THE WORLD OF Construction

THE WORLD OF Construction

DONALD G. LUX • WILLIS E. RAY, Co-Directors

Industrial Arts Curriculum Project

A. DEAN HAUENSTEIN, Assistant Director

Curriculum Development

McKNIGHT & McKNIGHT PUBLISHING COMPANY

Bloomington, Illinois

Fourth Edition

Lithographed in U.S.A.

SBN: 87345-462-6

Foreword

The World of Construction will provide an opportunity for you to become more familiar with the man-made world around you—that part of the world built by the construction industry. Just how important construction is can be observed by tracing your steps backwards for the past few days.

You live in a house or an apartment house which was constructed. You get to school over roads and streets that were built for safe travel. You study in a school, and members of your family work in factories, office buildings, or other structures built for special purposes. The water you drink comes through pipelines built by the construction industry, and the TV you watch is made possible by transmission lines and towers built for you by the construction industry. There isn't much that you can do that can't be traced back to the efforts of the construction industry. This course, developed in conjunction with all aspects of the construction industry, provides you an opportunity to better understand construction.

The first edition of this textbook was written in 1967; and, since then, many representatives of the construction industry have participated in revising and updating this material to its present form. As the text states, "They (labor and management) work together in many areas such as (1) training programs, (2) work promotion, and (3) safety programs." Through this joint venture, materials have developed which help point out that labor and management do have disagreements, but our common goals are achieved by cooperative efforts which overcome the differences.

The text ranges over the entire construction industry. Coupled with laboratory activities, the text should help you gain a working knowledge of what construction personnel do. The program is not intended to provide you with the knowledge or skill to perform as experts, but it can help you understand what experts know and do.

Representing major groups within the construction industry, we recommend *The World of Construction* as an important area of study. Students who may later join the industry as contractors or craftsmen want to know much about the team they are joining. Regardless of their career choice, the construction industry will be important to them.

Welcome to *The World of Construction.*

William E. Dunn C. J. Haggerty

William E. Dunn
Executive Director
The Associated General
Contractors of America

C. J. Haggerty
President
Building and Construction
Trades Department, AFL-CIO

Preface

You are about to begin a new and exciting kind of education. You will gain first-hand knowledge about the man-made world you live in. With this knowledge you will be able to view this constructed world with greater understanding, appreciation, and insight. Until now few students have had a chance to study man's practices in construction. To provide that opportunity, this educational program has been developed.

You may find the World of Construction so fascinating that you will want to make construction your life's work. Even if your life's work is in some other field, you still need some basic knowledge about construction. You will soon be a voting citizen. Then you will make decisions that affect the nature of the man-made environment. Whether or not society builds a satisfying and beautiful environment, or a frustrating and ugly one, depends on people's knowledge of the constructed world.

This textbook was written by professionals in the construction field, so you can be sure that what you read is accurate and up-to-date. The readings will help you form concepts or mental pictures of what the construction world is like. In the laboratory, working with a *laboratory manual,* techniques, tools, and materials, you will solve real construction problems that relate to the readings. In solving these problems, you will learn to use some of the basic practices of modern construction.

The World of Construction is a part of the answer to the growing demand for educational programs that deal with important industrial concepts. This program provides an excellent basis for advanced industrial education programs and for future life in our society.

Dr. Donald G. Lux
Dr. Willis E. Ray
Co-Directors

Acknowledgments

The readings in this textbook have been developed using the following procedure: 1) the over-all structure of the textbook was conceived with the assistance of specialists from the fields of management, labor, personnel, architecture, engineering, and production representing the construction industry; 2) outlines for each textbook reading were developed by the Project staff; 3) persons from industry qualified on the subject of each reading were asked to prepare a manuscript of approximately 1500 words; and 4) editorial staff of the Project edited these manuscripts for style and age-graded the materials.

INDUSTRIAL ARTS CURRICULUM PROJECT PERSONNEL

Co-Directors
Donald G. Lux
Willis E. Ray

Assistant Directors
James J. Buffer, Evaluation
A. Dean Hauenstein, Curriculum Development
John D. Jenkins, Dissemination
Henry J. Sredl, University of Illinois Division

Advisory Committee

Mr. Finlay C. Allan (Deceased)
First General Vice President
United Brotherhood of Carpenters and Joiners of America
Washington, D. C.

Dr. Max Beberman, Director
UICSM Mathematics Project
University of Illinois
Urbana, Illinois

Dr. Rupert N. Evans (Chairman)
Professor of Vocational and Technical Education
University of Illinois
Urbana, Illinois

Mr. John E. Harmon
Executive Vice President
National Employment Association
Washington, D. C.

Mr. Daniel MacMaster, President
Museum of Science and Industry
Chicago, Illinois

Mr. M. A. Maurer
Vice President
Northrop-Ventura
Newbury Park, California

Mr. C. I. Mehl
Assistant Executive Director
The Associated General Contractors of America
Washington, D. C.

Dr. M. Eugene Merchant
Director of Research Planning
Cincinnati Milling Machine Company
Cincinnati, Ohio

Mr. Nicholas J. Radell, Vice President
Cresap, McCormick, and Paget, Inc.
Management Consultants
Chicago, Illinois

Mr. Bernard M. Sallot
Assistant General Manager
Technical Divisions
Society of Manufacturing Engineers
Dearborn, Michigan

Dr. Jerome M. Shostak
Educational Consultant
Nanuet, New York

Mr. Charles W. Staab
Former Executive Vice President and Business Manager
Cincinnati Enquirer
Cincinnati, Ohio

IACP FIELD EVALUATION DIRECTORS AND TEACHERS

Center	*Personnel*	
California Long Beach	* Glenn Warrick ° William Welch	Gary Bos Warren T. Warken Robert Galvin
Florida Dade County	* James Morris ° Don Reinhofer ° Ronald Halden, on leave	Richard C. Altman Richard D'Aurora Leonard Smith
Illinois Chicago-Evanston	* Henry Sredl ° Ronald Mackert	Sheadrick Tillman Jerry Kowal Charles Vitello
New Jersey Trenton-Hamilton Township-New Brunswick	* J. Russell Kruppa ° Nelson Gray	Robert Starr John Trout Kenneth Vliet
Ohio Cincinnati	* Jack Ford ° Russell Henderly	John Fannin George Jones Paul Morehart
Columbus		Erwin Wagenknecht
Texas Austin	* Donald L. Clark ° Myron Ross	Lloyd R. Gober Vernon Coleman William E. McFarland

* Center Director
° Head Teacher

RESEARCH ASSISTANTS AND ASSOCIATES

Norman L. Asper
Vern M. Bonar
Walter R. Bortz
Roy A. Buckingham
John Butala, Jr.
Paul C. Caley
John S. Chilson
Donald L. Clark
Vincent C. D'Ambrosio
Donald E. Darrow
Ralph Dirksen
Charles R. Doty
William E. Dugger
James N. Fancher
Phillip A. Fazzini

Bill S. Frye
Nathaniel M. Griffin
Ronald L. Hoenes
Lawrence A. Inaba
Lewis D. Kieft
Richard A. Kruppa
Paul D. Kuwik
Robert C. Lampl
Sam Leles
Howard R. Maier
Arthur P. Martin
Kenneth C. Murray
Ronald M. Paige
Richard F. Peter
Bradford L. Pryce

David M. Richards
Arthur J. Rosser
Stanford D. Ruggles
Joseph F. Santoro
Lyle R. Schroeder
William L. Toner
Frederic E. Wachter
Lorin Waitkus
Floyd B. Walgren
Robert E. Weber
Robert E. Wenig
William E. West
James W. Wheeler
Darius R. Young

WRITERS AND REVIEWERS

Affiliated International Unions,
Building and Construction Trades
Department, AFL-CIO

Affiliated Local Unions,
Columbus Building Trades Council

American Institute of Architects

American Society of Civil Engineers

Associated General Contractors
of America

Ohio Contractors' Association

Ohio State Employment Service

B. P. Bellport
Office of Chief Engineer
U. S. Department of Interior
Bureau of Reclamation
Denver, Colorado

John D. Bristor, Professor
Department of Building Construction
University of Florida
Gainesville, Florida

A. Brinton Carson, Civil Engineer
Bureau of Engineering and Construction
Commonwealth of Pennsylvania
Harrisburg, Pennsylvania

James Deagle, Contractor
Columbus, Ohio

Joan H. Donnelly
Elementary School Teacher
Forest Hills, New York

David R. Dreger
Civil Engineer and Surveyor
Columbus, Ohio

Leo Gable, Technical Director
United Brotherhood of Carpenters and Joiners of America
Washington, D. C.

Lonnie Gaither, Jr.
International Organizer, Sheet Metal Workers' International Association
Washington, D. C.

Laurence C. Gerckens, Professor
City and Regional Planning
The Ohio State University
Columbus, Ohio

S. H. Hallock, Director
Center of Science and Industry
Columbus, Ohio

J. E. Hahn
Senior Application Engineer
Construction Machinery Division
Allis-Chalmers
Milwaukee, Wisconsin

Eugene E. Halmos
Magazine Editorial Consultant
Information Research Group
Washington, D. C.

Reese Hammond
Director of Research and Education
International Union of Operating Engineers
Washington, D. C.

Robert Jones
Ohio State Employment Service
Columbus, Ohio

Narbey Khachaturian, Professor
Department of Civil Engineering
University of Illinois
Urbana, Illinois

L. Brent Kuhnle, Assistant Vice President
J. A. Jones Construction Company
Seattle, Washington

Bruce G. Martin
Assistant Executive Manager
National Roofing Contractors Association
Oak Park, Illinois

John M. Norvell, Professional Engineer
Alexandria, Virginia

William Oviedo, Coordinator
United Brotherhood of Carpenters and Joiners of America
Apprenticeship and Training Department
Washington, D. C.

David Reyes-Guerra, Guidance Director
Engineers Council for Professional Development Inc.
New York City

William F. Roark, Director
Mason Relations Department
Structural Clay Products Institute
Washington, D. C.

King Royer, Construction Engineer
Standard Fruit Company
Costa Rica

William C. Schmitt
Center of Science and Industry
Columbus, Ohio

L. R. Shaffer, Professor
Department of Civil Engineering
University of Illinois
Urbana, Illinois

James Seyler, Professor
Division of University Extension
University of Illinois
Urbana, Illinois

Robert Siegel
Ohio State Employment Service
Columbus, Ohio

Carl Snyder
Ohio State Employment Service
Columbus, Ohio

John S. Spangler
Assistant Executive Director
National Asphalt Pavement Association
Riverdale, Maryland

Joseph E. Taylor, Director
Skill Improvment Training, International Brotherhood of Electrical Workers
Washington, D. C.

George B. Tobey, Jr.
Landscape Architect
Columbus, Ohio

B. R. Wellek, Assistant Director
Advertising & Public Relations
Master Builders
Cleveland, Ohio

John Winters
Manager of Sales Training
Caterpillar Tractor Company
Peoria, Illinois

Many other individuals in the construction industry freely gave support, advice, and counsel to the Project staff. To these individuals, we also express our appreciation.

SOURCES OF ILLUSTRATIONS

Allis-Chalmers
Milwaukee, Wisconsin
American Airlines
New York, New York
American Institute of
Steel Construction, Inc.
New York, New York
American Institute of
Timber Construction
Washington, D. C.
American Plywood Association
Tacoma, Washington
American Society of Civil Engineers
New York, New York
American Telephone & Telegraph
New York, New York
Armco Steel Corporation
Middletown, Ohio
Armstrong Cork Company
Lancaster, Pennsylvania
Asphalt & Vinyl Asbestos
Tile Institute
New York, New York
Association of American Railroads
Washington, D. C.
Atomics International
Division of North American
Rockwell Corporation
Canoga Park, California
Bethlehem Steel Corporation
Bethlehem, Pennsylvania
Better Lawn & Turf Institute
Marysville, Ohio
The Boeing Company
Seattle, Washington
British Overseas Airlines Corporation
New York, New York
Brown & Root Inc.
Houston, Texas
Brown Shoe Company
St. Louis, Missouri
Buckman, Inc.
Memphis, Tennessee
Bucyrus-Erie Company
So. Milwaukee, Wisconsin
Building & Construction Trades
Department, AFL-CIO
Washington, D. C.
Candelite Homes, Inc.
Columbus, Ohio
J. I. Case Company
Racine, Wisconsin
The Philip Carey
Manufacturing Company
Miami-Carey Division
Middletown, Ohio
Caterpillar Tractor Company
Peoria, Illinois
The Ceco Corporation
Chicago, Illinois
Celanese Plastic Company
Division of Celanese Corporation
Columbus, Ohio
Center of Science & Industry
Columbus, Ohio
Centron Corporation
Lawrence, Kansas
A. B. Chance
Pitman Division
Grandview, Missouri
Chapmans Shoes
San Rafael, California
Chesapeake Bay Bridge & Tunnel
Commission
Cape Charles, Virginia
Chicago Association of
Commerce and Industry
Chicago, Illinois
Chicago Bridge & Iron Company
Oak Brook, Illinois
Chicago & North Western Railway
Chicago, Illinois
Clark Equipment Company
Buchanan, Michigan
The Cleveland Trencher Company
Cleveland, Ohio
Colorado Department of Highways
Denver, Colorado
Columbus Area Chamber of Commerce
Columbus, Ohio
Columbus Dispatch
Columbus, Ohio
Constructor Magazine
Washington, D. C.
Corning Glassworks
Corning, New York
Davis-Dunlop, Inc.
Washington, D. C.
Eugene Dietzgen Company
Chicago, Illinois
Dobbs & Tidwell Construction Company
Pinson, Alabama
Dodge Construction News
New York, New York
Dravo Corporation
Pittsburgh, Pennsylvania
E. I. Dupont de Nemours &
Company, Inc.
Wilmington, Delaware
Ebasco Services Incorporated
New York, New York
Electric Heating Association
New York, New York
Erico Products, Inc.
Cleveland, Ohio
ESCO Corporation
Portland, Oregon
Euclid Division of General Motors
Hudson, Ohio
Farmland Industries, Inc.
Kansas City, Missouri
Firestone Tire & Rubber Company
Akron, Ohio
Flaherty Chip Spreader
Gale Products
Div. of Outboard Marine Corporation
Galesburg, Illinois
General Electric Company
Schenectady, New York
General Mills
Minneapolis, Minnesota

General Motors Corporation
Detroit, Michigan
General Trade & Labor Group
W. R. Grace & Company
New York, New York
W. A. Graham
Hardwood Plywood Manufacturers Association
Arlington, Virginia
Hercules Incorporated
Wilmington, Delaware
Home Builders Association of Greater Columbus
Columbus, Ohio
Hot Mix Asphalt Association
House & Home Magazines
New York, New York
Huber Corporation
Marion, Ohio
Ideal Cement Company
Denver, Colorado
Insulation Board Institute
Chicago, Illinois
International Brotherhood of Electrical Workers
Washington, D. C.
International Business Machines Corporation
Armonk, New York
International Harvester Company
Chicago, Illinois
Jamestown Foundation
Williamsburg, Virginia
Johns-Manville Corporation
New York, New York
Johnson & Johnson
New Brunswick, New Jersey
Joy Manufacturing Company
Claremont, New Hampshire
Kaiser Aluminum & Chemical Corporation
Oakland, California
Kelley Steel Erectors
Bedford, Ohio
Kelly Industrial Photography Inc.
Kennametal, Inc.
Latrobe, Pennsylvania
Koehring Company
Stockton, California
Libbey-Owens-Ford Company
Toledo, Ohio
Louisville & Nashville Railroad
Louisville, Kentucky
Louisiana Department of Highways
Baton Rouge, Louisiana
McCabe-Powers Body Company
St. Louis, Missouri
Marathon Oil Company
Findlay, Ohio
Marble Institute of America
Washington, D. C.
Masonite Corporation
Chicago, Illinois
Master Builders
Cleveland, Ohio
Merkle Press, Inc.
Washington, D. C.
Millers Falls Company
Greenfield, Massachusetts
Milwaukee Electric Tool Corporation
Brookfield, Wisconsin
Mobile Drilling Company, Inc.
Indianapolis, Indiana
Morgen Manufacturing Company
Yankton, South Dakota
National Archives & Records Service
Washington, D. C.
National Editorial Services
Royal Oak, Michigan
National Lead Company
New York, New York
National Park Service
Washington, D. C.
New York Convention-Visitors Bureau
New York, New York
Niagara Mohawk Power Corporation
Syracuse, New York
Nordberg Manufacturing Company
Milwaukee, Wisconsin
Northrop Corporation
Beverly Hills, California
Ohio Department of Highways
Delaware, Ohio
Ohio State University
Department of Photography and Cinema
Columbus, Ohio
Pan American World Airways, Inc.
New York, New York
Patent Scaffolding
Division of Harsco Corporation
Long Island City, New York
Philadelphia Naval Shipyard
Philadelphia, Pennsylvania
Chamber of Commerce of Greater Pittsburgh
Pittsburgh, Pennsylvania
The Plastering Industries
Seattle, Washington
Port of New York Authority
New York, New York
Portland Cement Association
Salt Lake City, Utah
Power Authority of the State of New York
Niagara Falls, New York
Prestressed Concrete Institute
Chicago, Illinois
Radio Corporation of America
New York, New York
Ransdell, Inc.
Washington, D. C.
Red Cedar Shingle & Handsplit Shake Bureau
Seattle, Washington
Reno News Bureau
Greater Reno Chamber of Commerce
Reno, Nevada
Republic Steel Corporation
Cleveland, Ohio
Rock Hill Contracting Company
Rock Hill, South Carolina
Rockwell Manufacturing Company
Pittsburgh, Pennsylvania

Rohm & Hass Company
  Philadelphia, Pennsylvania
Roofing, Siding, Insulation Magazine
  Duluth, Minnesota
Schiavone Construction Company
  Chicago, Illinois
Schramm, Incorporated
  Chester, Pennsylvania
O. M. Scott & Sons
  Marysville, Ohio
Sheet Metal Workers
    Air Conditioning Association
  Elgin, Illinois
Sheet Metal Workers
    International Association
  Washington, D. C.
Sierra Electric Corporation
  Gardena, California
Sikorsky Aircraft
  Division of United
    Aircraft Corporation
  Stratford, Connecticut
Sjostrom & Sons, Inc.
  Freeport, Illinois
Smith Kline & French Laboratories
  Philadelphia, Pennsylvania
Soiltest, Incorporated
  Evanston, Illinois
Stanley Tools
  Division of The Stanley Works
  New Britain, Connecticut
Stearns-Roger Corporation
  Denver, Colorado
Structural Clay Products Institute
  Washington, D. C.
Symes & Olds Company
  Cleveland, Ohio
Tell-Pics
  San Antonio, Texas
Tennessee Valley Authority
  Knoxville, Tennessee
Texaco, Inc.
  New York, New York
Tinius Olsen Testing Machine Company
  Willow Grove, Pennsylvania
U. S. Army Corps of Engineers
  U. S. Department of Defense
  Washington, D. C.
U. S. Department of the Interior
  Bureau of Reclamation
  Washington, D. C.
U. S. Naval Photographic Center
  Washington, D. C.
Union Pacific Railroad Company
  Omaha, Nebraska
Upjohn Company
  Kalamazoo, Michigan
Up-Right Scaffolds
  Berkeley, California
Vulcan Materials Company
  Birmingham, Alabama
Warner & Swasey Company
  Cleveland, Ohio
West Coast Lumbermen's Association
  Portland, Oregon
Western Wood Products Association
  Portland, Oregon
Westinghouse Air Brake Company
  Pneumatic Equipment Division
  Sidney, Ohio
Weyerhaeuser Company
  Tacoma, Washington
Wild Heerbrug, Ltd.
  Farmingdale, Long Island, New York
Wire Reinforcement Institute
  Washington, D. C.
Youngstown Pneumatic Concrete
    Company, Inc.
  Youngstown, Ohio
Zonolite
  Division of W. R. Grace & Company
  Cambridge, Massachusetts

Table of Contents

Foreword v *Preface vi* *Acknowledgments vii*

READING		PAGE
1	Man and Technology	1
2	Construction Technology	7
3	Applying Technology to People	12
4	Managing Construction	17
5	Beginning the Project	23
6	Selecting a Site	30
7	Buying Real Estate	38
8	Surveying and Mapping	45
9	Soil Testing	53
10	Designing and Engineering Construction Projects	60
11	Identifying the Design Problem	65
12	Developing Preliminary Ideas	68
13	Refining Ideas	71
14	Analyzing the Design	74
15	Selecting the Design	78
16	Making Working Drawings	83
17	Writing Specifications	87
18	The Designing and Engineering Cycle	94
19	Selecting a Builder	97
20	Contracting	102
21	Estimating and Bidding	107
22	Scheduling	114
23	Working as a Contractor	119
24	Collective Bargaining	125
25	Hiring Construction Personnel	133
26	Training and Educating for Construction	140
27	Working Conditions	145
28	Advancing in Construction	148
29	Construction Production Technology	154
30	Getting Ready to Build	160
31	Clearing the Site	168
32	Locating the Structure	174
33	Earthmoving	182
34	Handling Grievances	189
35	Stabilizing Earth and Structures	194
36	Classifying Structures	200
37	Setting Foundations	206
38	Building Forms	212
39	Setting Reinforcement	220
40	Mixing Concrete	226
41	Placing and Finishing Concrete	231
42	Completing Foundations	237
43	Building Superstructures	244
44	Building Mass and Masonry Superstructures	249
45	Erecting Steel Frames	255
46	Erecting Concrete Frames	261
47	Building Wood Frames	268

48 Installing Utilities 278
49 Installing Heating, Cooling, and Ventilating Systems 285
50 Installing Plumbing Systems 291
51 Installing Piping Systems 297
52 Installing Electrical Power Systems 304
53 Installing Electrical Communications Systems 310
54 Making Inspections 320
55 Mediating and Arbitrating 325
56 Enclosing Framed Superstructures 330
57 Roofing 336
58 Enclosing Exterior Walls 342
59 Striking 349
60 Insulating 353
61 Applying Wall Materials 359
62 Applying Ceiling Materials 364
63 Laying Floors 368
64 Finishing the Project 376
65 Painting and Decorating 381
66 Installing Accessories 387
67 Completing the Site 393
68 Transferring the Project 400
69 Servicing Property 405
70 Building Dams 410
71 Bridge Building 417
72 Road Building 423
73 Building Skyscrapers 428
74 Constructing in the Future 433
75 Constructing Housing 439
76 Your Dream House 443
77 Selecting and Purchasing a Lot 448
78 Planning the Living Space 453
79 Preparing Working Drawings 459
80 Writing Specifications 468
81 Financing and Contracting 474
82 Building the Substructure 478
83 Building Walls 484
84 Building Floors and Ceilings 487
85 Building Roofs 491
86 Enclosing Exteriors 496
87 Roughing in Utilities 500
88 Working on the Interior 505
89 Completing the House 510
90 Landscaping Homesites 515
91 City and Regional Planning Factors 519
92 Planning Community Services 523
93 Housing People 529
94 Planning Business Facilities 534
95 Planning Schools and Recreational Facilities 539
96 The Economics of Community Development 544
97 Managing Community Development 547

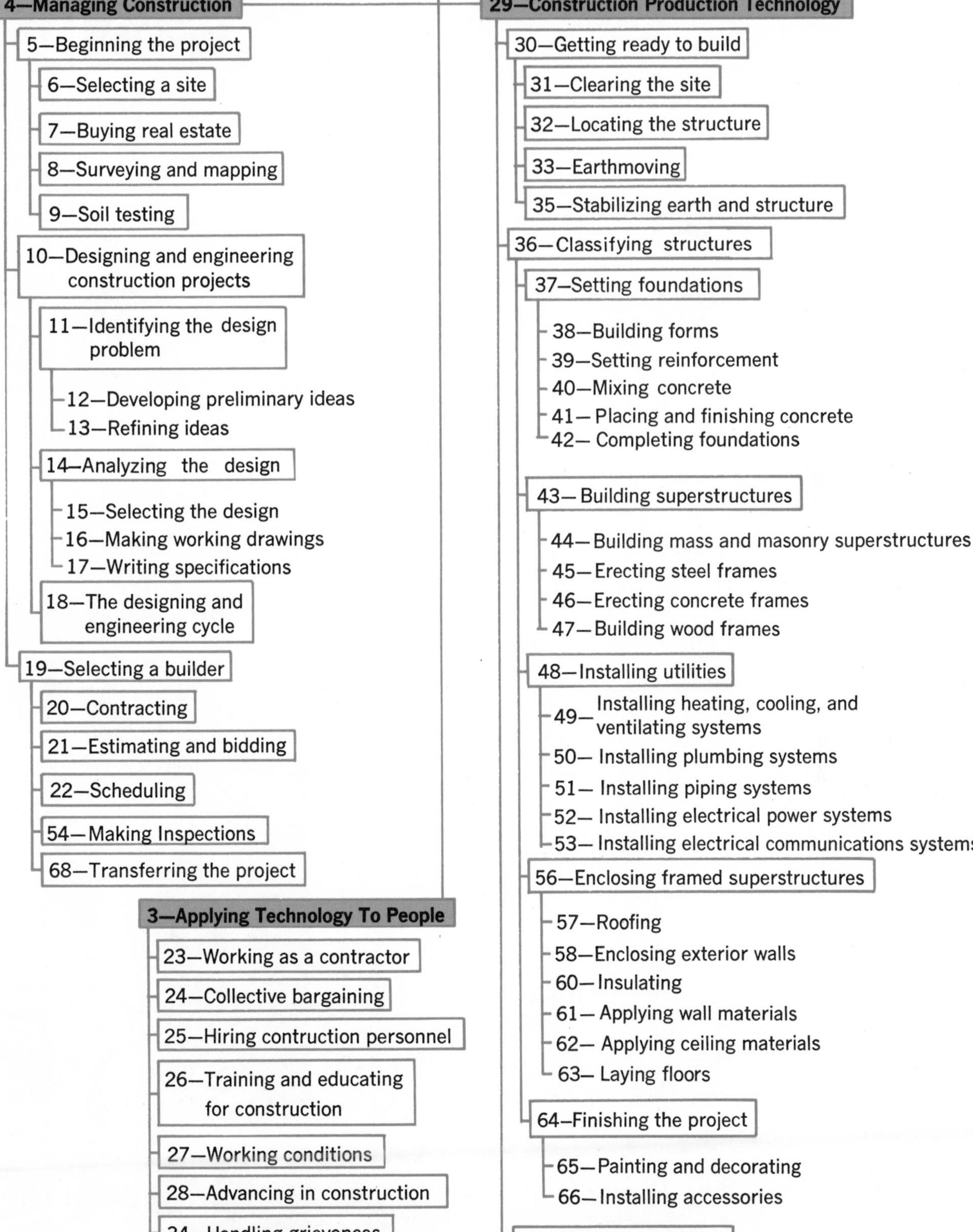
1—Man and Technology
2-Construction Technology
4—Managing Construction
5—Beginning the project
6—Selecting a site
7—Buying real estate
8—Surveying and mapping
9—Soil testing
10—Designing and engineering construction projects
11—Identifying the design problem
12—Developing preliminary ideas
13—Refining ideas
14—Analyzing the design
15—Selecting the design
16—Making working drawings
17—Writing specifications
18—The designing and engineering cycle
19—Selecting a builder
20—Contracting
21—Estimating and bidding
22—Scheduling
54—Making Inspections
68—Transferring the project
3—Applying Technology To People
23—Working as a contractor
24—Collective bargaining
25—Hiring contruction personnel
26—Training and educating for construction
27—Working conditions
28—Advancing in construction
34—Handling grievances
55—Mediating and arbitrating
59—Striking
29—Construction Production Technology
30—Getting ready to build
31—Clearing the site
32—Locating the structure
33—Earthmoving
35—Stabilizing earth and structure
36—Classifying structures
37—Setting foundations
38—Building forms
39—Setting reinforcement
40—Mixing concrete
41—Placing and finishing concrete
42—Completing foundations
43—Building superstructures
44—Building mass and masonry superstructures
45—Erecting steel frames
46—Erecting concrete frames
47—Building wood frames
48—Installing utilities
49—Installing heating, cooling, and ventilating systems
50—Installing plumbing systems
51—Installing piping systems
52—Installing electrical power systems
53—Installing electrical communications systems
56—Enclosing framed superstructures
57—Roofing
58—Enclosing exterior walls
60—Insulating
61—Applying wall materials
62—Applying ceiling materials
63—Laying floors
64—Finishing the project
65—Painting and decorating
66—Installing accessories
67—Completing the site
69—Servicing property

Man and Technology

In the beginning, the heavens, the earth, and man were formed. Man, from the past to the present, has changed the form of the earth's resources to satisfy his wants. The way man makes these changes is called *technology*. Let us think of what technology is and how technology has changed our lives.

The Dawn of Man

Imagine that you are living almost two million years ago. You don't go to school, because there are no schools. You have nothing but your physical and mental ability. You have no clothes, no tools, no home, no religion, no food saved, and no cities. Other than your family, you don't see many other human beings. Too many people in the same place cut down the food supply.

You might be running across a grassy plain somewhere in Africa. You see your mother, far away, chasing some animal to get food for you. You haven't had anything to eat for a long time. Your father is out hunting too, and you haven't seen him for many days. All at once, there is a loud squeal. Your mother has gotten some food for you by killing an animal. Together you rip it apart and eat the raw meat.

Just then, there is a rustle in the bushes. You are afraid because you don't know what it is. When you look up, you see it is your father. He can't say much to you, because you really don't have a well developed language. He grunts and makes sounds. You understand some of these sounds, but most of what he tells you is by motions. You notice something. Your father has been bleeding a lot. His legs and stomach are covered with blood. He must have been attacked by some large animal. Man, compared to many animals, is not very strong. Man does, however, have a very important advantage over animals. *He can think* and outwit the animals which hunt him.

Now that your father has come back, you want to go home. But you don't have a house or even a cave. All you can do is find a bush or a tree. There you lie down and sleep until you wake up and hunt for some more food. It may be the middle of the night, or it may be the next day when you get up. It doesn't make any difference, because you don't know what time is. You don't know about time as we know it today.

After some sleep, a sound wakes you. Something must be wrong because of all the noise. An animal is about to attack you and your parents. Because of fear, your father does something that you have never seen him do before. He picks up a stone and throws it at the animal. Because of a very lucky shot, he kills it.

Something important has happened just now. No one has ever done this—used a stone to protect himself and to kill an animal. What was that stone? Was it a *tool*? The word has not yet been made up. However, it is a tool. Your father used it to protect himself and to get food for another day. Could this have been how the first tool was discovered? What we know about the past tells us that the first tools were just stones, Fig. 1-1. They were sharp or jagged for killing and cutting. These stones helped man keep alive in his dangerous world.

The way early man made and used stone tools to get food and to protect himself can be called *technology* (knowing how to use tools and techniques efficiently). Because of his lucky shot with the stone, your father learned something he had never known before. Since it killed the animal, he now knew that he could both get food and protect him-

Fig. 1-1. Technology took a big step forward when man began to use tools to satisfy his wants.

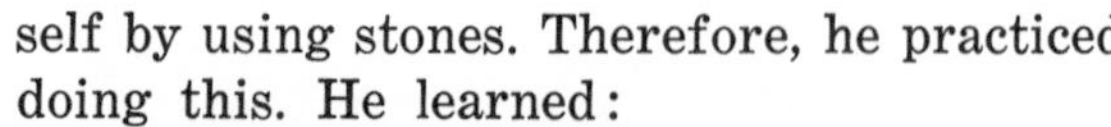

self by using stones. Therefore, he practiced doing this. He learned:

1. How big the stone had to be,
2. How hard to throw it,
3. How close he had to be to animals to kill them, and
4. Where to hit the animals.

He learned technology (how to use his stone tool to get the best results).

Now you have two advantages over animals and creatures around you. You can think and reason, and you have tools to increase your physical ability. Tools were one of the first great steps forward for mankind. Man increased his production (Fig. 1-2) by using technology to make and use larger, faster tools (Fig. 1-3).

The Beginning of an Economic System

When man developed new tools to help him with farming or hunting, he worked with stones. Then he discovered metal. He found copper in Egypt about 5,000 years ago. Bronze was then developed about 3,500 years ago. Not long after this, iron was first used

Fig. 1-2. Man using a shovel to move earth.

Fig. 1-3. Man using a machine to move earth.

in Europe. Using metals gave man more control in his struggle against nature. He also began to develop a new technology for making tools.

At this point in history, not everyone had to spend all his time getting food. Some people could spend more time doing other things that interested them. They began to specialize or do those things they could do best. For example, they made clothing, built shelter to live in, developed government, taught, or, perhaps, became entertainers. A man using a shovel (Fig. 1-2) can move more dirt than if he used only his bare hands. This same man can move more earth with a specialized tool, Fig. 1-3. He can now work at a similar task, but he has a higher output and he has better working conditions. A specialized worker can trade or sell the work he does to others. Then he can, in turn, get what he wants from this trading and selling.

Early men had to make for themselves whatever they wanted. Now men specialize and use technology to make an abundance of products. These are distributed by an economic system. This system provides you with most of what you use.

The products traded in the economic system are usually divided into goods and services. Goods are materials such as homes, radios, streets, and milk shakes. Services are such things as a haircut, a bus ride, or the chance to see a movie. Technology is used to provide both goods and services, but in this course you will study mostly about the technology which produces goods or materials.

Processing Economic Goods

There are two ways of getting materials:

1. Extracting from nature
2. Natural reproduction

Most of these materials are *processed* before we use them for our wants. There are two ways of processing materials:

1. Construction
2. Manufacture

The following paragraphs explain each of these.

Extraction is the process of getting materials from where they are found in nature. Examples of this are:

1. Getting crude oil by drilling a hole in the ground and pumping out the oil,
2. Panning a stream and collecting the gold,
3. Digging a beach in South Africa to mine for diamonds, and
4. Digging gravel out of a gravel pit.

All of these are processes of getting useful materials by *extraction,* Fig. 1-4.

Reproduction is a process of nature. Using seeds to grow a tree for your front yard, getting a puppy from a mother dog, and seeding your yard so you will have grass are all part of the process of reproduction. *Reproduction is the normal life process,* Fig. 1-5.

Fig. 1-4. Some materials, such as coal, are taken directly from the earth and are used up. This taking of natural resources from the earth is called extraction.

Fig. 1-5. Some materials such as these tree seedlings and the lumber they will someday become, are grown. This natural reproduction provides us with many of our materials.

Construction is building something on a site. Examples of construction are:

1. Building a house,
2. Putting in a sewage system, and
3. Building a bridge over a river.

These are all examples of taking raw materials, processing them, and assembling them (putting them together) at a certain location to make something that you want.

Manufacture is producing products in a factory or plant. Making a radio or an automobile, building a jet airplane, or putting together a coloring book are all *examples of manufacturing*.

Industry

You have learned that there are four ways to produce the material things that you want:

1. Extraction,
2. Reproduction,

Fig. 1-6. Many material goods are constructed on the site. This year you will study the technology that makes these things possible.

3. Construction, and
4. Manufacture.

Reproduction uses a product that is found in nature. *Extraction,* although it might be complicated, still uses nature's products. Neither of them do much to change the materials they produce. Sometimes extracted or reproduced materials are greatly changed in form (processed). *Industry is the part of the economic system that changes the form of a material. Construction* and *manufacture* are the two major parts of industry.

Now that you know what industry is, what would you say *industrial arts* is? An *art* is usually defined as an ability or skill. *Industry* is changing the form of materials. When you put "industry" together with "arts," industrial arts can be defined as *the study of the use of tools and techniques to construct and manufacture goods and to service these goods.* Therefore, industrial arts is the study of construction and manufacturing technology. This year, you will study *construction technology,* Fig. 1-6.

Summary

As technology developed, man began to specialize and to do the things he was best at and that he liked to do. He learned to trade or sell what he had to others who wanted it. In turn, he could get what he wanted from this trading and selling. This specialization led to the development of an economic system.

There are many products that each of us may want. These can be put into two different groups: (1) material goods and (2) services.

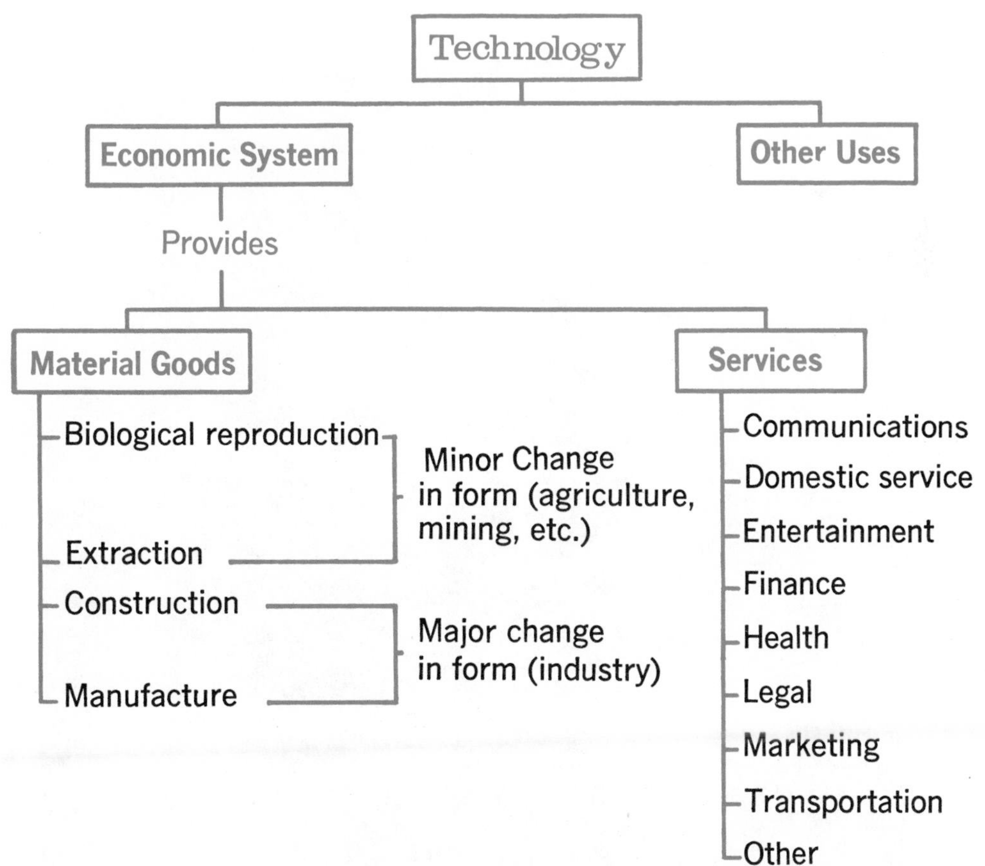

Material goods can be gotten by: (1) extraction and (2) reproduction. They can be processed by: (1) construction, and (2) manufacture. Of these four, construction and manufacturing (industry) change the shape, form, or size of materials the most.

An art is usually defined as an ability or skill to do certain things. When you put "industry" together with "arts," *industrial arts can be defined as the study of the use of tools and techniques to construct and manufacture goods and to service these goods.*

Terms to Know

tool
technology
specialization
industry
industrial arts
materials
extraction
reproduction
construction
manufacture
technique
process
material goods
economic system

Think About It!

1. How did *specialized tools* and technology lead to the development of an *economic system*?
2. Give three examples of materials which are:
   a. extracted
   b. reproduced
   c. constructed
   d. manufactured
3. Explain the difference between a *constructed product* and a *manufactured product*. Give three examples of each.

Construction Technology

Today you depend on the work of other people to help you live and to enjoy life. Industry plays a major role in giving all of us the material goods which mean so much to our lives.

As you live each day and take part in society, you and your family ask yourselves many questions about industrial technology. What kind of car shall I buy? How can I repair a wall in my house? How do I fix a transistor radio? What kinds of materials should I buy to make a doghouse? What products would I buy for my dream house? These questions or ones like them are asked by all people who live in an industrialized society. An *industrialized society* is one in which people have the ability to make and use constructed and manufactured products to help them in their daily lives. In the future, if you want to make intelligent decisions about what kinds of things are best for your needs and how to go about doing things for yourself, you will want to know something about industrial technology.

Remember that there are two broad parts or divisions of industrial technology. The first is building something at a site. This is *construction technology.* This is what you will study this year. In order to study construction technology you should know the parts of this field and see how each part relates to the others. Only then can you understand the whole field of learning which is construction technology. Next year you may study the second part of industrial technology which is the knowledge of manufacturing techniques.

Beginning of Construction Technology

Construction technology has always been a very important part of man's life. Even the earliest thinking man began to make things with simple stone tools. What do you suppose were the first things man constructed? We believe they were probably shelters or kinds of homes for himself and his family.

The first construction might have been only a crude lean-to shelter to protect man from wind and rain. Maybe the first construction was the act of digging or improving a cave to make a very crude home and to protect man against the weather. For about a million years, this is perhaps all that man ever tried to construct. As his knowledge of things around him increased, he began to design and build structures to make his life more comfortable.

Later man built bridges to make his travel easier. He built *aqueducts* to carry water to

Fig. 2-1. Construction technology makes it possible for man to work awe-inspiring changes in his surroundings.

Fig. 2-2. Many men and materials and specialized knowledge are required to build construction projects such as this dam.

Fig. 2-3. Modern machines and the skills of the operators make it possible to do in one hour what hundreds of men used to work for days to accomplish. This man is moving tons of earth with this machine.

his developing cities. He constructed huge pyramids which he thought would contain the remains of Egyptian rulers forever. He constructed the famous colosseum in Rome for entertainment. He built large churches for worship. Through the ages man has designed and constructed the many wonders of the world that we have today, Fig. 2-1.

Construction Technology Today

Construction technology is a very important part of today's economy. To understand construction in today's society, we should take a look at how much construction has taken place in recent years.

The way we, in the United States, measure goods and services produced is by the *GNP* (Gross National Product). We can say that, if you bought everything that was produced in one year, it would cost you the amount of the GNP. Construction accounts for about 16% of this amount. This means that it would have cost you over ninety billion dollars to buy everything that was constructed in 1970.

Sixteen cents out of every dollar spent each year is spent to buy such things as homes, roads, bridges, and dams, Fig. 2-2. You can see that construction technology is a very important part of our society. Do you think construction will continue at such a rapid pace in the future? Is man's need for constructed things increasing?

In the past one hundred years there has been a great increase in home construction. To meet our needs and wants, great factories have been constructed at a rapid rate. Office buildings increase in number and size to house the services we want. Miles of roads and bridges are constructed yearly to make it easier for us to travel and to transport products more rapidly, Fig. 2-3. The trend would seem to indicate a continued growth in the field of construction to meet the ever new needs and wants of our ever growing population.

Construction Technology in the Future

What kinds of construction might you see in the future besides the kinds of construction that you see today? New construction techniques are being tested to improve or replace even the best practices today.

In the not too distant future, engineers say we will be constructing not only on the earth but in other places. Serious thought is being given to building a huge space station hundreds of miles above the surface of the earth. When we get to other planets, we may build structures on them. The structures used for housing, such as on the moon, will have to be built so they will contain their own atmosphere and temperature control systems.

As we travel to other planets, we will have to think of new designs in construction to meet the needs of man as he conquers his universe. Already the space age has caused us to build one of the largest buildings known to man. This building houses the Saturn V rocket which launched astronauts to the moon, Fig. 2-4.

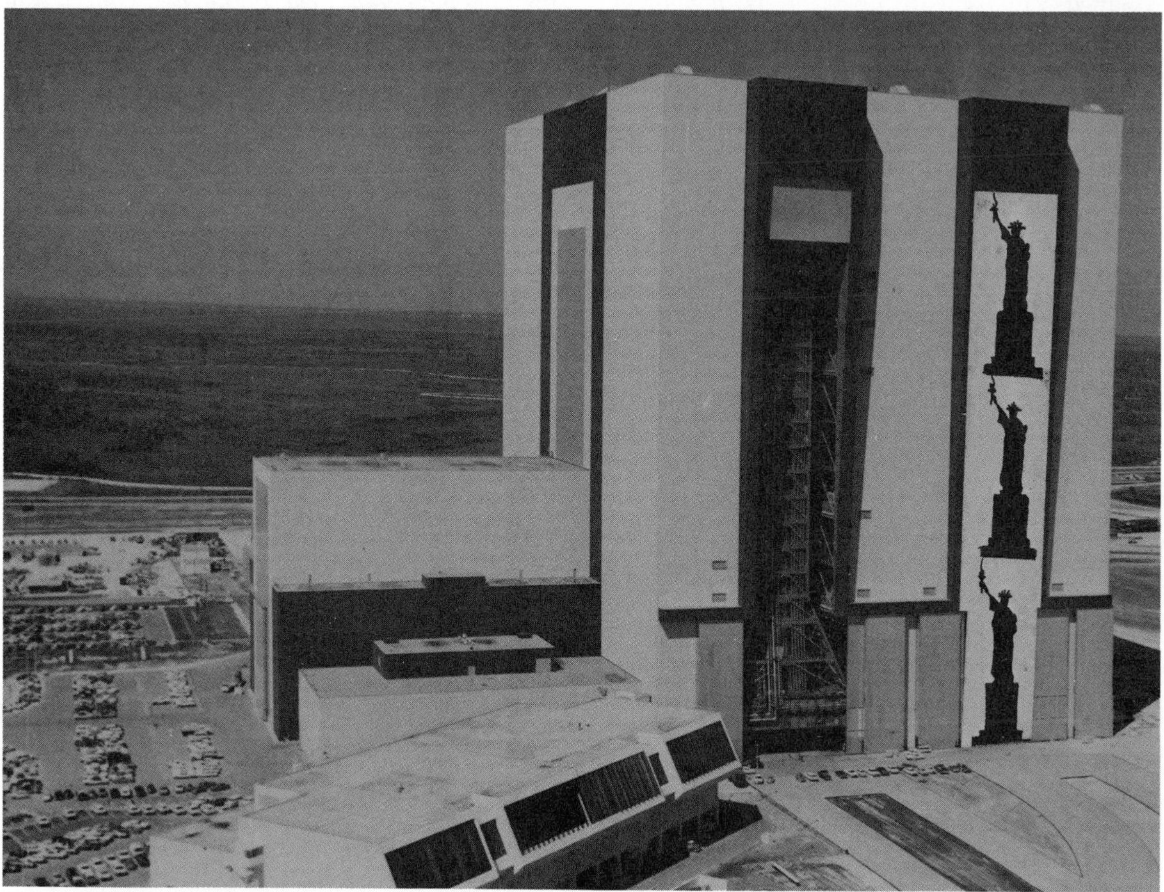

Fig. 2-4. One of the largest buildings ever constructed by man, the Vehicle Assembly Building at John F. Kennedy Space Center, represents the products of modern technology. Note the size of the automobiles in front of the building. Also note that the front doors are three times the height of the Statue of Liberty. The symbols of the statues shown in the door opening are drawn to the same scale as the building. This building encloses nearly twice the space enclosed by the huge Pentagon in Washington, D. C.

How Construction Technology Is Achieved

We have already seen that anything built on a site is a result of *construction technology* (knowing how to use tools and techniques to build something on a site). We know that if man did not exist, there would be no construction technology as we know it.

You might ask yourself, "How do we get all the structures that we see around us?" First, someone has to want the structure at a certain place. Would anything be built if nobody wanted it or was willing to pay for it? Once someone wants and is willing to pay for something, it must be designed and developed. Thus a *plan for action* is developed. Then a sequence (the steps) to be followed during construction is prepared so that the construction will be completed as planned.

Then the services of many different skilled people must be contracted. A plan is submitted or given to contractors who can handle most of the steps of building a structure. The contractors bid on the job and the bid of the least amount of money usually is selected.

Once a contractor's firm has been chosen to construct the object, how does the firm begin? First the location or where the object is to be built must be chosen. Then the site must be prepared. If a dam is to be constructed, water might have to be rechanneled so that the men can reach the bedrock to begin construction. In building a house, trees might have to be removed, the ground leveled, and earth removed to make a place for the foundation. You can see that, no matter what you are building, the site must be prepared in some way.

After the site is prepared, the structure must be built. Because of the many different things involved in building most structures, many people with special skills are needed. Because of the *specialization of techniques or skills*, we can build greater structures for less money.

After the structure is built, the site must be finished by *landscaping* (the finishing touches). The materials are cleaned up, shrubbery and trees are put in place to add beauty; and lighting, roads, sidewalks, and other things are installed to make the site ready to use. The constructed object is then complete.

All constructed objects must be continually maintained due to wear by use or *deterioration* from weather or corrosion. This is part of postprocessing (servicing).

Elements of Construction Technology

Management, personnel, and production technology together make up construction technology. Management technology has to do with *planning, organizing, and controlling* all the men and materials used in construction. Personnel technology is how to *hire, train, work, advance, and retire* constructon workers, Fig. 2-5. Production technology has to do with the *preprocessing, processing,* and *postprocessing* (servicing) of materials. All of this technology will be studied in detail in this course.

As you study and work on daily assignments, make an effort to figure out how each particular assignment is related to major parts of construction technology. If you make this effort, the details of your daily activities will help you to understand both the details of construction as well as the workings of the entire construction industry.

Construction technology is a vast body of knowledge. However, it can be simplified into common elements. As an example, *planning* is done by bricklayers, architects, draftsmen, carpenters, contractors, and many others in construction. However, they all use common planning practices. In this course you will learn some detailed planning techniques (practices). However, you also should try to use the study and experience with detailed techniques to help you understand the more general ones. That is to say, you may plan a particular object, but the techniques learned in doing this should be related to the common planning techniques used in planning all types of construction.

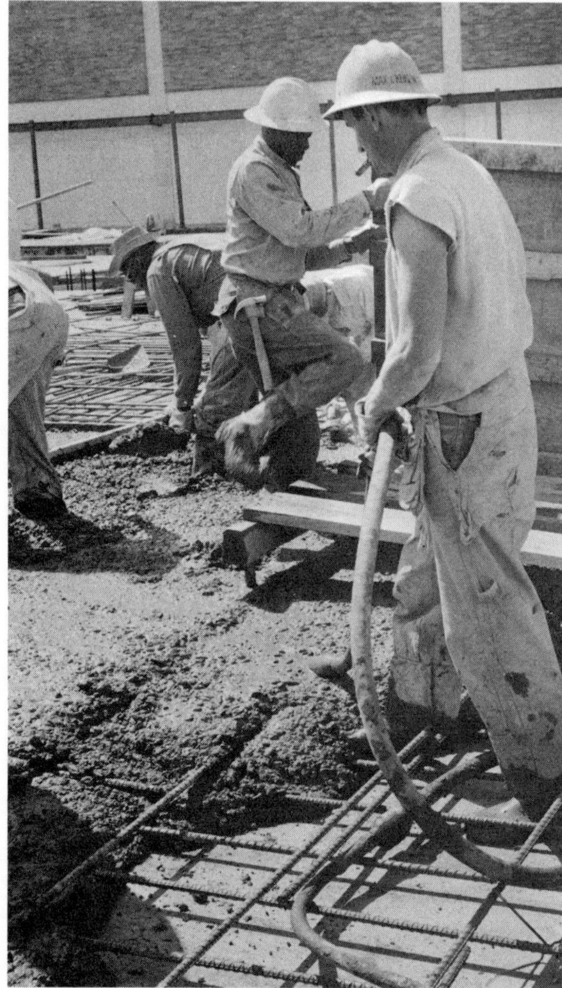

Fig. 2-5. These trained men were hired for their skill in working with concrete.

Summary

Construction is a large part of our society today. It has always been a part of man's society. As our society grows and our needs become greater, we need more and more constructed objects. Although our needs for objects may change and some new objects might be developed in different forms, the tools and techniques used to build all constructed objects are much the same.

Construction technology may be subdivided into elements which can be studied. Both the elements and their relationships to each other are important. As you study, you should try to place each day's study in relation to the studies completed and the studies to come. If you have a good knowledge of construction practices and constructed objects, you can better understand the world in which you live.

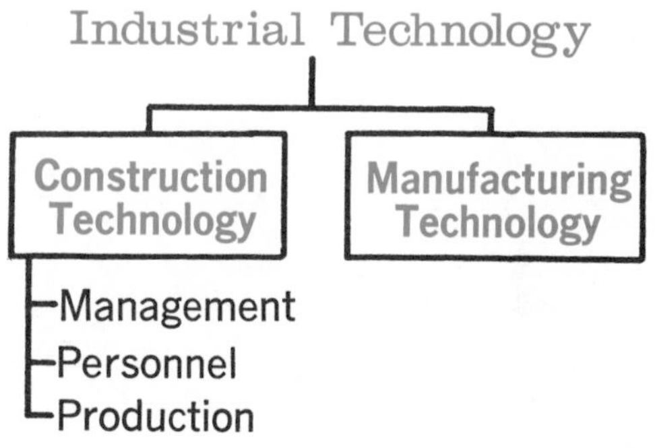

Terms to Know

industrial technology
technique
specialization
personnel
production
preprocessing
processing
postprocessing
economy
Gross National Product
contracted
deterioration
corrosion
elements
construction technology

Think About It!

1. What are the three main functions of management technology?
2. What are the five main functions of personnel technology?
3. What are the three main functions of production technology?

READING 3

Applying Technology to People

Everyone's life is changed when he uses industrial products. With a bicycle, you can go around a paper route quickly. Inside a comfortable house, you can forget about a rainstorm. The ways industrial products change the lives of people are studied as part of school subjects like geography or history, Fig. 3-1. In industrial arts we study how industrial production affects industrial workers as well as how to make and use industrial products.

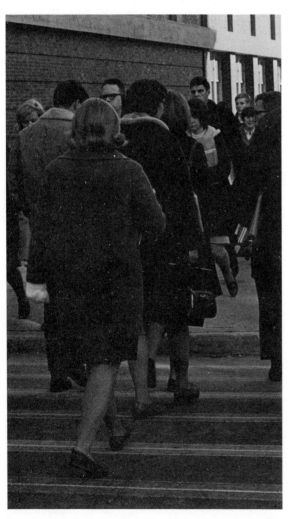

Fig. 3-1. Everyday you are in contact with constructed and manufactured products. Can you identify some of both kinds of products?

You will learn about the workers (personnel) in construction and the technology which is all around them. Later you will learn about workers in manufacturing. In this lesson *both construction and manufacturing workers* will be introduced, along with a brief look at the other major groups of workers in the labor force. These are the people who work for wages. The labor force does not include those who work at school studies or those who are full-time housewives, as examples. Personnel technology will also be defined.

About two out of every seven students in your school will begin working in industry when they finish their schooling. Perhaps you will be one to begin your career in industry. Therefore, it is important that you know about industrial employment and different types of jobs in order to decide whether or not you want to work in industry. Your knowledge about the different kinds of workers and their work will help you choose the type of job which you will be able to do and which you can enjoy.

Industrial Workers in the Labor Force

Table 3-1 shows how many workers there are in the major employment groups as reported by the United States Department of Labor. Manufacturing workers now make up the largest employment group. Construction workers make up one of the smallest employment groups. However, information about the growth of each employment group is important when you look at employment possibilities. Table 3-2 shows how fast each of the employment groups is growing. Table 3-2 shows that construction is one of the three fastest growing employment groups. It also shows that the number of manufacturing workers will not be increasing as fast as the numbers in the labor market as a whole. Construction employment increased 57% between 1947 and 1964. Manufacturing employment increased only 11% in the same time.

Services (see Table 3-2) is one of the major employment groups in the report by the United States Department of Labor. *Services to dwellings* is one of the smaller groups that makes up this larger group. All these workers could be called construction workers as well, because they make their living by working on constructed products. In the same way, "automobile repair" is a smaller group in "services," and all these employees could be called manufacturing personnel. All of them make their living by working on manufactured products. Thus, both the construction and manufacturing employment groups are larger than labor force reports show. We can estimate that more than one million service workers are servicing con-

Table 3-1

Workers in Major Employment Groups, 1964

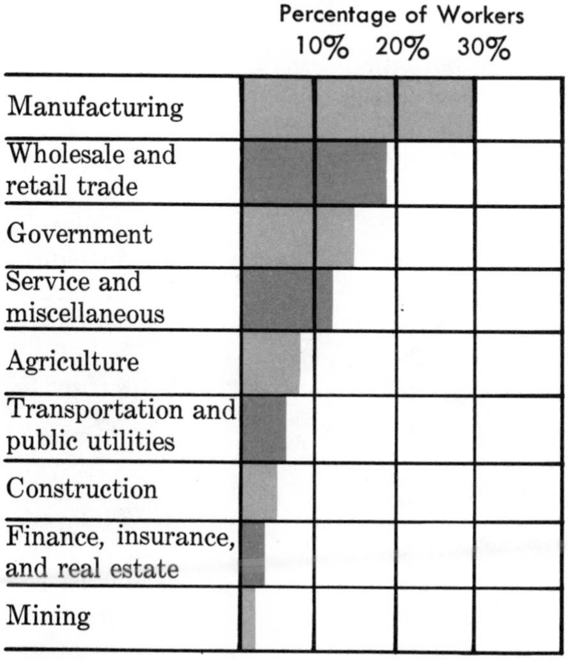

Percentage of Workers

	10%	20%	30%	
Manufacturing				
Wholesale and retail trade				
Government				
Service and miscellaneous				
Agriculture				
Transportation and public utilities				
Construction				
Finance, insurance, and real estate				
Mining				

Table 3-2

While Total Employment Will Go Up by One-Fourth by 1975

Growth Rates Will Vary Widely

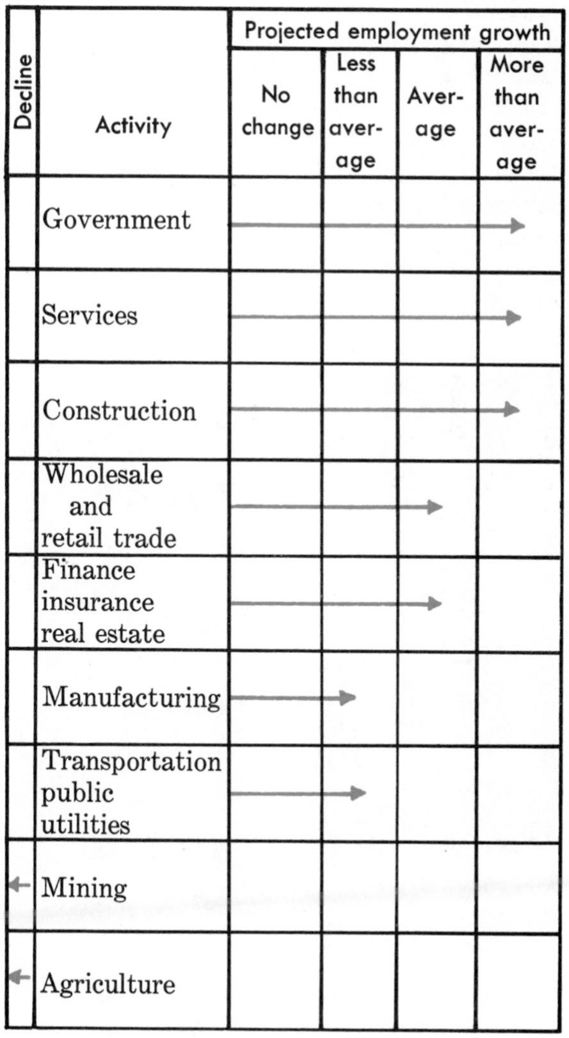

Decline	Activity	Projected employment growth: No change	Less than average	Average	More than average
	Government				→
	Services				→
	Construction				→
	Wholesale and retail trade			→	
	Finance insurance real estate			→	
	Manufacturing		→		
	Transportation public utilities		→		
←	Mining				
←	Agriculture				

structed and manufactured goods, Fig. 3-2. They work in the *postprocessing* of industrial products and could be considered to be industrial employees.

Personnel Technology

This year you will study and work with much of the technology used in making constructed goods. Also you will study the technology which affects the workers who make these goods. *Personnel technology* can be called "ways of causing people to do things." It has a great bearing on the daily work of millions of industrial workers.

The whole idea of personnel technology is a new one. A look at the "coffee break" will help explain problems of personnel technology. The coffee break has become an American tradition. It is accepted, often without question or explanation, as something that should be given to workers. To be called personnel technology, the coffee break would need to be studied from many points of view. With a coffee break, production may go up even though the time worked may be less. On the other hand, some workers may believe that others are getting a longer coffee break. This may make their production drop. In the same way, you may believe that someone else has less homework than you do. Therefore, you may do your homework poorly because you spend some of your time worrying about how to get less homework or, perhaps, how to get

Fig. 3-2. The work these construction men are performing can be classified as repair.

Fig. 3-3. These construction workers work for wages and benefits.

Fig. 3-4. In cold areas, working conditions are improved by the use of temporary plastic enclosures.

the other person more homework. The problem is that it is hard to find the best way to affect people. In personnel technology, the coffee break would be studied to see if it does help people do their jobs better. With more study, another way might be found to help them do their jobs better.

The technology which helps us form materials is very exact. The technology that helps us affect workers is not. Materials can be carefully tested and measured until each piece is very much like another. We are not able to make all people alike, and most people would even question if we should try. Even with the problems which exist in personnel technology, there is much that has been done. By studying what we do know about it, we can better understand personnel problems and practices in industry.

Personnel technology is used to cause workers to work safely and efficiently, to make them feel fairly treated, and to help them find jobs they like and do well. Personnel technology can be grouped in many ways. A simple way to group personnel technology is to consider all of the practices which are directed toward efficient (1) hiring, (2) training, (3) working, (4) advancing, and (5) retiring of personnel. Later in this course, you will study in greater detail each of these major types of personnel practices as they are used in construction.

Summary

As you go through this course, you will meet and do the work of many construction people. If you see how they are hired, trained, worked, promoted, and retired, you will learn how different personnel practices are used for different kinds of workers. You will better understand both what the practices are and why they are used. Also, you will be better able to decide the kind of work you will someday want to do.

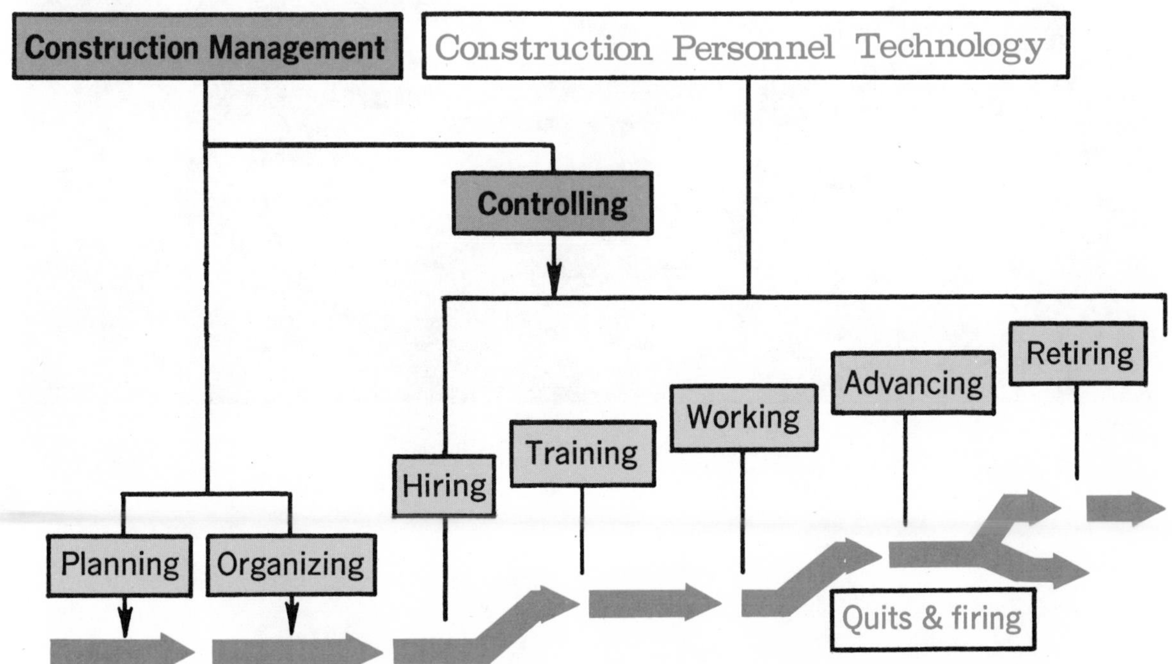

Terms to Know

labor force
wholesale
retail
estimate
organizing
personnel technology
employment
work
career

Think About It!

1. Compare a coffee break on a job with a recess at school. Do people always work harder or better after a break? Why or why not?
2. Since people are not all alike, a *personnel problem* may need several *solutions*. Suggest two or three ways to handle each of these problems.
   a. A construction worker does not like to wear his safety helmet.
   b. A worker who is very friendly wastes time talking.
   c. A man who works very hard thinks he is not paid enough because other workers get the same wages and do less work.

Managing Construction

Management is not hard to understand if you take a careful look at the actions or activities of managing. This lesson is a brief introduction to managing construction.

You have learned that man has improved his standard of living through technology and specialization of human activity. In industry, man has developed two systems for improving his world. They are (1) construction and (2) manufacture. Since construction is the subject of your study this year, we will look at the efficient actions or technology of construction management.

Management Activity Is Universal

You have seen your parents manage family and home affairs. At school you have seen your principal and others manage buildings, playgrounds, classes, teachers, and students. Your city or town is managed or run by elected or appointed officials. Likewise, state and federal governments are managed. Religious activities are managed. In fact, all human activity is managed to some degree.

A common definition of management is "getting work done through other people." In a special sense, then, a person cannot manage himself. He must have some authority over other people to be called a manager. However, if we look at management closely, we find that each person manages most of his daily activity, whether he thinks about it or not. Think back to this morning when you got out of bed. You planned ahead to see which socks would match the rest of your clothing. You organized yourself and picked them out of the drawer. You controlled your selection by making sure you got a pair of socks that were the same color and pattern.

Management involves the actions of:

1. Planning,
2. Organizing, and
3. Controlling.

These actions, activities, or functions as they are sometimes called, are common to all human work and play.

Management in Construction

Management in construction is much the same as in business, in agriculture, in the factory, or in the home. Management in construction involves the planning, organizing, and controlling of construction projects, Fig. 4-1. Well-managed projects usually make a profit for an individual or a company. If management practices are not done well, much money can be lost and a contractor or a construction company *may go out of business.*

Managing involves three major activities or functions:

We will now take a close look at the activities within each of these categories (groupings).

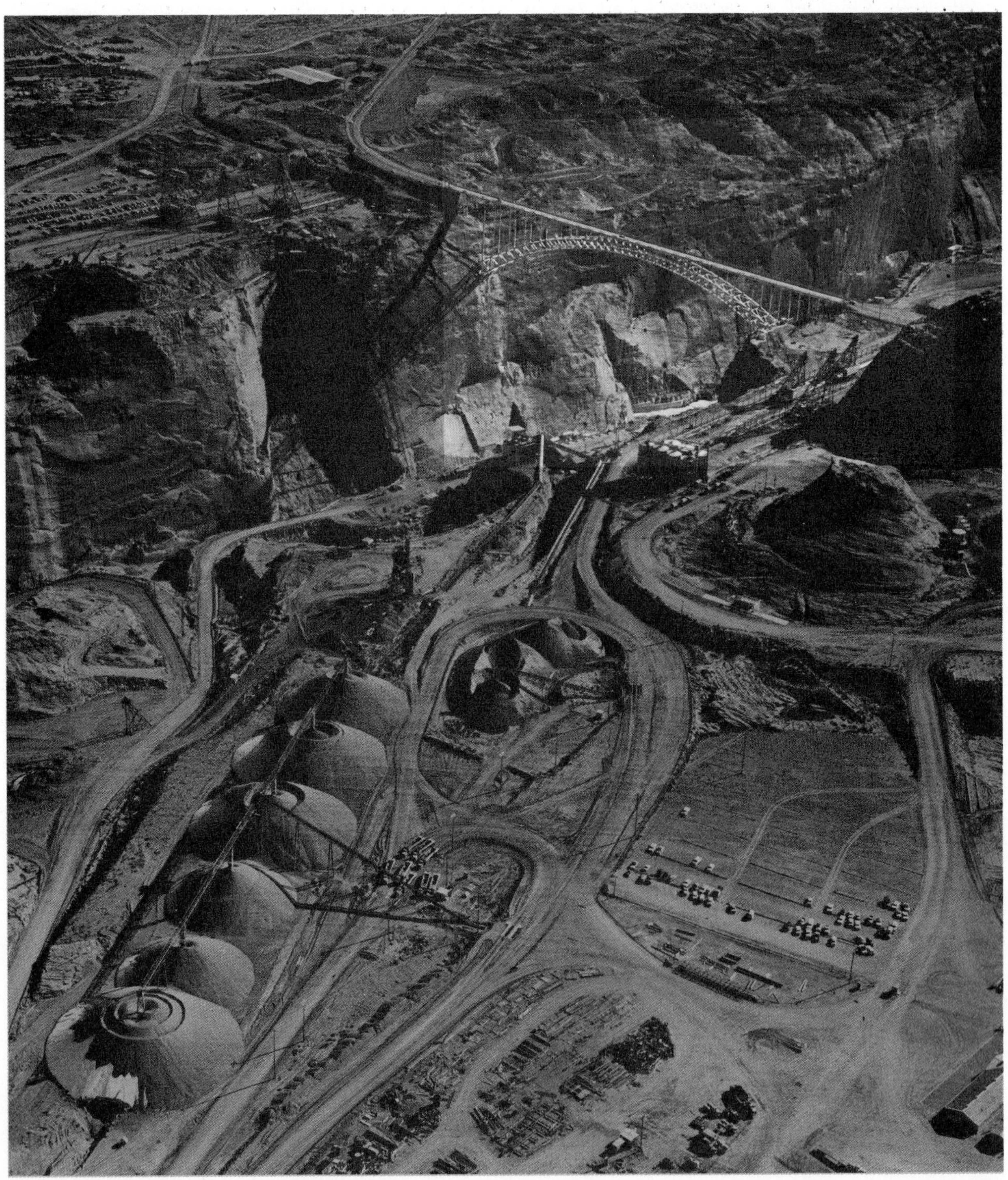

Fig. 4-1. Everything and everybody on a construction site is planned, organized, and controlled.

Planning

The first major category of management is planning. *Planning* is made up of formulating, researching, designing, and engineering.

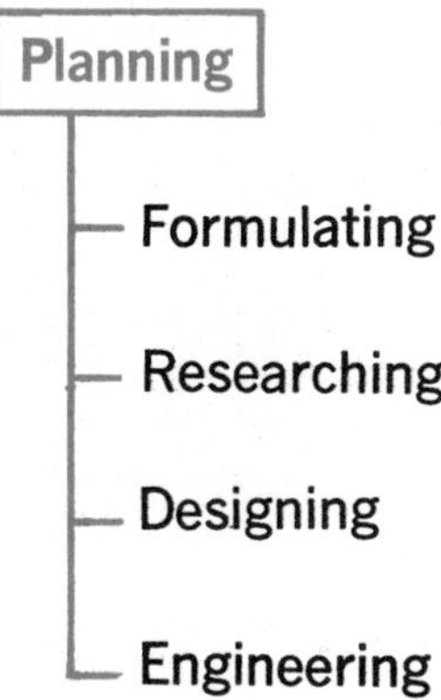

Formulating has to do with setting goals. It means making the first decisions about what is to be constructed and why. *Should it be built? Can it be built? Is there a need for the construction?* Individuals or groups of persons (private or public) take part in formulating well before a project is started at the site.

Researching is needed to find the correct answers to important questions or problems. Some researching (like testing the hardness of soil) is carried on at the construction site. Some research (such as finding where a water pipe is buried) is done in architect's and engineer's offices. Research is also done at universities and research institutes where, for example, wood or iron beams may be tested under great loads to find their breaking point. Researching helps to answer questions of:

1. *What was* (retrieving),
2. *What is* (describing), and
3. *What will be* (experimenting).

In construction, architects, engineers, and sometimes contractors work at designing. *Designing* involves deciding, for example, what function a structure must perform or what job it must do. Several solutions to the design problem will be created, and sketches and models may be made. The best design or the one most satisfying to the designer and customer will be refined and improved, Fig. 4-2. *Designing is very creative.*

Once the best design is selected, details of how to build the structure are considered. This is the *engineering* part of planning. Engineers, estimators, and draftsmen work at engineering details:

1. Detailed drawings are made from the sketches and models.
2. Specifications for building materials are given.
3. Costs are estimated, and building processes are decided upon.
4. The whole project is scheduled as to what must be done first, second, and so on until the project is completed.

Construction bids grow out of engineering activity.

Fig. 4-2. Complicated models sometimes are made to help in the making of management decisions.

Organizing

The second major category of management is *organizing*. This involves the activities of structuring and supplying the organization.

Organizing
- Structuring (forming)
- Supplying (men and materials)

The construction contractor, for example, must plan, structure, or form his organization. This means he must have men and materials to do each job. He forms or structures his company by deciding:

1. What work is to be done,
2. What workers will do it, and
3. When and where they will do it.

Following through with the example of the contractor, he must next supply his structured organization with workers, tools, and materials. He may obtain workers from a union hall or simply "off the bank" (anyone that is around and available). He owns or rents special tools. He buys materials from the concrete plant or the lumber yard. He may subcontract the plumbing or electrical work. He directs men, materials, and subcontractors to get the job done as planned by the engineers.

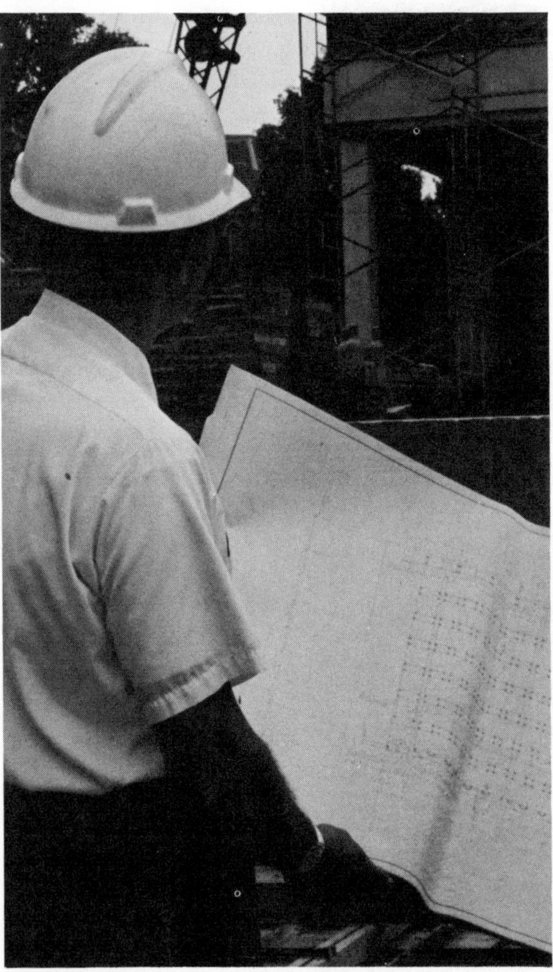

Fig. 4-3. Some managers work on the site.

Controlling

The third major category of management is controlling. *Controlling* includes the activities of directing, monitoring, reporting, and correcting.

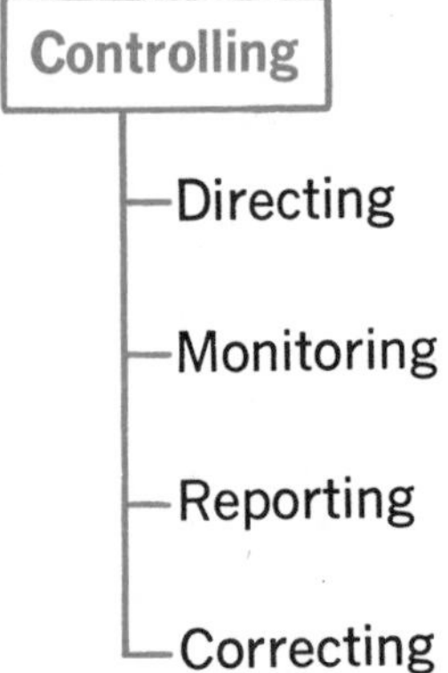

Workers must be supervised. Men and materials must be coordinated. This is called *directing*, and it helps get the work done. All managers are supervisors to some degree, but on the construction job the foreman is the key man, Fig. 4-3. He directs the men in their work with proper tools, equipment, and materials.

Monitoring means that the foreman oversees the work and makes sure it is going smoothly. He is a monitor. The architect and the engineer are monitors because they keep a constant check on the work in the field. The building inspector checks to make sure all building codes (laws) are being followed. He is a monitor. Men who take inventory of supplies and materials are doing monitoring. The timekeeper is a monitor. However, monitoring is often done by machines and not by men. A time clock with punch-in and out cards is an example of monitoring by machines. Monitoring means making sure the work is being done according to plan.

Reporting is the feedback of information about the work which is given to persons in responsible positions. Some reports show that all is going well. Other reports show that something is wrong and that changes are needed. Inspectors may find that electrical wiring does not meet the building codes of the area. The foreman may see that the materials are of poor grade and report this fact to the contractor.

Correcting completes the cycle of controlling. Changes are made by responsible persons if the work is not going according to plan. Correcting may mean only that the foreman tells the carpenter to use a 12 penny nail rather than the smaller 8 penny nail. Correcting sometimes involves replanning on the part of the architect or engineers.

Many Persons Perform Management Activity

The examples given in this lesson have shown that there are many persons in construction management. Managing is done by many different persons with special duties at different levels of authority, Fig. 4-4. We have seen that the owner or client is involved in management activity. The contractor is a businessman, builder, and a manager. The architect and the engineer do

Fig. 4-4. Some managers work in offices.

most of the planning and controlling of construction jobs. Building inspectors perform management activity. The supervisor and foreman take part in management. In fact, each production worker is performing the management activity of controlling. An example is the carpenter who measures, lays out, and checks his work against a plan. However, he may not, technically, be a manager because he is not "getting work done through other people."

Summary

Many persons in construction perform management activities. Three major management functions in construction, as in all human activity, are (1) planning, (2) organizing, and (3) controlling. They do not have to take place in any special order. They often take place at the same time. Planning, organizing, and controlling each have several subactivities.

Your next lesson begins the management story. Someone must first get things going by formulating. Formulating is one part of the larger activity of planning. Planning is one part of the larger activity of managing. As you read this textbook, try to think how each activity relates to the others.

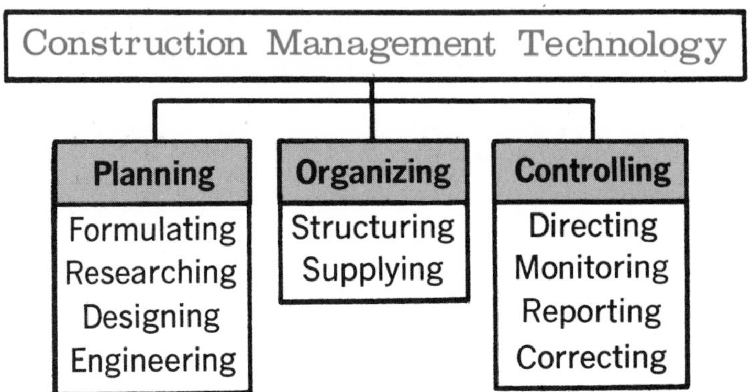

Terms to Know

management
managing
specifications
category
planning
- a. formulating
- b. researching
- c. designing
- d. engineering

subcontract
draftsman
controlling
- a. directing
- b. monitoring
- c. reporting
- d. correcting

monitor
building code
involve
organizing
- a. structuring
- b. supplying

Think About It!

1. For a class party at school, what *planning, organizing,* and *controlling* tasks would each of these committees have?
   - a. Food committee
   - b. Decorating committee
   - c. Entertainment committee
2. Name some of your activities that fit into each research category.
   - a. *Retrieving* (What was?)
   - b. *Describing* (What is?)
   - c. *Experimenting* (What will be?)

Beginning the Project

Everything that has ever been constructed in the world was begun because someone needed it or wanted it to be built. The man who has the idea and who gets a project started is said to begin (initiate) the construction, Fig. 5-1. He is called the *initiator*. After the initiator takes the first step, he or someone else needs to decide whether the project can and should be built. Information is collected and studied. A decision based on the information then is made to go ahead with the project, to delay it, or to forget it.

Initiating Public and Private Projects

Projects may be of two kinds. First, there are those which are publicly owned such as schools or state highways. Second, there are privately owned projects such as the house in which you live or television stations. The procedure for starting or initiating a public project is somewhat different from that for a private project, Figs. 5-2 and 5-3.

Public projects may be small or large. An example of a small public project would be building a sidewalk in front of a school. This would cost only a few hundred dollars. An example of a large public project is the development of the vast Mississippi River system for flood control and water transpor-

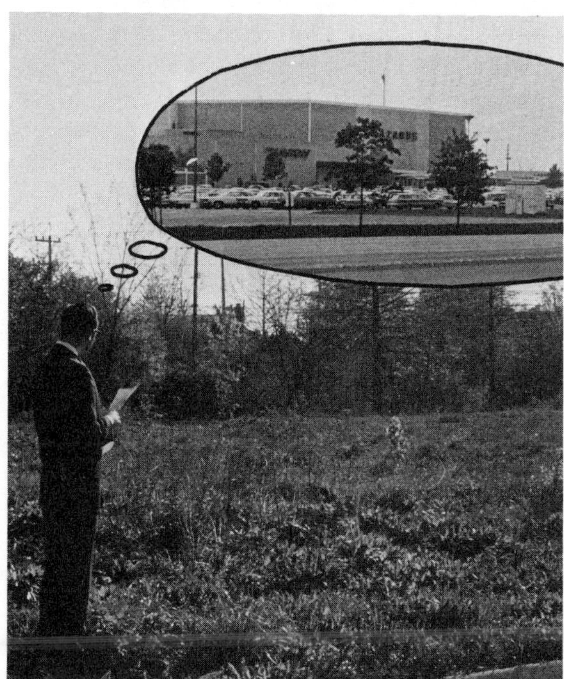

Fig. 5-1. This man, the initiator, has a vision of a finished project on a particular site.

Fig. 5-2. As an example of a public project, we see a state highway being constructed.

tation. This project has cost billions of dollars since it began in 1824, Fig. 5-4. Regardless of project size, the steps for starting most projects are much the same. This is true even though they may take many years to complete and be very difficult—especially if they are major public works.

First, an *initiator* has to see the need for something to be built. An initiator may be anyone—either a private citizen or a public official. Not only must an initiator see the need for a project, but he must also do something about it to get things going. This *second step* of "doing something" usually means pointing out this need to others and getting them to support the project, Fig. 5-5.

Fig. 5-3. Utility lines are being installed as part of a private project.

Fig. 5-4. This is an aerial view of a portion of the Mississippi River flood control and transportation system.

For public projects, the initiator and those who agree with him that there is a need for the project then make the need known to public officials such as city councilmen, county commissioners, or members of legislatures. Sometimes the initiator passes around *petitions* (requests for the project) and gets other interested citizens to sign them to show their support. Often a public official will call a meeting, called a *public hearing,* where the project is discussed and at which the desires of those who are interested are made known. Usually, at the public hearing, the initiator will try to point out good reasons for building the project. The initiator must work very hard to get a project going until final approval is given and until the money is made available for the project.

Usually, the agency of the government which is in charge of a particular project takes over and gets the job done once the project is approved and there is money to build it. The initiator may not take any further active part in buying the property, preparing the plans, and the actual construction. Whoever awards the contract for the actual construction usually is called the *owner of the project.* In public works, the

Fig. 5-5. An initiator is discussing a project with his staff.

owner generally is a governmental agency such as a state highway department or a city park commission.

In private as in public projects, the initiator is the man who has the idea and who does something about it. However, in private projects, the initiator and the owner usually are the same person. The initiator of a private project usually wants something for himself. In the public project, the want is a bit less personal—it is for the community or the region as well as for the initiator.

The initiator of a private project wants something built that he or his company can use for themselves or that he or his company can use for the purpose of making money. For example, a man might want to build a house in which to live. Or he might want to build a house which he can sell at a higher price than it cost him to build so he can make money on it. Perhaps the initiator wants to build a garage in which he can make money by repairing automobiles. Or he may have an idea that his company should build a new plant to produce something which is needed in a certain area.

Fig. 5-6. An initiator is making a proposal to an executive of a private company.

For the private project, the initiator who is building for himself must either have money in hand or convince people who lend money that they should put their money in or invest in his project. If he works for a manufacturing company, he must convince the executives or the owners of the company that the project should be constructed, Fig. 5-6. Unlike the initiator of a public project, the initiator of a privately owned project does not have to gain public support for his project. However, his project must follow public laws and regulations.

Questions to be Answered

If the initiator has proved the need for either a public or a private project, there are many questions to be answered. First, *can the project really be built*? The need for the Panama Canal was known for almost 400 years before the worker welfare, engineering, and earth-moving problems could be solved! We cannot build a highway bridge across the Atlantic Ocean. Even if we could build it, it would cost so much that it would bankrupt every country on earth. The point is that workers, technical skill, money, and time are all needed in building a project. If we don't have them, the project cannot be built.

Second, if the project can be built, *will it work*? If a hydroelectric power plant is to be built, there must be enough water to keep the generators turning. If there is not enough water, it will not be a workable facility.

Third, *is the project the best kind of project to meet the need*? As an example, suppose that a bridge is to be built across a river used by boats. Someone has to decide if the need is best met by building a bridge high enough so that the boats may pass under it or if the need might be met better if the bridge would swing or lift out of the path of the boats. A tunnel might be even more efficient. All the possible ways of doing things should be looked at to find the best answer before a project is started.

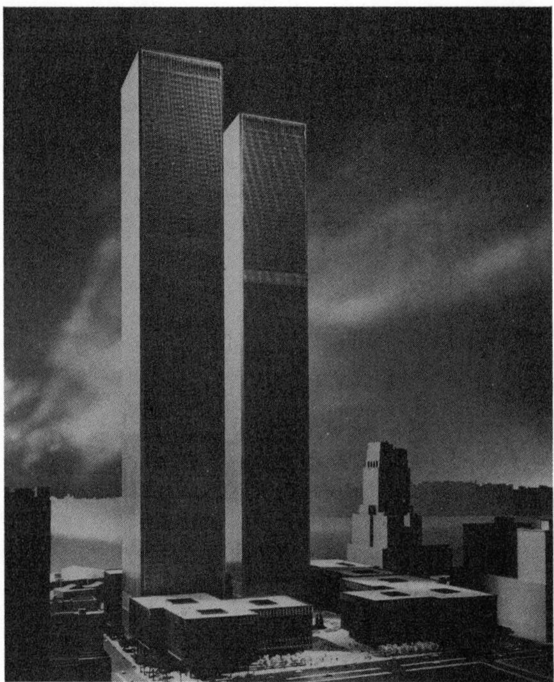

Fig. 5-7. Would you consider it feasible to build these buildings in your community?

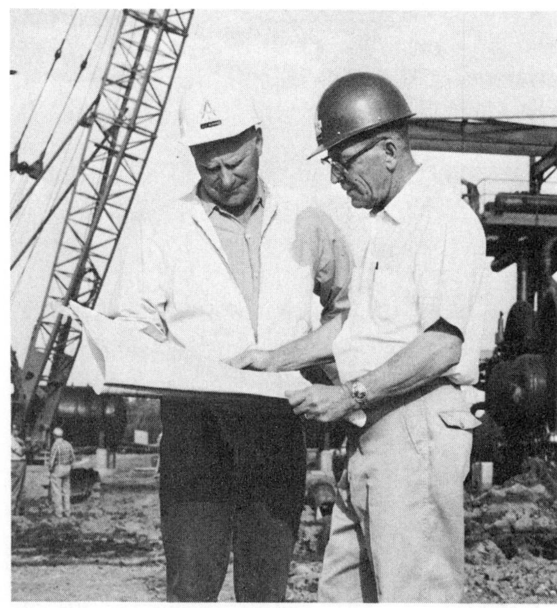

Fig. 5-8. An engineer studies blueprints of other similar projects to determine the feasibility of the owner's project.

Fourth, *will the project add to the well-being of a community or make money for a company?* The wrong project may result in the waste of millions or even billions of dollars. Even a large corporation can be forced out of business by a project which never should have been built or which was built in the wrong place or in the wrong way. On the other hand, a good project means economy in government or profit and success in business.

Someone has to find the answer to these questions. There may be several thousand different ways a project can be built. Even to build a house on a lot 100′ by 100′, there are thousands of different houses which might be constructed. Who is the person who answers the questions?

1. He may be a regular employee of a government agency or a company.
2. He may be someone hired by the government agency or company.
3. He may be the owner or contractor.

To get the answers, this person must study the project. Such a study will tell whether or not it is a good idea to build the project, Fig. 5-7. If it is a good idea, the project is said to be *feasible* (practical). The study itself, which determines whether or not the project is feasible, is called a *feasibility study,* Fig. 5-8.

The Feasibility

If the owner or contractor needs special help in making a feasibility study, he hires specialists who are called *consultants* (advisors). Large construction firms may have a regular staff of consultants. Smaller firms hire independent consultants who work for many firms, Fig. 5-9. The four types of consultants are:

1. Financial,
2. Management,
3. Technical, and
4. Public relations.

Whether a feasibility study is made by the owner, the contractor, regular employees, or an outside consultant, there are certain things that are done in a feasibility study. First an outline of all reasonable alternatives (different ways of building the project) is made. For example, if a road leads to a river, should a ferry boat or a bridge carry the traffic across the river? If a bridge is best, what kind of a bridge should it be and where should it be put?

Fig. 5-9. Consultants spend much time discussing the feasibility of a project.

Fig. 5-10. This bridge could not be built until industrial technology made its construction feasible.

Second, many facts are found by research and by visiting the site. Maps are collected and surveys are made. Holes are drilled into the ground to see what kind of soil is under the surface. The location of roads and utilities is checked, and the kinds of transportation which may be used are checked. Everything that has to do with the project is found out and collected.

Third, the facts that are gathered are studied. Cost, time, and the usefulness or value of the project all are considered.

Fourth, exact recommendations are made such as:

1. The project should not be built at all,
2. The airport should be built at this exact place, or
3. A new plant to make furniture should be constructed close to Newville.

The Decision

After the feasibility study has been made and given to the owner, a decision is made

Fig. 5-11. This completed bridge is the end product of an initiator's dream.

about whether or not to go ahead with the project. A further decision usually is made about the general nature of the project. For example, a decision may be made to build a road on the south side of the river rather than on the north side. These decisions usually are made at the highest level in the organization. In the case of a public project, the decision is made by the governing body. In the case of a corporation thinking of building a new plant, the board of directors makes the decisions.

Summary

This assignment has covered how projects are begun and has shown some of the questions to be answered before deciding whether a project can or should be built. The major questions to be answered and the use of feasibility studies made by the owner, contractor, by their regular employees, or by outside consultants also was discussed. This assignment should help you understand how the final decision to build or not to build is made.

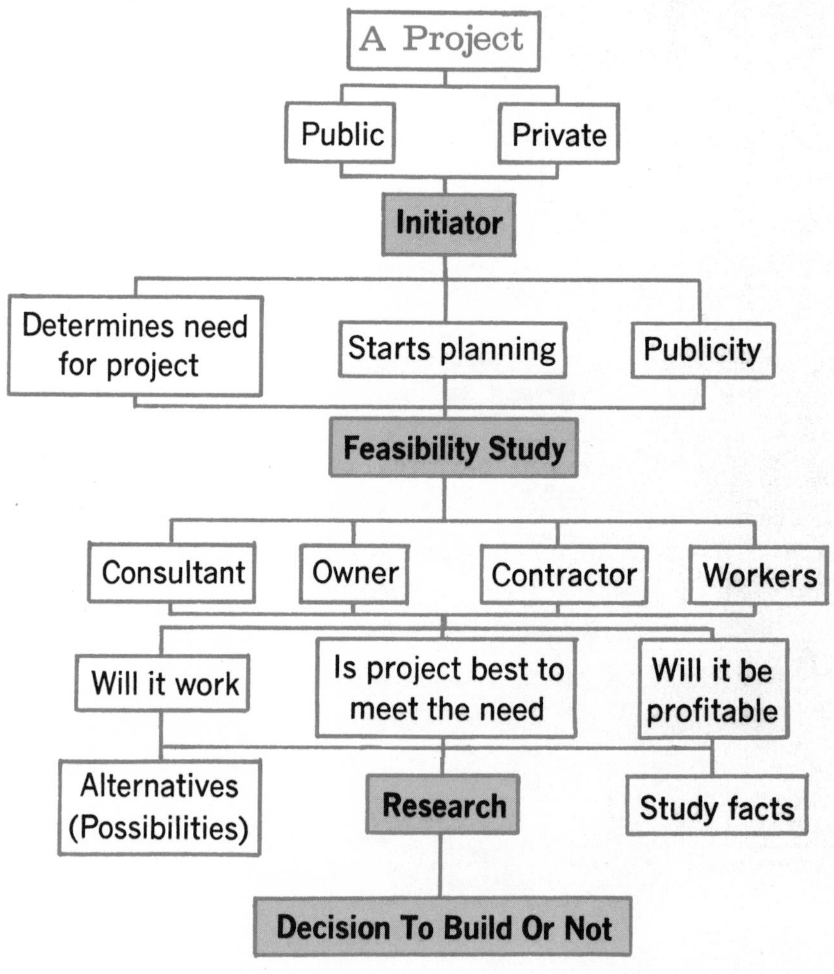

Terms to Know

public hearing
petition
feasible
feasibility study
initiator
survey
utilities
consultant
corporation
recommendation
bankrupt
hydroelectric

Think About It!

1. Suppose that a friend of yours wants to have the community build a recreation center for teen-age boys and girls. He is thinking of bowling alleys, billiard tables, and a gymnasium.
   a. What would be important reasons for spending *public funds* to build this project?
   b. If it is planned as a *private project,* who might provide the money, and why?
2. To help decide if a recreation center is *feasible,* what else would your friend need to find out?

READING 6

Selecting a Site

The *initiator* (or project starter) takes the needed steps to begin a project. Next, a feasibility study is made to find out whether or not the project can or should be built. Then a *site* (location for the construction) is selected and obtained.

Importance of the Site

A good site is a key to the success of a project. The selection of the best site available for the purpose usually means (1) the lowest overall cost and (2) the highest amount of usefulness. For these reasons, selecting a site is done with great care after a long and detailed study, Fig. 6-1. For example, the route for the second Panama Canal has been under study for over 40 years.

One other reason for careful study is that once a location is selected, the site cannot be moved. Many sites for state capitals were chosen from 100 to 250 years ago. They are now in the wrong place for today's distribution of population, Fig. 6-2. Our national capital, once in the center of population, is now more than 1,000 miles from many population centers such as Dallas, San Francisco and Chicago. Yet so much money has been spent on these sites that it would be too expensive to move them to a better location.

Who Selects the Site

Sites are always approved by top management in corporations or in government agencies, Fig. 6-3. If the owner is one person, the owner has the final say about the site for a project. The recommendation (a suggested decision) for a certain site generally is made as part of the *feasibility study* which is made by the owner, the owner's staff, or a hired consultant. During

Fig. 6-1. This picture shows a logical site for a dam.

Fig. 6-3. Top management approves a site for a proposed project.

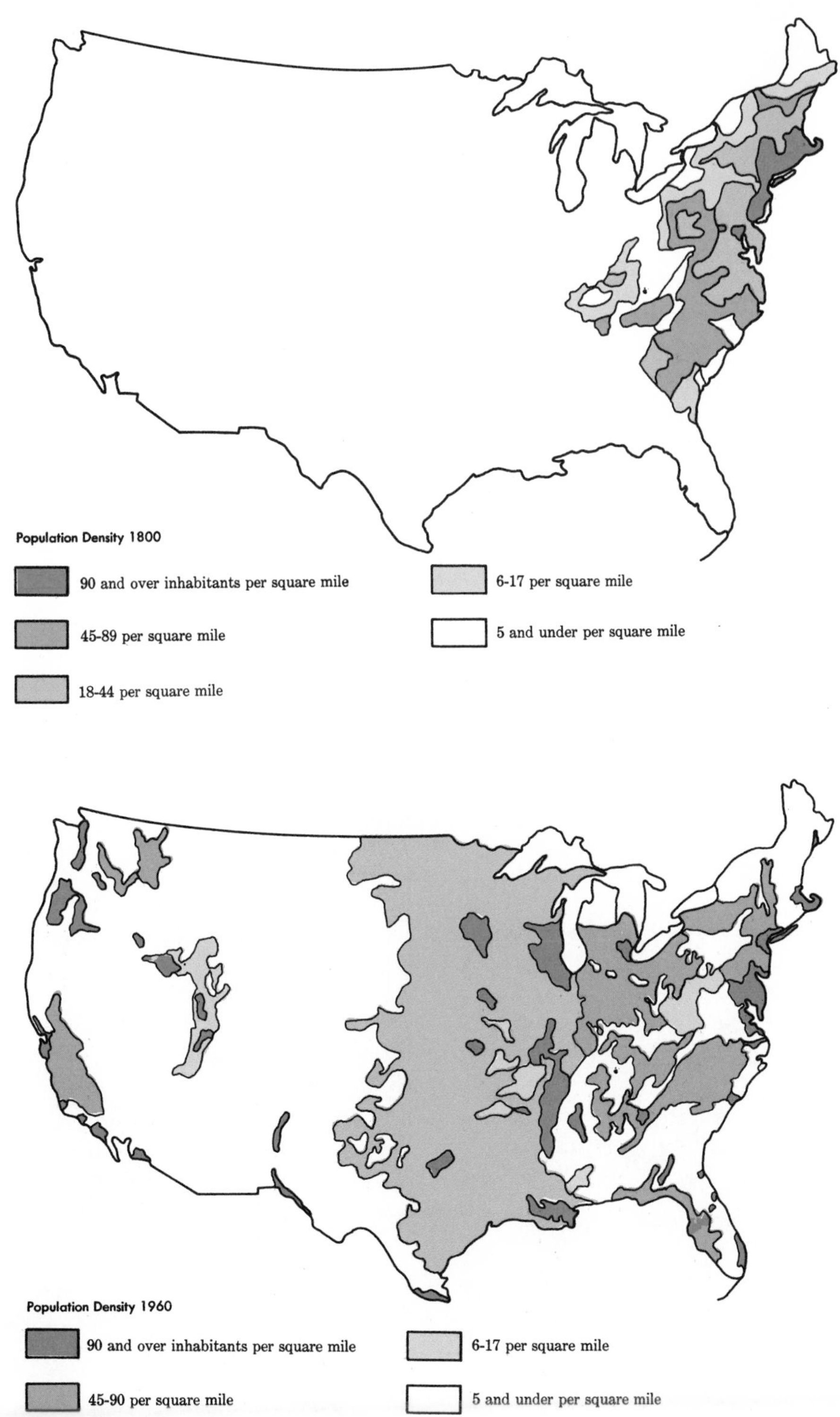

Fig. 6-2. Population density from year 1800 to 1960.

this study many sites may be considered. Generally, information about each site is collected. Then the most promising sites are visited. After this, the choice is cut down to a few sites which are examined in detail. From these few, one is recommended to top management or to the owner who then makes the final choice.

Criteria for Selecting a Site

Criteria are *rules or tests by which something is judged.* The exact criteria for choosing a site depend on the kind of project to be built. A site for a canal would have different criteria for selection than would a site for a railroad. Many criteria are used in site selection.

Perhaps the most important of all criteria for choosing a site is the usefulness of the location for the intended purpose of the project, Fig. 6-4. The site which *best serves the purpose of the project* is the one which should be selected, even though the land or construction cost at other sites may be cheaper. Even though land and construction might cost less on the edge of a community, a bank should locate near the business center of a city where it is needed.

Whether or not the site is available is important. There are usually many good sites, but they may already be in use by someone else or may be owned by someone who does not want to sell.

As criteria for a site, a *market for the products* or a public need must be present. For example, a factory making snow shovels probably would be located in the North and not in Florida.

There must be a *supply of labor* for construction, for operating, and for maintaining the structures to be built. Not only must there be labor, but the workers must have the skills needed, Fig. 6-5. Places where labor contracts have a history of being broken by "wildcat" strikes (sudden stopping of work) often are not chosen as sites.

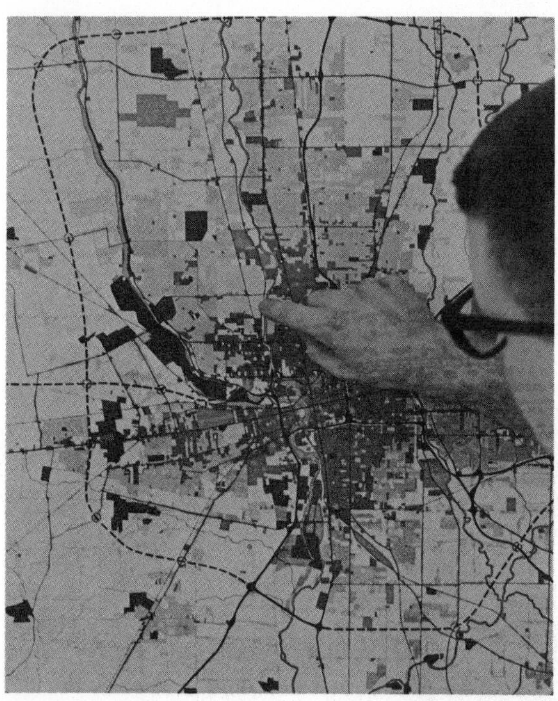

Fig. 6-4. The best site available for a project is selected.

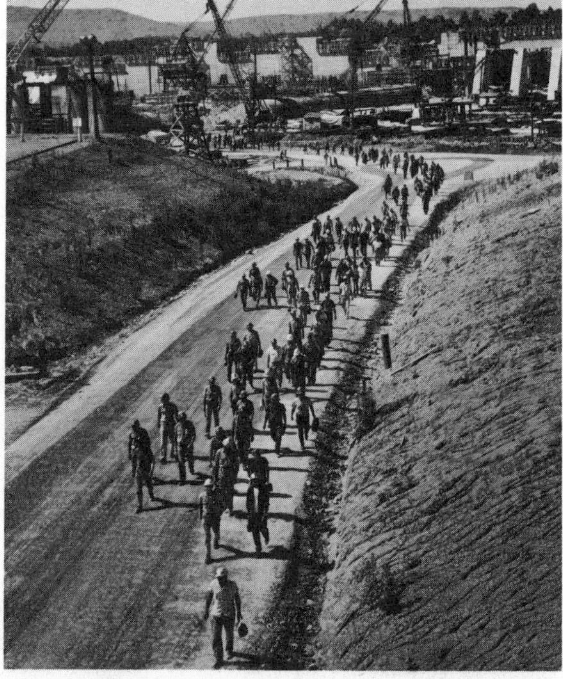

Fig. 6-5. There must be an abundance of labor to construct the project.

A good *community environment* is important in selecting a site, Fig. 6-6. Most companies like to go where they are welcomed. Good schools for children of the company's employees are wanted. If the company employs large numbers of scientific personnel, it may wish to be near one or more universities. Good facilities for recreation also are important. Also, many companies want things like donations of sites, long-term low-interest loans, provision of utilities, and favorable tax treatment.

There must be *transportation* to and from a site. If a company makes large, bulky materials, it will want railroads, good highways, and, sometimes, waterways, Fig. 6-7. If a company ships most of its products by air or if its personnel travel a great deal, it will try to locate near a city with airline service.

Utilities are important for all kinds of projects. A good supply of clean, pure, fresh water is needed. Most industry needs large amounts of water for processing, heating, cleaning, drinking, and cooling. For this reason, as well as for water transportation, heavy industry and electric power plants often look for sites on major waterways. Sewage treatment and water

Fig. 6-6. A good community environment is important for a new industry.

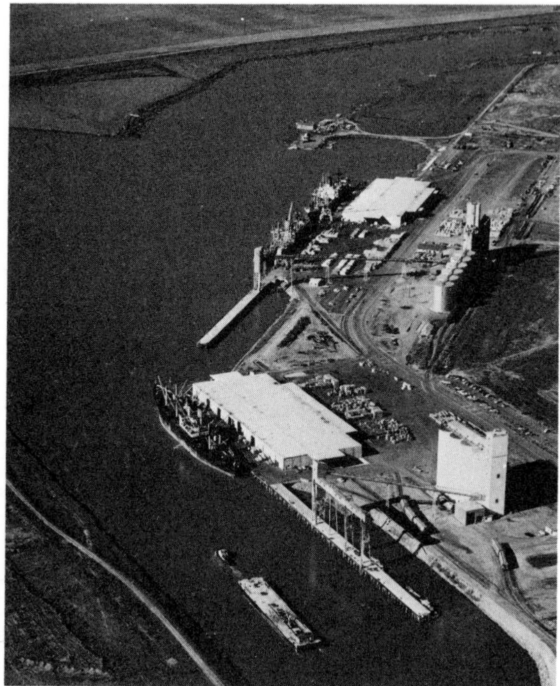

Fig. 6-7. A good industrial site has to have good transportation facilities. Here we see an example of a waterway, a railway, and a highway.

disposal utilities are needed, Fig. 6-8. Nearly all projects need some electric power. Some manufacturing processes need large amounts of low-cost electricity. Therefore, many plants locate near sources of hydroelectric power. Communications like telephone, telegraph, and teletype services must meet the needs of the project. Some industries need large amounts of natural gas or petroleum and, therefore, locate near pipelines.

Raw material availability is often a major factor in selecting a site. Cement plants are usually near limestone quarries. Plywood plants are near forests.

A *suitable climate* also is desired. Certain manufacturing processes need either a dry or a wet climate. Other processes require high or low temperatures. Some others must stay away from areas where temperatures are extremely high or low.

The *physical characteristics* of the site itself are quite important. These include drainage, the amount of site preparation needed, subsurface conditions, and the size of the site. *Subsurface conditions* tell if the

Fig. 6-8. Utilities such as water and electricity are essential in most site selections.

Fig. 6-9. Good physical conditions make the project easier and cheaper to complete.

ground or the underlying rock will hold up the structures needed for the project without very expensive foundations. There must be enough land for all the features of the project, Fig. 6-9. Whether or not roads, bridges, power lines, and underground utilities have to be moved and how much these will cost also are important.

Land restrictions sometimes prevent the use of a good site. Zoning laws, one type of land restriction, have been passed in many places. These laws tell what kind of building can be placed in each location or on each block. The purpose of these laws is to prevent a "mixed-up" community in which factories are built among residential houses. Usually, zoning laws divide a city into residential, business, and industrial areas. Any site selected must be in an area with the right zoning, Fig. 6-10.

Local taxes play an important part in selecting a site. Sometimes property taxes, sales taxes, or income taxes are so great that it is not wise to build a project in an area.

All of the above criteria for selecting a site are looked at in terms of (1) cost of construction, (2) cost of operation and maintenance of the completed project, or (3) cost per unit of production. The site which best can meet the needs of the project at the least cost is generally the one selected.

Acquiring a Site

Once the site is selected, steps must be taken *to buy it or to acquire it.* Sometimes this is easy and takes only a few days. Generally, it takes much longer. In the case of one office building in New York City, it took almost 50 years. Some of the owners of the property on which the building was to be erected insisted on very high prices for their land. Also, some of the properties were owned by two or more people who did not agree upon how the property was to be sold.

Fig. 6-10. Some communities have land restrictions and zoning laws.

The two general ways of acquiring real estate are (1) negotiation and (2) condemnation. *Negotiation* begins when the buyer and the seller talk to each other. They may *reach an agreement* as to price, the date on which the property will change hands, and what portion of the existing property, if any, the seller may remove. For example, a buyer and a seller might negotiate the sale of a house on the following terms: the price to be $20,000, the seller to vacate or be out of the house on April 1, and the seller to leave the draperies but take the electric dishwasher. Sometimes the buyer and the seller talk directly to each other. Often they may have other people, usually realtors (real estate agents), negotiate for them.

Negotiating an agreement between a buyer and seller is by far the better way to acquire real estate. Both parties usually are satisfied with the arrangements made. For this reason, negotiation is used more often than condemnation.

Condemnation may have to be used when public projects need one or more pieces of land. There has to be a way by which a single owner of one piece of property cannot stop the project from being built by a stubborn refusal to sell or by asking too high a price. In such cases, governmental units like federal, state, county, and city governments have what is called the "power of eminent domain." *This is the right to take or condemn real property for public purposes even against the objection of the owner.* This taking process is called "condemnation." However, even though a property is taken away from its owner against his will, the United States Constitution and all state constitutions require that the owner must be paid a fair price for his property. Many utility-type corporations such as railroads, pipelines, and telephone companies also have a limited power of eminent domain when property is needed for their purposes.

Condemnation of property is very unpopular, and those who have this power generally try to negotiate with the owner. If negotiations result in a disagreement over price, the matter is taken into court where the amount is fixed in what are called "condemnation proceedings." These proceedings also are used when the owners cannot be found or when there are problems with the title to the property, Fig. 6-11.

Summary

This assignment has covered how the site is selected and acquired. Typical criteria for site selection are: (1) will it be useful, (2) is it available, (3) are contractors and labor available nearby, and (4) are transportation and utilities handy?

Sites are usually acquired through negotiation. When this does not work and public needs demand that the site be used, the property may be taken by condemnation.

The next assignment tells about how the outside limits of the property are determined and about some of the legal steps taken when property for a project is bought.

Terms to Know

site
criteria
raw materials
pipelines
restrictions
residential
zoning laws
acquiring
negotiation
condemnation
environment
power of eminent domain

Fig. 6-11. A condemnation proceeding is held in a court of law to secure a needed site.

Fig. 6-12. A complete community has been planned by a group of city planners.

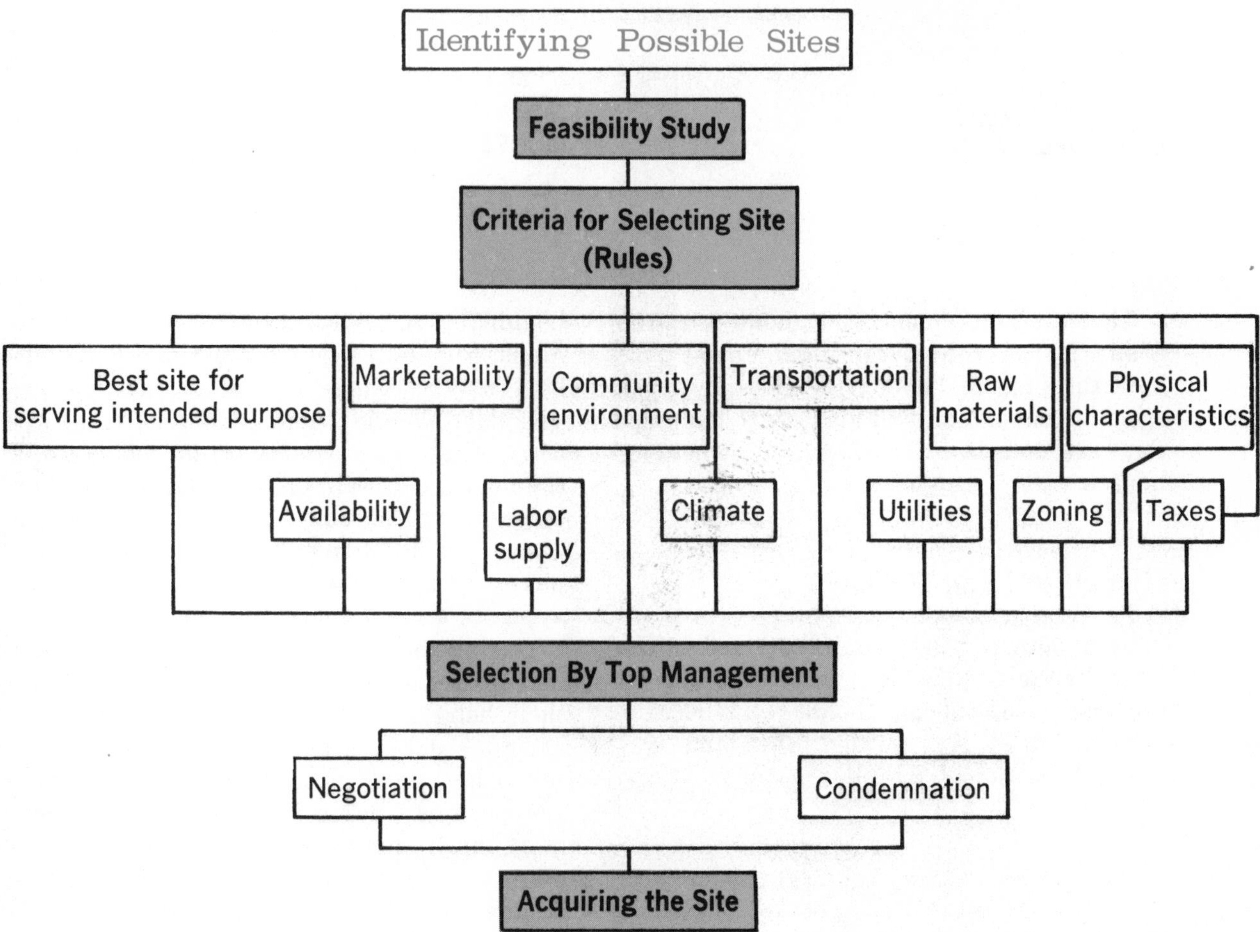

Think About It!

1. Electric power is one of the *general needs* for almost all construction projects. Name some other general needs that people must keep in mind, in deciding where to build the following projects.
   a. A new airport
   b. A shopping center
   c. A factory
2. Suppose that you are *negotiating* to buy a garage where auto bodies are repaired and customized. Name several things that you and the *seller* must agree on before you buy this garage.
3. If you only want to buy the *site* and have no need for the garage building or equipment, how will this affect the *negotiation*? For example, is the land worth more to you with the building or without it?

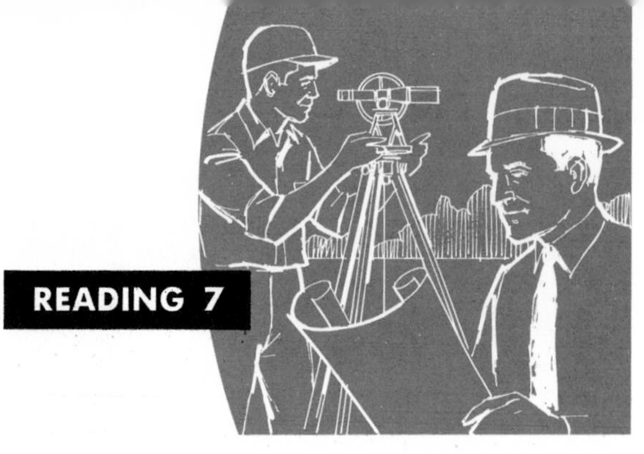

READING 7

Buying Real Estate

The last assignment told about selecting a site for a project. This assignment tells how the outside boundaries or edges of a site are found. You will also study the steps that are followed for changing owners of land.

History of Land Holdings

To understand how land is divided in the United States today, it is helpful to look at the history of its land holdings. When the United States was settled, the land was bought or otherwise acquired from the Indians, Fig. 7-1. Most of it became the property of the kings of the colonial powers (England, France, Spain, Holland, and Sweden). These kings made *grants* (gave away the land) to certain of their people—usually those who had come to the New World. These grants divided the land into large pieces. Some of the land grants were as big as states as we know them today.

Fig. 7-1. Land in the United States was first acquired from the Indians.

During the Colonial Era (1492-1776), the persons receiving the grants (grantees) and their heirs (those who were given the land after the death of the grantees), decided to sell or give away most of their land holdings. The persons who first got the land and their heirs have divided it into smaller pieces many times over. Today there are millions of landowners of the original pieces of land. These are called *parcels* or *tracts of land* and are owned either by some person, company, or by the government.

After the United States was formed and while the United States was getting more land, such as the Louisiana Purchase of 1803, the federal government took title to all the land held by the foreign powers and much of the land which was given to the first people who settled here. Some of this land then was sold or given away. Today, the government still owns one-third of all the land. Government land is of two types. The government has developed some land such as parks, the sites for post offices, and military bases. The balance is undeveloped land which has never been sold or developed land which has been returned to the government for nonpayment of taxes, Fig. 7-2. Most of the undeveloped land is in the Rocky Mountains of the West and in Alaska.

Records

Because there are millions of parcels of land, there is a need for a system of permanent records telling just who owns each piece of land. Records are used to show the *boundaries* (outside lines) of each piece of land. Such records of land ownership generally are kept in county courthouses by a person called a *county registrar* (recorder of deeds), Figs. 7-3 and 7-4. Included in these records are both the present and past owners, the dates of acquisition and transfers of title, tax information, the location of the land, sometimes with plats or maps, and even all past titles, deeds, and mortgages.

A *legal description* tells, in words, what is included in a piece of land. There are many kinds of legal descriptions. However, most of them are similar to one of the three examples which follow.

The first example of a legal description is:

Lot 74 of Libby Heights, a subdivision as per plat recorded in Plat Book 'E', page 92, of the public records of Alachua County, Florida.

Fig. 7-3. This photograph shows a county courthouse where records of land ownerships generally are kept.

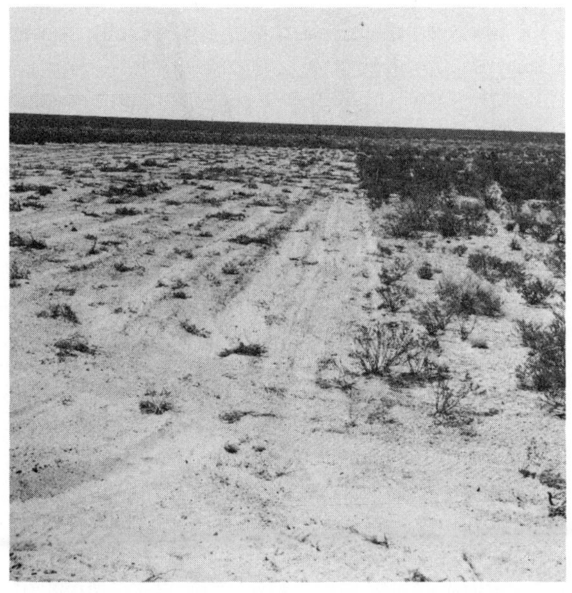

Fig. 7-2. An example of undeveloped government land is shown here.

Fig. 7-4. Here we see a county registrar working in a county courthouse.

A subdivision is an area of land which is divided up into smaller sized lots. The small lots may be easier to sell or improve. In this case, the Libby Heights Subdivision consists of five blocks of land divided up by the land developer into lots about 100′ by 100′. Each lot is numbered so that it can be located easily at the county seat. The map or plat of the subdivision shows the exact boundaries of each lot in the subdivision.

A second example of a legal description follows:

> **Beginning at a concrete and steel monument located 40.1 feet south and 63.2 feet west of the intersection of the center lines of Lexington Avenue and Elm Street in the Town of Norwich, County of Northfield, State of New Jersey, thence:**
>
> **South 4° 3′ east along the westerly line of Elm Street for a distance of 237.3 feet to an iron pin; thence;**
>
> **South 86° 54′ west for a distance of 109.7 feet to the center of a 4′ concrete post; thence. . . ;**
>
> **All bearings being referred to a true meridian; the tract containing a calculated area of 7.59 acres, more or less; and being shown on the plat drawn by George Jones, Registered Land Surveyor, which is attached hereto and made a part hereof.**

This type of description is called a description by "metes and bounds." It is used to describe the land in the 13 original colonies, Kentucky, Tennessee, and parts of Texas and Hawaii. Sometimes it is used in other places for odd-shaped tracts.

The above description starts with a known point—the concrete and steel monument—and goes at a certain angle for a certain distance to an iron pin. Then it goes at another angle to a concrete post, and so on, until it gets back to the starting point—thus enclosing the parcel of land.

Here is a third legal description:

> **Northwest quarter of Section 9, Township 2 North, Range 3 West of the Fifth Principal Meridian, County of Clay, State of Illinois, containing 160 acres, more or less, according to the United States Survey.**

Parts of the country not based on metes and bounds surveys, as in the legal description just before this one, are divided by meridians and base lines. *Meridians* run north and south. *Base lines* and *parallels* run east and west. The area in between is further divided into *townships* which are six miles on a side. They are 36 square miles in size. The townships are further divided into *sections* which are one mile square and contain 640 acres. Sections are divided into *quarter sections* of 160 acres. Quarter sections are often divided again into quarters of 40 acres. After that, division is into *lots* which are subdivided according to a developer's plat or map.

In the place of legal descriptions, some states allow the use of only a map. This map is called a *plat*. Plats are made from surveys done by registered land surveyors, Fig. 7-5. They show the boundaries of a tract of land. Plats always are made when land is subdivided and may or may not be made when land changes ownership. They are filed with the county recorder of deeds, Fig. 7-6.

Fig. 7-5. A surveying team is shown surveying a piece of property.

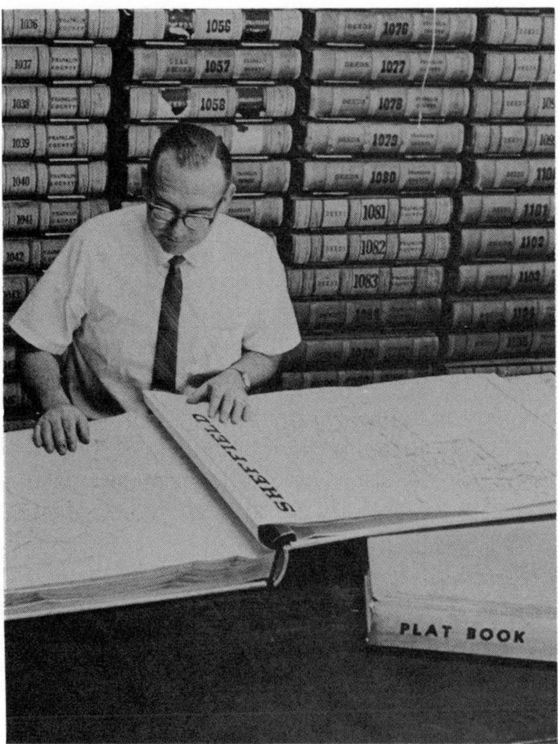

Fig. 7-6. Plats are recorded in plat books and are easily accessible for making a title search.

Fig. 7-7. Shown is the inside of a lending institution where mortgage money can be obtained.

Plats show:

1. Boundaries;
2. Improvements, such as buildings, pavements, and other structures; and
3. Natural features such as lakes.

Plats also show easements. *An easement gives someone the right to put something on the owner's land.* For instance, the electric power company may be given the right to put power lines over a certain part of a piece of property. In addition, plats include what are called encroachments. *An encroachment is a structure owned by someone who does not own the property on which the structure is built.* The fence of a neighbor which is two feet past his property line and on another person's property is an encroachment on that property.

A *title* is a certificate of ownership of a piece of property. A *deed* is a written legal document by which the person who sells the land transfers his ownership to the person who buys the land. Deeds usually are made up of several things. First, there is a legal description of the property. Next, a deed includes mortgages on the land. *Mortgages* show the money owed on the property, Fig. 7-7. A deed also may include restrictions. An example of a restriction might be that every house must be at least a certain size—1,000 square feet, for instance. Easements, as mentioned above, also are included in a title. Easements may show whether or not mineral rights on the property have been sold. As an example of a mineral right, a farmer may own a section of land, but he or an owner before him may have sold the right to drill for and extract oil to someone else. This other person holds the mineral rights. Mineral rights may be for all minerals or for just one mineral such as coal, oil, or gas.

Titles and Surveys

The buyer of the land on which the project is to be built wants to be sure he has a good title to the property. In nearly all cases, the people who lend money to build a project will insist that the property have a *good title.* A "good title" means that the land has been legally transferred and the land has no claims (mechanic's liens) against it. A *lien* means that the previous owner owes someone money for work done on the land or building. The buyer or his construction consultant can check the title by hiring a specialist to examine it.

The hired specialist usually is a real estate attorney—a lawyer who is qualified by training and experience to give an opinion about the title. As the basis for his opinion, he makes what is known as a *title search.* He searches the records at the courthouse which relate to that particular property, Fig. 7-8. Instead of going to the courthouse himself, he often buys an *abstract.* This is a document prepared by an abstract company. The document is based on the courthouse records of important information about the piece of land being bought.

Fig. 7-8. Here we see an attorney making a title search at the county registrar's office.

Title insurance also can be bought. A title insurance company has or hires a lawyer to read the abstract and give an opinion. If the title is good, the owner gets an insurance policy. This policy insures him against mistakes in the title and promises to defend lawsuits which may come up if there are such mistakes.

If a title is defective or has mistakes, the owner gets an attorney to correct them. This means that he "cures" the title of its problems. Sometimes this work means only finding a missing heir to the land. At other times, court action is brought to clear the title of its defects.

Either the owner or the people who lend him money for the project usually insist on a survey as well as a title search. This survey must be done by a registered land surveyor. In some states, a registered professional engineer may do it. The surveyor first gets all known surveying facts about the site. Then, starting at a known point, he measures angles and distances along the boundaries. He checks the legal description and makes a new one if it is needed. Then he prepares the plat or map.

Fig. 7-9. The buyer, seller, lawyer, real estate broker, and the representative for the lending institution are shown at a property closing.

Changing Owners

After the title search and survey, the seller, the buyer, a representative of the mortgage company, and their lawyers meet at what is called a "closing." The buyer gives money to the seller. The seller then hands the buyer the deed. This is the formal transfer of ownership of the property, Fig. 7-9. The deed then is recorded at the courthouse, Fig. 7-10.

Fig. 7-10. Records are kept up to date at a county registrar's office.

Summary

Land holdings in the United States have been divided many times over. Today there are millions of parcels of land. All are owned privately or by the government. Many records of land ownership are kept. These are legal descriptions, plats or maps, titles, and deeds. Title searches and surveys are made to get an exact description of pieces of land. These are done mostly when land changes ownership.

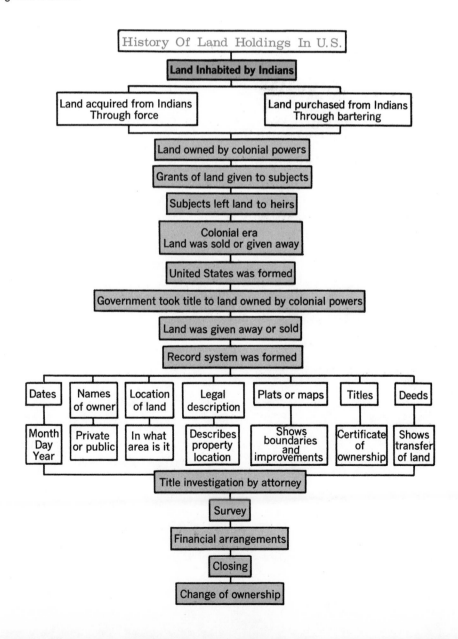

History Of Land Holdings In U.S.

Land Inhabited by Indians

Land acquired from Indians Through force

Land purchased from Indians Through bartering

Land owned by colonial powers

Grants of land given to subjects

Subjects left land to heirs

Colonial era
Land was sold or given away

United States was formed

Government took title to land owned by colonial powers

Land was given away or sold

Record system was formed

Dates	Names of owner	Location of land	Legal description	Plats or maps	Titles	Deeds
Month Day Year	Private or public	In what area is it	Describes property location	Shows boundaries and improvements	Certificate of ownership	Shows transfer of land

Title investigation by attorney

Survey

Financial arrangements

Closing

Change of ownership

Terms to Know

boundaries
registrar
plat
subdivision
legal description
meridians
base lines
parallels
townships
sections
quarter sections
lots
easements
encroachment
titles
deeds
parcel
abstract
title insurance
mortgage
title search
surveyor
closing
lien

Think About It!

1. A *plat* (map) of a piece of land may show all the kinds of information listed below. You may use examples to explain each term.
   a. *Boundaries*
   b. *Improvements*
   c. *Natural features*
   d. *Easements*
   e. *Encroachments*
2. When a piece of land is sold, the seller must give the buyer a *deed* (legal paper) showing several kinds of information. If you were buying a building lot, what information could you expect to be recorded on the deed?

Surveying and Mapping

The last assignment told about the boundaries and legal description of a site. This lesson tells how the natural and man-made features of the site are surveyed or measured and put on maps to be used for designing the project, Fig. 8-1.

Types of Surveys

Surveys are classified as to their function. *Land surveys* are made to establish boundaries and provide records and maps which show the proper location and subdivision of lands in any specified area. *Topographic surveys* are conducted to gather data showing both the natural and man-made features of the terrain. *Route surveys* are made to determine alignment (route), grades, and the amount of earthwork needed in connection with the construction of highways, railroads, canals, airports, and pipelines, for example. *Hydrographic surveys* are made to record data about the shore lines of bodies of water and to determine the shape of the area underlying the water surface. *Aerial surveys* are to record the features of a large area of land. Topographic maps may be made from aerial surveys. *Construction surveys* are made to properly locate on a site all of the facilities that are to be built.

Surveys are made by employees of the project owner, construction consultants, or by a surveying firm hired to make them. In making a topographic survey, many steps are taken.

Research

Many times a record of information about a site is already available. Any information about a site that can be found beforehand will lower the amount of required work and the cost of the survey. It also will help check any work that is done. Therefore, all the facts already known about a site are collected first. This gathering together of facts is called *research.*

There are many places where facts can be found. Most of the country has been mapped by the United States Geological

Fig. 8-1. Before a project can begin, natural and man-made features of the site must be accurately located and mapped.

Survey. Copies of these maps and some field work facts can be requested from their files. Other federal, state, and local governmental agencies have large amounts of surveying data (information). For example, the Department of Agriculture has air photographs of most of the cropland. County or city surveyors often have information. Sometimes surveyors who have made topographical surveys of the area before will give out information about a site. People who have owned the site before sometimes have good topographic maps or other facts about the site. Public utilities, railroads, and city and county engineers may have helpful information.

Almost all surveys are really *resurveys.* This means surveying again what has been surveyed before. A resurvey usually is done for a different reason and in more detail than surveys which were done before. A resurvey must start from known points of location and elevation which have been found by research.

Finding Known Points

Finding the location of known points is called *horizontal control.* It is based upon a process known as *triangulation.* The term "triangulation" refers to accurate surveys which have been made of the whole country to find the corners of a large number of triangles. Each side of the triangle may be several miles long. From the triangle corners, other surveys have been made to find the location of millions of additional points.

Elevations of known points are called *vertical control.* These *elevations* are distances above a certain fixed level on the earth's surface. *Usually the mean* (average) *sea level at a certain point is used as a fixed level.* For example, the elevation of Lake Superior may be 602′. This means that at some point the level of the lake is 602′ above the average level of the ocean. In this case, the ocean level at New York was used. A point in Death Valley, California, may be minus 125′. This is 125′ below the average height of the surface of the ocean.

Things other than average sea level sometimes are used as a fixed level. Very careful surveys, generally along railroads, have been made throughout the country. As a result, the elevations of these lines from the level of the ocean are well known.

Monumenting

When important surveys are made to find out either the *location* (where a point is) or the *elevation* (how high above the ocean level it is), permanent markers are placed on the point so that future surveys can be started from that point. These markers, called *monuments* or sometimes *bench marks,* are firmly set in place. Early surveyors used large stones set in the ground as markers. Today concrete posts are used. The location and elevation of the marker often are placed on a brass plate on the marker, Fig. 8-2. The readings are taken from the very center (the center is the highest point on the top surface of the bench mark). The foundation for a bench mark is shown in *B* of Fig. 8-2. The foundation supports the bench mark so that it will not move out of position. All bench marks are placed very accurately so readings can be taken for new constructions. The marker's location and elevation are always put in the surveyor's notes. These notes then are carefully recorded and saved. Anyone wishing to make a resurvey finds a marker as a place to start or end his survey. Finding these markers, some of which were placed over 100 years ago, is sometimes a major problem for the surveyor.

On the project site, the surveyor works from a known point which is related to a marker. He then drives wooden stakes or metal pins to mark locations and elevations which help the construction workers in earthworking and locating the structure.

Survey Parties

The size of the survey group and the skills of the people in it depend on the size and the difficulty of the job to be done. Most survey parties have from two to eight people in them. The *chief* of the surveying party plans and supervises the work. On small parties, he also may record survey findings in the field notebooks. Sometimes another person, called a *recorder,* does this. The *instrument man* sets up and operates the surveying instrument over a known point. The *rodman* holds the rod used in surveying over another point. Sometimes an *axeman* is needed to clear brush and trees so that the rod may be seen from the instrument. If any measurements

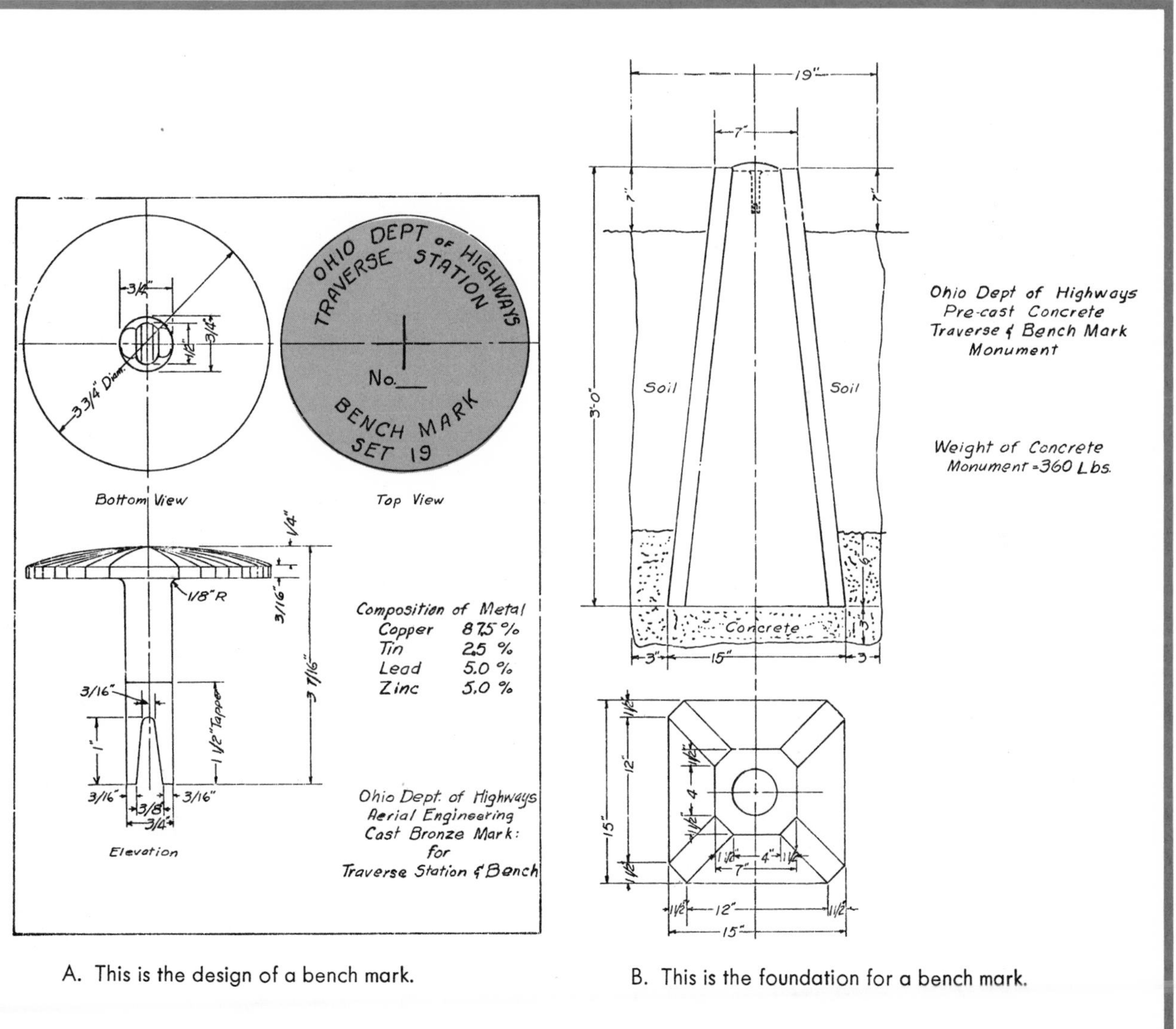

A. This is the design of a bench mark.

B. This is the foundation for a bench mark.

Fig. 8-2. The construction of a bench mark.

are to be made with a steel tape (called a *chain*), two or more *chainmen* may be in the survey group.

Fig. 8-3. A team of surveyors may travel to remote areas.

Location Surveys

The instruments used most often to find a location are the transit and the plane table. The *transit* measures horizontal and vertical angles, Fig. 8-4. It also may be used for leveling, but a *level* usually is used instead, Fig. 8-5.

When points are known, the transit is set up and leveled over one point. One rod is placed on the known point. Another rod is placed at the unknown point. The transit measures the angle between the line from the transit to the known point and the line from the transit to the unknown point.

The transit also can be used to measure the distance from the transit to the points by reading numbers on the rods. However, on very careful surveys, this distance usually is chained or measured with a steel tape. By making repeated setups of the transit and by measuring angles until another or the same known point is reached, all the land is measured. The transit may be set up to measure angles and distances to certain features of the site when their location is wanted, Fig. 8-6.

The *plane table* is a simple form of transit. It is used in much the same way as a

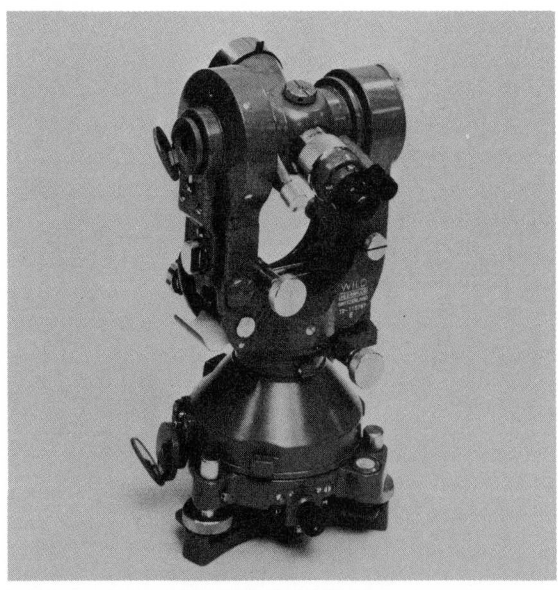

Fig. 8-4. A transit is used by surveyors to measure horizontal and vertical angles.

Fig. 8-5. A level is used by surveyors to measure elevations.

transit. The *theodolite* is another survey instrument. It is a more precise form of transit used for very accurate measurements. Other modern instruments are used for measuring angles and distances. Some of these new instruments make use of electronics.

Elevation Surveys

The instrument used most often for finding elevations is the level. The *level* is a telescope which is set up and is, itself, leveled. The *level rod,* which is marked in feet, is set on a point of known elevation or height. The level is set up, and the measurement is found on the rod, Fig. 8-7. Then the rod is put on a point where the elevation is not known, and the measurement is found. The difference between the readings is the elevation of the unknown point.

For example, suppose the elevation of a known point is 100′. A reading on the rod at the known *point A* is 3′. The reading at the unknown *point B* is 5′. The difference between these two readings is 5′ minus 3′, or 2′. The unknown point, then, is 2′ lower than the known point. 100′ minus 2′ equals 98′, which is the *elevation on the unknown point.* If the level is now moved to another position, the rod may be placed on *point B,* which is now a known elevation, and then on an unknown *point C* to find the *elevation of C.* In this manner, a line of levels may be run by repeating measurements until another known point (or the first known point) is reached. A line of levels may also be run by setting up the level in one position and moving only the rod from point to point, referring back to just one known elevation. This method can be used only when the ground is quite flat and there are few obstructions.

Other instruments used for elevation surveys are the *surveying altimeter* and the *elevation meter.* Although both are very expensive, work can be done more quickly with them than with the level.

Plotting Data

As surveys are made, the measurements are recorded in *field notebooks.* The note-

Fig. 8-6. The transit is leveled accurately before readings are taken on the construction site.

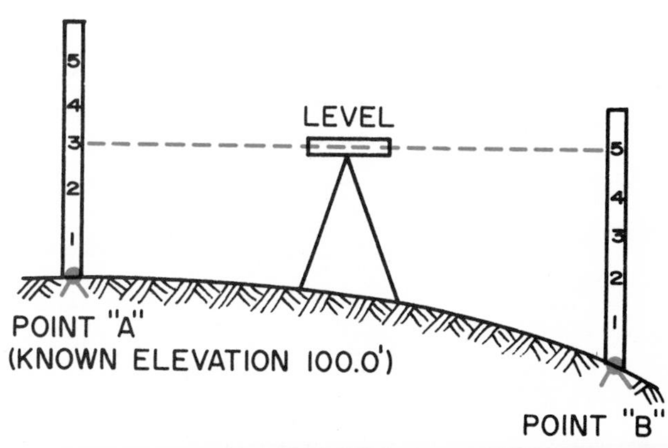

Fig. 8-7. A level is used to find the elevation of an unknown point from a known one.

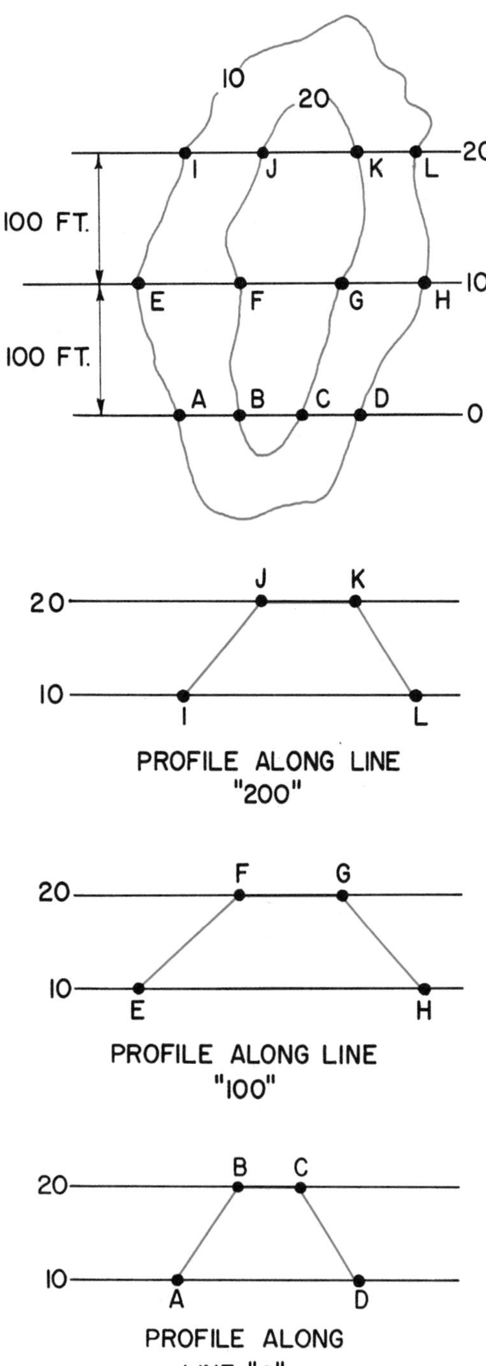

Fig. 8-8. A series of elevations along parallel lines can be made into profiles of the terrain along the lines.

books then are taken to the office where figuring is done. The next step is to *plot* (find the location of) each important point on a topographic map. To show the shape of the land, which is found from the elevations, two methods are used:

1. Grid system
2. Contours

A simple *grid system* often is used for small sites. The site plan is divided into squares to form a grid. Elevations are shown at the corners of squares. When adjoining squares show elevations which are about equal, the land is flat. When adjoining squares show differing elevations, the person reading the grid knows the site is uneven.

A *contour* is a line made by connecting every point on a grid which is at the same height. Contours have several features. First, contours never cross except in the rare case of an overhanging cliff. Contours *spaced closely together* mean a steep slope. When they are *spaced far apart,* they show a gentle slope or fairly flat land. *Closed contour lines* mean either a hill or a low spot in the land.

In some cases, mostly for roads and airfield runways, *cross section surveys* are made. A cross section survey is made by finding a series of elevations along parallel straight lines, Fig. 8-8. The survey lines usually are spaced about 100′ apart. The elevation points can be connected on profile drawings. These drawings are used to estimate how much earth moving must be done on a site.

Surveys of Large Areas

Modern instruments are valuable for surveying sites which are large in area. Also, aerial photography can be used for such surveys. Photographs taken from the air show the features of the ground. However, horizontal and vertical control also are needed to plot what the photographs show. Techniques have been developed by which approximate elevations may be found from aerial photographs. However, these methods require expensive and complicated equipment such as multiplex projectors and stereocomparagraphs.

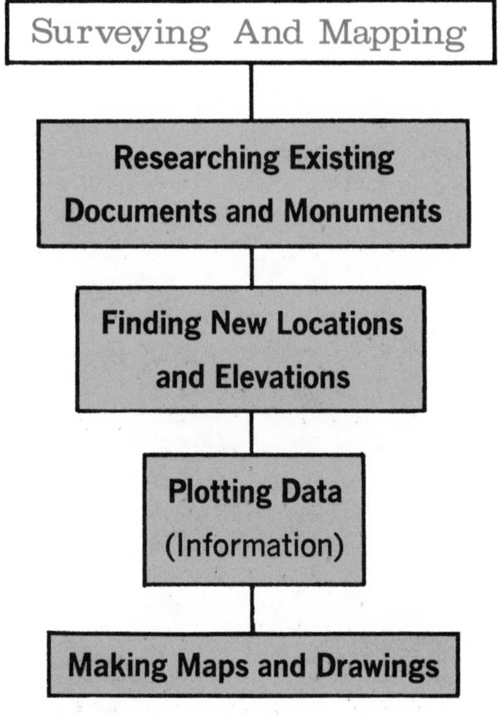

Summary

Topographic surveying is measuring land to show the exact natural and man-made features of the site. These surveys are made so that maps can be drawn for the designer to use in designing a project.

Surveys begin with finding known points. Locations and elevations are very important, Fig. 8-9. The transit and plane table are used for finding locations. Elevations are found by using a level. The grid system and contours or cross sections are used to show the lay of the land.

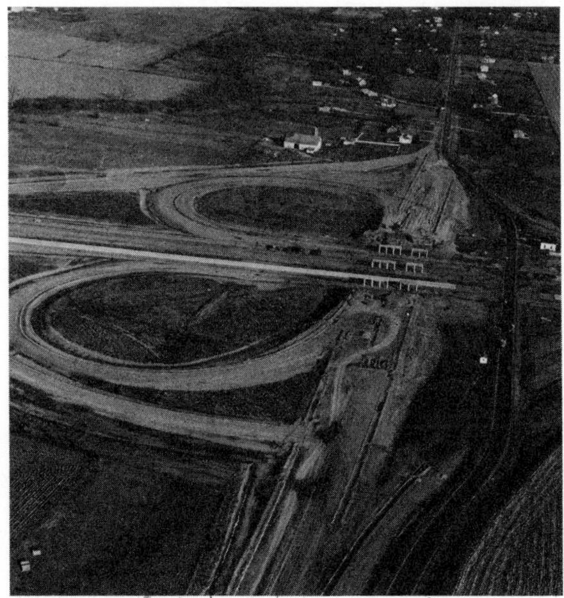

Fig. 8-9. Imagine the surveying, mapping, and construction drawing which had to be done before this construction work could be started.

Terms to Know

research	fixed level
location	contour
level	plot a point
surveying	transit
resurvey	monuments
horizontal control	bench marks
vertical control	data
triangulation	grid
elevation	mapping

Think About It!

1. Why does a *surveyor* begin measuring from a *monument* or *bench mark*?
2. What *natural features* may have existed, on and near the site of your school, before the land was settled and developed?
3. On a *topographic map* of your school grounds, what *improvements* would be shown?

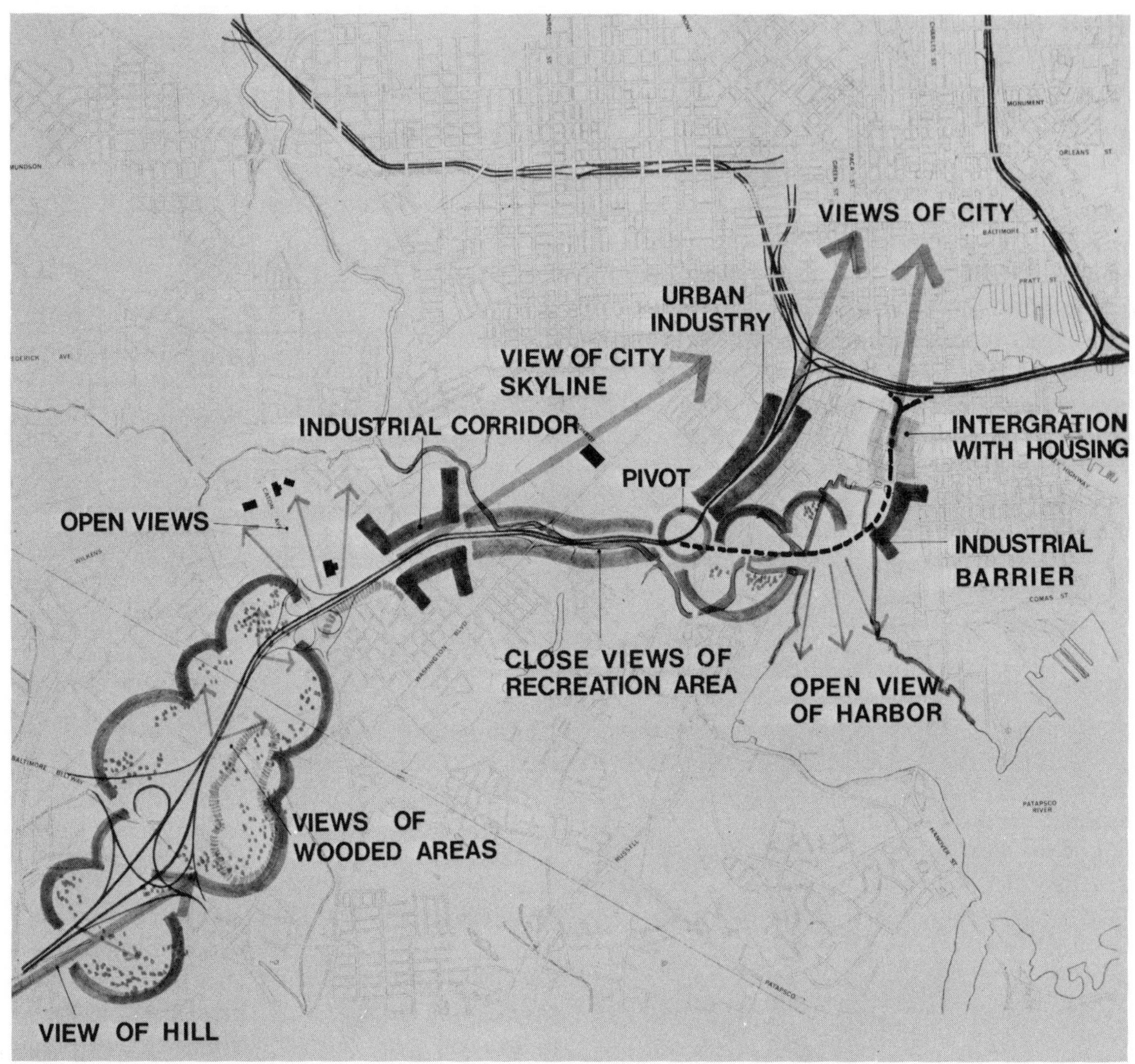

Fig. 8-10. A surveyor's map may show the location of existing structures with regard to the planned project. This map shows the different views that the motorist will have from the new highway.

READING 9

Soil Testing

You have read how land surfaces are measured and described. This assignment will help you understand the nature of the soil which forms the upper layer of the earth. Soil sometimes is used in the construction of a structure such as an earthen dam. Generally, however, soil provides the *load-bearing surface* upon which the foundation (base) of a structure rests. No matter what the structure may be, it must have a strong and sturdy foundation. To be sure of the strength and stability (firmness) of the foundation, the construction designer must know what the soil is like where the foundation is to be built.

The Earth's Crust

The crust of the earth is made up of rock and soil, Fig. 9-1. Since rock is a hard material, it requires great force to excavate or remove it. There are several kinds of rock. *Bedrock* is under all of the earth's surface. It may be deeply below the earth's surface, or in other cases, it may be exposed and can be seen on the surface. *Boulders* are large, loose pieces of rock. They are from about 8″ to many feet in diameter. *Cobbles* are small pieces of rock. They are about 4″ to 8″ in diameter.

Soil is composed of loose parts of the earth's surface. It is made up of grains of different sizes. *Gravel* is in pieces which range from the size of peas to the size of cobbles. *Grains of sand* range from the size of granulated sugar to the size of peas. The texture of *silt* varies from that of powdered sugar to that of granulated sugar. *Clay* is of a very fine, powder-like texture, much like that of flour.

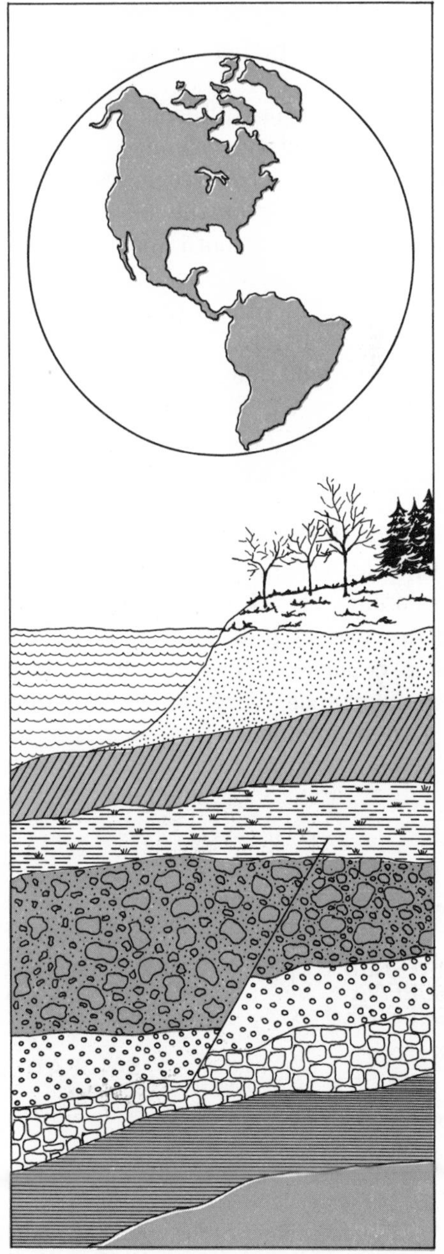

Fig. 9-1. The earth's crust is made up of rock and soil.

Most soil is made up of textures varying from that of fine clay to large boulders. For example, a so-called silt may be made up of 75% silt, 15% clay, and 10% sand.

Topsoil is the soil which lies near the surface of the earth. It is generally covered with grass, crops, or weeds. It is a mixture of soil and decayed vegetable matter.

Soil Characteristics

Different soil has different characteristics. Some characteristics depend on the soil particles. Other characteristics depend on the action of water on the soil particles. Soil particles are not smooth like marble. They are different in size and shape. Sometimes they are rounded. More often they are jagged with sharp corners. Because of the way they are shaped, they may not fill the whole space they are in. There are usually spaces between the particles which are called *voids*.

Much soil, especially clay, is quite *cohesive*. This means that the grains stick together. In fact, some kinds of soil stick together so strongly that they are nearly like cement. This kind of soil is almost as hard to work with as solid rock. Other clays often are plastic. They can be molded into different shapes very much like modeling clay can be molded.

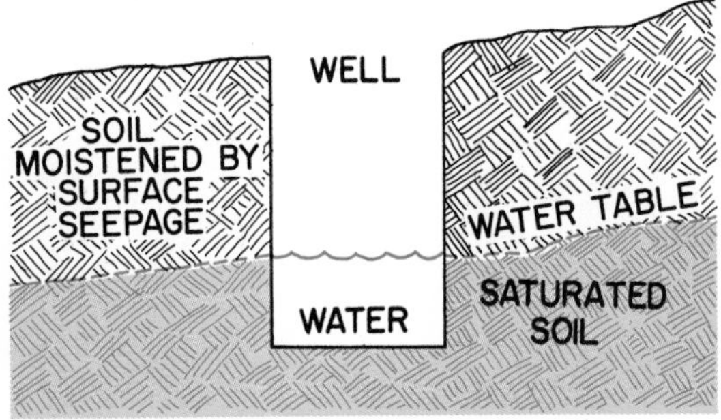

Fig. 9-2. The water table generally follows the surface contour of the land. In different parts of the country the water table is found at different depths from the surface.

When the grains have large spaces or voids between them, the soil is called *loose*. When the voids are small, the soil is called *dense*. Density can be made greater by putting pressure or weight on soil. Most soil is compressible. This means that it can be *packed down* or *compressed*.

The characteristics of soils depend a great deal on the amount of water which they contain. This water is of two kinds. At least a small amount of water from surface seepage (drainage) is in the spaces between grains of nearly all soils. In addition, there are rivers and lakes of water under the surface of the ground. This water fills and flows through the spaces between the soil grains. The top of this underground water, which can be found by digging an open pit, is called the *water table*, Fig. 9-2. The water table is not flat like the surface of an aboveground river or lake. Instead, it is found at differing depths from place to place around the world. It generally follows the surface contour of the land. Like surface water, most of this water is in motion or has a current.

In general, most soil (especially that with a lot of clay in it) swells as moisture is increased and shrinks when it is taken away. Some clay *slakes* (turns into a soft mass) when it becomes wet. A firm clay may lose its strength when there is water in it.

When water freezes and becomes ice, it expands and takes up more space. If the water in the soil freezes, the soil also expands and takes up more space. This raises the surface of the ground. Then, when the ice thaws, water forms and the soil becomes very wet. The depth of frost in the ground depends on the weather.

When most soil is excavated or dug up, it expands or swells. This happens because, when soil is disturbed, air gets into the spaces between the particles. One hundred cubic yards of a certain soil in its natural state might become 114 cubic yards if it were taken out and loaded onto trucks. Then it might be placed in a foundation for a building where it might be placed under pressure to reduce the voids or spaces between the grains. After this is done, it might be only 85 cubic yards, Fig. 9-3.

Soil Analysis

On large projects, or when there are unusual soil drainage or groundwater problems, soil specialists may be hired to do a *soil analysis.* They study the soil and make recommendations about how to work with it, Fig. 9-4.

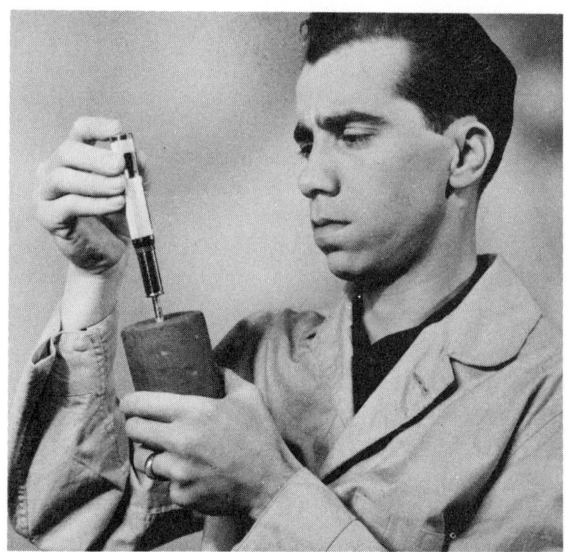

Fig. 9-4. A soil tester is using a pocket penetrometer to check soil strength and its classification.

There are many ways to get information about what kind of soil or rock is under the surface of the ground. The cheapest way is to find out what is already known about the soil. This is done by checking with government agencies, the neighboring property owners, drillers, and soil laboratories to see if they already have facts about the soil under study. Another inexpensive method used to analyze soil is to look at and feel the type of rock or soil which is on top of the earth's surface.

Holes may be bored with drills. By seeing the type of soil which comes out of the hole,

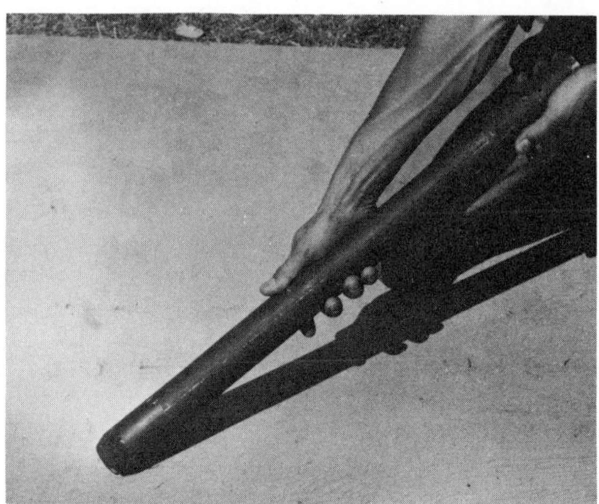

Fig. 9-5. A split-spoon core container with both halves together is shown here.

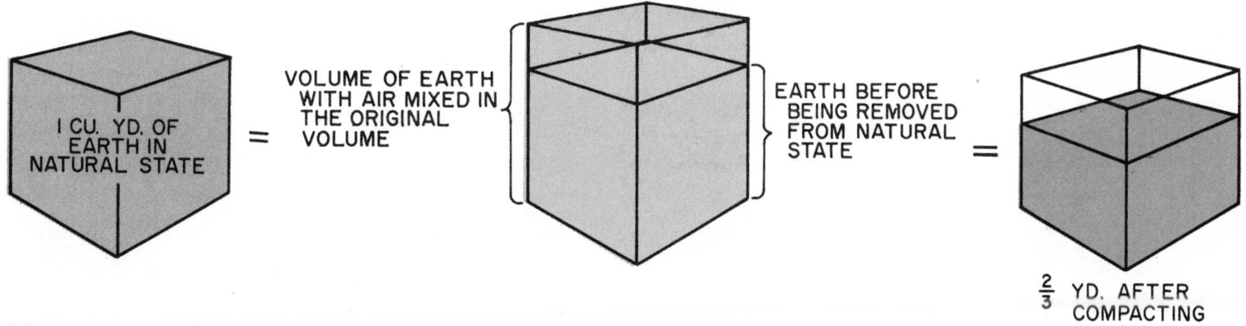

Fig. 9-3. When soil is removed from its original position, it is loose because of the air it now contains. Also, it has become large in volume (amount). When the soil is packed to hold a load bearing surface (a foundation), it then becomes smaller in amount.

it is possible to tell what kind of soil is at different depths in the ground. Some drills are made so that they bring up to the surface a cylindrical sample (shaped like a round pencil) or core of the soil, Figs. 9-5 and 9-6. These cores may be sent to a laboratory for analysis.

Sometimes, large holes are dug in the ground so the soil tester may look at and take samples of the soil at various depths. These holes, which are dug by hand or machinery (Fig. 9-7), are called *test pits*.

Soil tests in the field are of two different kinds. First, there are *plate bearing tests*. In these, heavy weights are placed on about four square feet of the earth's surface. The tester then observes the vertical and horizontal stability of the soil. That is, he measures how much the load tilts or leans. Also, he measures how much the load sinks into the soil. These are measures of *soil stability* and *settlement*. Second, there are *density tests*. Soil is put in a standard cylinder and is hit with a certain number of blows

Fig. 9-6. The split-spoon container with one half removed shows the soil sample.

Fig. 9-8. A soil tester is performing a sand density test.

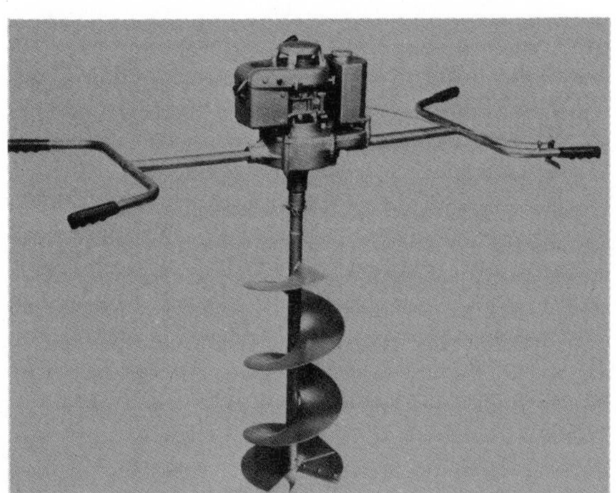

Fig. 9-7. An auger powerhead is used for large diameter or deep hole drilling to obtain soil samples.

Fig. 9-9. A laboratory technician is preparing a core sample of cohesive soil for determining its shear strength.

with a hammer. This shows how much the soil packs together, Fig. 9-8.

Laboratory testing is done to find out about (1) soil strength (Figs. 9-9 and 9-10), (2) water in the soil (Fig. 9-11), (3) soil plasticity, and (4) soil compressibility (how much it will pack down, Fig. 9-12). Geophysical tests using explosives or the

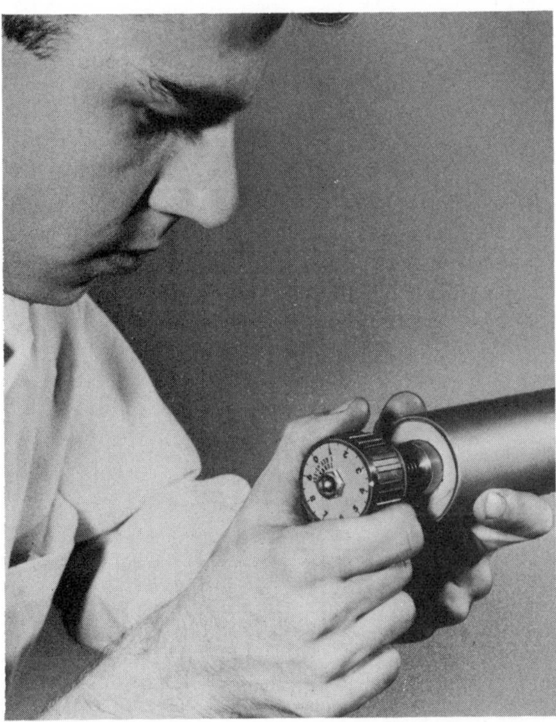

Fig. 9-10. A shear strength testing device is being mounted in a soil sample.

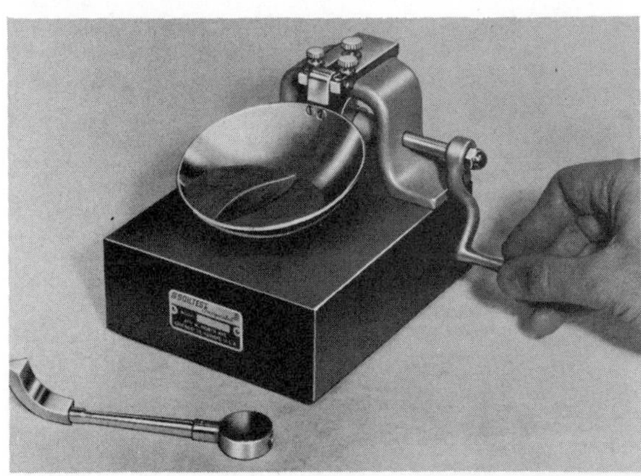

Fig. 9-11. A liquid limit testing device is used in the laboratory to determine the amount of water needed to cause the soil sample to become fluid.

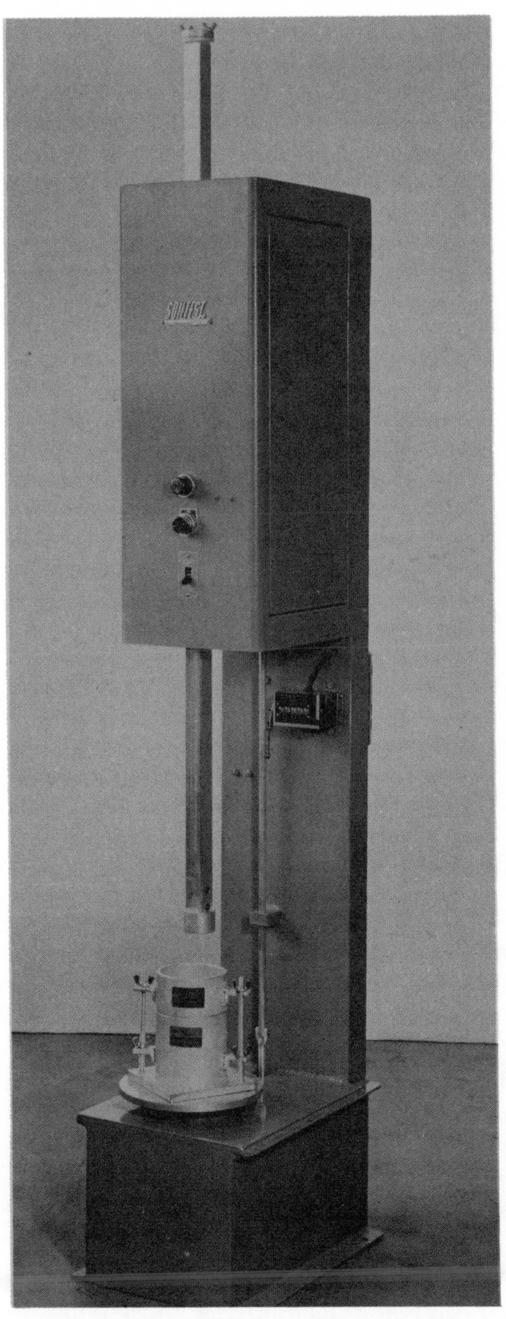

Fig. 9-12. A laboratory soil compactor is used to measure the ability of a soil to be compacted.

electrical resistance of the ground often are used. They are very helpful in finding how deep the bedrock is buried below the surface, Fig. 9-13.

Fig. 9-13. Here soil testers are performing a geophysical test using a seismograph to determine how deep the bedrock is beneath the soil.

Soil and Construction

The soil under a foundation must be stable enough to hold up the load of the structure which is built on it. It must not erode or wash away, and it must be kept from heaving as a result of freezing or extra water in the soil. Soil must not settle too much or unevenly. This would cause the structure to crack.

Soil is often used as a construction material in making earthen dams. It must be stable and not heave or settle too much. It must be placed so water can drain away without eroding the fill. In addition, when trenches are dug, some soils need to be held in place by supports which are called *shoring*, Fig. 9-14. This keeps them from caving in or falling on the workers. *Firm soil* may not need to be shored. Excavating crews must know with which soil type they are working to prevent dangerous caving in.

Fig. 9-14. Shoring is used to hold soil in place.

Soil Engineering

From the soil tests and the laboratory reports, the construction consultant determines how the soil in its natural state will be affected by the structure. He also decides what has to be done to or with the soil to take care of the needs of the structure and the safety of the workers. Sometimes a large amount of soil must be removed and replaced by soil which is better for use. In other cases, pressure must be applied by heavy rollers to reduce the spaces or voids between the grains of the soil so that it can hold a greater load. Often the composition of the soil itself is changed by adding a different type of soil or even some other substance, such as cement, to it.

The construction consultant decides how steep the man-made slopes should be. He also decides how to take care of extra water and how to prevent *frost heave.* In the case of foundations, he determines how much weight the soil can hold without collapsing or settling too much or too unevenly. He may even find that the soil is so soft that pilings must be put in for support. Based on the strength of the soil, a design for the structure may now begin.

Summary

In this assignment you have read that the earth's crust is made up of rock and soil. Characteristics of various types of soil have been described. The designer or soil consultant tests the soil and decides what needs to be done with the soil so it will support the structure that is being planned.

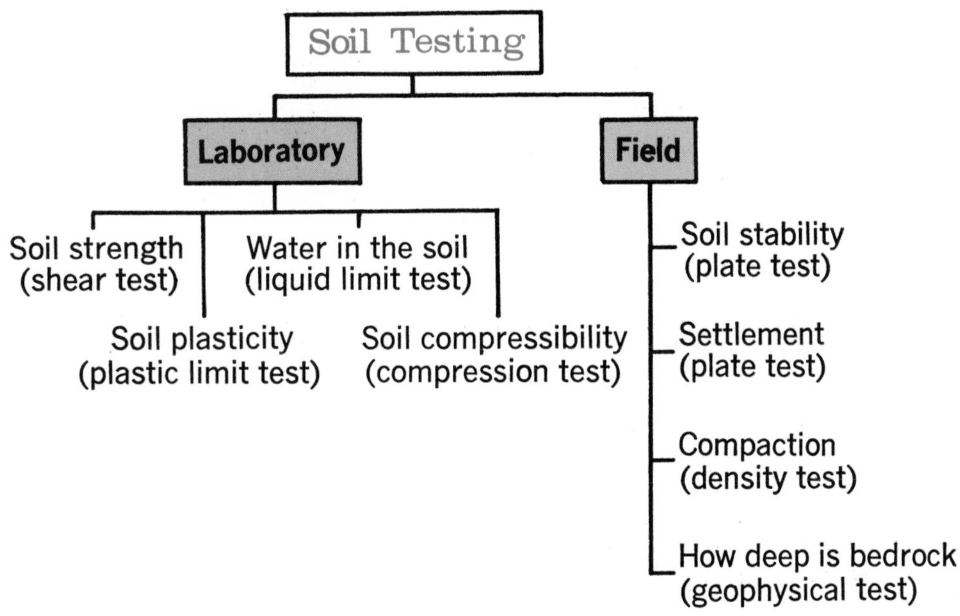

Terms to Know

voids
bedrock
topsoil
slakes
cohesive
loose soil
dense soil
compress
water table
cubic yard
analysis
sample
stability
laboratory
geophysical
shoring
piling

Think About It!

1. Describe the soil in your community.
2. How does the soil in your community affect the following:
   a. water supply
   b. building foundations
   c. basements
   d. roadways
   e. drainage
   f. plant growth

READING 10

Designing and Engineering Construction Projects

The previous reading assignments have discussed how a project is begun and a construction site selected. The next step in the project is the developing of a working plan of action. This is a process known as *design*. The design process was actually begun before the selection of the site, because the site must fit into the master design plan. If this had not been done, a poor site might be selected. This assignment will introduce the design process of construction involving: (1) architects, (2) engineers, (3) contractors, and (4) craftsmen.

What is Design?

Designing is finding a solution to a problem. A design does not need to be entirely different from any other designs. It may be a combination of ideas arranged in a different way, Fig. 10-1. A traffic system for a neighborhood would probably be the result of a design of this kind. The designer would probably use standard materials, basic measurements, and standard curbing and drainage methods. However, his use and arrangement of these features might be very unusual, Fig. 10-2. The result would likely be something entirely different from other designs of this kind. Because requirements, purposes, and other limitations may change with each situation, each design is usually unique.

Some problems require entirely new solutions. There might be no past experience or usable background information that would apply to the planned project. "No past experience" means that the designer must be very creative. He must experiment with de-

Fig. 10-1. The Mormon Tabernacle in Salt Lake City is a solution to one designer's problem.

Fig. 10-2. After the general shape of the design has been determined, the details are engineered.

signs. Examples of problems of this kind are:

1. A nuclear-powered generating plant,
2. A space station, and
3. A neighborhood nuclear fallout shelter.

Each of these problems might require information and use of materials different from routine construction projects. Also, there is usually little past reference information available for the designer to see what others have done on each of the three problems. To design a nuclear-powered generating plant, the designer must learn the scientific principles involved so his design can meet the needs of the project. A space station will require many new materials and techniques. The design for a nuclear fallout shelter would be based on conditions that could not be tested without having a nuclear explosion. Thus, the designer must think of each problem in very fine detail to develop a workable design.

In general, the process of designing is the art of finding a new solution to a problem. The final product of a designer is a completed project such as a building, a community, or a bridge that satisfies a given need. The final design is usually presented in the form of drawings and specifications that can be used by the builders to produce the final project.

Design Considerations

Regardless of the type of design project being developed, there are basic factors that are common to all designs. Several of these factors are: (1) function, (2) appearance, (3) cost, (4) construction materials, and (5) strength. These factors are closely related and overlap, making it hard to separate them.

Almost all design projects begin with a budget that outlines how the money is to be spent on the project. The most important part of a construction design is its function or its ability to meet the problem's needs. For example: a foundation must support a building. If it will not, the design is unsatisfactory regardless of how economical or attractive the foundation may be. Another type of function is flow of traffic in a parking lot. The design is a failure if automobiles cannot enter and leave the parking spaces in an efficient manner without causing traffic jams.

The use of materials and strength of a design are important to the project. Although leather or steel could be used as the material for a door hinge, steel would be better. A steel hinge would give more strength while holding the door securely in position. Dams may be constructed from earth or concrete with each material having certain advantages over the other.

The Design Process

The designer's procedure for arriving at his final solution may vary with the individual; however, he will always approach the design process in an *organized manner*. The steps given below outline a procedure that is commonly used by most designers.

1. **Problem Identification:** A problem is identified to prove that there is a need that must be satisfied. Background information must be gathered and evaluated to understand the full need. For example, a need is recognized for a design to provide automobile traffic to cross a riverbed. Identification of the problem would include (1) setting up dimensions, (2) finding the depth of water, (3) finding the width of the riverbed, (4) estimating the number of people who would need to make the crossing, (5) finding historical records which show high water levels, and (6) studying other information of this type to better understand the problem.

2. **Preliminary (Beginning) Ideas:** After the problem has been fully identified, the designer should consider as many solutions as possible with little regard to the details as to whether or not a solution will work. Sketches, notes, and ideas are jotted down as fast as possible in hopes that one idea might lead to another. Using the riverbed crossing as an example, the designer might consider rerouting the river, building a bridge, using a ferry or other ideas. At this point, these ideas have no limits.

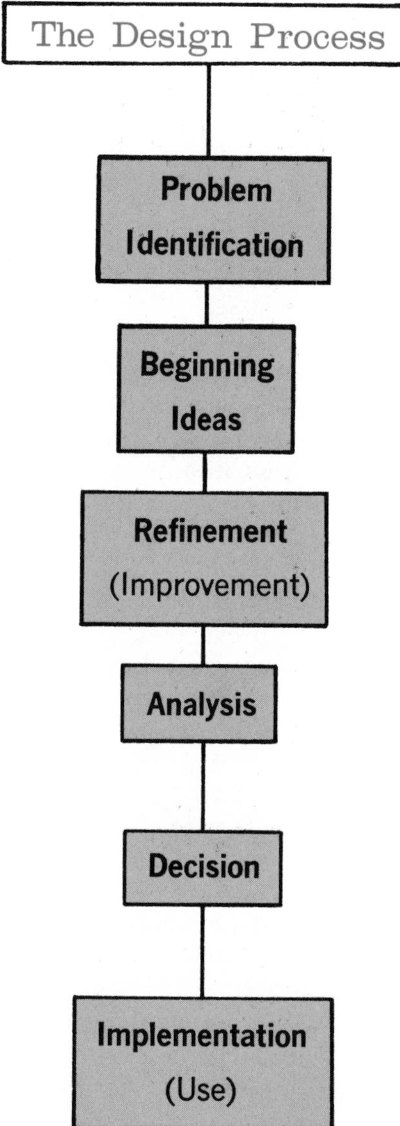

3. **Refinement (Improvement):** After the designer has a number of beginning ideas, he will select several of his better ideas for refinement. Refinement usually means that specific details are improved so that the designer can judge his design. Usually, scale drawings are made that will specify dimensions, shapes and other factors that will describe the designs. At this time, it is better to improve several designs rather than select only one.

4. **Analysis:** Analyzing a design is the process of finding the strength needed in each part of the design. This phase of the design process is more closely related to engineering than any other. If a bridge were to be used to cross the river, the proposed structure would be analyzed to decide the size needed for each beam and column.

5. **Decision:** At this point, more than one design has been improved and analyzed. It is necessary for the designer to make a decision or present his ideas to a group for its decision. A decision may be made to (1) accept one design, (2) combine several design features or the best solutions, or (3) turn down all designs, and repeat the design process. A design for a riverbed crossing would probably be presented to a building committee or a city council responsible for the final decision.

6. **Implementation (Use):** When the decision is made to accept a design, the designer supervises the preparation of the plans and specifications from which the project will be constructed. Minor changes in the design may be made during construction which may require that the designer assist in supervising the construction.

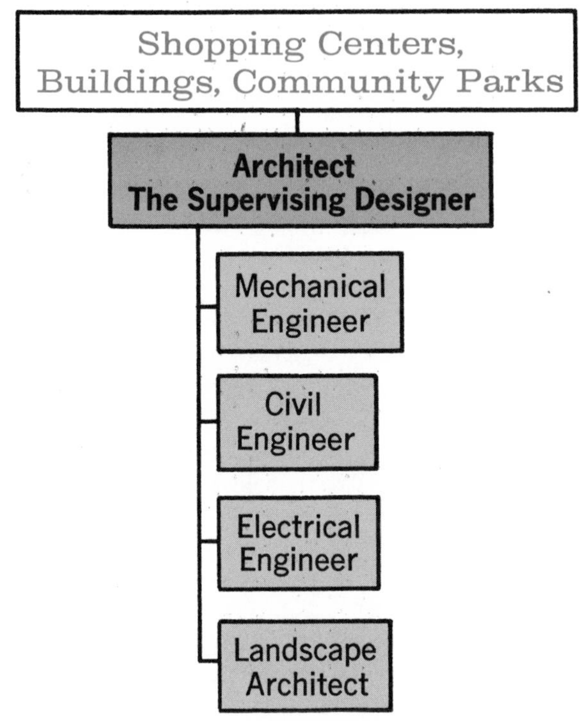

Who Designs?

Construction projects may be designed by either an architect or an engineer depending upon the nature of the project. Architects develop master plans for buildings, shopping centers, and community developments. Engineers are more concerned with bridges, dams, highways, and utility systems. The architect in charge of a shopping center design will be responsible for the master plan, but he will rely on the engineer for designing certain parts of the project. For example, the engineer will design the utility system, the drainage of the site, and the structural system of the building.

An Example of a Design Problem

The reading assignments which follow will discuss each of the steps of the design process as they apply to the following problem:

> **A Camping Facility:** A plot is available for a camp site that joins a lakeshore. This site will be used for a weekend camp for a troop of 20 scouts. The scouts will need housing, parking space, utilities, fishing area, boating facilities, and similar improvements that would help them enjoy their weekends when visiting this camp.

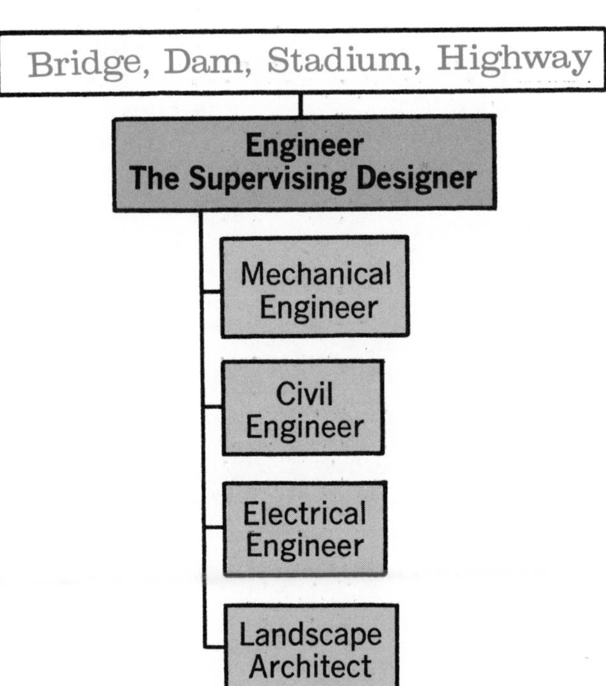

Summary

The design process is a systematic method of developing a plan for constructing a project. The design process does not end until the project has been completed. The six steps of the design process are: (1) problem identification, (2) preliminary ideas, (3) refinement, (4) analysis, (5) decision, (6) implementation. The following reading assignments will outline each step of the design process in greater detail. To illustrate these steps, reference will be made to the camping problem stated above.

Terms to Know

requirements
budget
vary
problem identification
designing
designer
efficient
preliminary
refinement
analysis
analyze
dimensions
decision
implementation
utility systems
data
design process
supervising

Think About It!

1. You have been asked to design a neighborhood playground. What do you need to do to:
   a. Identify the problem
   b. Develop preliminary ideas
   c. Define these ideas
   d. Analyze the design
   e. Select the final design
   f. Get the playground built (implement the design)

Identifying the Design Problem

Before a design is attempted, the problem must be clearly defined in the mind of the designer. He must understand what is to be designed and why it is necessary. This step of the design process is called *problem identification,* Fig. 11-1.

Whether the designer is an architect designing a community development or an engineer designing a highway, he must know the total needs and requirements of the problem. The basic steps of identifying a design problem include: (1) identification of needs, (2) gathering information, and (3) judging information. These terms are explained in this reading.

Identifying Needs

A design is always based on a need. A bridge is designed to span a canyon. A reservior is designed to store water. A camp is designed to serve the needs of campers. If a number of camping grounds were available at a low cost and at a convenient location, perhaps the need would not exist. However, if a troop of boy scouts could obtain a camp that was better than those available, it would be a desirable project. The need could be stated as follows:

A camp is needed to provide recreation for Scout Troop 403 on Lake Indian that would be better than those that are available and would be reasonable in cost.

To clearly define the purposes of the design, the design statement should be written out on a work sheet. This should be done for a skyscraper project as well as a hot dog stand.

Gathering Information

Additional information is needed to identify the problem and its limitations. For example, it would be necessary to know:

1. How many boys would be using the camp on a typical outing?
2. How often would the camp be used?
3. What kinds of activities would be provided?
4. Would there be a number of automobiles to be parked?

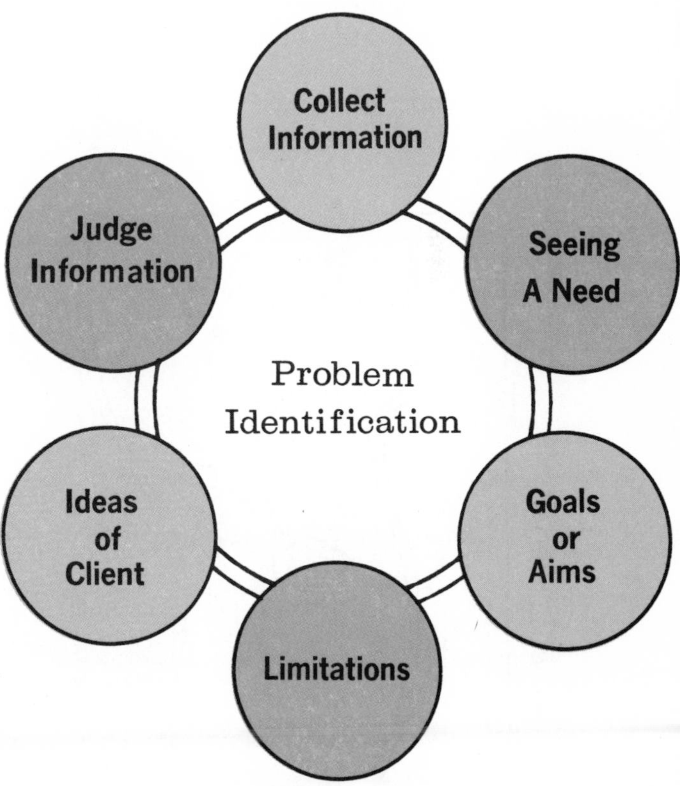

Fig. 11-1. Areas that must be considered to identify the problem.

5. Would there be boats to be housed?
6. Would a permanent bunkhouse be required?

Information of this type must come from those involved in the project as they will be the ones to decide what features are desired. Likewise, an architect must learn about the businesses that are to be included in a shopping center that he is to design.

If a certain site has been donated to the scout troop, the problem would involve a study of the site to decide the best way to take advantage of its best features. On the other hand, it may be necessary to gather information on a number of available sites before selecting the one that is best suited to the needs of the scout camp. Information must be collected about the specific site selected for the camp: (1) lot contours and dimensions, (2) the location of trees, (3) the minimum and maximum rainfall, (4) the high and low levels of the lake, and (5) other characteristics of this type.

Indentifying the problem for a camp is very similar to identifying the problem for the designing of an apartment building. In both cases, there are many small problems that must be identified within the total problem. For example, if the site shown in Fig. 11-2 is to be used for the camp, a bridge will be needed; and perhaps a parking lot and bunkhouse will be identified as major parts of the total problem.

Judging Information

Information that has been gathered concerning the site's characteristics, the desires of the scout troop and other factors affecting the design plan should be judged (evaluated) to obtain a better understanding of the problem. Evaluation could be improved by drawing graphs to show past records and to make predictions for the future, Fig. 11-3. Information such as: the ages of the scouts, the number in the troop during the year, and rainfall records are examples of information that can be shown in a graph. Diagrams can be used to represent the various activities that have been identified, as in Fig. 11-4.

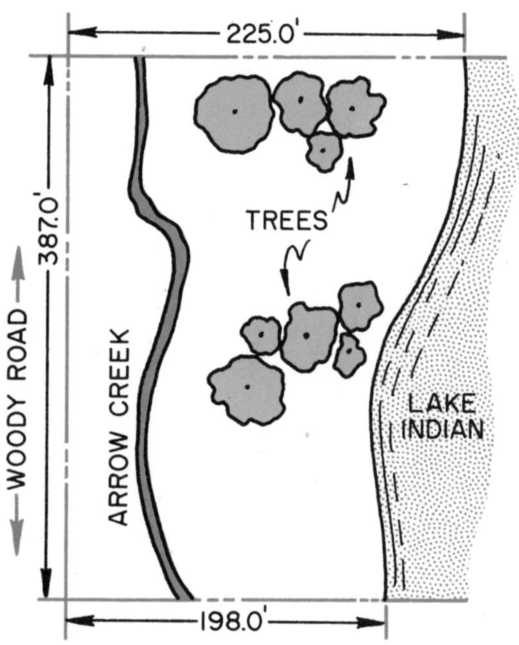

Fig. 11-2. The site of the camping facility.

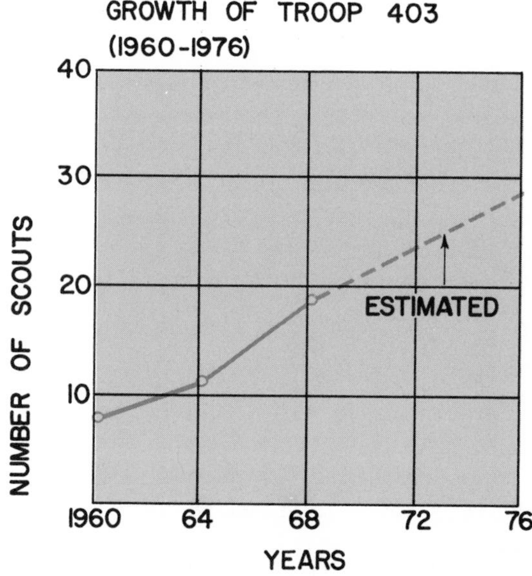

Fig. 11-3. Graph showing membership trend.

Summary

After identifying a problem, the architect or engineer will be in a better position to suggest solutions. He *must* understand the problem before he can design. The three basic steps of the identification process are: (1) identification of a need, (2) gathering of information, and (3) evaluation of information. Graphs and diagrams can be of help in evaluating information.

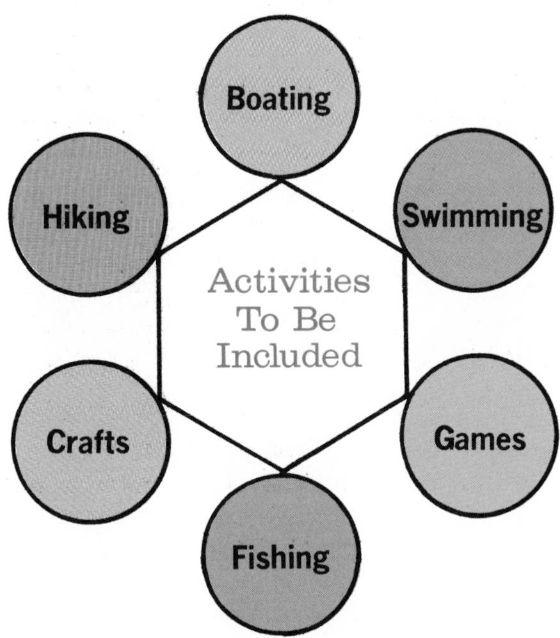

Fig. 11-4. A schematic diagram used for identifying the problem.

Terms to Know

identify	minimum
problem	evaluate
limitations	architect
maximum	evaluation

Think About It!

1. To *identify a problem,* the designer first must ask, "What is needed?" Describe the general needs that these structures fill.
   a. Warehouse
   b. Garage
   c. School
   d. Hospital
   e. Factory
   f. Department store
2. As a way of *gathering information,* the designer asks many questions. Imagine that your city needs a new, three-story hospital. How would you move people from floor to floor?
3. *Evaluate* your answers to 2. How will they affect the building design?

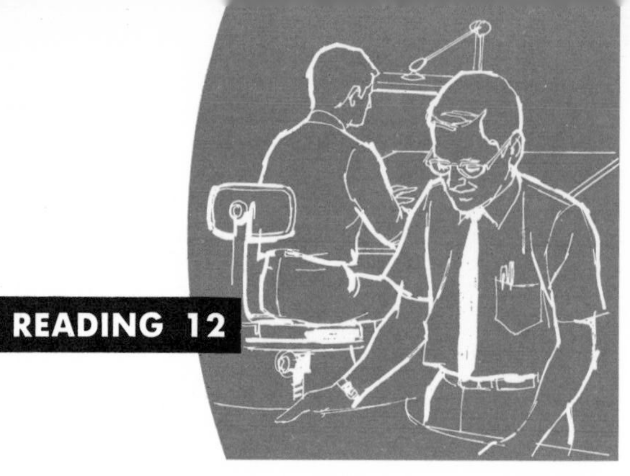

READING 12

Developing Preliminary Ideas

After a problem has been well defined, the designer should think up several different solutions to the problem. A number of ideas are likely to be more valuable to the final solution than are only one or two. In general, preliminary (beginning) ideas will be related to the problem limitations that were found in the identification step of the designing process.

Beginning Ideas and Creativity

Beginning ideas are ideas that come to the designer when he first thinks about possible solutions to the problem. He should not try to study these ideas, but instead, simply list or sketch the ideas as they come. Being critical of the first ideas can limit the designer's freedom of thought. He should look for solutions that are different from existing solutions for similar problems.

Since the designer is completely unlimited at this point, *this is the most creative step of the designing process.* Suggesting new solutions might result in a new idea. Perhaps the new idea will improve older methods or will give an entirely new way of looking at the problem.

An engineer responsible for providing a water supply for a city may list several older ideas: (1) a well, (2) a lake, or (3) a pipeline. He might also develop unusual suggestions such as making new roofs for every home in the community. These roofs would hold water and provide each home with its own water supply. This new idea might work. All ideas should be considered, even if they do not seem reasonable at first glance.

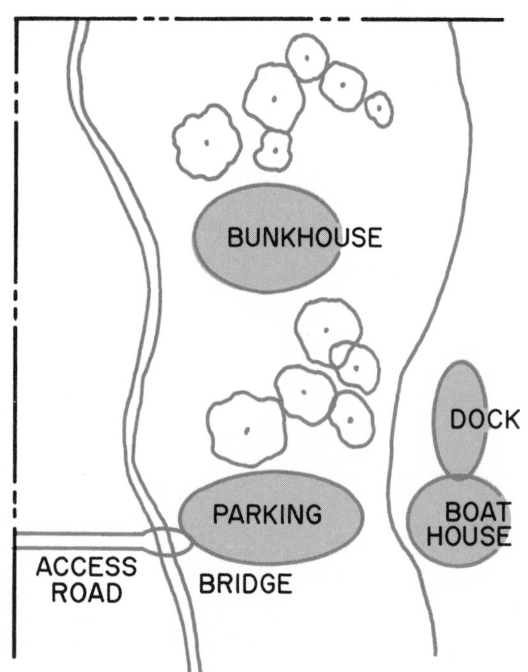

Fig. 12-1. Preliminary idea #1 for the site plan of the camping facility.

Recording Beginning Ideas

If the first ideas are not written down as they come to mind, they might be forgotten. It is even better if freehand drawings are made. Even if the drawing is a diagram, it will help detail the idea. Notes can be added to drawings. Making notes and drawings help the designer find other ideas. Once the ideas begin to come, he should draw and write as fast as possible to keep up the flow of his thoughts. Work sheets should be used as permanent records of his ideas. The designer can refer to this work sheet in the designing process.

Beginning ideas for the camp design will involve a general layout of the various parts to be included. For example: the entry road, parking lot, bunkhouse, and water facilities should be studied by using the technique shown in Fig. 12-1. General areas may be defined by using loose diagrams to show the general relationships of the parts. Another camp plan is suggested in Fig. 12-2. There, the bunkhouse is built on piers above the water and off the shore of the lake. This process of sketching general relationships helps the designer see a number of possible combinations.

The designer will apply the same technique to each part of the overall plan. Using this approach, he will need to decide the layout for the bunkhouse. The diagram in Fig. 12-3 shows the general relationship of the major activities within the bunkhouse. Making several diagrams like this will provide a basis for the development of a rough floor plan as shown in Fig. 12-4. More than one diagram should be sketched so the designs can be compared with others.

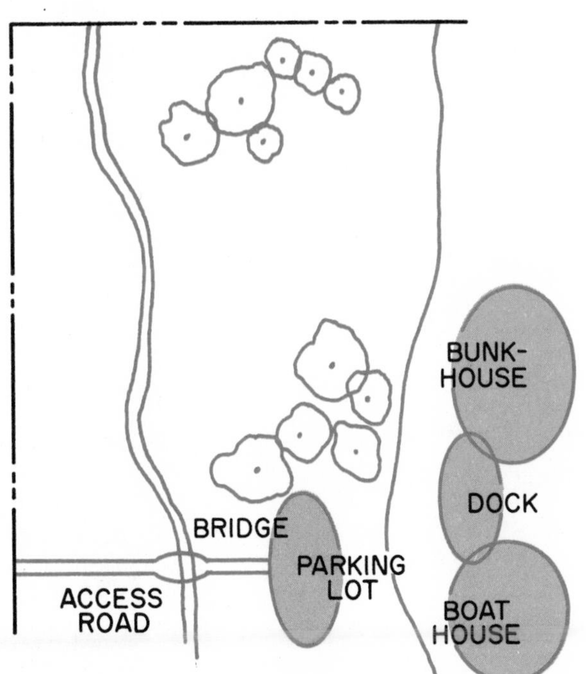

Fig. 12-2. Preliminary idea #2 for the site plan of the camping facility.

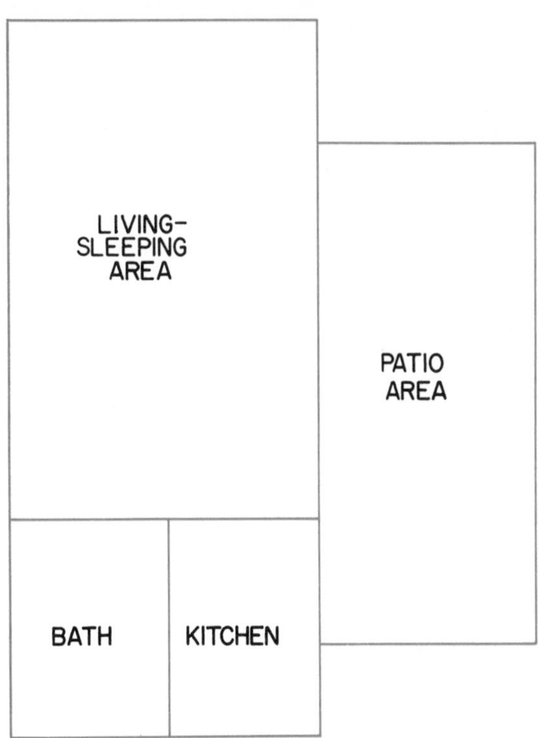

Fig. 12-3. A preliminary idea for the bunkhouse plan.

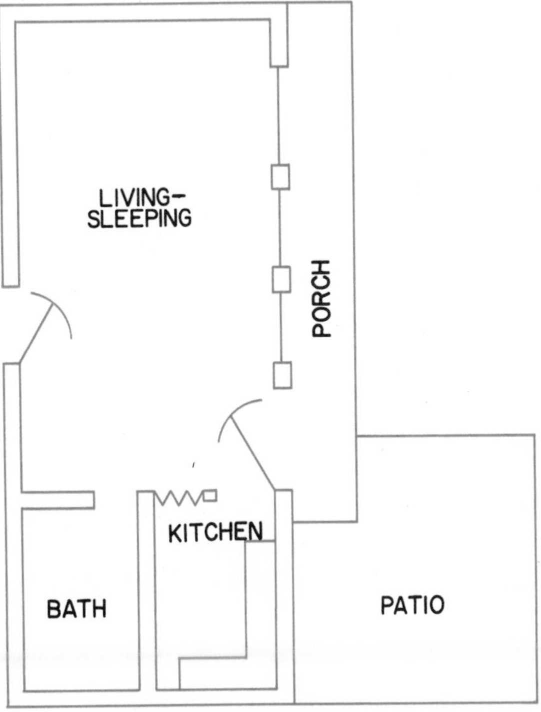

Fig. 12-4. A sketch of a preliminary floor plan of the bunkhouse.

Summary

The most creative phase of the designing process is the step in which beginning (preliminary) ideas are developed. These ideas can be as unusual as the designer would like, with little concern, at this time, for the feasibility of a particular concept. Each new idea may suggest additional ideas from which new methods may be developed. Preliminary ideas should be listed on work sheets with general notes to outline the idea. A good solution is more likely to come from a large number of preliminary ideas than from a single one. Freehand drawings may be in the form of pictures or diagrams. The next step of the design process will be the refining of several of the better preliminary ideas.

Terms to Know

preliminary
problem
creative
layout
solution
diagram
relationships

Think About It!

1. *Preliminary* means "before the main business." Why should a designer sketch and write his *preliminary ideas,* before he works out exact dimensions?
2. At a "brainstorming" session, several people work together to create new ideas for solving a problem. Each person is free to borrow and change the ideas of others, but no one criticizes an idea in a negative way. Try "brainstorming" to create one of these structures.
   a. A house than can be cleaned inside and out; using hot water from a garden hose.
   b. A combination garage and storage area that can be kept free of animals, insects, and excess dampness.

READING 13

Refining Ideas

The problem has been identified. Preliminary ideas have been collected. The next step is *refinement* (improvement). During refinement, the designer will develop several of his preliminary ideas into more complete form. Some of the first ideas may appear to be workable in rough, freehand form, but may not be acceptable when they have been refined and drawn to scale.

Drawing to Scale

Preliminary ideas have been drawn freehand, with very little attention to dimensions, shapes, and sizes. The plan for a parking lot may be in the form of a general area sketched on the *site plan*. When actual dimensions are not used, it is very easy for a freehand sketch to be misleading. A parking lot sketch could be much too small for the number of cars that are to be parked. Thus, to decide whether or not the preliminary ideas will work as planned, they should be drawn again to scale. It might then be necessary to turn down a preliminary idea or to improve it so that it will be workable.

More than one of the first ideas should be improved to give a selection of ideas and a comparison of different concepts. The designer should not select a solution to the problem too early. Selecting a solution too soon could eliminate ideas that might be better. The designer should refer to his first ideas and sketches on his work sheets and refer to his problem identification work sheets. Idea refinement requires the designer to do more thinking and use less creative expression than in the previous step of the design process. During the refinement step, the designer tries to use the best ideas for a workable solution. The solution can then be constructed to give the best results at the best cost.

Refining a Boathouse Design

An example of the refining process can be shown in the development of a boathouse design for the scout camp problem. While the problem was being identified, it was decided that four boats would be stored and housed for protection at the lake's shore. A preliminary idea is shown in Fig. 13-1 in a general layout form. This sketch gives only a rough idea as to how the boathouse might be designed, but it is not drawn to scale. Then this preliminary sketch is drawn to scale with more specific dimensions and details.

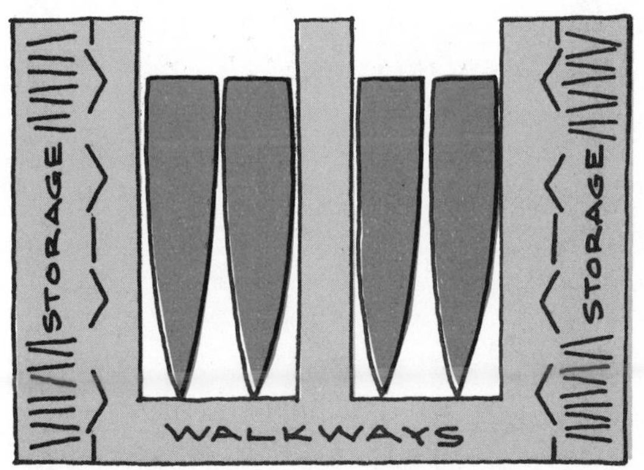

Fig. 13-1. A preliminary sketch of a floor plan of a boathouse.

A scale drawing of the boathouse floor plan is shown in Fig. 13-2. Notice that the dimensions of the boats, the items to be stored, and the width of the walkways have been used as the basis for the dimensions of the boathouse.

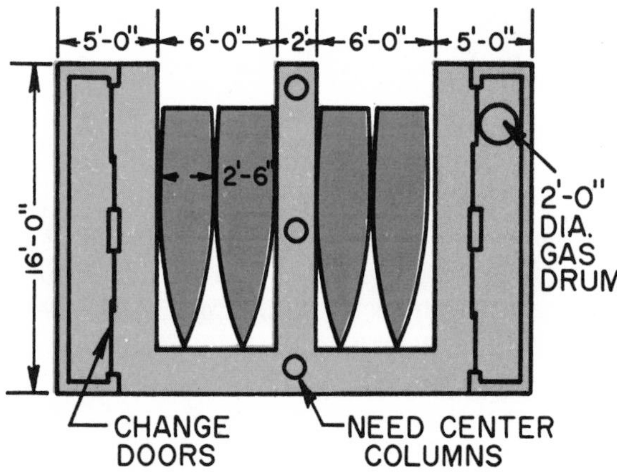

Fig. 13-2. A refinement of the preliminary boathouse plan.

Although the floor plan is the beginning point for a workable design of this type, thought must also be given to the type of roof, outside walls, height, and the general exterior of the building. An exterior refinement is shown in Fig. 13-3. As the design is improved, details of construction (ways of hoisting boats out of the water, what material to select, and how much construction will cost) become important. As the refinement process continues, suggestions must be made for each of these items.

Rejecting Refined Ideas

At any point during the design process, the designer may discover that his design will not work. If this happens, he must re-

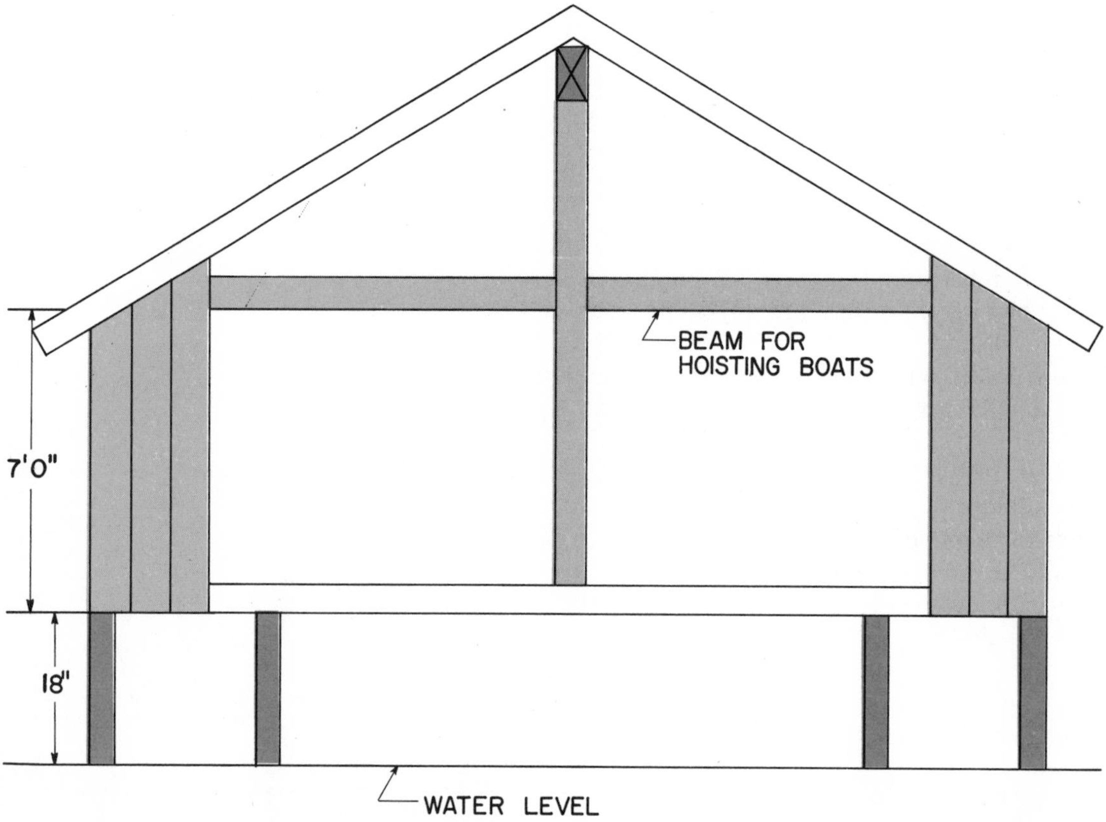

Fig. 13-3. Refined drawing of exterior of the boathouse.

turn to his earlier steps (his preliminary ideas) to select another idea to be developed. This procedure is repeated until he feels that the best solution has been obtained.

An engineer may select a site for a bridge that seems to be the most likely location. After studying the site in greater detail, he may find facts indicating that this site would be highly expensive or impractical for the bridge. He may then consider other sites that might be better and that could serve the same purpose at a lower cost. If the cost of moving the highway to the new bridge site would be much higher than the cost of the bridge, perhaps the added expense for the bridge in its original location would be justified. Cost or time limitations may cause the engineer to reject the preliminary ideas.

Summary

Refining is the first step in judging the beginning ideas with respect to the master plan. The beginning ideas are improved, drawn to scale, and studied to obtain a realistic idea of the size, form, and details of the design. Dimensions such as roof height, square footage, storage space, parking areas, and structural parts can be checked as the design is improved and drawn to scale. Refinement drawings are not finished plans from which the project could be constructed. They are general scale drawings that will show important details that should be defined as early as possible before the design is analyzed.

During the refining of a preliminary idea, the designer may see problems that cannot be as easily solved as he had once thought. He should select other preliminary ideas to improve. The designer should then try to adapt several of the better ideas of the rejected design to his new ideas. Rejection is not to be considered a failure in the design process, but merely a natural procedure in finding a solution to a problem.

Rather than putting all his efforts into a single idea, the designer should develop and refine several workable ideas. He will then be in a better position to select the best design. Before he can make a final decision on which design is actually the best, he must study his design for function, strength and cost. This is the next step of the design process which is covered in the following reading assignment.

Terms to Know

refinement	preliminary ideas
drawn to scale	rejection
sketch	creative
exterior	

Think About It!

1. When a design idea is to be *refined,* exact sizes become important. What dimensions and activities need to be studied if you were designing a classroom for school music activities.
2. Suggest some things that could go wrong if a designer did not carefully "work out" the music room sizes and dimensions.

READING 14

Analyzing the Design

When a preliminary design has been refined, it must then be *analyzed* (studied) to determine its acceptability, Fig. 14-1. When an engineer has refined a design, he must analyze (study) his design to decide what will give (1) the best structure, (2) the best use of the site, and (3) the most useful project.

Structural Analysis

A simple structural analysis is illustrated in Fig. 14-2. A diving board has been drawn to scale. The maximum load of impact (when a swimmer jumps) at the end of the board has been figured. The problem is to figure the load at *point A* that would be necessary to anchor the board when a maximum load of 600 pounds is applied at *point C* (the end of the board) by the diver. Since the board is supported at *point B*, the *principle of the lever* can be applied to the design.

The ratio of loads at each end will be opposite in proportion to the *dimensions AB* (3′) *and BC* (6′). Notice that *BC* is twice as long as *AB*. Thus, the load at *point A* must be twice as much as the load at *point C*. The engineer's technique in making this analysis, using mathematics and physics, is shown on his analysis worksheet in Fig. 14-3. Notice that he has sketched the diving board in a diagram form to help him define his analysis problem in its simplest terms.

After the engineer has completed his figuring, he has found that a load of 1,200 pounds would be required to anchor the diving board to offset the maximum load applied by a diver. A safety factor of 2 is applied to make sure that the anchor is adequate. A number of rocks could be used to apply a *dead weight* of 2,400 pounds. Concrete could be used in place of the rocks,

Fig. 14-1. Hydraulic engineers are checking water flow patterns for spillways on a model of a dam.

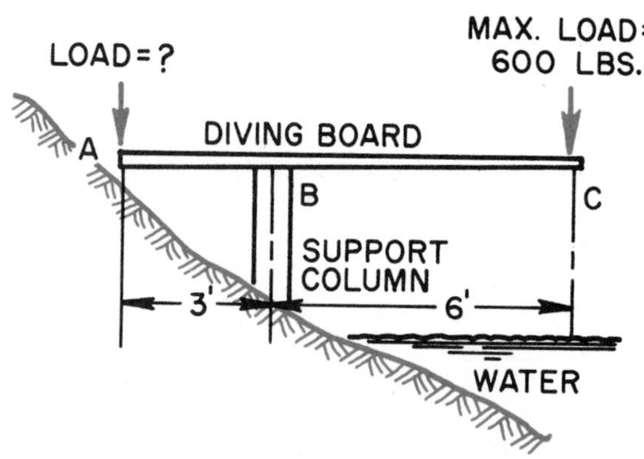

Fig. 14-2. Even the design of the diving board must be analyzed.

or pilings could be driven in the bank. If pilings were to be used as the anchor, the engineer would have to analyze how to fasten the board to the pilings and the holding power of the soil on the pilings. The engineer would know which type of anchor to use after his study.

Site Analysis

Analysis of a design might involve the analysis of a construction site in order to prevent problems of drainage, allow pathways for access, and to permit grading or excavation (leveling or digging earth). For example, the contour map of the scout camp would need to be analyzed to determine how the rainwater would drain. Notice that a bunkhouse located in the position shown in Fig. 14-4 would be in the path of the water drainage. Draining water could cause damage to the building.

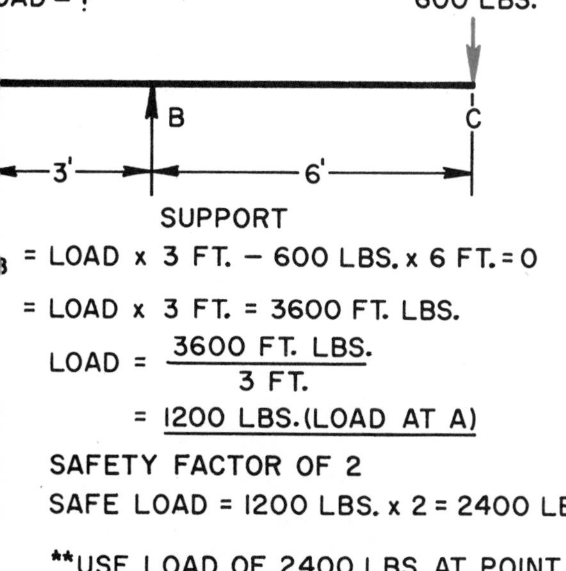

ƆAD = ?
600 LBS.
B
C
3'
6'
SUPPORT
= LOAD x 3 FT. – 600 LBS. x 6 FT. = 0
= LOAD x 3 FT. = 3600 FT. LBS.
LOAD = 3600 FT. LBS. / 3 FT.
= 1200 LBS. (LOAD AT A)
SAFETY FACTOR OF 2
SAFE LOAD = 1200 LBS. x 2 = 2400 LBS.
**USE LOAD OF 2400 LBS. AT POINT A TO ANCHOR DIVING BOARD

Fig. 14-3. Engineers use mathematics and physics as their tools to analyze this diving board design.

Some areas of the site are better suited for certain activities than others. For example, a parking lot should be located where the site is most level and nearest to the road. This will reduce earthmoving and the length of the access road.

The steepness of the ground will also affect the feasibility of a roadway. A scale drawing could be used to analyze the problem of unloading a boat in the lake. It can be seen in Fig. 14-5 that it would be hard to back a boat trailer to the lakeshore without site and roadway preparation. If the incline

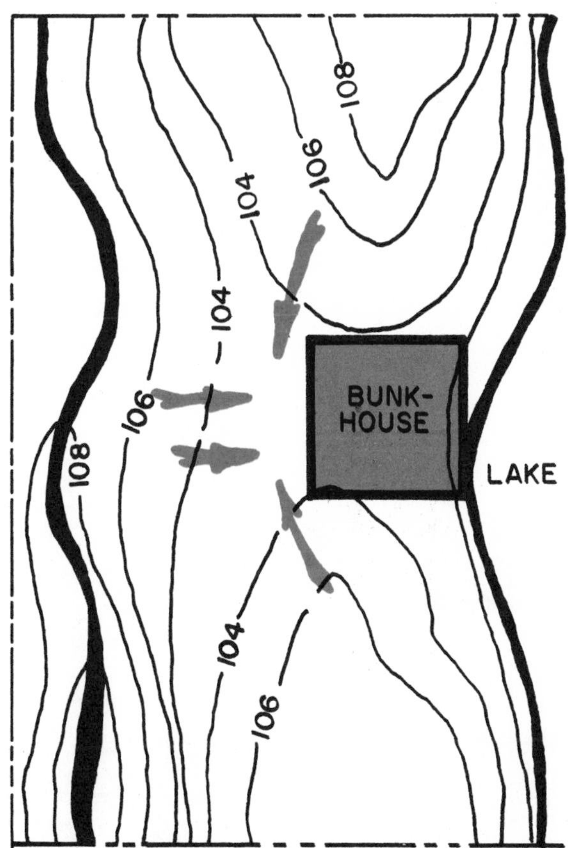

Fig. 14-4. Site and structure must be analyzed to see if they fit together.

is too steep, it will be impossible for a car to pull the trailer and boat uphill. Analysis of the boat launching problem and many other problems is all a part of *site analysis* at the proposed camp.

Functional Analysis

Another type of analysis is *functional analysis*. This type of study will show if the idea or design will work. This involves the analysis of such things as (1) materials to be used, (2) ease of operation, and (3) flow or movement (as in the case of a hallway, driveway, or fishing dock). For example, a long fishing dock would not work if it were so narrow that one fisherman could not walk past another. Likewise, an access road to the bunkhouse should provide space for turning a car around so that the driver would not have to back out the entire distance.

Fig. 14-5. Boat-launching inclines must be figured.

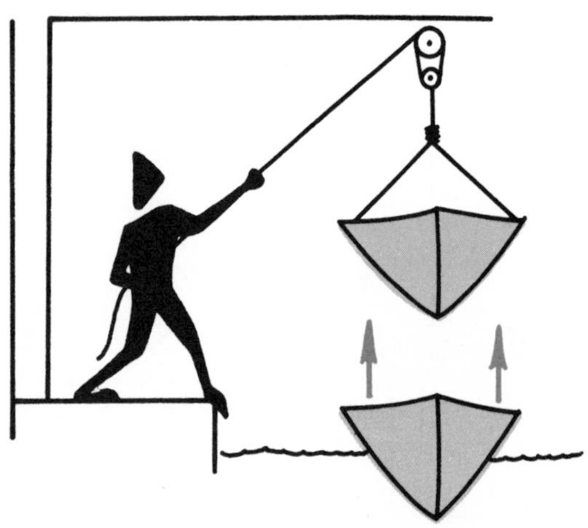

ANALYSIS OF THE PROCEDURE OF
LIFTING A BOAT FROM THE WATER
FOR DRY STORAGE IN A SUSPENDED
POSITION

Fig. 14-6. Boat-lifting procedures must also be considered.

The boat house must be designed with thought for safety and human use. For instance, if the boats are to be hoisted out of the water with a pulley system, the designer must decide (1) how much pull must be used, and (2) the distance above the water that the boats will be held. Then he must provide the necessary space for this to be done. Figure 14-6 shows the procedure of pulling the boat out of the water. Using the weight of the boat and the pull that must be used to hoist the boat, the designer must provide enough space for a person to safely stand while hoisting the boat. This involves an analysis of human factors and the body movements that would be needed to apply the pull. A crowded area would make this a difficult task.

The act of getting out of a boat onto a platform at the side of the boat would need to be thought out and a means for steadying the boat decided upon. The necessary handrails and safety devices that would improve this situation would have to be provided. Sometimes an analysis of this kind must be performed at the site of the project, where the conditions of the problem can actually be seen.

Summary

Analysis is the process of determining whether or not a design solution will actually work under specific conditions. The structural members are analyzed to make sure that they have been adequately designed. This type of analysis is structural analysis. Other types of analysis that apply to most construction projects are: (1) site analysis and (2) functional analysis. The analyzing process may identify problems in the proposed design solution. These problems might make it necessary for the designer to return to another preliminary idea that would give a more workable solution.

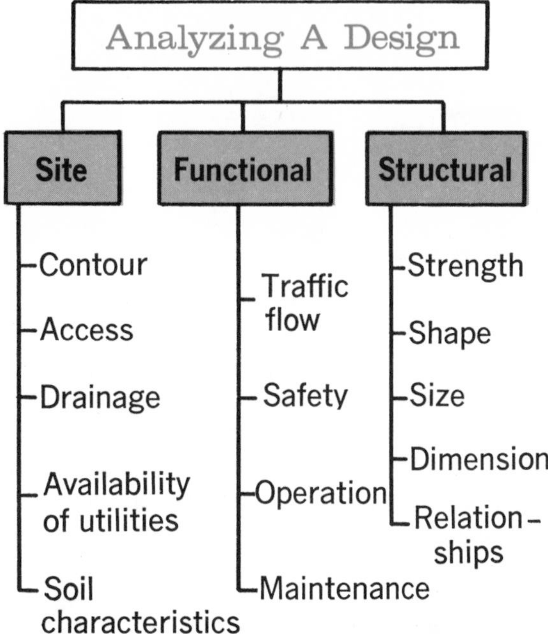

NOTE: These are only a few factors considered in making an analysis.

Terms to Know

structural analysis
functional analysis
analyze
adequate
maximum
ratio
principle of the lever
proportional
site analysis
hoist
pilings
feasibility
physics

Think About It!

1. Suppose that you have been asked to purchase and install recreation equipment for a neighborhood playground.
   a. What special *structural problems* do you think should be considered?
   b. What *functional problems* need your study before you install the equipment?
   c. What *site problems* do you need to study before you install the equipment?

READING 15

Selecting the Design

When several designs have been refined and analyzed and found to be satisfactory, the one that will be constructed must be selected. The process of choosing is called the *decision* step of the design process. This is an important step. There is always the possibility of rejecting the proper solution or accepting the wrong solution. The responsibility for making the final decision on a design solution may lie with the designer, an individual owner, or a committee of individuals, such as the city council. The designer of an outdoor patio would probably make the decision as to which design he would select. On the other hand, the designer of a utility plant would have to present his designs to a city council for its decision of which one would be best at a cost that could be afforded. See Fig. 15-1.

Fig. 15-1. The design of this city sewage plant had to be approved by a city council.

Decision by the Designer

The designer who will decide which design will be built will go through much the same process as he would if he presented his design to a group. The main difference would be in the process of presenting his ideas. Since the designer is familiar with the problem, he would make several sketches, scale drawings (Fig. 15-2), and pictorial views of each design to help him compare the designs that he is considering. His next step would be to list the advantages and disadvantages of each design. This list could serve as a guide in arriving at his final choice. In effect, he is communicating with himself through sketches, drawings, and notes to make sure that all aspects of the solutions are considered.

Decision by Others

If the designer must get permission from someone else or a group, he must approach the problem in much the same way as noted above. He must, however, place more emphasis on explaining his ideas. In order for the deciding individual or group to have a sound basis for making a decision, the designer must explain his ideas step by step. One design may be far better than another, but it may cost more. Perhaps the deciding person or committee would change the budget to make the more expensive design possible, if it were clear that this expensive design would cost less in the long run.

The designer does not wish to trick anyone. He wants to present both sides of the issue. A deciding committee is often made up

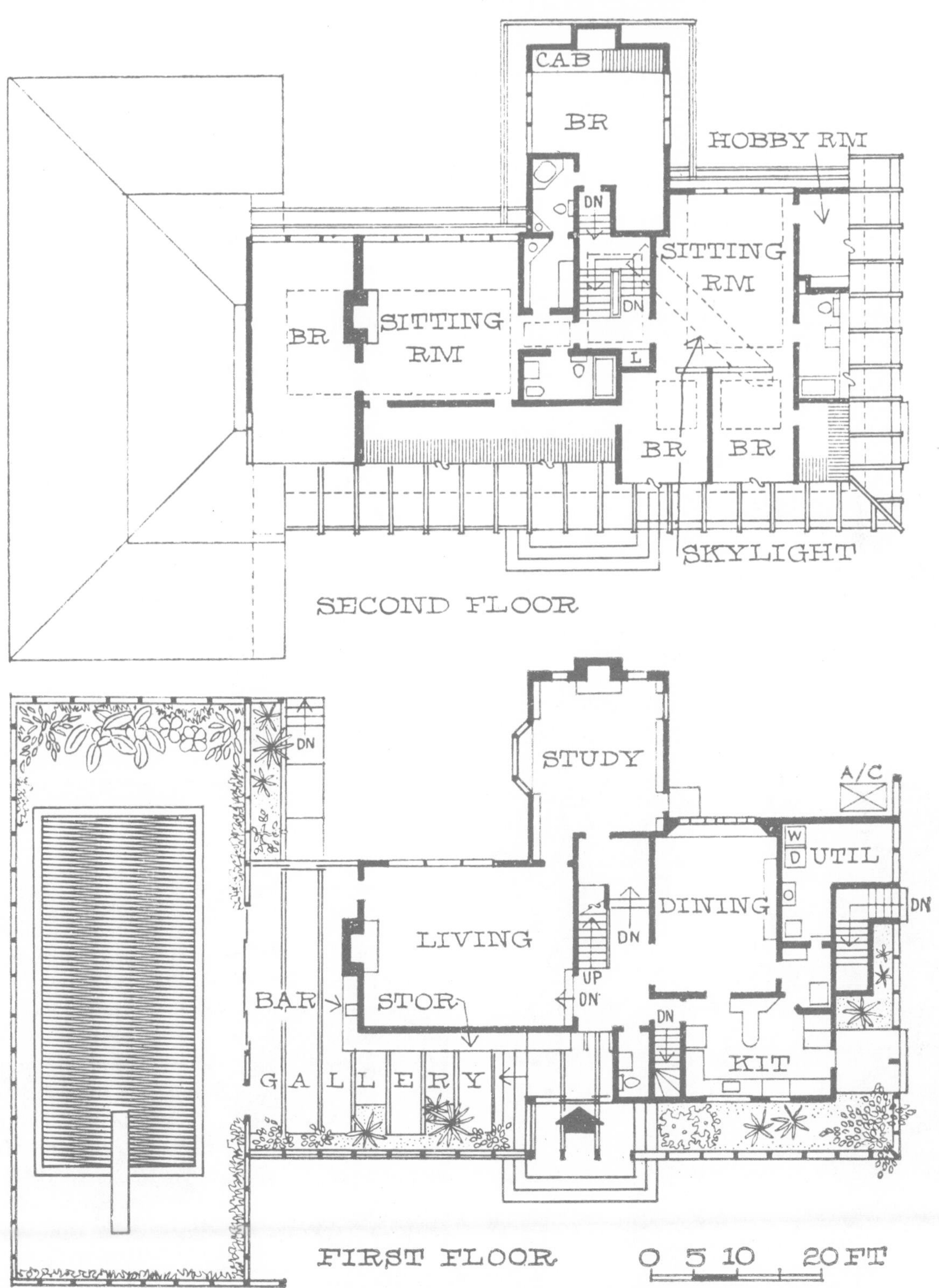

Fig. 15-2. The designer makes scale drawings of the structure to help him consider alternatives.

of people who have different backgrounds and who may not understand the technical aspects of the problem being presented. In such a case, the designer must prepare visual aids that will make it possible for him to explain the details of his design and to identify the factors that must be considered in the decision, Figs. 15-3, 15-4, and 15-5.

Presentation of the Design

In order for the designer to present his design, he may use a number of visual aids. He may use models, flip charts, slides, pictures, diagrams, graphs, or any similar techniques. Architects may construct a scale model of an entire city development. Since the average person can understand a model much more easily than he can understand a detailed drawing, models are excellent for this kind of presentation. When a model cannot be used, pictorial drawings are used to show the appearance of the project in its finished form. Photographic slides of similar design solutions may also be used as an example of the kind of design that is being proposed.

Tables of figures, costs of construction, and other information of this type are easy to analyze if plotted on a graph. A graph permits easy analysis of the trends and past histories of such information as population figures, cost of various materials, and the trends of labor costs. Simple bar graphs and line graphs can be easily drawn on a flip chart and presented and explained to several people at one time. Without many hours of study, it would be impossible for a person who was unfamiliar with the problem to make a wise decision as to which design would be the best. The designer can stop this waste of time by developing his presentation with his audience in mind.

The presentation may be given to an individual, a small group of four or five people,

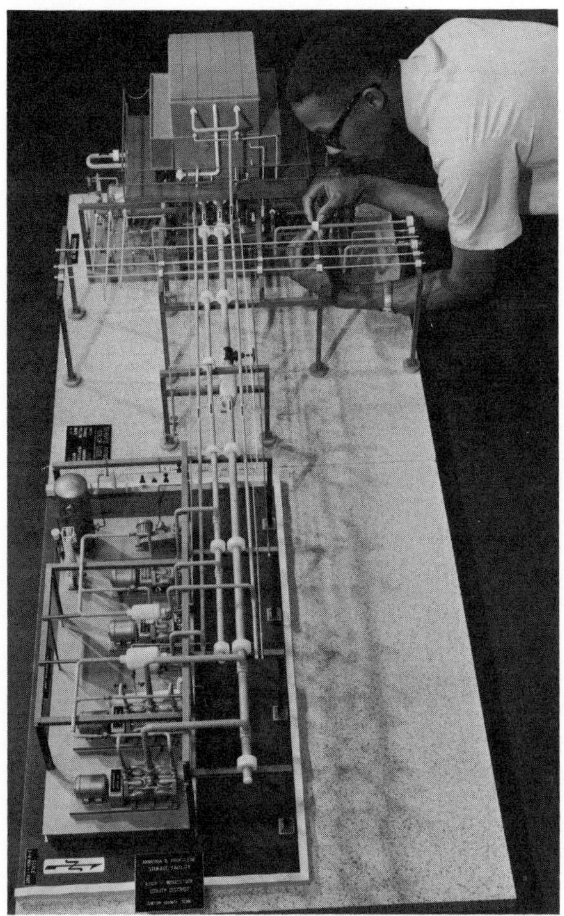

Fig. 15-3. Scale models help in decision making by enabling one to see the project.

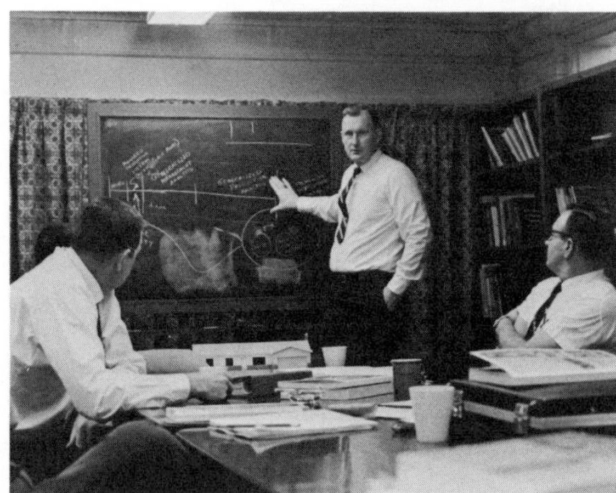

Fig. 15-4. The designer presents his designs to a group to aid them in making a decision.

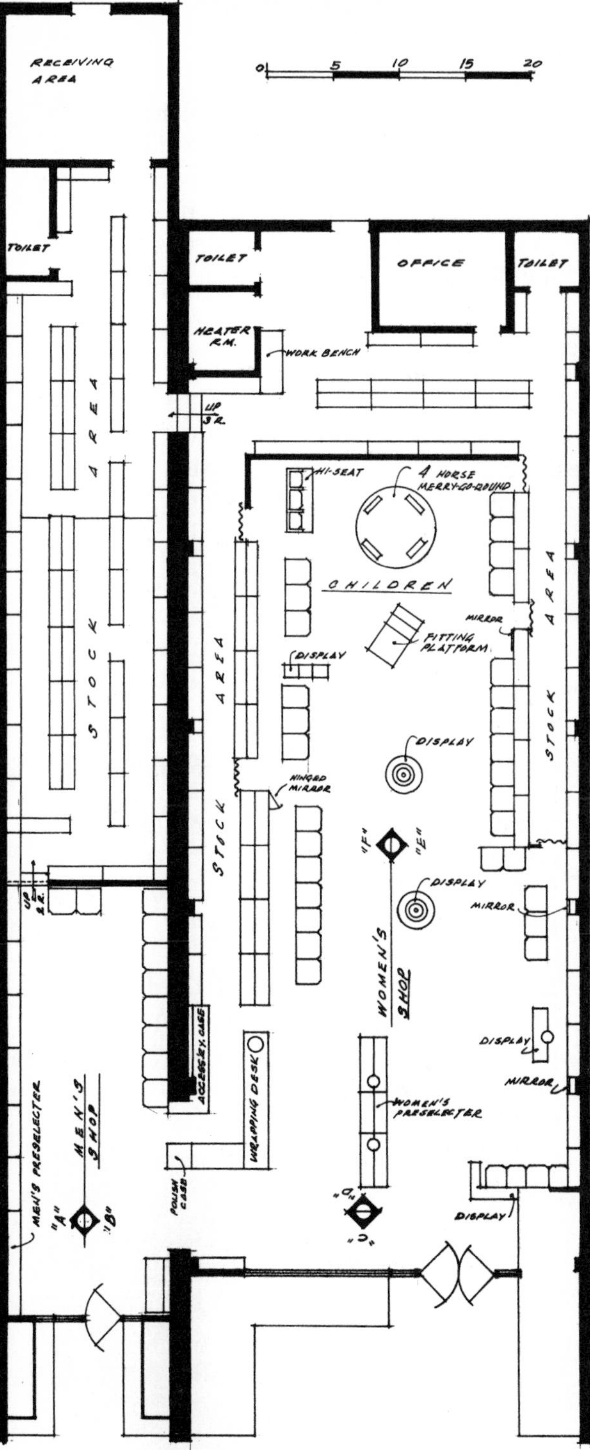

Fig. 15-5. When the designs are rather simple, a set of working drawings may be presented to the committee. The sketch here is one example of a plan and elevation of a shoe store attached to a men's store.
A. Left wall, men's shop.
B. Right wall, women's and children's shop.

or it may be given to a larger group of a hundred or more. This would be the case if presentation were given to members of a community who were responsible for voting on the construction of a new school. The presentation would outline the advantages and disadvantages of the project and make a suggestion for a solution. The overflow of present school facilities and the expected number of children in the next few years would be important factors to point out. The location and the convenience of the school would also be important factors.

Working Drawings

If the project is rather simple, such as a design for a service station or a paved parking lot, the completed working drawings may be presented to the committee. Completed working drawings are drawings that are fully detailed and dimensioned, and could be used in constructing the final project. They will be supplemented with sketches, pictures, and other diagrams as mentioned above. On the other hand, the proposed design for an apartment building would probably be presented in general form before the investment was made in preparing additional detailed drawings. The proposed plans would show the appearance of the building, its general site layout, the floor plan, and sufficient details to provide a complete impression of what the finished design would look like. Once the proposed plan has been approved, the detailed working drawings and specifications would be prepared.

The presentation for the bunkhouse design for the camping site would need views of the outside, an accurate floor plan, and diagrams explaining the foundation and proposed construction methods. The designer would use these drawings and diagrams to present his idea to the troop. The troop would then decide which arrangement seemed best and should be accepted.

Summary

In the design process, a decision must be made to (1) accept, (2) change, or (3) reject the design. It is necessary for the designer to present his ideas and suggestions as clearly as possible to the individual or group responsible for making the decision. An excellent design may be rejected if the designer is unable to present his ideas in an understandable form. In most cases, he will need to make use of visual aids, expecially pictures, to present his ideas.

The designer must develop his ability to discuss design problems with groups and make suggestions based on facts and his analysis of the problem's needs. If his design is properly thought out and he can obtain approval from the deciding committee, the next step will be the *implementation* of this design. This will begin with the preparation of detail working drawings from which the project will be constructed.

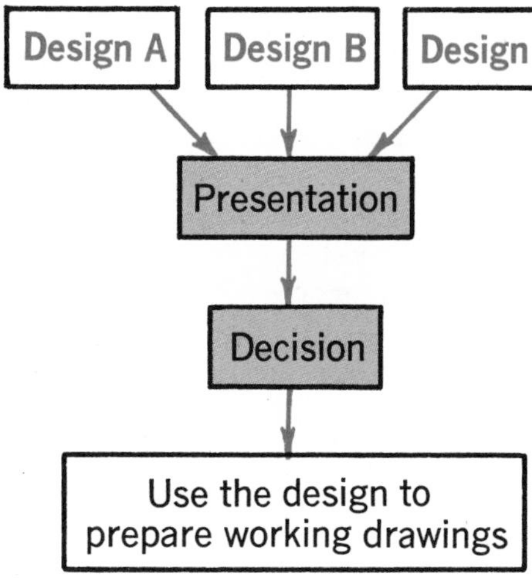

Design A
Design B
Design C
Presentation
Decision
Use the design to prepare working drawings

Terms to Know

decision
designer
advantages
disadvantages
scale model
scale drawing
presentation
visual aids
working drawings
investment

Think About It!

1. Imagine that you have designed two plans for a neighborhood park. A committee of businessmen, parents, teachers, and city officials may choose one of your plans. What questions might these people ask, before they *decide* on one plan?
2. How might you use each of the following devices to help answer their questions?
   a. *Models*
   b. *Photographs of similar projects*
   c. *Bar graphs and tables of figures*
   d. *Diagrams that show function or movement*

Making Working Drawings

The *working drawings* in the construction contract for a project give the physical details needed to build the project. They are used by all people responsible for the construction of the project. They are used especially by the construction contractor and his workmen, Fig. 16-1. Working drawings that are even more detailed than those in the construction contract are often made in the offices of the contractor and his subcontractors. This is done to guide their own work. These working drawings are called *shop drawings.* See Figs. 16-2 and 16-3. The contract drawings and shop drawings for a project must be accurate and complete if the project is to be successfully constructed.

A Set of Working Drawings

The working drawings in the contract for a small, simple construction project may have: (1) a site plan, (2) a foundation plan, (3) floor plans, (4) a roof plan, (5) elevations, (6) sections, and (7) details. In simple projects, all of the physical details of the project are shown in this one set of drawings. Each drawing shows not only the physical form of the project, but also all of the mechanical, electrical, and structural parts of the project, Fig. 16-3.

In larger or more difficult projects, separate sets of drawings are made. One set shows the details of the site plan such as excavation (earth removal) limits, paving requirements, river control, or detour construction. These are called *civil drawings.*

When necessary to the project, other sets of working drawings also are prepared. *Architectural drawings* are made to show many details of the physical form of the project. *Mechanical and electrical drawings* show: (1) heating, (2) cooling, (3) drainage, (4) plumbing, (5) elevator and moving stair, (6) ventilating, (7) lighting, and (8) electrical requirements. *Structural drawings* also are made to show the detailed structural needs of the project.

The set of working drawings in the contract for a project may have architectural, civil, mechanical and electrical, and structural drawings all separated into sets. This is done so the drawings can be read easily without getting them mixed up.

In very complex projects, these sets of working drawings may, in turn, be further divided into more sets. For example, separate sets for heating, plumbing, and electrical distribution may be made. A complete set of working drawings for a large, complicated project may have hundreds of separate drawings.

Accuracy

Each of the drawings in a set of working drawings must be accurately drawn to scale and *dimensioned.* That is, *the lengths, widths, and position of each part of the project must be noted as well as drawn to scale.* This is a must, because the paper on which drawings are made and reproduced shrinks and stretches with changes in the amount of moisture in the air. A large drawing, accurately drawn to scale today, may not be exactly the same size tomorrow. Also, a drawing of a large project (Fig. 16-1) cannot be drawn full size.

The dimensions of a drawing's parts must be put down so they may be quickly and accurately read from the drawings. If every workman had to scale the size of every part of the project he worked on, many mistakes would be made, and much valuable time would be lost.

Accuracy in dimensioning is very important. All of the dimensions on a drawing must add up. For example, all of the dimensions of rooms inside a building, plus the thickness of the outside walls and the walls separating rooms, must add up to the dimensions given for the outside width and length of the structure. A mistake in any one dimension might result in a part of the project being mislocated.

Care also must be taken to make sure that dimensions shown on separate drawings relate to one another. All of the dimensions

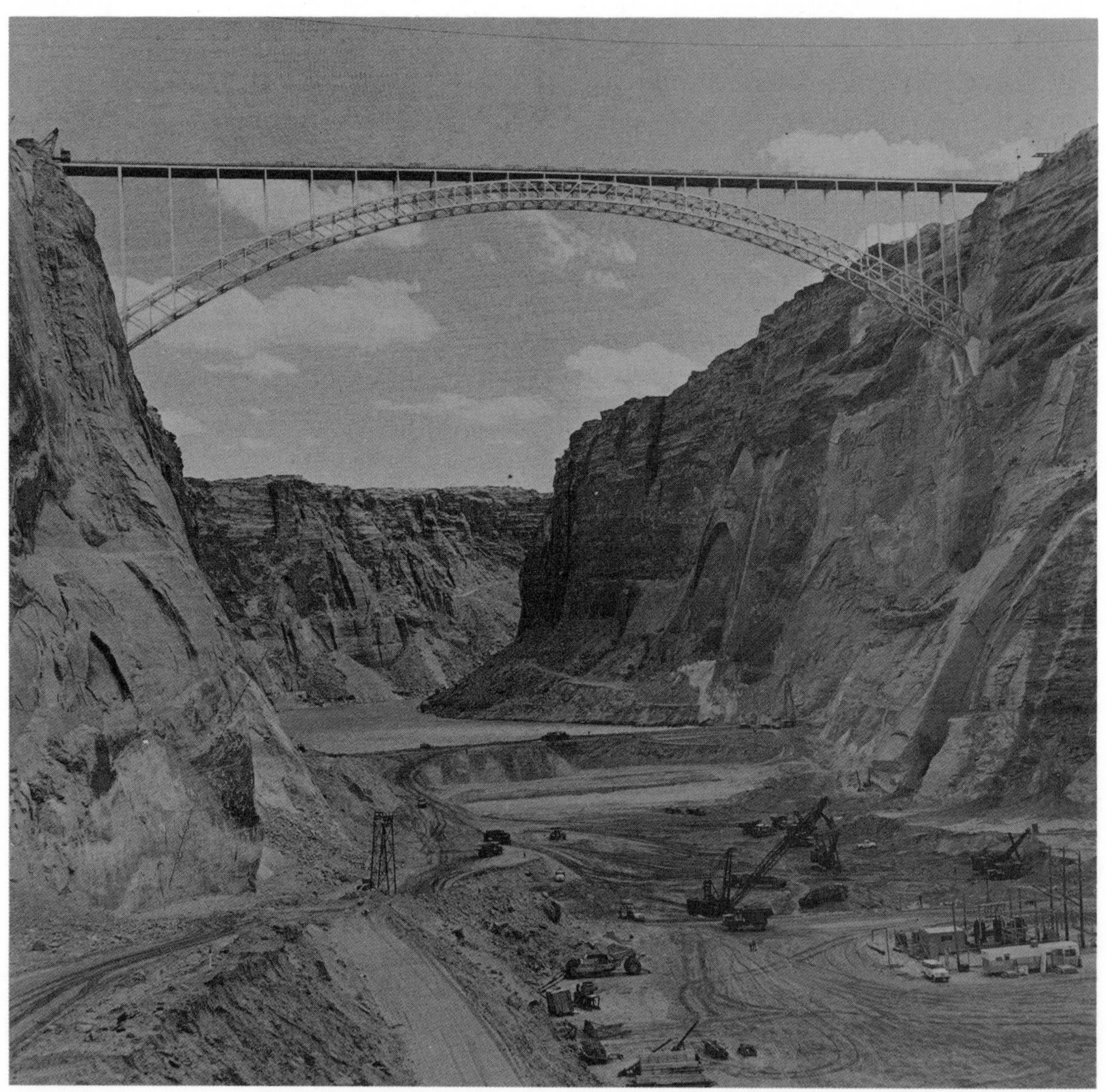

Fig. 16-1. This bridge is being built from working drawings.

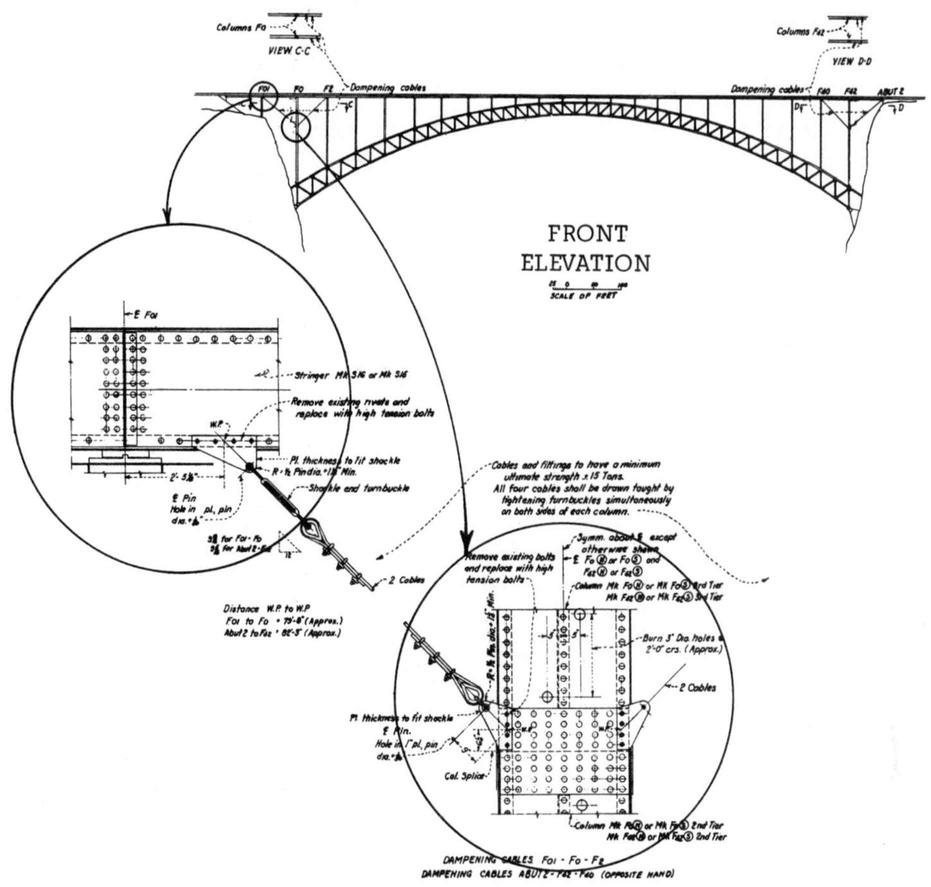

Fig. 16-2. This drawing shows details of a part of the bridge.

Fig. 16-3. This working drawing shows the front elevation and the top view of the bridge.

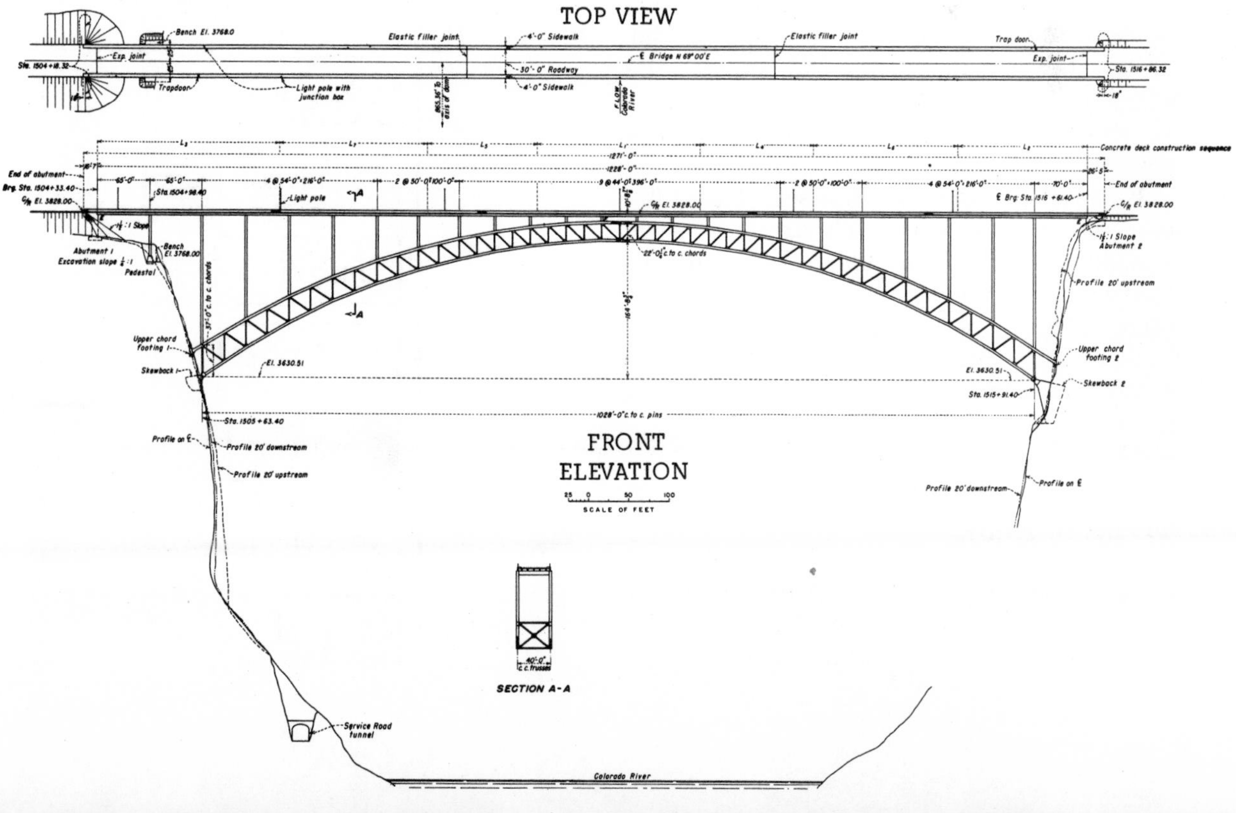

TOP VIEW

30'-0" Roadway

4'-0" Sidewalk

Elastic filler joint

Concrete deck construction sequence

1028'-0" c. to c. pins

FRONT ELEVATION

SCALE OF FEET

SECTION A-A

Service Road tunnel

Colorado River

of a foundation plan might add up, and all of the dimensions of the first floor plan might add up. However, column dimensions on the first floor plan might not be located so they rest on top of the foundation dimensions on the foundation floor plan, unless the plans are carefully checked to make sure that they do.

Summary

Working drawings may be one of two kinds. They may be either *contract drawings* or *shop drawings*. Shop drawings are made by construction contractors or their subcontractors to guide their own work. Contract drawings are made by the project designers and their consultants. They spell out the physical conditions the contractor must provide when he builds a project.

A basic set of working drawings may be made up of seven kinds of drawings: (1) site plan, (2) foundation plan, (3) floor plans, (4) roof plan, (5) elevations, (6) sections, and (7) details. In simple projects, this one set of seven drawings is used to show all of the physical details of the project. In more complex projects, separate sets of working drawings are made for the architectural, civil, mechanical and electrical, and structural features of the project. In very complex projects, even more sets are needed.

Each of the drawings in a set of working drawings must be accurately drawn to scale and dimensioned. The outside (overall) dimensions must equal the sum of all the dimensions in a straight line. Also, the location of each part of the project on one drawing must match the locations shown on all the other drawings of the set.

Terms to Know

contract drawings
working drawings
shop drawings
constructed
complex
dimensions
civil drawings
contractor
subcontractor
dimensioned
accuracy

Think About It!

1. What types of working drawings will you need to explain the layout and construction details for a neighborhood playground?

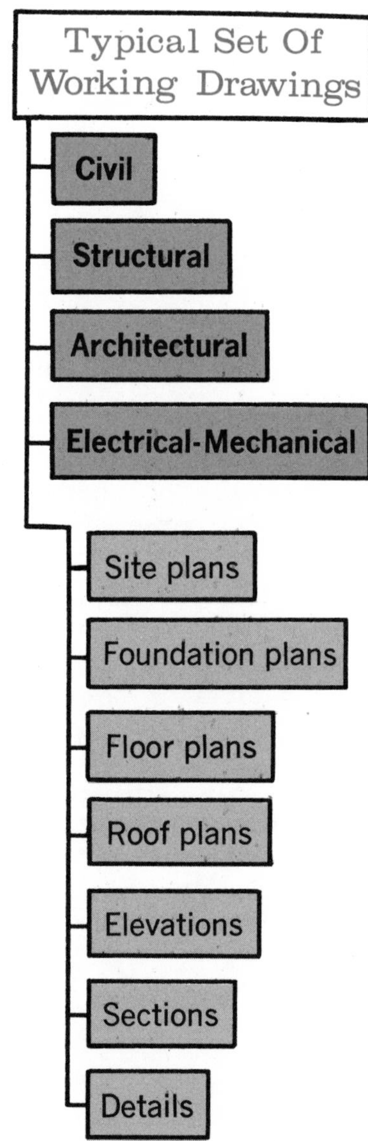

Writing Specifications

Construction specifications are written instructions to the builders about a project to be constructed. They match and are used along with working drawings. They are important because they give details and instructions about the construction job which are easier to put into words than into drawings. Also, when there is a difference between the drawings and the specifications, the specifications are followed.

Specification Content and Uses

Specifications tell about the materials and work needed for a construction project, Fig. 17-1. They describe the work to be done and give the limitations set by the owner, such as job completion deadlines, penalty clauses, payments, change of orders, and procedures. The kind and quality of workmanship, fixtures, materials, and equipment wanted are all written out in specifications. They also give instructions dealing with different parts of the project, such as plumbing, electrical fixtures, and wiring. The materials to be used and the finishes for these materials are also given in specifications.

General conditions of the project (such as guidelines to be followed about performance standards, order and importance of job performance, and the way the work is to be done) are given in specifications. Special conditions for very difficult work which need to be pointed out and clearly defined also are given. In short, *specifications tell all about a construction project in writing*. Figure 17-2 lists several factors, individuals, and groups that influence the specifications of a construction project.

Specifications are used by contractors to estimate a bid on a job. After a bid has been accepted, the specifications are used as a part of the contract between an owner and the contractor. They can be added to the contract and become part of it when it is signed by the owner or the contractor.

Sometimes a book of written contract documents, referred to as the *specifications*, is divided into four kinds of documents. These include: (1) bidding requirements,

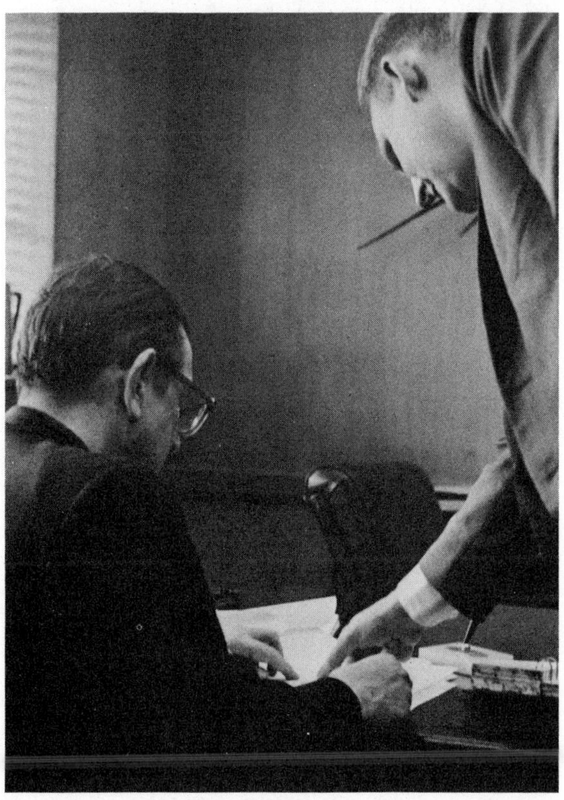

Fig. 17-1. Specifications are prepared by men who have knowledge about construction materials, costs, and building codes.

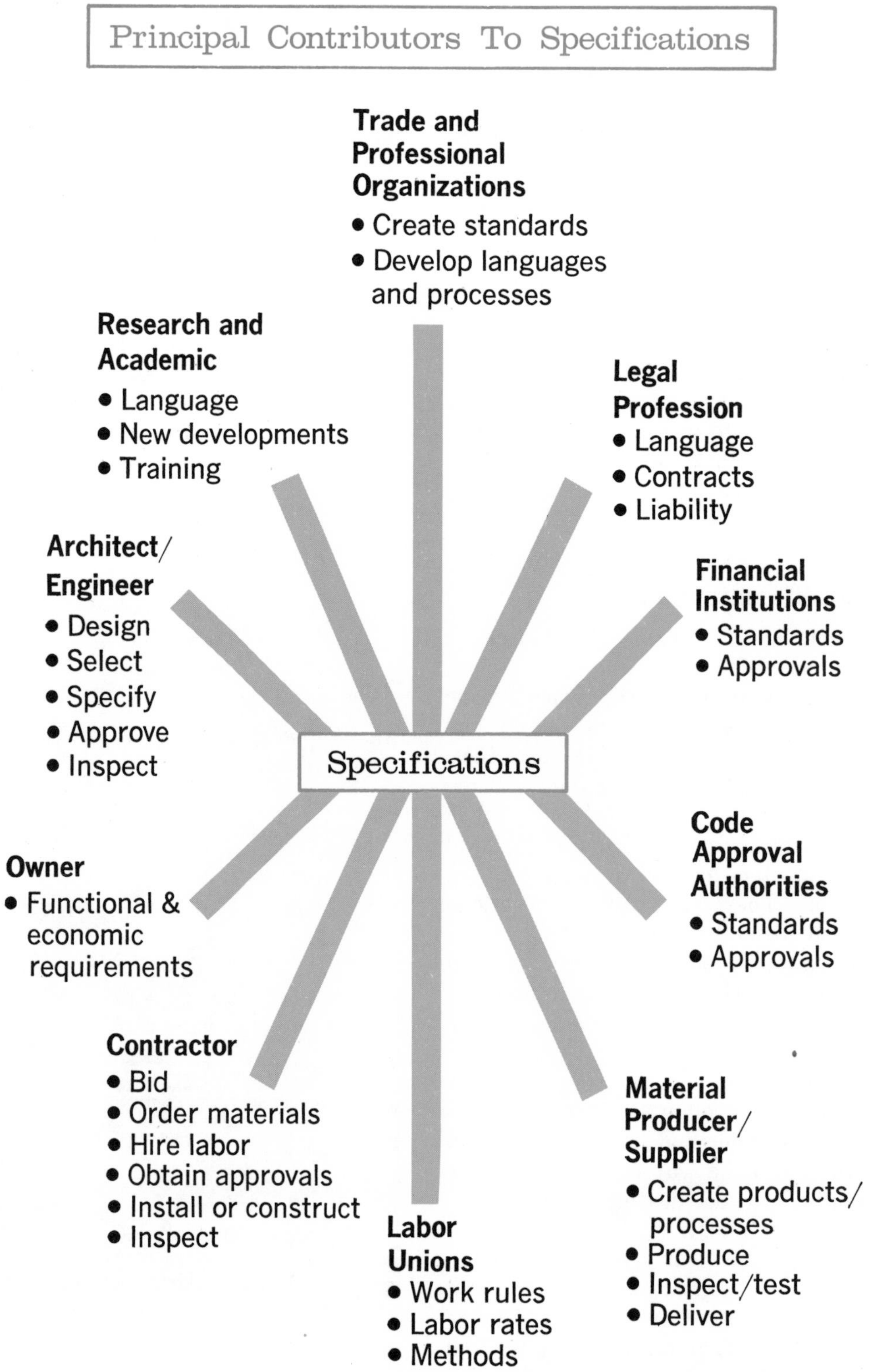
Principal Contributors To Specifications
Specifications
Trade and Professional Organizations
• Create standards
• Develop languages and processes
Research and Academic
• Language
• New developments
• Training
Legal Profession
• Language
• Contracts
• Liability
Architect/Engineer
• Design
• Select
• Specify
• Approve
• Inspect
Financial Institutions
• Standards
• Approvals
Owner
• Functional & economic requirements
Code Approval Authorities
• Standards
• Approvals
Contractor
• Bid
• Order materials
• Hire labor
• Obtain approvals
• Install or construct
• Inspect
Labor Unions
• Work rules
• Labor rates
• Methods
Material Producer/Supplier
• Create products/processes
• Produce
• Inspect/test
• Deliver

Fig. 17-2.

SPECIFICATIONS

General Conditions

1. The building permit and all other permits and inspections required shall be obtained and paid for by the contractor.
2. A portion of the site will be allotted the contractor for the prosecution of his work.
3. All water and electricity used on the work will be furnished by the owner.
4. All surplus materials to be removed shall become the property of the contractor and shall be removed from the premises.
5. The contractor shall pay for all materials, labor, tools, and transportation necessary for the completion of the work.
6. The contractor shall maintain such insurance as will protect him from claims under workmen's compensation acts.
7. The owner will be responsible for maintaining fire insurance and liability insurance.
8. The contractor must present a claim for extras before performing any extra work.
9. The owner has the right to require the contractor to furnish bonds covering the faithful performance of the contract.
10. The owner may withhold final payment and any retained percentages until he is entirely satisfied that the contractor has paid all bills.
11. The contractor must submit a list of subcontractors for the architect's approval.
12. The contractor shall at all times keep the premises free from accumulation of waste materials or rubbish caused by his employees or work.
13. Specific payments will be made to the contractor after he has completed the floor and foundation and the roof.

Fig. 17-3. The general conditions which relate to a project, such as those above, commonly are written and attached to the specifications.

(2) contract forms, (3) general conditions Fig. 17-3, and (4) specifications. This assignment is mainly about specifications. The other documents will be studied later.

Kinds of Specifications

There are four major kinds of specifications. These are: (1) outline specifications, (2) standards specifications, (3) guide specifications, and (4) project specifications. *Outline specifications* are made up when the design phase of a project begins and preliminary drawings are made. These specifications give only an outline (the main facts) about materials to be used and how they are to be used for the job.

Standards specifications are those which are made up by different companies about the use of their own materials. These are usually standard or the same for each material used. If a company specification is used for a certain product, it may also have an "or equal" term tagged on the end. See items "C" and "D", Fig. 17-4. This means

SPECIFICATIONS

Lathing and Plastering

Materials

A. Metal Lath: 3.4 lb. copper-bearing steel, 3/8″ diamond mesh, galvanized, or coated with rust inhibiting paint after fabrication.
B. Tie Wire: No. 18 W & M gauge, weighing not less than 475 pounds per 1,000 ft.
C. Expanded Corner Beads No. 1 "Milcox," 26 gauge, galvanized (or equal).
D. Casing Beads or Plaster Stops: No. 66 "Milcox", 24 gauge, galvanized (or equal).
E. Portland Cement: ASTM C 150, Type I.

Fig. 17-4. Shown here is a typical materials specification for one feature of the work to be done.

that another company's material of the same kind and quality may be used if written permission is given by the architect or owner. The *American Society of Testing Materials* has standard specifications for many materials. In addition, *Sweets Catalog* gives many specifications for many kinds of work and materials.

Guide specifications are a kind of check list which can be used for writing specifications. They tell about things which may be needed for a job. Guide specifications are put together in order and have blanks which a specification writer can fill in to show the specifications he needs for a job. They act as a guide for writing project specifications and help a specification writer organize the specifications in the right order.

Project specifications are usually made up of outline specifications, standards specifications, and guide specifications. They are the finished specifications which have been made for one special construction project.

When Specifications Are Made

Specifications cannot be made until most of the decisions about materials and equipment have been made. However, because of time limits and deadlines, specifications are usually started as soon as the preliminary drawings are done. Work which is not likely to be changed later is started at this time. Examples of specifications which can be done early are those for general conditions of the project, earthwork, and concrete work. As more drawings are made, the specification writer continues identifying and preparing complete specifications. By working along with the drawings in this way, specifications can be finished soon after final drawings are done.

Specification Writers

In a small office, the man who makes the working drawings may also make the specifications. However, in larger firms, there may be one or more people whose only job is to write specifications and to keep a *specification file* up to date. A specification writer must have knowledge and experience. He must know about construction practices and materials. He must know the newest materials and ways of using them, Fig. 17-5. He also needs to know where to go for information and facts he doesn't know. He must be able to find state, county, village, and city building codes or ordinances so his specifications will agree with them. Information from trained men in the construction industry and standard specifications is helpful to a specification writer. He must know where to get this information. With experience, a specification writer is able to write specifications correctly, to do them without wasting time, and to organize them well.

How Specifications Are Made

There are at least four ways to make specifications. **First,** a specification writer may *get a set of old specifications* written for a job much like the one he is working on now. He can write it over, adding or taking away anything needed or not needed for this project.

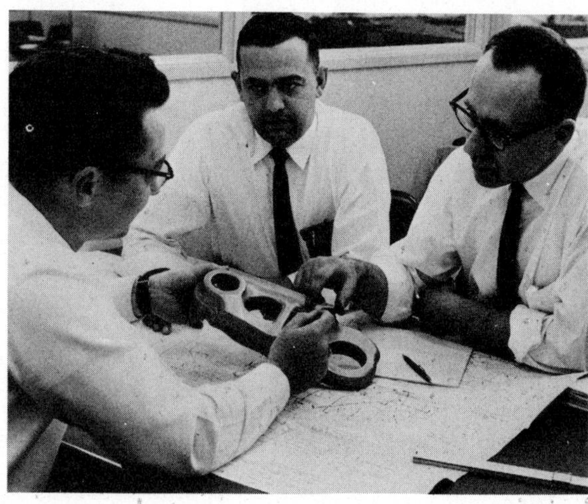

Fig. 17-5. The specifications writer must keep up with new materials and their uses.

Bidding Requirements

Invitation to Bid
Instruction to Bidders
Form of Bid Proposal

Contract Forms

General Conditions
Supplementary General Conditions
Special Conditions

Specifications

Division 1—General Requirements
0170 Alternates

Division 2—Site Work
0211 Demolition
0221 Site Grading
0222 Excavation and Backfilling
0274 Irrigation System
0281 Soil Preparation
0282 Lawns
0284 Trees and Shrubs

Division 3—Concrete
0310 Concrete Formwork
0320 Concrete Reinforcement
0331 Heavyweight Aggregate Concrete
0341 Precast Concrete Panels

Division 4—Masonry
0410 Mortar
0422 Concrete Unit Masonry

Division 5—Metals
0551 Metal Stairs
0570 Ornamental Metals

Division 6—Carpentry
0621 Wood Trim
0622 Millwork

Division 7—Moisture Protection
0711 Membrane Waterproofing
0751 Built-up Bituminous Roofing
0762 Metal Roof Flashing and Trim
0790 Calking and Sealants

Division 8—Doors, Windows, and Glass
0812 Aluminum Doors and Frames
0820 Wood Doors
0839 Revolving Doors
0852 Aluminum Windows
0860 Wood Windows
0870 Finish Hardware
0885 Glass and Glazing

Division 9—Finishes
0913 Gypsum Lath
0915 Plastering Accessories
0916 Plaster
0926 Gypsum Drywall System
0927 Gypsum Drywall Finishing
0931 Ceramic Tile
0941 Cast-in-place Terrazzo
0957 Wood Parquet Flooring
0965 Resilient Flooring
0990 Painting
0995 Wall Covering

Division 10—Specialties
1013 Chutes

Division 11—Equipment
1132 Audio-Visual Aids
1197 Stage Equipment

Division 12—Furnishings
1240 Carpets and Mats
1250 Drapery and Curtains

Division 13—Special Construction
1385 Swimming Pool

Division 14—Conveying Systems
1420 Elevators

Division 15—Mechanical
1510 Basic Materials and Methods
1521 Water Supply Piping
1522 Domestic Hot Water System
1526 Soil and Waste Piping
1529 Roof Drainage System
1530 Plumbing Fixtures and Trim
1580 Air-Tempering System
1590 Refrigeration
1595 HVC Controls and Instruments

Division 16—Electrical
1610 Basic Materials and Methods
1630 Electrical Distribution System
1640 Lighting Fixtures
1651 Telephone Equipment
1671 Motors and Motor Controls
1695 Lightning Protection System

Fig. 17-6. The Construction Specifications Institute outline for specifications.

Second, if he does not have a set of old specifications much like the job he is working on, a specification writer may gather together several sets of specifications. Then he may use the *cut and clip procedure.* To do this, he cuts out the sections of the specifications which he needs for this job. Then he clips them to a page and puts in additions where they are needed. By doing this, he is able to build up a new set of specifications without writing all parts from the beginning.

Third, a specifications writer may write specifications by the *paragraph procedure.* To do this, he uses a specifications file. This file has file cards in it. Each file card has a single statement paragraph on it. The writer gets all the cards needed for the specifications he is working on, puts them in order, and makes up a set of new specifications from the cards.

Fourth, guide specifications can be used. These are forms which are organized in order and have blanks for filling in needed information. The specification writer fills in the blanks he needs to make a set of specifications.

Specification Format

Specifications are set up and written in the same order that the job is to be done. The sections are kept in order, and everything about one part of the job is kept together. For example, everything about earthwork is put together. Everything about plumbing is in one section, and so on, until the whole job is described. Writing specifications in this way makes it easier for a contractor to *estimate* a job and to decide who is going to do each part of a job. A sample set of specification sections and divisions is shown in Fig. 17-6. These have become widely used in the construction industry.

Specifications are usually written on 8½″ by 11″ paper. This makes them easy to work with. The *title page* comes first. The title page includes: (1) the title of the specification, (2) the kind of work the specifications are for, (3) where the work is to take place, (4) the name and address of the owner, (5) the name and address of the architect, (6) the date, and (7) the job number. Next, there is usually a table of contents. The specifications follow this. Specification information is usually titled, numbered by sections, and written in paragraph form. See Fig. 17-4.

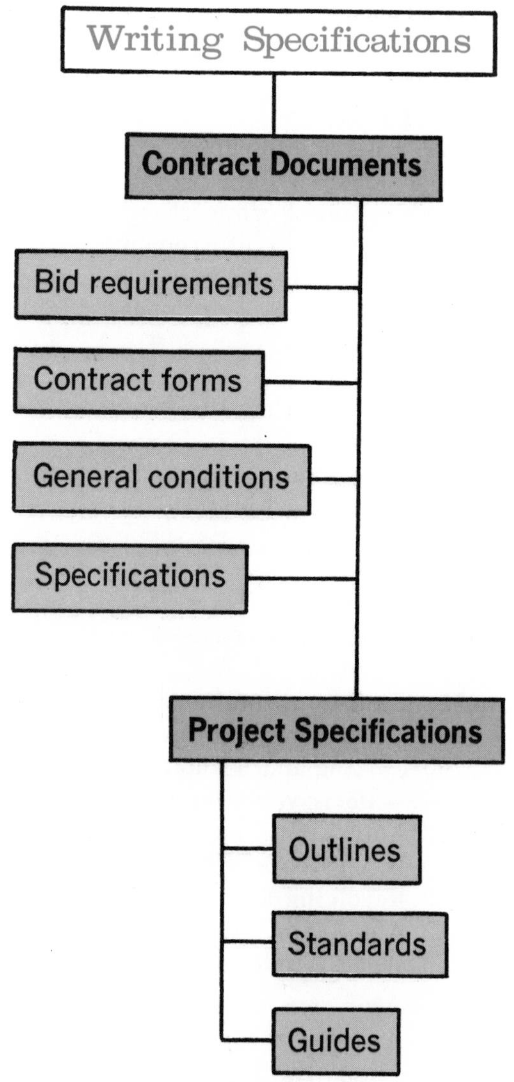

Summary

Construction specifications are written instructions to the builder about a project to be constructed. They tell about the materials and work needed for a construction project. They are used by contractors to estimate and bid for a job, and they become part of a contract after a bid has been accepted.

There are four parts to specifications. While drawings for a project are being made, specifications are started. By working along with the drawings, specifications can be finished soon after final drawings are done.

Specification writers need both knowledge and experience. They write specifications in four ways. These are: (1) getting an old set of specifications and working it over for the new job, (2) using several sets of specifications and cutting and clipping them to get one new set, (3) writing them by the paragraph procedure which requires the use of a specification file, and (4) using guide specifications.

Specifications are written in sections in the same order that the job is to be done. This makes it easier for a contractor to estimate a job and to decide who is going to do what job.

Terms to Know

construction specifications
- a. outline specifications
- b. standards specifications
- c. guide specifications
- d. project specifications

fabrication
liability
allotted
an estimate
a bid
"or equal"
specifications file
building codes
ordinance
format

Think About It!

1. You have been selected as the contractor to build a playground. What are some of the specifications you would need, in writing, about:
   a. General conditions
   b. General requirements
2. What could you do if some of the specified materials could not be purchased in your area?

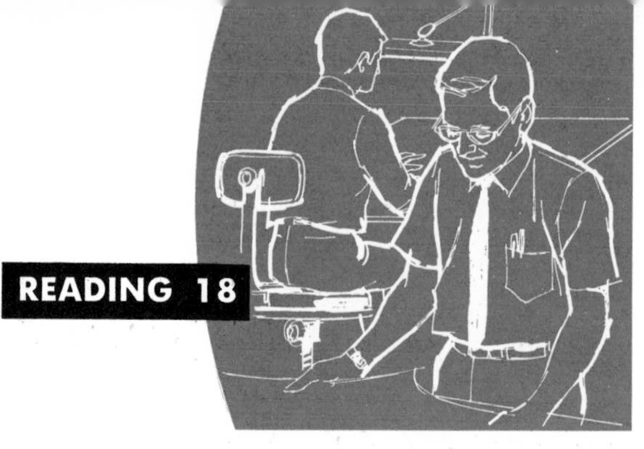

READING 18

The Designing and Engineering Cycle

The previous reading assignments have discussed six steps of the designing process as they would be applied to different types of problems of the construction industry. These suggested steps are not rigid steps that must be followed in every detail to arrive at a completed plan of action, but they should serve as a general guide for the designer. He must consider each of the steps of the design process as presented, but he may change the order of the steps. Usually, a better design will result from an organized approach rather than from an unorganized effort.

Steps in the Design Process

The design process is composed of six steps: (1) problem identification, (2) preliminary ideas, (3) refinement (improvement), (4) analysis, (5) decision, and (6) implementation (use).

The first step in the designing process is problem identification. Someone must see the need for a problem's solution. In the construction industry, this is usually a private investor, a public agency, or a business corporation. For example, the Ajax Corporation may wish to build a manufacturing plant in a certain area of the state. They may see the need for the plant to increase their present production, or to enter a completely new field of manufacturing for a new product. Once they have seen this need and have agreed to begin with the project, they will hire an architect or engineer to set up a working plan from which the new plant could be constructed. At this point, *the person in charge of the project becomes the designer*; however, his design must follow the general requirements and desires of the corporation for whom the plant is being built.

The designer is unable to find a solution to the problem until he fully understands the problem and its requirements. During the identification phase, the designer will gather the following information: (1) the desires of the client (the corporation), (2) the needs of the plant, (3) the facilities required, and (4) the building regulations at the site, to name a few. The designer must also consider: (1) future expansion, (2) availability of resources, (3) power, (4) utilities, (5) labor, and (6) costs. An evaluation of this information can be used to help him understand the problems that he must solve with his design.

Step two in the design process is the development of preliminary (beginning) ideas. These first ideas are thought up in great numbers to provide a wide variety of solutions to the design problem. These ideas usually are recorded as freehand sketches and notes to be used as a guide for further study. All ideas are collected for review, whether or not they seem to be practical. Sometimes unusual ideas, when applied to a new situation, will give a new solution to a problem.

To refine (improve) these beginning ideas, scale drawings are made of several of the better ones (step three of the design process). Exact information, such as sizes, shapes, lengths, and angles, is necessary before the design can be analyzed in the next step of the designing process. Refinement is the improvement of a beginning idea into a more detailed form. Several ideas should be refined, rather than only one idea selected early in the process.

During step four, each of the refined ideas is analyzed in these areas:

1. Selection of structural materials of the necessary strength,
2. Analysis of the site to decide upon the best possible layout, and
3. Deciding as to whether or not the idea is efficient by analyzing the functions of important areas.

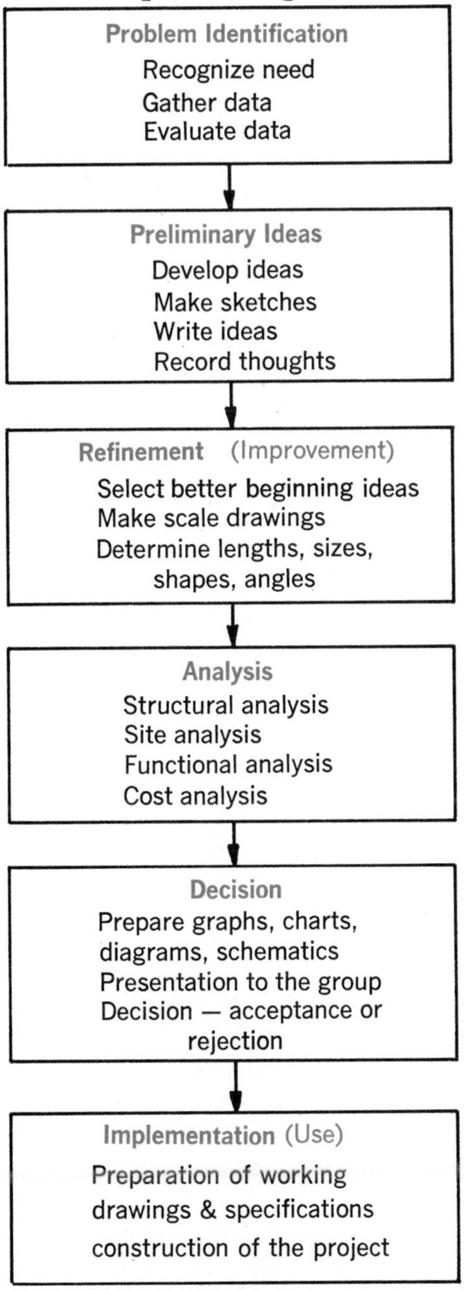

When the design process has reached this point, the most desirable design must be selected for construction (step five—decision). In the case of the corporation, the officers and directors of the company will be responsible for this decision. The designer must present the background of his design and the process by which he approached its solution.

After it is decided which design is to be constructed, the designer will prepare plans and specifications that will explain the details of construction to the builders. The process of preparing these plans and specifications and the construction of the project are called *implementation.* (This is the last step of the design process.)

The designer often closely watches the construction of the project in order to make changes in the plans as the need arises. It is very difficult to prepare plans that will cover every detail completely. Therefore, the builders must help in suggesting ways to improve weaknesses in the details of the plans. On a large project, to a limited extent, the contractor, technicians, and craftsmen participate in the designing process.

Plans, working drawings, and specifications are prepared in the last step of the design process before construction begins. This area is closely related to the field of drafting. The engineers and architects develop construction details that are drawn by draftsmen in standard form. These details will be blueprinted and given to the builders and contractors who will construct various parts of the project.

The Complete Design Process

Problem Identification
Recognize need
Gather data
Evaluate data

↓

Preliminary Ideas
Develop ideas
Make sketches
Write ideas
Record thoughts

↓

Refinement (Improvement)
Select better beginning ideas
Make scale drawings
Determine lengths, sizes, shapes, angles

↓

Analysis
Structural analysis
Site analysis
Functional analysis
Cost analysis

↓

Decision
Prepare graphs, charts, diagrams, schematics
Presentation to the group
Decision — acceptance or rejection

↓

Implementation (Use)
Preparation of working drawings & specifications
construction of the project

Changes in the Design Cycle

The design process is outlined as a set of six steps that are usually followed in arriving at a design solution. This does not mean that a single idea should be taken through each of the six steps one at a time. Instead, a number of ideas should be developed before an attempt is made to develop a final solution. Several ideas should be refined and analyzed to give other solutions. As ideas are carried through the steps of the design process, reasons may be found for turning them down. For example, a solution may be found to be too expensive, not strong enough, or too small. In this case, the designer will return to another idea or, perhaps, return to the first step of the design process and develop other solutions that will be carried through the steps of the designing process again. This cycle could be changed at the decision step if the *client* (person hiring the designer) disagrees with the designer's solution.

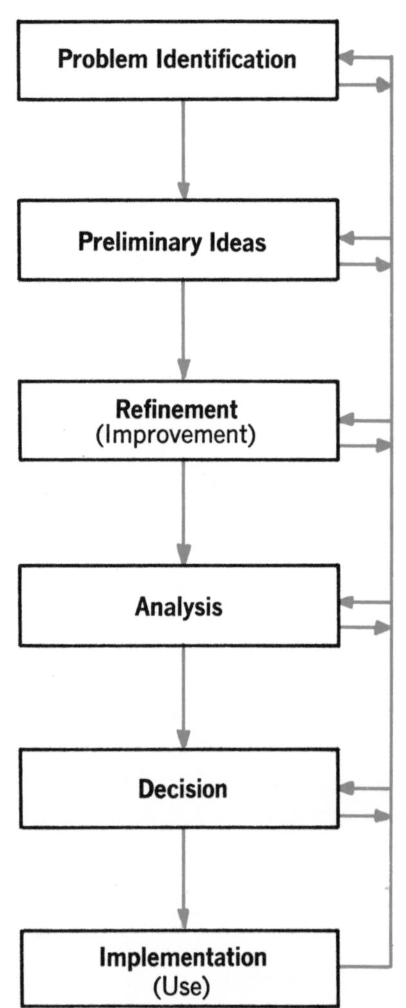

Summary

The designing process is the step-by-step approach used by a designer to find a solution for a problem. A recognized series of steps is used for all construction projects (an athletic stadium, highway, or any other structure). This cycle can stop at any step, and the designer may go back to a previous step and develop new ideas. A designer does not design by chance, but through a systematic approach. The end result of the designing process should be a constructed project which best meets the original needs of the project. Since changes in the master plan may need to be improved during construction, the designing process does not end until the project has been completed. Without careful planning and designing, a completed project might turn out to be unsatisfactory.

Terms to Know

design cycle
organize
construct
scale drawings
architect
engineer
client

Think About It!

1. Suppose you are asked to design the stage sets for a school play. What questions might you ask to help identify the *design problem*?
2. After you *sketch* and *note* many *preliminary ideas,* you will *refine* some of them.
   a. What dimensions will you need before you start *drawing to scale*? (Think of the curtains, the ways of entering and leaving the stage, and all the other size limits.)
   b. Why will you need to know what the actors do on the stage?

READING 19

Selecting a Builder

Let us now suppose that the design is completed. The next decision the owner must make is who will do the construction work? In general, the owner has three choices:

1. He might do the work himself.
2. He might select a construction consultant who is also a builder.
3. He might choose a construction contractor.

The owner does not often build a project by himself. This is only done if the job is very small, if the owner and his employees have the necessary skills to do the work, or if the owner has enough construction jobs to keep a complete construction crew of his own busy at all times, Fig. 19-1.

Sometimes a *construction consultant* both designs and builds a project. The consultant who does this is often called an *architect-engineer-constructor*. The job itself is sometimes referred to as a "turnkey" job, because one company prepares the plans and constructs the project, and then turns the key over to the owner. The advantage of this method is that only one organization, the architect-engineer-building company, is responsible for seeing that everything is done. The disadvantage is that this may be an expensive way to get a project built, for very often there is little competition.

Commonly, a construction project is built by a contractor who has competed with others for the job. The owner chooses the contractor by comparing what several contractors say it would cost them to do the job. The owner makes the contract with the one who has said he can do the job correctly for the least amount of money. *The contract is an agreement between the owner and the contractor as to how much the owner will pay to have that contractor build the project,* Fig. 19-2.

Fig. 19-1. Large companies such as railroads employ their own architects, engineers, and construction crews.

Fig. 19-2. This contracting company probably was awarded this job contract after submitting the lowest bid.

Kinds of Contracts

In the construction business, there are four general kinds of contracts: (1) fixed price, (2) cost plus a fixed fee, (3) cost plus a percentage of cost, and (4) incentive.

Fig. 19-3. A contractor must consider the cost of any new equipment needed to do the job.

Fig. 19-4. Contractors consider the cost of all the materials in making a bid estimate.

In the *fixed price contract,* the contractor agrees to do all the building according to the owner's plans and specifications for a set sum of money which is to be paid by the owner. Sometimes, especially for buildings, this amount is stated as a single lump sum. For example, Bill Smith, a painting contractor, might agree to paint John Jones's house for $600. The $600 is called a single lump sum (fixed price).

The *unit price contract* is a different kind of *fixed price contract.* The unit price contract is often used for any project which uses heavy construction equipment. For example, if there is to be excavating and paving for a project, there might be one price for the excavation and one price for the paving. The price might look like this:

103,000 cubic yards of common excavation at 30 cents per cubic yard	$30,900
12,700 square yards of asphalt pavement at $5.00 per square yard	63,500
Total	$94,400

The contract itself would have an estimated quantity of cubic yards or square yards. Payment would be made on the actual quantity. If, on the above project, only 100,000 cubic yards were actually excavated, the contractor would receive 100,000 x 30 cents or $30,000.

In the *cost-plus-a-fixed fee* (CPFF) *contract,* the owner agrees to pay the contractor whatever it costs to do the job (materials, use of equipment, and labor) plus a fixed sum. (See Figs. 19-3 and 19-4). For example, the ABC Construction Company might agree to build a plastics factory for what it costs them to build it, plus a fee of $100,000. This fee of $100,000 is to cover ABC's *overhead* (such as the cost of its home office) and profit.

The CPFF contract is used in many cases. It is most often used when large industrial plants are to be built and whenever the work must begin before plans and specifications are completed.

Some owners find that CPFF is a very good way to get their projects built. Other owners feel that the contractor has too little reason to be economical or efficient because the owner pays the cost no matter what it is. Also, the expenses involved in bookkeeping and accounting for a CPFF contract are very high. Some contractors like CPFF because they believe that the fee gives them a good profit without much risk. Others like to take the risk involved in a fixed price contract because they think their efficiency will help them make a greater profit than they would get from the fee of a CPFF.

The *cost-plus-a-percentage-of-cost contract* (CPPC) is one in which the contractor is paid a flat percentage of his cost. For example, he may be given a contract to build a plastics factory for the amount of whatever it will cost him ($1,500,000) plus an 8% fee ($1,500,000 x .08 or $120,000). This kind of contract is rarely used. In fact, on most public work the CPPC contract is illegal. This is because a poor contractor (one who is not economical or efficient) will receive higher fees than an efficient one.

In the *incentive contract,* a target estimate is made. If the contractor should do the job for less than the estimated cost, he gets to keep a part of the saving. If it should cost more than the estimated amount, his fee is reduced. Thus, the contractor has a good reason (incentive) to keep the cost down.

Suppose the owner and contractor agree that the plastics factory should cost $1,500,000 and the contractor will get a fee of $120,000 for building it. They might also agree that if the factory actually costs $1,300,000, the contractor would get half of whatever he saved plus his regular fee of $120,000, a total of $220,000. The contract might further state that if it should cost $1,700,000, the contractor's fee would be reduced to $50,000. Use of the incentive contract is usually limited to work that costs more than $1,000,000.

Advertised and Negotiated Contracts

Most public contracts and many private contracts are advertised. That is, the owner places notices in newspapers, magazines, and with contractors' associations asking contractors to send in their bids (the amount for which each could do the job), Figs. 19-5 and 19-6. Public contracts are usually advertised because it is thought fair to give every qualified contractor the chance to bid, since they are also taxpayers. Private contracts are sometimes advertised because the competition created by advertising usually results in the lowest cost for the project.

Any contractor who can convince the owner that he is able to build the project is usually eligible to bid. Advertised contracts are generally fixed price contracts. Because the various contractors are bidding against one another, each contractor is encouraged to turn in his lowest possible bid. This tends to lower the price that the owner has to pay.

Negotiated contracts are any contracts in which the owner and the contractor talk together to reach an agreement on the terms of the contract. The price is always one of the terms. Sometimes the owner compares

ADVERTISEMENT FOR BIDS

Legal Notice

SEALED PROPOSALS WILL BE RECEIVED at the Office of the Secretary of the Board of Education of the City of Chicago, up to the hour of 12 NOON of MONDAY, MARCH 11, 1971, for the following school work:
SUNDRY SCHOOLS — General Work in connection with ALTERATIONS and IMPROVEMENTS.

Plans and specifications may be obtained at the Board of Education, Bureau of Architecture, Room 564, 228 North LaSalle Street, Chicago, Illinois 60601.

SAUL SAMUELS, Director Bureau of Architecture
EDWIN A. LEDERER, Associate Superintendent in Charge of Operation Services

February 23, 1971
DCN, Feb. 23, 1971 — 172

Fig. 19-5. Public contracts often are advertised in newspapers.

prices by trying to negotiate with more than one contractor.

Negotiated contracts are useful in certain circumstances. For example, the owner might want to limit the bidders to those contractors he is sure are qualified for the specific project he needs to have built. If only four contractors were known to have had experience in building a certain kind of industrial plant, the owner might decide to limit bidding to those four. Negotiated contracts might also be used if it were important to save time and to begin the work before plans and specifications were completed. By their very nature, some kinds of contracts, like CPFF, CPPC, and incentive require some negotiation.

general building

low bidders, contract awards

CHGO 23 #472 199B
1ST REPT 2-9-68

ADMINISTRATION BUILDING (INT ALTS) — $45,000
AURORA ILL (KANE CO) 152 GLENWOOD PL
G C-PLBG-HTG-VENTG-AIR CONDTG & ELEC AWARDED-START WORK SOON
OWNER-BD OF EDU-WEST SIDE SCHOOLS-DIST #129-HAROLD G FEARN (SUPT) 152 GLENWOOD PL-AURORA ILL
ARCHT-BERGER-KELLEY-UNTEED & SCAAGS-501 W UNIVERSITY-CHAMPAIGN ILL & 1612 W NORTHWEST HWY-ARLINGTON HEIGHTS ILL
ENGR (PLBG-HTG-VENTG-AIR CONDTG-ELEC) — BELING ENGRG-807½ S NEIL AVE-CHAMPAIGN ILL
INCLS MINOR PLBG WK-AIR CONDTG-HTG & ELEC CHANGES-CARPT WK - ACOUST TILE - VINYL ASB TILE-CARPETING & PTG WK
G C INCLS ALL TRADES EXCEPT PLBK-HTG-VENTG-AIR CONDTG & ELEC
G C - BANKS & WEGMAN-755 N OHIO-AURORA ILL
PLBG-HTG-VENTG & AIR CONDTG-R J O'NEIL INC-900 S UNION-AURORA ILL
ELEC-GLENN PIERCE ELEC INC-311 ASHLAND AVE-AURORA ILL

CHGO 27 #472 880

CAR WASH-$15,000
CHICAGO ILL (COOK CO) 2717 E 95TH ST
PERMIT GRANTED-WORK TO BEGIN AT ONCE
OWNER - JM V CORP-11435 S WENTWORTH-CHICAGO ILL
ARCHT-WM CONVEY-20 E MAIN ST-GLENWOOD ILL
MAS EXT WALLS-1 STY-NO BASMT-28x105 FT DIMS
OWNER AWDS SEP CONTS

Fig. 19-6. Contract awards commonly are listed in special reports or in trade publications.

Others Who Help to Build the Project

So far, we have considered that the job is to be done by the contractor's company. Actually, few contractors do all the work with their own employees. Contractors are usually *general contractors*. They are called general, because they are the ones who have the overall or general contract with the owner.

The general contractor subcontracts parts of the job to specialists, Fig. 19-7. For example, The Smith Construction Company, a general contractor who is to build a house, might subcontract all of the plumbing work to the Jones Plumbing Company. The agreement between the Smith Company and the Jones Company is called a *subcontract*. It would be the same if the Smith Company would decide to buy their lumber from a particular lumberyard. This lumberyard would be called the *supplier* and the contract

Fig. 19-7. The superstructure on this bridge is being set up by a subcontractor. Other subcontractors may set the foundations, install utilities, and do the painting.

between the two companies would be called a *supply contract.*

Summary

The usual way for an owner to get his project built is to hire a general contractor. The agreement between the owner and the contractor may be one of four kinds of contracts: fixed price, CPFF, CPPC, or incentive. The owner may advertise or negotiate for the project. The general contractor may subcontract parts of the job to specialists and must nearly always buy materials for the project from a supplier. In the next three lessons on contracting, we shall assume that the owner has already had the plans drawn by a construction consultant. It also will be assumed that a fixed price contract has been awarded to a general contractor.

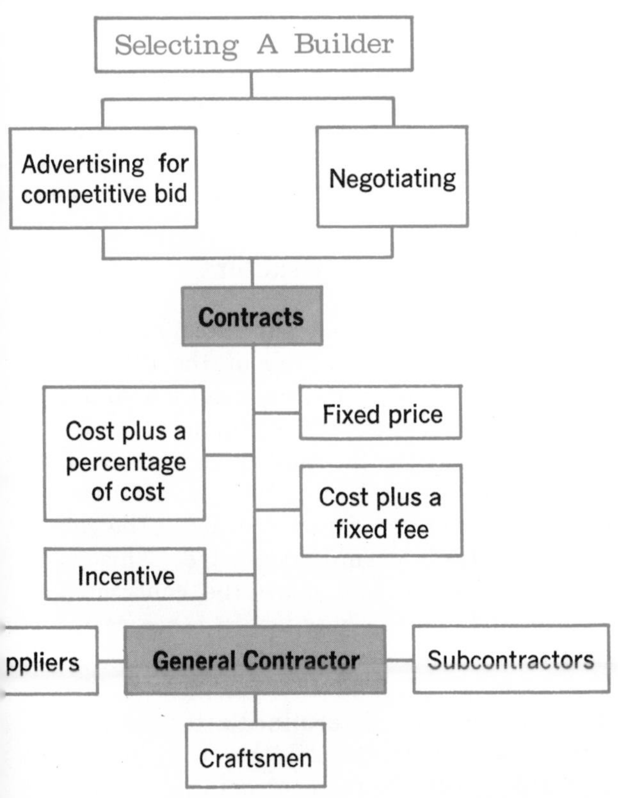

Terms to Know

construction consultant
"turnkey" job
single lump sum
overhead
submit a bid
fixed price contract
unit price contract
cost-plus-fixed-fee contract
cost-plus-a-percentage-of-cost contract
incentive contract
awarded
a target estimate
advertised
competition
negotiated contracts
general contractors
subcontractors
supply contract
supplier

Think About It!

1. The *owner* of a building site usually does not buy all the *materials,* rent *equipment,* and hire *workers* to put up a structure.
   a. Why do most landowners hire a *general contractor* for a construction project?
   b. Why does a *general contractor* often hire *subcontractors?*
2. Match each kind of *contract* with the way the contractor is paid:

Payment

a. He is paid what the job costs him, plus a profit that is *decided in advance.*
b. He is paid what the job costs him, plus a profit that goes up as his costs go up.
c. His payment is decided in advance, and is not changed.
d. He estimates the cost in advance. If he does the job for less, his *fee* goes up. If the job costs more than his *estimate,* his fee goes down.

Kind of Contract

1. *Fixed price*
2. *Cost plus fixed fee*
3. *Cost plus percentage of cost*
4. *Incentive*

READING 20

Contracting

Let us now assume that the plans and specifications are completed. The owner has decided to select a contractor to build the project by advertising for bids and then awarding a fixed price or unit price contract. We shall now outline the steps which are followed between completion of the plans and the actual start of work. Although different owners have different methods of bidding and awarding contracts, the procedure outlined below is typical of a fair and honest way to select a construction contractor.

Advertising

The first step in selecting a construction contractor is to notify all bidders who might be interested in the fact that bids will be received. This is done by an *invitation to bid,* a short notice which states: (1) the type of work, (2) the location, (3) the time and place of the bid opening, and (4) where and how plans and specifications are to be made available.

The invitation to bid is mailed by the owner or the architect-engineer (who represents the owner) to contractors who might be interested. Sometimes the invitation to bid is actually advertised in newspapers and magazines, Fig. 20-2. It is sent to contractors' associations, such as local chapters of the Associated General Contractors of America. There are also companies, such as the F. W. Dodge Corporation, which publish reports of jobs being bid. On public work, especially, great effort is made to notify all possible bidders.

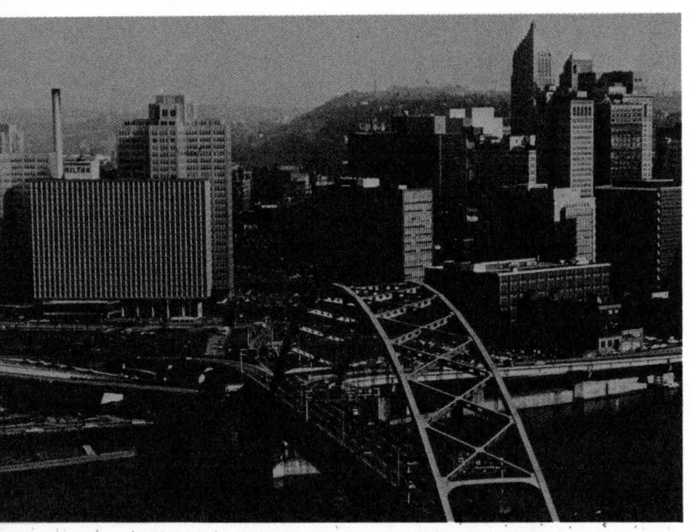

Fig. 20-1. Most of the construction projects around us were built by contractors who bid for the contract to do the work.

Qualifications of Contractors

The owner or his architect-engineer always satisfies himself about the contractor's ability (experience, financial resources, integrity, personnel, and equipment) to do the job. Sometimes this ability is determined before bidding, and only those contractors who are considered capable of doing the job are invited or permitted to bid. This is called *prequalification* since the contractor must qualify before bidding. In other cases, such as on much federal government work, anyone may bid, and the qualifications of the low bidder are determined after the bids are opened but before the contract is *awarded* (given) to the contractor.

bidders column

Call 467-7139 in case of error or omission. Two days are required for listing.

February 23, 1971

(A) Church (B) Rectory (C) Parochial Grade School (addn & alts), Summit, Ill., (a & b) 75th St. & 72nd Ct. (c) 5641-73rd Ave. (ATB on GC & mechl trades) due Feb. 23 at 4 p.m. for St. Joseph Parish. (A) Stade, Dolan, Emrick & Assocs., 819 Busse Hwy., Park Ridge, Ill. 459 897

Peter Hansen & Sons Inc., 9505 S. Prospect. (HI 5-0300)
Talsma Bldrs., 12642 S. Springfield, Alsip. (597-0500)
George Kohler & Sons Inc., 2355 E. Oakton, Arlington Heights. (430-3910)
R. Rudnick Co. Inc., 3957 N. Ashland Ave. (935-5007)
Geraghty Trainor Const. Co., 10200 S. Cicero Ave., Oak Lawn. (499-0550)
Midway Const. Co., 1801 S. Busse, Mt. Prospect (439-5100)

(A) Assembly Plant Bldg. #8 (B) Wheel Press Bldg. #10 (C) Paint & Grit Storage Bldg. #12 (D) Truck Assembly Bldg. #9 (addn) (E) Stenciling Bldg. (addn) (F) Bldg. #7 (alts), East Chicago, Ind., 151st & Railroad Ave. (ATB on GC) by invitation only, due Feb. 23 at 2 p.m. for Union Tank Car. (A) Metz, Train, Olson & Youngren Inc., 1 E. Wacker, Chicago. 468 376

Edward Gray Corp., 12233 S. Ave. O. (BA 1-8400)
Campbell, Lowrie, Lautermilch Corp., 6317 N. Broadway. (338-0300)
J. L. Simmons Co. Inc., 506 S. Wabash. (WE 9-2355)
Morrison Const. Co., 1834 Summer, Hammond, Ind. (219-WE 2-5036)
J. M. Foster Co. Inc., 7500 W. 5th Ave., Gary, Ind. (219-949-4020)

Fig. 20-2. Trade magazines may have special columns in them to advertise projects on which bids may be made.

Bidding Documents

When a contractor indicates to the architect-engineer his decision to bid, he is given several documents. Among these are the instructions to each bidder. The instructions tell the contractor how to submit his proposal (proposal and bid are the same thing), how the rules of the bidding will be conducted, and how the award will be made. The contractor also receives plans and specifications, including the conditions of the contract into which he will enter if he is awarded the job. The contractor is also given blank forms which are to be used (1) for bonds, (2) for a questionnaire about his qualifications, and (3) for submitting his proposal. All of the bidding documents should be completed so that the bidders may know all the details they need for preparing bids. Subcontractors and suppliers also obtain plans and specifications so that they may furnish prices to the general contractors for their own parts of the job.

The Bid Opening

How the contractor makes his estimate and prepares his bid (Fig. 20-3) is described in the next lesson. Accordingly, we shall pass directly to the bid opening itself. The bids are usually opened about 30 days after the invitation to bid is issued or advertised. This period, during which the contractors prepare their bids, may vary from 10 to 90 days.

At the bid opening, each contractor submits his proposal. The *proposal* is a form, usually supplied by the architect-engineer, on which the contractor writes in the amount for which he will build the project. If it is a lump sum job, he would submit

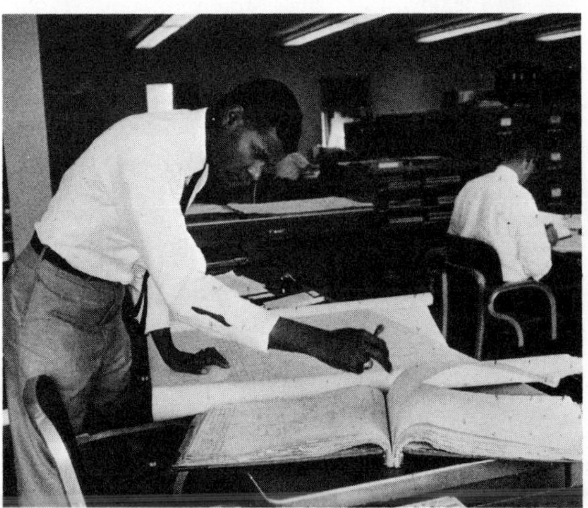

Fig. 20-3. The contractor checks records from his previous jobs to help make decisions about new bids and contracts.

just one amount. For instance, he might bid $325,700 to construct a certain school building. On a unit price job, such as paving a parking lot, the price schedule in the proposal might look like this:

20,500 cubic yards of excavation @ $0.50	$10,250
5,000 cubic yards of select fill @ $2.00	10,000
3,000 square yards of asphalt paving @ $5.00	15,000
Total	$35,250

(Note: @ means *each.*)

In addition to the proposal, each contractor usually submits a deposit or *bid bond.* The owner wants to be sure that the bidder will enter into the contract at the price bid. A bid bond is a guarantee on the part of a bonding company (usually a large insurance company) that the contractor will enter into the contract. Bid bonds are often for 20% of the face value of the bid. If the bidder accepts the contract, the bid bond no longer serves a purpose. If the low bidder refuses to take the contract, the owner collects the difference between the low bid and the next lowest bid, up to the amount of the bid bond.

Other things which may be submitted by the contractor at the bid opening, if required by the architect-engineer, are:

1. A list of the qualifications of the contractor,
2. A list of subcontractors,
3. A list of construction equipment to be used by the contractor to build the job, or
4. A list of makes and models of equipment the contractor will install in the structure.

So that all bidders may be treated fairly, very strict rules on bid openings are carefully observed. One rule is that no bid may be submitted or changed after the time set for the bid opening. Bids must be submitted in sealed envelopes, but changes made by telegram are usually permitted before the bid opening. In the case of public work, each contractor's proposal is read aloud at the public opening. Anyone may attend the bid opening, and may examine any contractor's proposal, Fig. 20-4.

The Award

After the bids are opened, each bid is carefully examined by the owner or the architect-engineer. The purpose of this examination is to determine the lowest *responsive bid.* A bid is responsive if it matches in every detail the conditions set forth in the bidding documents. To be responsive, a bid must be complete. Normally, any exceptions (changes) that the contractor plans in his bid make it not responsive. Should the owner specify maple flooring and the contractor says in his bid that instead pine will be furnished, the bid is not responsive to the owner's requirement that maple be furnished.

If the contractors have not been prequalified (qualified before the bids were opened), the architect-engineer checks on the qualifications of the lowest responsive bidder. He finds out if the bidder has the knowledge, the money, the honesty, the people, and the equipment to do the job.

Fig. 20-4. The bid opening is a public meeting where individual proposals are available to be examined.

Information about a contractor can be learned (1) from the bidder's statement of qualifications, (2) from banks, (3) from other owners for whom the bidder has worked, and (4) from other businessmen.

After identifying the lowest responsive bid of a qualified contractor, the architect-engineer suggests to the owner that an award be made. Then the owner sends a *notice of award* to the successful bidder. Usually he sends along with the notice of award, agreement forms and blank performance and payment bonds.

Bonds

A *performance bond* is one in which the bonding company (an insurance or surety company) guarantees that the contractor will build the project according to the owner's plans and specifications (that is, that the contractor will perform the contract). If the contractor does not fulfill his duties under the contract, then the insurance company itself will fulfill them. If this should happen, the insurance company would probably hire another contractor to complete the work.

A *payment bond* is one in which the bonding company guarantees that the contractor will pay his subcontractors and suppliers (and sometimes employees) for any amount due them. If the contractor does not pay a subcontractor for work satisfactorily performed, the bonding company must make payment.

Performance and payment bonds give the owner a considerable amount of protection, and are generally required on most major projects. The cost is rather small, about one cent per dollar of the contract amount. It is quite rare for a contractor not to fulfill his obligations to the owner, his subcontractors, and his suppliers. Accordingly, bonding companies do not often have to take over the contractor's job or the payment of his bills. Needless to say, bonding companies are very careful about which contractors are given bonds. To obtain a bond a contractor must have ability, financial resources, and a good reputation.

The Agreement

The *agreement* is a brief statement of the work to be done under the contract and the price. It refers to the other parts of the contract, the plans, specifications, instructions to bidders, general and special conditions, and the bonds. It is signed by the owner and the contractor.

Notice to Proceed

It usually takes from five to ten days for the contractor to complete arrangements for his payment and performance bonds. He then signs the agreement and forwards the agreement and the bonds to the owner. The owner then signs the agreement and issues the *notice to proceed,* which gives the contractor permission to begin the work.

Fig. 20-5. The contractor is given the notice to proceed on a huge building project.

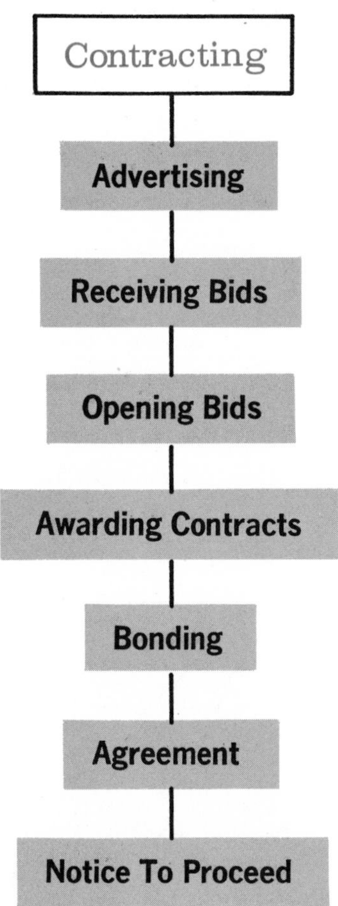

Summary

This lesson has traced the steps for selecting the construction contractor from the advertising of the contract through the bidding to the awarding and signing of the contract. The next assignment will cover how the contractor prepares his estimate of how much the project will cost and how he makes up his bid or proposal.

Terms to Know

invitation to bid	performance bond
prequalification	payment bond
qualify	bonding company
proposal (bid)	notice of award
questionnaire	agreement
bid bonds	notice to proceed
responsive bid	integrity

Think About It!

1. A contractor must prove he is able to do a job, either before he *bids* or before he is *awarded the contract.* What kinds of information will show an owner or architect-engineer that a contractor is *qualified* (has the ability) to do a construction job?
2. A contract usually is awarded to the contractor who *submitted the lowest responsive bid.*
   a. What is a responsive bid?
   b. What might happen if bids did not have to be responsive? Give some examples.

READING 21

Estimating and Bidding

The last lesson covered the actions of the owner and architect-engineer in the bidding and the awarding of construction contracts. In this lesson, we shall take a look at what the contractor does to bid for a contract. When the contractor receives an invitation to bid, he has to decide whether or not he is interested in bidding the particular job. If he is, he must then prepare his bid estimate (proposal) and submit it. Different

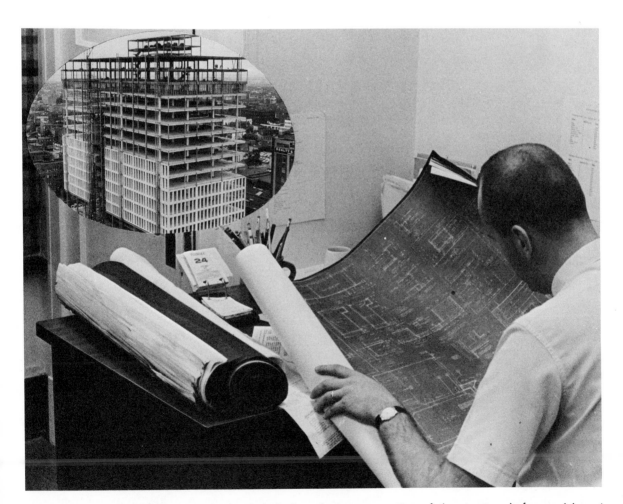

Fig. 21-1. The contractor must visualize and think through the construction of the structure before arriving at a decision to bid.

contractors prepare their bids in different ways, but the procedure below shows one typical process.

Fig. 21-2. When an estimate is prepared, a price is figured for the material to be used.

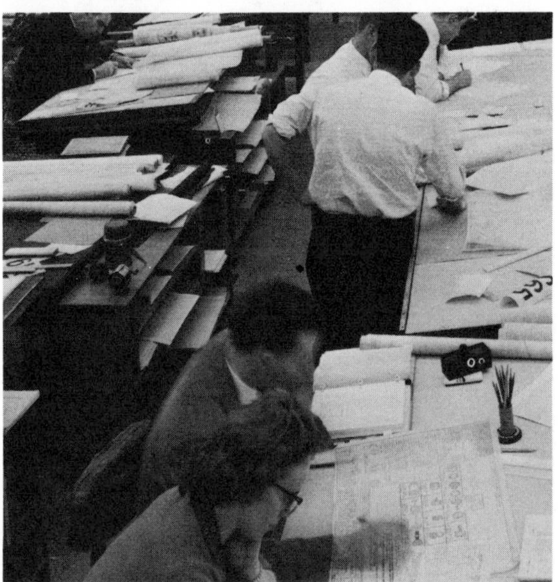

Fig. 21-3. The estimator must be able to read drawings and understand specifications. He computes the cost of material, labor, equipment, and overhead.

To Bid or Not to Bid

While deciding whether or not to bid, some of the questions the contractor might ask himself are: Is this the type of work I know how to do? Do I have a chance of being the lowest bidder? Can I make a profit? Is the job very risky? Do I want to work in the area of the job site? Can I hire the employees? Do I have the money to carry a job of this size? Do I have too much to do elsewhere? Do I have or can I rent the equipment? Is this job too small, too big, or just the right size for me? What kind of an owner and architect-engineer shall I be working for? Will the bonding company give me the necessary bonds? After carefully thinking over the answers to these questions, the contractor arrives at a decision either to bid or not to bid, Fig. 21-1.

The Estimate

The contractor bases his bid on an estimate. *An estimate is a careful calculation of what the job will cost.*

A small contractor may do his own estimating. Medium and large contractors hire an estimator to do the estimating. The estimator must understand construction practices. The estimator must be able to read drawings and understand specifications. (See Figs. 21-2 and 21-3.) He must have a good idea of the prices of materials, how much work a craftsman can do in a day under the conditions of the job, and what production may be expected from equipment. To estimate accurately, the estimator should be able to visit the site.

The success or failure of a contractor depends largely on the ability of the estimator. If his estimates are too high, the contractor will not be awarded any jobs. If the estimates are too low, the jobs will not make a profit. Since the contractor must depend on the estimate being correct, the chief estimator is a key man (and usually a highly paid one) in a construction firm.

Approximate ("shotgun") estimates are those made in the early stages of the design of the project—before the plans have been finished. In the case of buildings, they are often made on a per square foot or per cubic foot basis. For example, a man who wants a house which is 30′ x 50′ (1,500 square feet) might be given as an early estimate, a price of $15 per square foot, or $22,500 for the construction of this house. Almost never are approximate estimates used for bidding purposes.

When an estimate is prepared as the basis for a bid proposal, a price is figured for the *material, labor,* and *equipment* which will be used. To this is added *overhead* and *profit.* Each of these five items will now be considered.

Material

The amount of material is determined by what is called a takeoff from the plans and specifications. *Takeoff is the counting of how many times a certain item appears on the plans.* For instance, an estimator may count 20 windows on the plans. The specifications will tell him that they are of a certain size and kind. To get the cost of the windows without installation, the estimator may do several things:

1. He may get the price from a catalog.
2. He may call his purchasing department.
3. He may call a company that sells windows.
4. He may look up in his files what that particular window cost the last time he used it.

If the windows cost $25 each, delivered to the job site, the total cost of windows will be $25 x 20, or $500.

Labor

The estimator also figures the amount of labor necessary to do each job in the project, Fig. 21-4. In the case of the windows, the estimator would determine that it took 1½ hours of carpenter time and ½ hour of laborer time to set each window. The 1½ hours and ½ hour are called *labor productivity rates.* Tables of labor productivity are available to the estimator. He might buy some of these tables, but more often he will depend upon the experience of his own company in how long it takes to set a window.

If the carpenter receives $5 per hour and the laborer $3, the cost of labor per window will be 1½ x $5 + ½ x $3 or $9 per window. The 20 windows will cost $9 x 20 or $180 for installation only, not counting the windows themselves. To this must be added other costs for Social Security insurance, Workmen's Compensation (accident) insurance, and unemployment insurance.

Equipment

If a job involves equipment, the contractor determines the cost of the equipment per hour. If he is renting the equipment, this will be the hourly rental cost, plus the cost of fuel and repairs. Rental costs also include the transportation costs for moving the equipment to the construction site and back to the owner.

Fig. 21-4. The estimator must figure the labor requirements as well as the materials.

If the contractor owns the equipment, he will figure the hourly cost by adding the depreciation cost (*depreciation is the loss in value from year to year*), the investment cost (how much interest he has to pay on the amount of money he has borrowed to buy the machine), plus taxes, insurance, storage, and the cost of fuel and repairs. This total is divided by the hours worked to get an hourly cost of the equipment owned by the contractor, Fig. 21-5.

Unit Prices

A contractor who has experience figuring labor and machine productivity rates may be able to combine labor and equipment costs into a *unit price*. Use of these unit prices speeds up estimating. Let us take the case of a trenching machine. A certain trenching machine costs $8 per hour, including the cost of moving it to and from the job. From information in his files, the estimator knows that this trenching machine will dig a trench 2′ wide, 4′ deep and 150′ long in one hour. The operator is paid $4 per hour. The cost for 150′ is therefore $12. The cost for each foot is $12/150 or $0.08. The 8 cents per foot is a unit price. When the estimator sees 2,000′ of this trench on the plans, he can then estimate that it will cost 2,000 x $0.08, or $160.

Subcontract Work

As explained in a previous lesson, the general contractor often hires a subcontractor to do some of the specialized work, Fig. 21-6. The subcontractor, in preparing his estimate which he gives to the general contractor, follows much the same procedure as does the general contractor above in estimating material, labor, and equipment costs. To the sum of these three costs, the subcontractor adds his own percentage of overhead and profit in the same manner as will be described for the general contractor in the next two sections. The subcontractor then notifies the general contractor of the total price for his part of the work. This price is called a *quotation*, or sometimes just a *quote*.

Fig. 21-5. The cost of renting or purchasing special equipment must be estimated.

Fig. 21-6. The workers of specialized subcontractors may do only part of the total work on a project.

Overhead

Overhead costs of the contractor are those which pertain to the job as a whole and are not related to any particular feature like excavation or masonry, Fig 21-7. There are two types of overhead: home office costs and job overhead costs. *Home office costs* include: (1) the salaries of executives and employees, (2) office rent, (3) telephone and other utility expenses, (4) advertising and (5) travel. *Job overhead costs* include: (1) the salaries of the superintendent and employees at the site (other than craftsmen engaged directly in the work), (2) surveys, (3) office space, (4) testing, (5) barricades, (6) insurance, (7) storage, (8) building permits, and the like.

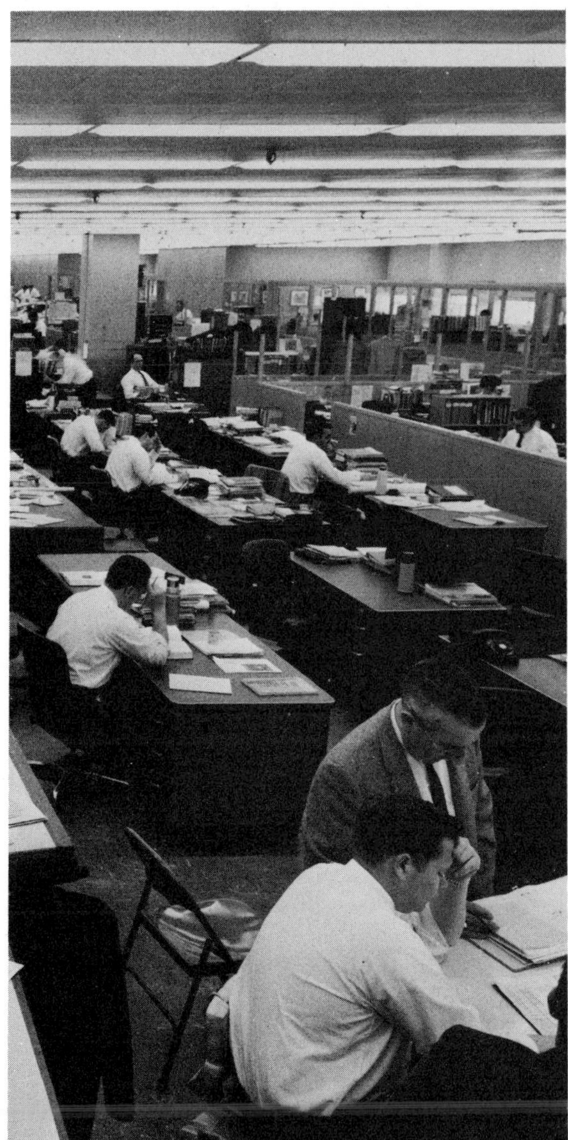

Fig. 21-7. Office personnel, rent, utilities and other overhead expenses are part of the estimate

Profit

The contractor is in business to make a profit on the capital or money he has invested in the business. The *profit* is the difference between the amount of money the contractor receives from the owner and the amount of money the contractor spends to do the job. Some of the factors considered in selecting a percentage of profit are: (1) the size of the job, (2) the risks involved, and (3) the eagerness of the contractor to get the job.

Profit is usually a management rather than an estimating decision as will be explained under the Bid Proposal. Profit is usually expressed as a percentage and is sometimes called a *markup*. For instance, if the total of material, labor, equipment, subcontract, and overhead costs is $1,000,000, and the contractor decides he should earn a 7% profit, he would add 7% of $1,000,000 or $70,000. His bid would then be $1,070,000.

The Summary Sheet and Bid Proposals

The estimator figures the cost of material, labor, equipment, and subcontract work for each part of the job. Then he puts together all items in a summary or recap sheet, an example of which is shown in Table 21-1.

The estimator's best estimate of the cost of the work must be carefully prepared. The bid proposal, which is based on the estimate, is a decision of management even though the estimator is consulted. Management may decide to increase or reduce the percentage of profit for many reasons:

1. Its expected competition from other contractors,
2. Its desire to be low bidder,
3. Its estimate of risk,
4. Its ability to secure better prices by making deals with major suppliers, subcontractors, and equipment companies, and
5. Its finding of a more economical way of doing the job.

In these cases, management may change the estimate of materials, labor, equipment, or subcontracting, and sometimes even overhead. After careful consideration of all these factors, management makes a final decision as to what price goes into the bid proposal.

Summary

Estimators prepare bid proposals. These bid proposals are based on estimates of the

Table 21-1

J & J Construction Company
Summary Sheet — Bid Estimate
Gymnasium — Camp Swampy

Item	Material	Labor	Equipment	Subcontract	Total Cost
Clearing		300	700		1 000
Excavation, borrow and compaction	3 000	4 000	5 000		12 000
Concrete and forms	50 000	23 000	2 000		75 000
Masonry	70 000	61 000	1 000		132 000
Carpentry and millwork	19 500	11 000	500		31 000
Steel				120 000	120 000
Roofing and flashing				112 000	112 000
Insulation	10 000	3 700			13 700
Lath, plaster and interior partitions	21 100	33 600			54 700
Wood flooring	42 200	20 900			63 100
Tile flooring	19 100	5 400			24 500
Painting				33 300	33 300
Hardware	19 800	2 100			21 900
Glass and glazing				14 700	14 700
Electrical				98 300	98 300
Plumbing, heating and air conditioning				212 000	212 000
Parking lot				23 400	23 400
Cleanup		4 300	500		4 800
	254 700	169 300	9 700	613 700	1 047 400
Taxes and insurance	10 300	23 800	200	24 500	58 800
					1 106 200
Overhead 7%					77 400
					1 183 600
Profit 6.5%					77 000
					1 260 600
Bond 1%					12 600
Total cost					$1 273 200

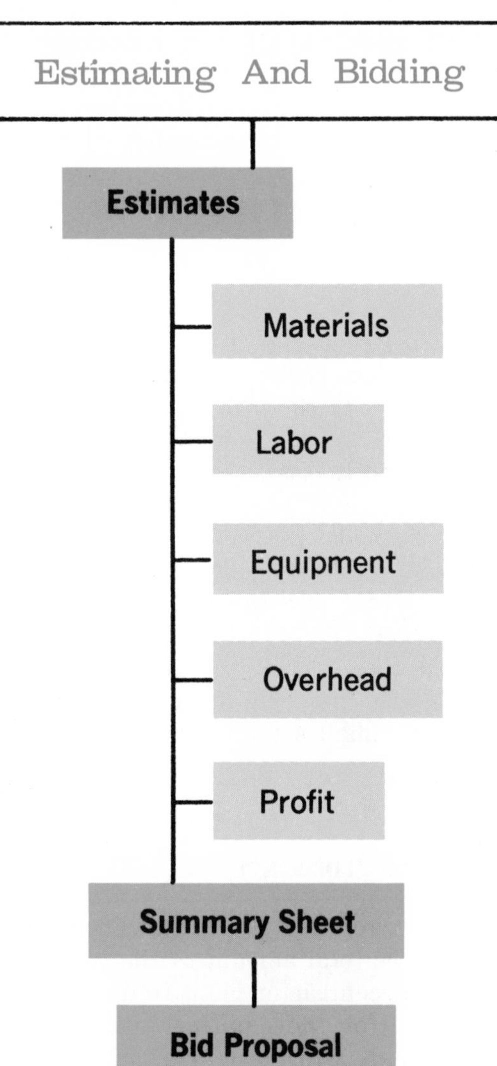

cost of materials, labor, equipment, overhead, and profit. These estimates are always carefully checked. The success or failure of a contractor depends very much upon the ability of the estimator.

Terms to Know

an estimate	investment cost
field experience	unit price
installation	quotation
takeoff	overhead
labor productivity rate	profit
depreciation cost	

Think About It!

1. In *preparing a bid* for a construction project, where does a contractor or his *estimator* get the following kinds of information?
   a. Sizes and kinds of materials needed
   b. Labor costs
   c. Equipment costs
   d. Overhead costs
2. What might cause a contractor to raise or lower the profit that is included in his bid?

READING 22

Scheduling

As soon as the contractor receives the notice of award, he prepares a *schedule* for the work, Fig. 22-1. Most owners and architect-engineers see to it that the contract includes a statement that a work schedule will be furnished by the contractor within a few days after his receiving the *notice to proceed.*

To prepare a schedule, the contractor makes a detailed study of the best way to use his men, machinery, materials, and money. The contractor must decide what work he will do with his own men, what parts of the job he will subcontract, and who the subcontractors will be. He also must decide where he will get needed manufactured items and material supplies, what craftsmen and equipment will be needed on the project, and how much money he must get together to do the job.

Fig. 22-1. This contractor is making a schedule.

Having made these decisions, the contractor goes on with the making of his schedule. He continues to define or list each part of the work and to estimate the time needed to finish it.

Two methods for scheduling work are commonly used by contractors. They are the *Bar Chart Procedure* and the *Critical Path Method* (CPM). These are both management tools used to get work done efficiently. To show how one of these methods is used, we shall set up a Bar Chart for a simple construction job.

Bar Chart Procedure

A contractor has the job of installing a flagpole. The total amount of the contract is $1,000. The contractor plans to do the entire job, except for the painting, with his own employees. He will use transit-mix (already mixed) concrete which will be delivered to the job. The contractor lists divisions of the work and estimates the cost and the percentage of each item in the total job, as shown in Table 22-1.

Analyzing the Job

The contractor sizes up the work as follows:

He knows that the pipe for the flagpole should be put together and ready to erect by the time the hole is completed. Also, assembly of the flagpole cannot begin until the pipe is ordered and delivered. The first step then must be getting the pipe. There is no point in finishing the hole until the pipe is ready. If it rains, the sides of the hole might cave in. After the hole is dug, and the pole is put together, erection of the pole may begin. After the pole is erected, concrete may be placed. When the concrete has been cured, painting may begin. Before the painting begins, the painting subcontract must be made.

Job Progression

Item, cost, and percentage of job are placed on a bar chart such as the one shown in Table 22-2. On the bar chart, the days are listed across the top and the items of work are listed down the left side.

The cross lines or bars indicate planned or scheduled progress. Notice that the first three days are left for the ordering of the pipe. By the end of day 4, it is planned for the pipe to be put together. If the hole has been dug, it is planned that the flagpole should be ready to erect during day 5. Since it takes two days to dig the hole, the hole should be started by the beginning of day 3. During the fifth day, the pole will be erected and the concrete ordered from the ready-mixed concrete supplier so that the concrete may be placed and cured during days 6 and 7. If the painting subcontract

Table 22-1

List of Work to Be Done, Cost and Time

Item	Cost	% of Job	Time *
Order and deliver pipe	$ 400	40%	3 days
Assemble pipe and fittings	100	10	1
Dig hole	100	10	2
Erect pole	200	20	1
Order concrete			1
Place and cure concrete	100	10	2
Make painting subcontract			3
Paint	100	10	1
Total	**$1,000**	**100%**	

*Note: Times are not totaled, as some of the items are done at the same time.

Table 22-2

T. & L. Construction Co.

Installation of Flagpole — Camp Swampy

Bar Chart

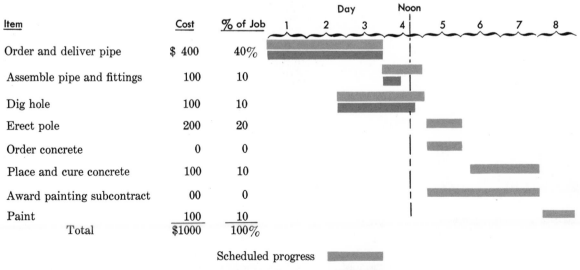

Item	Cost	% of Job	Day 1	2	3	4 (Noon)	5	6	7	8
Order and deliver pipe	$ 400	40%								
Assemble pipe and fittings	100	10								
Dig hole	100	10								
Erect pole	200	20								
Order concrete	0	0								
Place and cure concrete	100	10								
Award painting subcontract	00	0								
Paint	100	10								
Total	$1000	100%								

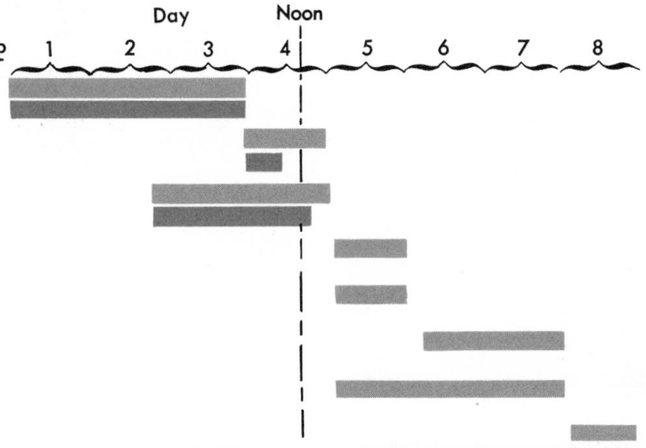

Scheduled progress

Actual progress

has been awarded, painting should then be done on day 8. Making a deal with the painting subcontractor and his preparations (buying paint, for example) takes 3 days. This should be started at the beginning of day 5 so that painting may begin the morning of day 8. At the end of day 8, the entire job is completed.

The colored line in Table 22-2 represents the work which has actually been completed (called *actual progress*) at any particular time. By looking at the chart, we can see that the contractor examined the progress of the job at noon on day 4. He found that the ordering and delivering of the pipe had been completed, but that assembling of the pipes and fittings was only ¼ of the way completed, when it should have been ½ of the way finished. He also found that the digging of the hole was ⅞ of the way com-

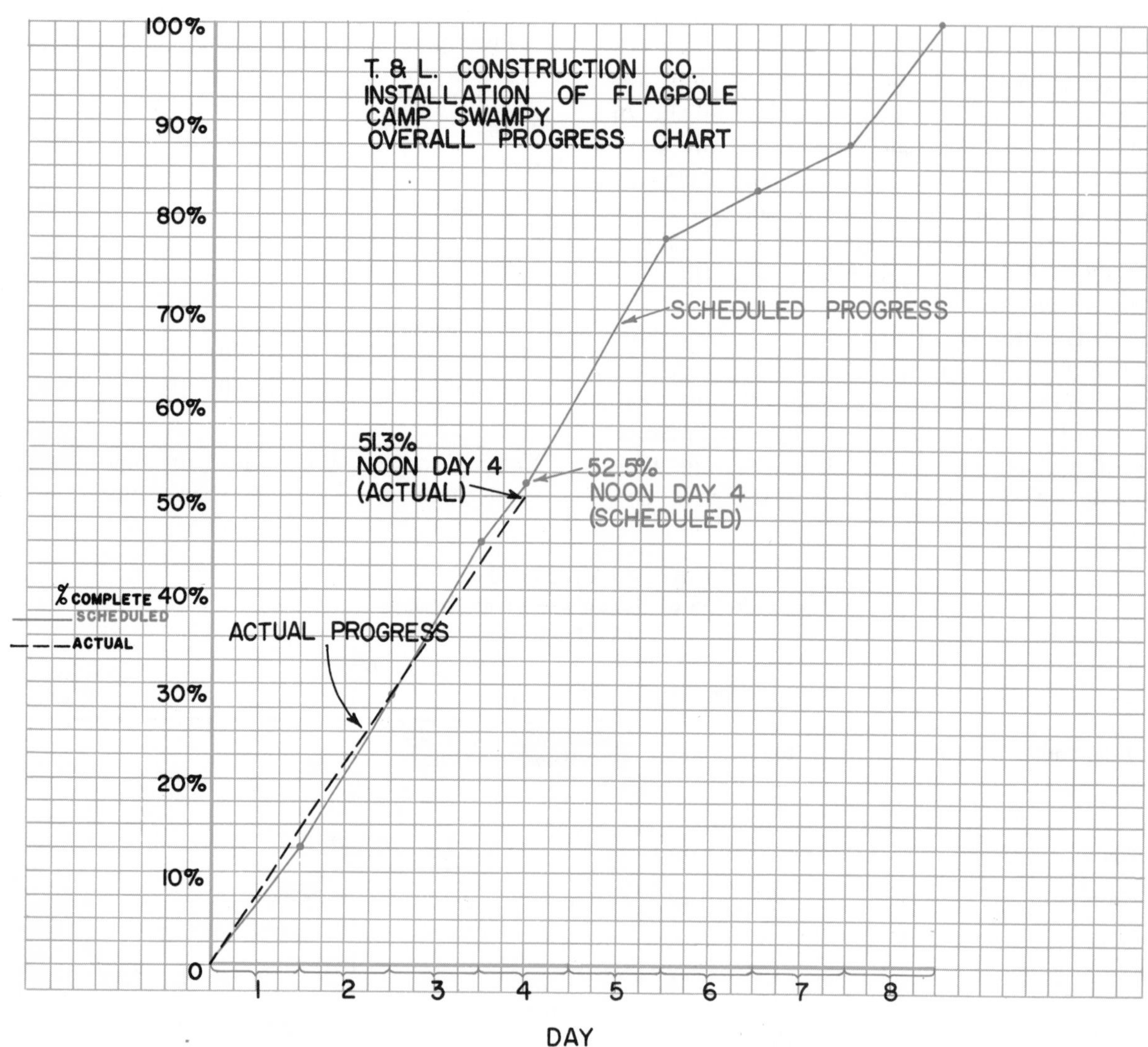

Fig. 22-2. A dotted line connects the points of actual progress. When the dotted line is above the solid line, the job is ahead of schedule. When the dotted line is below the solid line, the job is behind schedule. At day 3½, the point on the dotted line is at 51.3%, while the corresponding point on the solid line is at 52.5%. This means that the job is 52.5% (scheduled progress) minus 51.3% (actual progress) or 1.2% behind schedule.

pleted, when it only needed to be ¾ of the way done. Pipe assembly was ¼ day behind schedule, and the hole was ⅛ day ahead of schedule. The contractor decided then that more men or tools should be put to work on the pipe assembly in order to have the pole erected at the start of day 5.

Overall Progress Chart

Usually the *Overall Progress Chart* is placed at the top of the bar chart (Table 22-2), but since this might be a bit confusing, it is shown on a separate chart, Fig. 22-2.

The Overall Progress Chart is concerned with the cost of the job, in dollars, rather than with how much of the work has actually been done at the site. For example, at the end of day 2, the contractor has spent ⅔ of the $400 which is to be spent by the time the pipe will be delivered to the job. However, no actual work has been done by the contractor or his subcontractor. He is not supposed to put his own men on the job until the morning of day 3. Until he starts digging the hole, there is no progress that can actually be seen.

To find out the scheduled progress at the end of a certain time, we add the proportions of each item scheduled times the percentage of the job. For example at the end of day 1, ⅓ of the pipe ordering and delivery is scheduled to be completed. This item is 40% of the total. ⅓ x 40% gives 13.3 for overall scheduled completion. So, on the bottom line, starting at 0, we go right to the end of day 1 and then up to 13.3. This procedure locates the point on the Overall Progress Chart which shows how much of the project money should have been spent by the end of day 1. Each day is plotted by following this procedure.

As a further example, in Table 22-3, we figured that 45% of the scheduled work, in terms of total project cost, should have been completed on day 3. To plot this on the Overall Progress Chart (Fig. 22-2), we go right to the end of day 3 and up to 45% completion and mark a point. Lines are drawn to connect all plotted points.

To get the actual completion, say at noon of day 4, as indicated in the Bar Chart, the process is much the same, except that the actual rather than the scheduled progress is used. (Refer to Table 22-4.)

Meetings

The first schedule prepared for the job is really only an estimate of the time it will take to complete each separate part of the work. As parts of the construction work are actually finished, some of these estimates are found to be correct while others are found to be wrong. To find out how the

Table 22-3

Total Work at the End of Day 3

Item	% of Job	Proportion Scheduled to be Completed	% of Whole Job Scheduled to be Completed
Order and delivery of pipe	40	All: 16/16 = 1 (16 of 16 sq.*)	1×40 = 40%
Dig hole	10	½ : 2/4 = ½ (2 of 4 sq.)	½×10 = 5%
			Total 45%

*Note: sq. means squares on Fig. 22-2, and four squares equal 10%.

Table 22-4

Actual Progress Total at Noon, Day 4

Item	% of Job	Proportion Actually Complete	% of Whole Job Complete
Order and deliver pipe	40	All: 16/16 = 1 (16 of 16 sq.)	1×40 = 40%
Assemble pipe	10	¼: (1 of 4 sq.)	¼×10 = 2.5%
Dig hole	10	⅞: 3½ of 4 = ⅞ (3½ of 4 sq.)	⅞×10 = 8.8%
			Total 51.3%

job is going (whether or not it is following the schedule), and what can be done to improve the situation, meetings are held. The contractor is always there. Others who may be present are the architect-engineer, union representatives, the owner, subcontractors, and suppliers. Depending on how the job is going, meetings may be held weekly, monthly or irregularly. At these meetings, the progress of the work is checked against the schedule set up for it. It may be checked by looking at the Bar Chart or the Overall Progress Chart. If the job is behind schedule, measures to improve performance are discussed, Fig. 22-3.

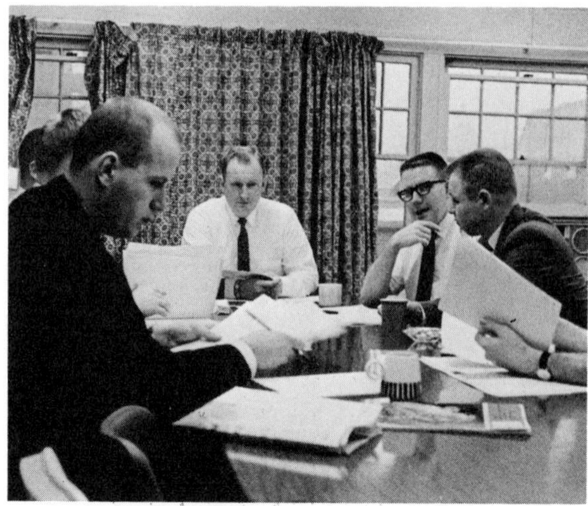

Fig. 22-3. The contractor and other necessary men are meeting to decide if the job is proceeding on schedule.

Updating and Revising Schedules

If construction work falls behind schedule or the owner or architect-engineer decides to change the project in some way, a new and more realistic schedule should be made. This new schedule must be set up in the same way as the first one. It is often better to set up another schedule after the job is underway. The time estimates can then be more accurate.

Summary

To finish a construction job within the time limit of the contract, the contractor sets up a schedule. This schedule is based on the contractor's idea of the best way to use men, money, machinery and materials. The contractor lists each part of the work along with an estimate of time. He then sets up the schedule. The schedule is changed from time to time because of events on the job or because of a change in orders from the owner or architect-engineer.

Terms to Know

notice to proceed
schedule
assemble
Bar Chart Procedure
Critical Path Method
Overall Progress Chart
install
erect

Think About It!

1. What might happen if a contractor made these errors in *scheduling*?
   a. The inside walls were plastered and painted before an electrician arrived to install wiring.
   b. The kitchen walls and floor were finished before the plumber did his work.
   c. A truck arrived with ready-mixed concrete, but the forms to hold the concrete were not built.
2. Suggest some other *scheduling errors* that might be very expensive mistakes.

Working as a Contractor

READING 23

Previous lessons told how the contractor was selected, and described the techniques of bidding, contracting, and scheduling. This assignment will explain in general terms (1) the contractor's duties, (2) the contractor's relationship to others (owners, architect-engineers, subcontractors, suppliers), and (3) the contractor's business organization.

Contractor's Responsibilities (Duties)

The job of the contractor is to furnish all the labor and materials for building a project. He also makes sure work necessary to the building of the project exactly follows the plans and specifications, Fig. 23-2. To supervise his own employees and the subcontractor's, the contractor must have an able superintendent on the job at all times. He must obey all laws relating to labor, job safety, traffic, sanitation, and licensing. He must protect the owner by providing the necessary insurance and bonds as stated in the contract. He must get the job done within the time of the contract. He must furnish samples and shop drawings as outlined in the contract. He must pay his laborers, suppliers, and subcontractors promptly. Usually, he must guarantee the quality of materials and workmanship for at least one year after completion of the job. Briefly, the contractor's responsibility is to get the job done according to the contract.

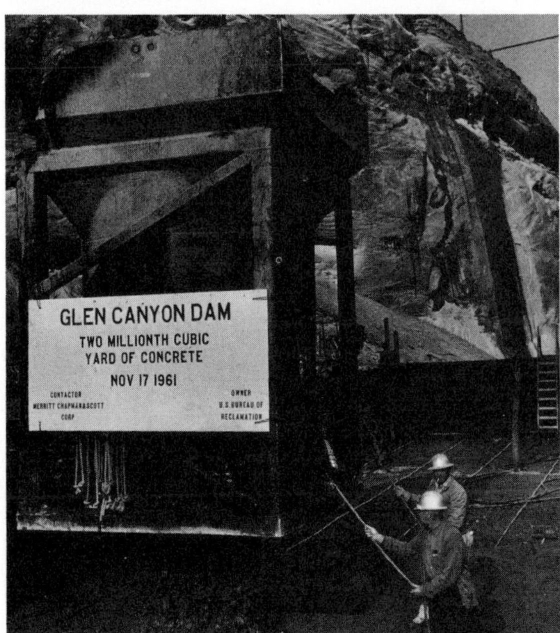

Fig. 23-1. The beginning, ending, or certain major steps of construction work may be marked by a ceremony. Here the contractor's foreman and the owner's representative place a special bucket of concrete.

Fig. 23-2. It is the contractor's duty to see that the job is done according to the contract.

Responsibilities of the Owner to the Contractor

The owner must supply the *real estate* (land) for the project, furnish the money to pay the contractor as stated in the contract, and make quick decisions as to what he (the owner) wants. The owner must request changes in plenty of time if he wants them made after the project is underway. The owner must not delay the contractor. If there is more than one contractor on the project, the owner must arrange for someone, usually the architect-engineer, to organize the work of the various contractors.

Responsibilities of the Architect-Engineer

During the progress of construction, the architect-engineer supervises the work being done by the contractor. In doing this, the architect-engineer checks to see that the contractor carries out the requirements of the plans and specifications.

Fig. 23-3. An architectural engineer inspects a plastic liner which is being injected into the ground.

The architect-engineer tests and approves all the samples provided by the contractor. For example, in a large brick structure, the contractor might give the architect-engineer samples of the brick. The architect-engineer may examine these for color and may test the strength of the brick and its ability to withstand freezing and thawing. The architect-engineer may also receive and approve shop drawings and equipment specifications sent in by the contractor. He may also approve the contractor's schedule, his general method of operation, the superintendent on the job, and often, the subcontractors.

The architect-engineer is also charged with explaining all the contract documents, including the plans and specifications. For example, if the specifications should require a certain lighting fixture, such as a Toledo No. 422 or one equal to it, the architect-engineer would rule on whether or not Sandusky No. 148, which the contractor wants to use, is equal. Or, if the contractor finds hard rock where the drawings showed soft sand, the architect-engineer would rule on whether or not the contractor should be paid an extra amount and, if so, how much. In short, the architect-engineer is the agent of the owner. In working with the contractor, he acts in place of or for the owner. See Fig. 23-3.

Contractor's Organization

A contractor gets his job done by using people, materials, tools, and equipment. At this time, we are interested in the *people*.

In order to make efficient and economical use of his people, the contractor assigns each of them a certain job. In so doing, he *organizes* his people so that each performs one or more duties or functions. The organization of a contractor's people may take many different forms depending on (1) the amount of business the contractor does, (2) the types of jobs for which he contracts, (3) the abilities of the various people he hires, and (4) the desires of the contractor himself. A typical organization chart of a medium-large construction company is shown on page 123. Keep in mind, however, that any particular contractor may be organized differently.

Home Office

At the top of the organization, there is usually an owner or president who is in charge of the construction company. He is the chief executive officer who runs the whole company. He has the overall responsibility and authority.

Below the president, there are usually three groups: *administrative, engineering,* and *construction.* Although the groups are shown separately on the organization chart, the people in the different groups work closely together. For example, if a superintendent in the construction group should need hardware for a building, he would send an order to the purchasing section of the administrative group.

Administrative Group

The administrative group may include sections for accounting, contracting, purchasing, and labor relations. The *accounting section* is in charge of handling the money or financial affairs: (1) it keeps the books, (2) makes up the payrolls, (3) pays the contractor's employees, subcontractors and suppliers, (4) prepares bills to the owner, and (5) often does the paper work for the hiring of personnel.

The *contract section* prepares contracts with owners, subcontractors, and suppliers. The contract section also prepares contract changes and handles bonds and insurance.

The *purchasing section* does many things: (1) makes sure that materials are available on the job when needed, (2) buys materials and equipment, (3) maintains a file of current catalogs and price lists, (4) handles rental of equipment, and (5) arranges for transportation of materials to the job.

The *labor relations section* handles matters pertaining to employees. It negotiates labor contracts with unions and represents the contractor in any labor disputes which might arise.

Engineering Group

The engineering group designs any temporary structures needed to build a project. For example, they might design the bridge on a temporary road over which trucks would haul rocks to the site. This group also (1) makes estimates for bids and for changes in the contract, (2) keeps cost records, (3) controls the costs on the jobs to see that they do not become too high, and (4) conducts tests and field surveys needed by the contractor, Fig. 23-4.

Construction Group

The construction group actually carries out the work for the job. It controls the field offices and the yards and shops. Often there

Fig. 23-4. Concrete is being tested at the site.

is a project manager located with the construction group at the home office. A project manager is responsible for one major job or two or more smaller jobs. He supervises the activities of the field office and acts as the home office representative of the superintendent on the job, Fig. 23-5. For example, if it appears that the work might be held up for a roller which needs to be rented, the superintendent would ask the project manager to have the purchasing section speed up renting the roller and getting it to the job site.

Fig. 23-5. In the field, the project manager inspects a job.

Fig. 23-6. The field office at this dam site is near the base of the dam. The field engineer's surveyor is at work in the foreground.

Field Offices

In the last section, we talked about the employees who work at the contracting company's home office—his place of business. Let us now turn our attention to the employees who are at the job site. Of course, the number and type of personnel the contractor has on the job depend largely on how large the job is and how complicated it is. Usually, there is a small field office at the construction site, Fig. 23-6. Often trailers are used. The man in charge of getting the work done at the site is called the *superintendent*. He usually has a clerk in the office, and on large jobs, he may have a field engineer. The *clerk* takes care of payrolls, receiving reports from timekeepers or foremen, and any other paperwork. The *field engineer* does whatever engineering is needed on the job and is responsible for seeing that the proper layout of the project is carried out. On large projects, the field engineer may have a survey crew.

Various foremen are also under the superintendent. Where several craftsmen of one trade are working, there is usually a foreman for that trade. For example, if eight carpenters are working, there is usually a carpenter foreman in charge. There may also be a steel foreman, a concrete foreman, or an earthwork foreman. Subcontractors also have foremen on jobs where more than two or three men work. On an extremely large job, such as doing all the electrical work for a skyscraper, the electrical subcontractor might even have a superintendent and several foremen. The superintendent for the general contractor supervises the work of the subcontractors as well as that being performed by the contractor's own employees.

Typical Organization Of A Construction Contracting Company

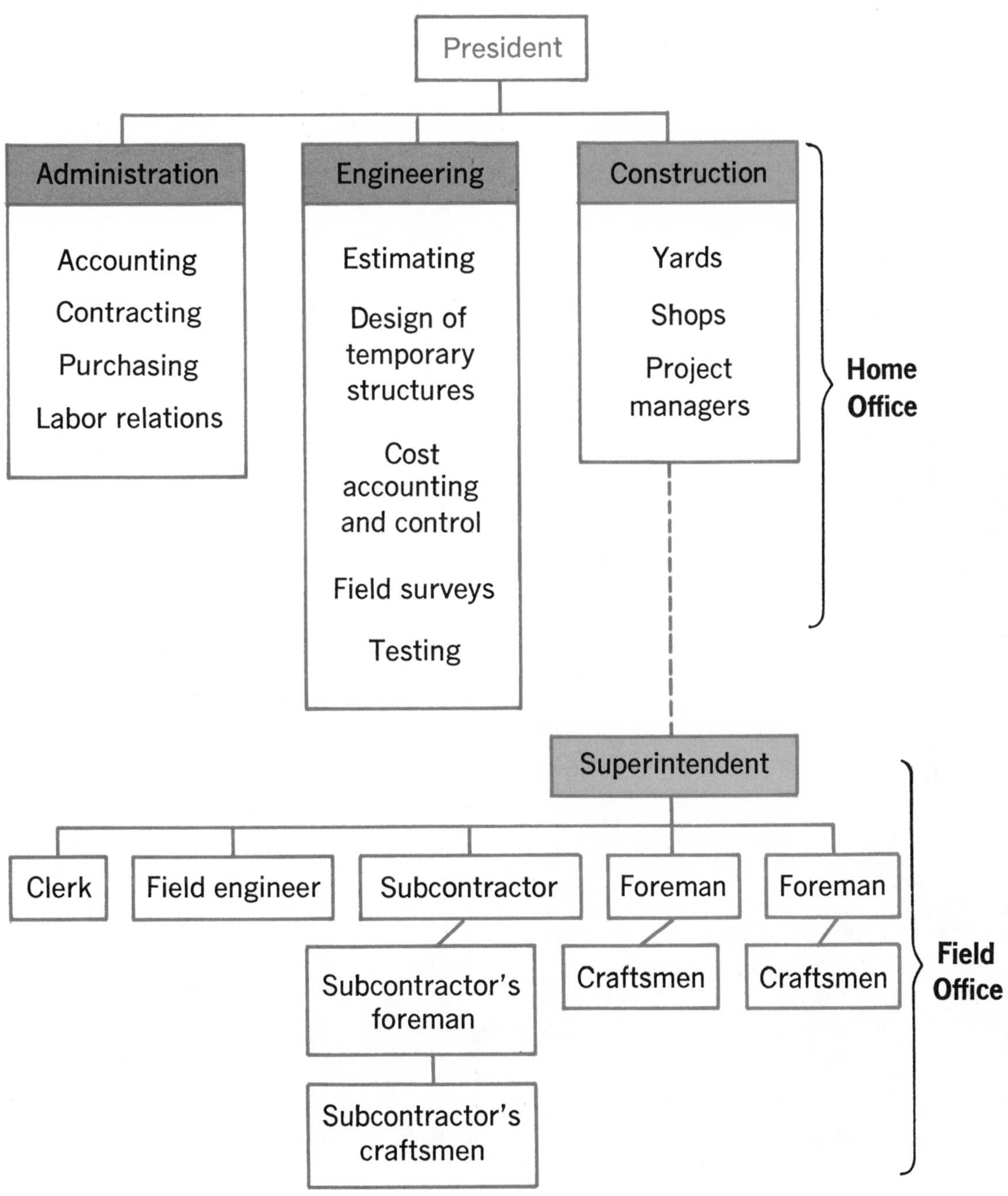

Summary

The main responsibility of the contractor is to get the job done. The owner's job is to furnish the money. The architect-engineer represents the owner to see that the job is built according to the plans and specifications. The contractor gets the job done with his employees, subcontractors, and suppliers. To work effectively, the contractor's employees are so organized that each performs a certain duty.

Terms to Know

responsibilities
supervise
construction group
foreman
superintendent
real estate
inspect
organize
administrative group
engineering group
craftsman
field engineer
clerk
field office
coordinate
pertaining

Think About It!

1. On a construction project the contractor must be sure that all the correct materials are used. What other *responsibilities* does he have?
2. If you were going to work in one of the groups in a contractor's office (administrative, engineering, construction), which would you choose? Why?

Collective Bargaining

READING 24

One person has little bargaining power. When people with common interests join together, they can jointly elect one person to speak for them all. This person has more authority than any other single member in securing benefits for them all. When this elected leader seeks benefits for the group, from the employer, he is doing *collective bargaining*. *Labor union* is the name given to a group of organized workers who wish to bargain collectively.

Labor unions, representing about one quarter of our labor force, play an important role in the complex economy of modern America. Union members work in such fields as transportation, communication, construction, and manufacturing.

By working together through a union, all the employees of a company can speak with one voice at the bargaining table just as the owner does. Part of dignity on the job is fair treatment in job assignments and performance requirements. But unions also *negotiate* (discuss and decide) for other benefits such as better wages, better working conditions, and a comfortable retirement for their members, Fig. 24-1.

Fig. 24-1. The dignity and integrity of labor comes from fair treatment in job assignments and performance requirements.

Fig. 24-2. The wages this electrician earns influence the cost of things we buy as well as the things he buys.

Unions are important in our everyday lives. The wages workers earn not only are part of the total cost of the things we buy, but these wages also determine how many things the workers can buy, Fig. 24-2. If workers made little money, they might not be able to afford to buy cars or television sets that other workers make.

Although many workers do not belong to unions, these organizations are important to everyone. Often the gains made by local unions are shared by unorganized workers. Also, the price of manufactured goods we buy, the cost of our homes, and even the size of a telephone bill are partly determined by the actions of labor unions. Perhaps you may one day belong to a union. In this lesson, you will study about the history, organizations, and activities of today's labor unions, particularly the building and construction trades unions. You will find out how you can join a union.

History of the AFL-CIO

The first labor unions in the United States appeared in the 1790's. The first of these organizations to become important was the Knights of Labor founded by Terrance V. Powderly in 1869. Although it claimed 700,000 members, it was unpopular and unsuccessful in reaching its aims. During the 1890's it collapsed.

Fig. 24-3. The construction labor force is composed of a mixture of people with varied trades, crafts, and skills.

A more successful union of the same period was the American Federation of Labor (AFL) founded by Samuel Gompers. It organized skilled craftsmen into unions. The AFL has grown since its beginning. In 1940 it had over 4,000,000 members, and after World War II about 7,000,000 members.

In the 1930's many labor leaders believed that a new sort of national association of unions was needed for workers not in skilled trades. In 1938 they set up the Congress of Industrial Organizations (CIO) in competition with the AFL. This union organized on an industrial basis. That is, all of the workers in industry from the unskilled to the skilled were in one union. It grew rapidly.

In 1955 these two great organizations joined together. Together they had 14,000,000 members in 140 unions. Today the membership of this organization, the AFL-CIO, is nearly one quarter of America's labor force. In addition, there are certain independent unions which do not belong to the AFL-CIO.

The Building and Construction Trades Department

Today's AFL-CIO is divided into departments. Each department is made up of unions in a certain category. One of the most important of these is the *Building and Construction Trades Department* which was founded in 1908. It has 18 member unions from Iron Workers and Boilermakers to Carpenters and Granite Cutters. Because it affects so many workers, the work of the Building and Construction Trades Department is far-reaching and important.

Unlike the manufacturing employee who may work during his whole career with one company, a construction employee may work with many different employers. Construction work is done on many different sites and with many different employers. Working conditions and employers' requirements could vary from one project to the other. Thus, construction employees need the union to protect their benefits as workers.

The Building and Construction Trades Department represents the welfare of the building trades. All of its officers are elected by delegates to a convention of the department. The duties of the department officers are:

1. To work with and to organize its members
2. To settle disagreements between members
3. To keep pace with the labor policies of the state, local, and national governments
4. To carry on a program of information and education on the place of the building trades in our economy

How Unions and Contractors Bargain

There are several causes of conflict between the union and management. These come from their differing goals. Management, such as a contracting firm, seeks to

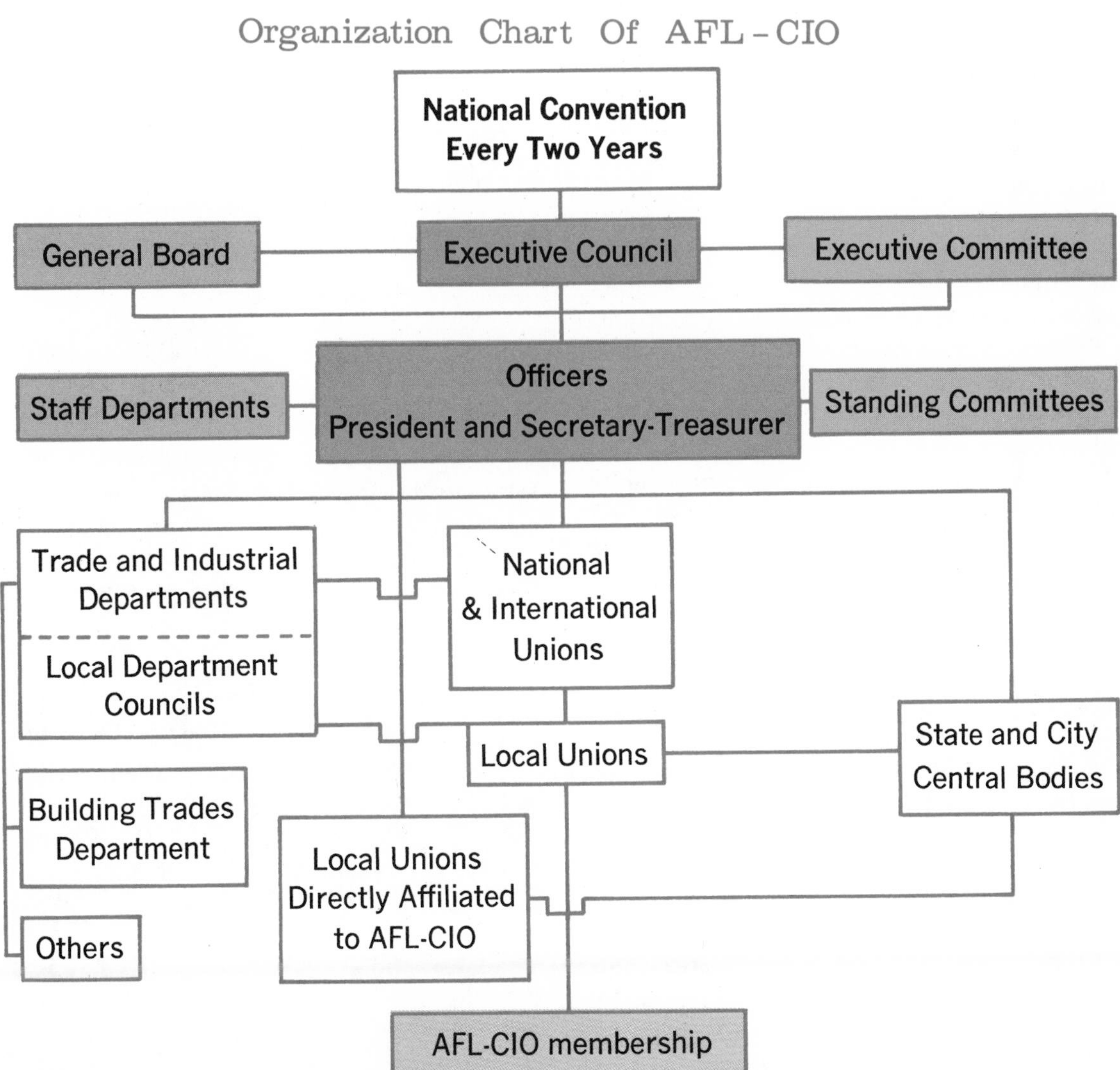

make money for the firm or company. The union tries to get as many benefits as possible for its members.

Four common causes of labor-management disagreements are:

1. Rate of wages
2. Working conditions or the environment in which the laborer works
3. Hours of work
4. Fringe benefits or extra privileges such as vacation

The union favors an improvement of these because they make life for the worker more pleasant. The employer seeks to limit them because they will decrease his profits and may even keep him from bidding successfully for projects, thereby putting him out of work. A fair balance must be found if everyone is to profit including workers, owners, and buyers. Collective bargaining is used to find this balance.

Before 1932, each of the 48 states had its own rules and regulations between employers and employees represented by labor organizations. Because such rules and regulations varied from state to state, it became necessary to set up a *national labor policy.* Congress has passed laws to provide this policy, Table 24-1.

Workers and employers use agreements and contracts to serve as the rules and regulations of their relationship. These agreements and contracts are reached through collective bargaining. Both sides must be willing to give and take on their goals if collective bargaining is to be a success. In the end, the agreement should be acceptable to both sides.

The union may use several procedures to achieve its aims by collective bargaining. It may attempt to settle differences by discussion or *negotiation.* If this is not successful, the union may resort to a strike. In general, unions and management seek to settle their differences by peaceful and businesslike relations. If labor and management cannot reach an agreement, an impartial mediator is requested by both parties to assist them in

Table 24-1

Labor Legislation

LAW	YEAR	PROVISIONS
Davis-Bacon Act	**1931**	**Requires the use of area prevailing wages in bidding public works. Prevailing wages are those which have been negotiated and are now in use.**
Norris-La Guardia Act	1932	Restricted the rights of federal courts to issue injunctions.
National Labor Relations Act (Also known as Wagner Act)	**1935**	**(as amended*) Gave unions the right to organize and bargain with employer. Set up National Labor Relations Board (NLRB).**
Walsh-Healey Act	1936	Improve working conditions and pay for workers under government contracts.
Fair Labor Standards Act	**1938**	**Sets up minimum wages and maximum hours for workers engaged in interstate commerce.**
Taft-Hartley Act* and Landrum-Griffin Act*	1947 1959	Amended National Labor Relations Act. Established rules for unions: (1) governing elections; (2) requiring the filing of statements about finances, handling of funds, qualifications of officers; (3) outlawing certain kinds of strikes and contracts; and (4) giving the government power to inspect union activities more closely.

reaching an agreement. Both parties discuss their disagreement with the mediator who attempts to end their differences by encouraging discussion. The mediator does not have the power to enforce his decision. If *mediation* does not work, a strike or arbitration may be used.

Sometimes, when the national security or public welfare is threatened, *arbitration* may be used. An arbitrator is appointed to *arbitrate* (settle) a disagreement while the work continues. An arbitrator is a third party (besides labor and management) who has the power to decide a settlement. Labor and management agree that compulsory (forced) arbitration is no substitute for free collective bargaining and the right to strike. They believe the directly involved parties should negotiate in good faith.

The last resort is the *strike*. When the strike is voted by the union membership, none of the members of the union go to work until a settlement is reached. Strikes are used by the union because loss of profits by the employer and pressure from those who need the employer's product may force management to bargain in good faith. Strikes are avoided by labor and management whenever possible. They hurt the union members because the workers are not paid by the employer for the days on strike. Though some unions have strike-benefit payments, the money is only a part of what wages would be. A strike hurts the employer because of loss of production and profits while overhead costs continue.

Fig. 24-4. Much construction involves dangerous work. Both labor and management want safe working conditions.

Labor-Management Cooperation

Labor and management do not always disagree. They work together in many areas such as (1) training programs, (2) work promotion, and (3) safety programs. In a world with rapidly changing production techniques, especially in construction, the union wants its members to be skilled so they will be hired by an employer and can demand a higher wage. Management wants skilled workers because they are more productive.

Work promotion is also favored by both management and labor. *Work promotion* means to support new construction. Management supports this because more contracts should mean more efficient use of resources and more profits. The union wants work promotion because more production means employment for members.

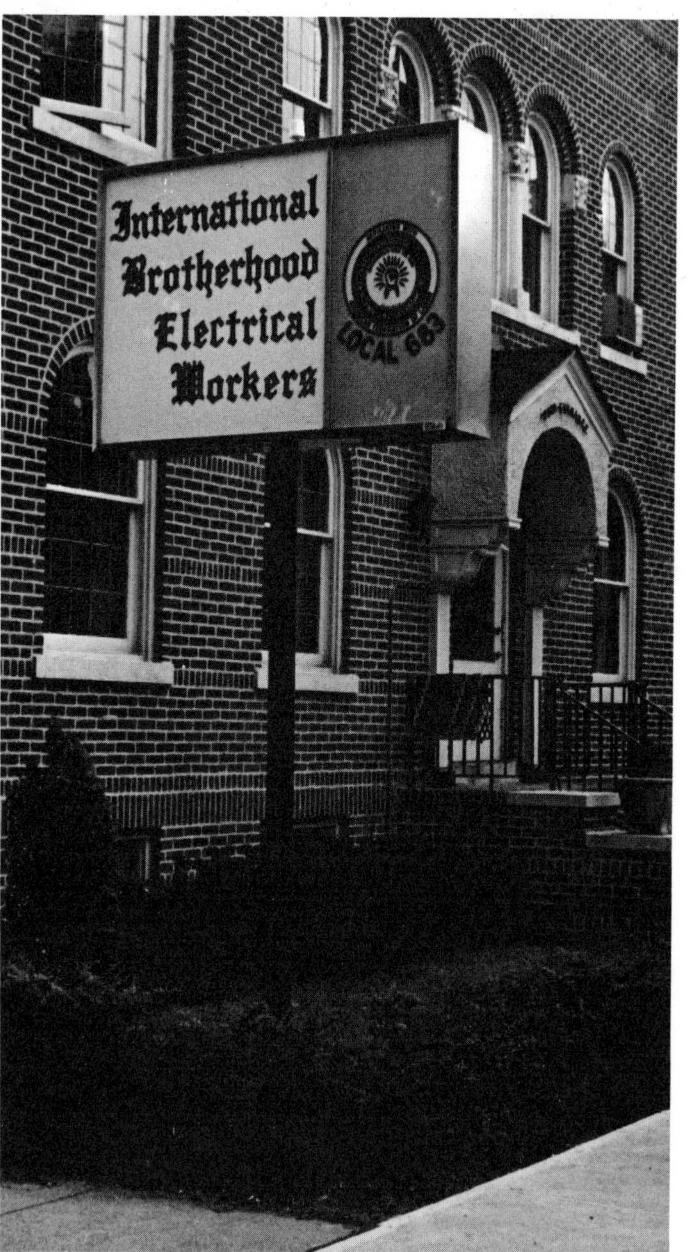

Fig. 24-5. Each local union has its own administrative center which follows the standards and requirements of the national organization.

Both labor and management have an interest in safety programs. The employer knows that the loss of a skilled craftsman because of injury is the loss of a valuable employee. Unions support safety programs because physical well-being is in the interest of their individual members, Fig. 24-4.

In order to run these programs and to deal with other problems (such as workers' complaints against the employer), the union and management may set up joint councils or committees. In these joint councils or committees, they try to solve their common problems.

Joining a Building Trade Union

If you are interested in joining a building trade union, you must meet certain requirements. These are different for each construction trade union. The Electrical Workers union and the Carpenters union, for example, each has its own separate standards, Fig. 24-5. Within the national union organization, each local, city, or plant union may establish membership rules. All national and local unions in every construction trade usually prefer that all members have a high school education and a sincere interest in the craft. *Apprentices* (new workers) enter the union through apprenticeship programs (training programs). These programs follow National Standards registered with the U.S. Department of Labor.

So that you understand more fully the rules for joining a union in the construction industry, let us look at a typical local union's membership standards. A local union of the United Brotherhood of Carpenters and Joiners of America, which governs the work of carpenters in Columbus, Ohio, is such a union. Carpenters who are employed on union construction projects in this city belong to this union and are either journeymen or *indentured apprentices.*

To join the union, the applicant must first have a high school education or its equivalent. He must be selected by a joint labor-management committee according to objective standards set by the committee. Then, he must serve a trial (probationary) period, usually for 90 days. If he is found to be satisfactory, he is allowed to join the union by paying an *initiation fee* (usually about $25). At the beginning, the rate of pay for an apprentice is about 60% of the journeyman rate. He receives increases every six months during his apprenticeship until he reaches the journeyman pay scale. The apprentice member must pay union *dues* equal to about $1\frac{1}{2}$ hours pay each month. For four years the apprentice receives on-the-job training under the supervision of a journeyman. Also, he must go to classes two nights a week during the school year. When he successfully completes his training program, the apprentice is granted membership as a *journeyman carpenter.* With this title he is eligible to work as a journeyman on any construction project within the *jurisdiction* (authority) of the union and to receive the wages negotiated for a journeyman. He may also transfer to other local unions.

The journeyman now has earned all benefits of union membership. Among them are: (1) membership in the welfare and retirement plans of the union in which he receives payments and medical care for himself and his family in the case of disability or retirement, (2) improved employment opportunities as a result of training programs and work promotion activities, and (3) the right to have his name placed on the unemployment list. (This is a list of journeymen out of work at a certain time.) If a contractor needs carpenters, he may contact the union and ask for the number of workers he needs. The union then contacts men whose names are on the unemployment list and refers them to the contractor. In this way, the union acts as an employment agency for the unemployed carpenters and for the contractor.

Fig. 24-6. Management and labor negotiate to resolve their disagreements.

Summary

Workers (unions) and employers (management) make agreements and contracts by a process known as *collective bargaining,* Fig. 24-6. Workers join together in unions so they can bargain with a single voice. Most international unions are affiliated (members of) with the American Federation of Labor (AFL) and the Congress of Industrial Organizations (CIO). The AFL and CIO joined together in 1955 to form the AFL-CIO. The Building and Construction Trades Department of the AFL-CIO is one of the most important parts of this union organization.

Requirements for joining a building trades union are set by each local of the national union. Usually the applicant must (1) have a high school education and (2) work under a training program for a certain length of time before becoming a journeyman member of the union.

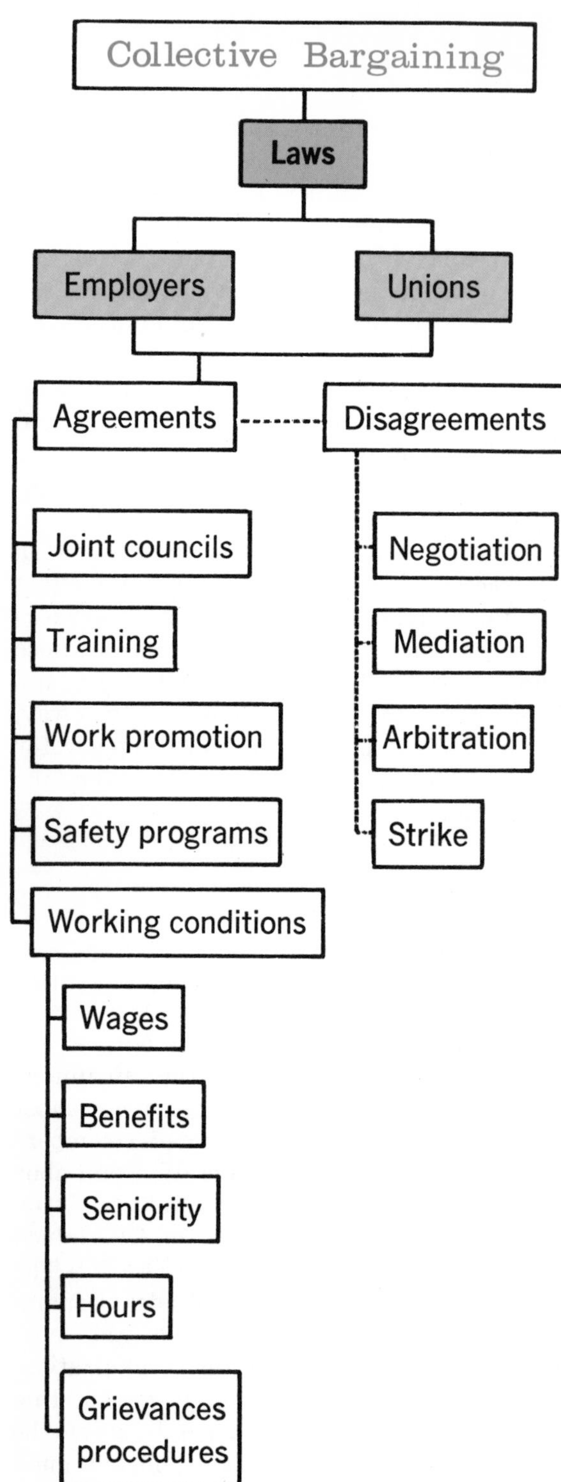

Terms to Know

labor union
trade union
AFL-CIO
skilled worker
unskilled worker
category
disability
employer
employee
NLRB
negotiate
arbitrate
mediator
labor
collective bargaining
management
the strike
wages
working conditions
fringe benefits
apprentice
initiation fee
dues
on-the-job training
jurisdiction
local
journeyman
protect
guarantee

Think About It!

1. Why do construction workers have special need for help from a union?
2. *Union members* and their *employer* reach an agreement through *collective bargaining*.
   a. What kinds of things do they bargain about?
   b. What can a *mediator* do to help *settle* a difference?
   c. What can an *arbitrator* do?
   d. Why does a union try to avoid a *strike*?
3. In what kinds of activities do *labor* and *management* usually work together?

Hiring Construction Personnel

READING 25

The importance of *hiring practices* becomes clear when you realize that each of the millions of construction workers was hired at least once. Many construction workers are hired a number of times each working season. This is because they often move from one employer to another as they move from one construction site to another, Fig. 25-1.

The next few lessons tell about the various personnel practices in construction. This lesson tells about one part of the personnel practices, that of *hiring*. In construction, there are three major practices in hiring: *recruiting, selecting,* and *inducting*. The following readings will help you understand other personnel practices such as training, working, advancing, and retiring.

Recruiting

Recruiting is the finding and attracting of needed employees. Recruiting may be fairly simple. A small construction contractor may hire someone who has been watching the construction work, Fig. 25-2. Or, for a large contractor, recruiting may be a long and expensive process. This is especially true when a specialist such as an architect, civil engineer, draftsman, foreman, or skilled craftsman is needed. In every case, the contractor must make the job attractive enough that employees will want to work for him.

Recruitment begins with the request to fill a job opening or hire someone for a new job. Although the request may come from the foreman or superintendent, the recruiting is done by the *personnel man*, or in a large organization, the *personnel department*. The personnel department has *job descriptions* which tell what each worker is expected to do. They will also have a description of the skills, education, and experience that the needed worker must have. The per-

Fig. 25-1. These construction workers will work at this job until it is completed. Then they will move on to another.

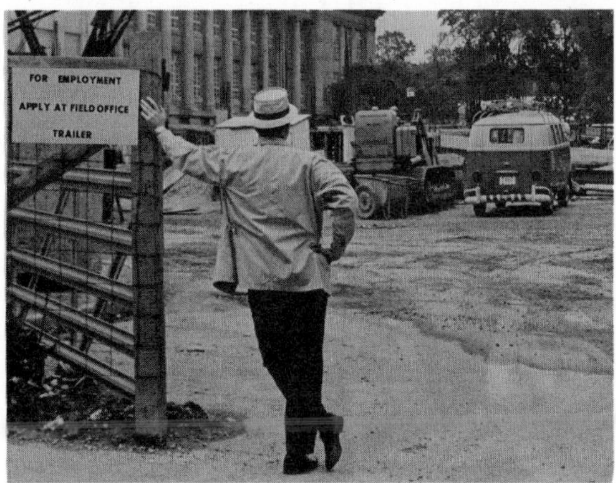

Fig. 25-2. This man who is watching the construction work may be hired by the contractor.

sonnel department may recruit workers in these ways: (1) by advertising in newspapers, (2) by checking with schools and colleges, or (3) by placing job orders with public and private employment agencies.

The way that union contractors in the building and construction industry recruit workers is usually provided for in the collective bargaining agreement. The union and employer have usually set up procedures by which the employer calls the union when he needs workmen. This is known as the *hiring hall* or referral provision. (See Fig. 25-3.) It is agreed in advance that the union will maintain a pool of skilled construction workmen. The employer then calls the union and places an order for the number of men needed. Then, the union refers the workmen to the employer for hire.

The referral provision has proven to be of service to everyone involved. It helps the contractor to be free to bid any size job, because he knows he has a source of qualified workmen. The worker is helped by receiving placement help and knowing that his wages and working conditions will be covered by an agreement.

Fig. 25-3. Skilled, union electrical workers can report at the union hall to find a job.

Selecting

Selecting is a screening process for choosing the best qualified person from among those who apply for each job. Selecting, like recruiting, may be an easy or a difficult process. It depends on what kinds of jobs have to be filled, the number of people who want the job, and the company's hiring policy. A good selection can be made only if many facts are known about the people who want the job and the job itself. These facts help the employer decide who is the best person for the job.

There are many ways to get facts about an *applicant* (the person wanting the job). First, there is an *application form.* See Figs. 25-4 and 25-5. This gives basic information and helps to show if the person meets the company's standards. For most jobs today, filling out some kind of application blank is required. In most cases, the form is filled out by the applicant, Fig 25-6. In some cases, however, it is done by the employer who asks the applicant questions. The way the applicant answers the questions and what he says help the employer to judge the applicant.

Testing may also be used to select a person applying for a job. There are two major kinds of tests: proficiency tests and aptitude tests. *Proficiency tests* measure such abilities as typing and bricklaying. They are given to applicants who want skilled positions in the construction industry. These tests require applicants to produce samples of work which the employer then compares to the work of successfully employed tradesmen. Proficiency tests may also require answers to oral or written questions. Generally, these operations and questions can only be performed and answered by an experienced person.

THIS FORM SHOULD BE COMPLETELY FILLED OUT TO RECEIVE PROPER CONSIDERATION

APPLICATION FOR EMPLOYMENT

(TO BE FILLED OUT BY APPLICANT IN OWN HANDWRITING)

DATE OF APPLICATION____________

NAME IN FULL__________ FIRST __________ MIDDLE __________ LAST

PRESENT ADDRESS__________ STREET AND NUMBER __________ CITY AND STATE PHONE NO.__________

LAST PREVIOUS ADDRESS__________

SOCIAL SECURITY No. __________ IF SCHOOL AGE HAVE YOU A WORKING PERMIT? __________

MALE* FEMALE* SINGLE MARRIED SEPARATED DIVORCED WIDOW(ER)

AGE__________DATE OF BIRTH*__________

HEIGHT__________WEIGHT__________COLOR OF EYES__________COLOR HAIR__________

ARE YOU A CITIZEN OF UNITED STATES?__________

IF MARRIED, IS WIFE (HUSBAND) WORKING?__________WHERE?__________

HUSBAND'S (OR WIFE'S) NAME IN FULL__________ FIRST MIDDLE LAST

LIVE WITH PARENTS__________RELATIVES__________BOARD__________LIGHT HOUSEKEEPING__________

In case of emergency, such as serious injury or illness, notify the following person:

NAME__________PHONE No.__________

ADDRESS__________CITY & STATE__________

FATHER'S NAME IN FULL__________

DO YOU HAVE LIFE INSURANCE?__________WHAT COMPANIES?__________

STATE NUMBER OF DEPENDENTS: ADULTS__________CHILDREN__________AGES?__________

Have You Ever Received UN-EMPLOYMENT COMPENSATION?__________HOW MANY TIMES?__________

FROM WHAT EMPLOYERS?__________

HAVE YOU ANY RELATIVES OR FRIENDS WORKING HERE?__________WHO?__________

WHAT IS YOUR No 1 HOBBY?__________OTHERS__________

DO YOU USE A TYPEWRITER?__________WELL__________FAIR__________VERY SLOWLY__________

DO YOU USE A CAMERA?__________OFTEN?__________SELDOM?__________FINISH YOUR OWN FILMS?__________

(IF APPLYING AS DELIVERYMAN) EVER CONVICTED FOR — RECKLESS DRIVING?__________SPEEDING?__________HOW MANY TIMES?__________

ARE YOU NOW EMPLOYED?__________IF SO— WHY DO YOU WANT TO CHANGE?__________

Have You Other EMPLOYMENT APPLICATIONS PENDING?__________WHAT FIRMS?__________

HAVE YOU EVER HAD A SURETY BOND?__________CANCELLED?__________REFUSED?__________

Form E-102

Printed in U. S. A.

EDUCATION:

GIVE NUMBER OF YEARS ATTENDED		NAME OF SCHOOL	CITY	STATE
GRAMMAR SCHOOL	YEARS			
HIGH SCHOOL	YEARS			
COLLEGE	YEARS			

WHAT SPECIAL COURSES?__________

EMPLOYMENT HISTORY: STATE FULLY HOW YOU HAVE BEEN PREVIOUSLY EMPLOYED OR ENGAGED FOR LAST 3 YEARS BEGIN WITH YOUR PRESENT OR LAST EMPLOYER. —GIVE FULL PARTICULARS AS REQUIRED BY THIS FORM.

FROM MONTH—YEAR	TO MONTH—YEAR	FIRM EMPLOYED BY	WHAT DID YOU DO?	EMPLOYER'S ADDRESS	NAME OF PERSON YOU WORKED FOR	WHY DID YOU LEAVE?

REFERENCES: GIVE THE NAMES OF THREE RELIABLE PERSONS TO WHOM WE CAN REFER, WHO ARE SUFFICIENTLY FAMILIAR WITH YOUR QUALIFICATIONS AND CHARACTER TO GIVE INFORMATION ABOUT YOU. DO NOT INCLUDE RELATIVES OR FORMER EMPLOYERS.

NAME	PRESENT ADDRESS	CITY AND STATE	TELEPHONE No.

DESIRE EMPLOYMENT IN: PHOTO LABORATORY__________ RETAIL STORE__________ OFFICE WORK__________ DELIVERY__________ JANITOR WORK__________

WHAT EXPERIENCE IF ANY FOR THIS WORK?__________ WILL YOU ACCEPT OTHER WORK?__________

HEALTH: THE FOLLOWING INFORMATION IS GIVEN IN LIEU OF A PHYSICAL EXAMINATION

Eyesight: __________Good__________Fair__________Poor

Hearing: __________Good__________Fair__________Poor

Have you a Hernia or Rupture?__________Yes__________No. If "Yes" is a truss worn?__________

Have you ever been advised to have a surgical operation?__________

Details__________

Have you ever received indemnity for accidents or occupational illness?__________

Details__________

Have you ever been told you had high blood pressure?__________

Have you ever had, been treated for, or been told you had any of the following? Epilepsy, Syphilis, Vertigo or dizziness, fainting spells, disease of the brain, nervous system, lungs or heart? (Underscore which ones, if any.)

IMPORTANT

"I hereby warrant that the information given by me in this application is true in all respects and I agree that if employed and it is found to be false in any respect, that I will be subject to dismissal without notice."

"I hereby authorize you or my former employers or references to furnish any information concerning my personal character, habits or employment record and I hereby release all such persons from any liability or damages on account of having furnished such information."

In return for this agreement that I will receive one week's notice or equivalent in pay in case my services are no longer required through no fault of my own. I agree if employed, to give one week of notice of my intention to discontinue my employment.

SIGNATURE OF APPLICANT X__________

*The New York State Law Against Discrimination prohibits discrimination because of age and sex. Fair employment practices laws of many other states as well as the Federal government prohibit discrimination in employment on account of race, color, religion (or creed), sex, or national origin, and some states include national ancestry and age.

Fig. 25-4. An applicant is asked to give information about himself on the application form.

CONFIDENTIAL

EMPLOYMENT INFORMATION

After analyzing and discussing applicant's information on pages 1 and 4, IF there is possibility you might hire immediately or at a later date,—then complete the interview and tests indicated on this page.
If hired, file in "EMPLOYEE RECORD" file.
If not hired immediately, file in "PROSPECT" file.
If tests indicate as unsatisfactory, file in "APPLICATIONS REJECTED."

FOR ____ SOCIAL SECURITY No. ____

ADDRESS WHEN EMPLOYED ____ PHONE No. ____

DATE		
____	ADDRESS CHANGES ____	PHONE No. ____
____	ADDRESS CHANGES ____	PHONE No. ____
____	ADDRESS CHANGES ____	PHONE No. ____
____	ADDRESS CHANGES ____	PHONE No. ____
____	ADDRESS CHANGES ____	PHONE No. ____

OTIS "RATE OF LEARNING" SCORE: NUMBER OF QUESTIONS ANSWERED ____ NUMBER CORRECT ____

"RATE OF MANIPULATION" SCORE: PLACING TIME ____ TURNING TIME ____

PHOTO APTITUDE SCORE: — SORTING TIME ____ ERRORS ____ MATCHING TIME ____ ERRORS ____

APPEARANCE: EXCELLENT ____ NEAT ____ FAIR ____ POOR ____

PERSONALITY: EXCELLENT ____ PLEASANT ____ FAIR ____ RESERVED ____

VOICE: LOUD ____ CLEAR ____ SOFT ____ IMPAIRED ____

APPEARS SUITED FOR: PRODUCTION WORK ____ SALES ____ EXEC. ____

APPARENT HANDICAPS:

GENERAL COMMENTS ON INTERVIEW: —

STARTED WORK — DATE ____ STARTING PAY $ ____ TIME CLOCK No. ____

HIRED FOR: (JOB CLASSIFICATION) ____ DEPARTMENT ____

EMPLOYMENT RECORD

ADVANCEMENTS: — PAY INCREASES

DATE OF CHANGE	POSITION ASSIGNED	REASONS ✓	✓	✓	APPROVED BY	NEW RATE PAY
		EXTRA SKILL	NEW ABILITY	LONG SERVICE		
		EXTRA SKILL	NEW ABILITY	LONG SERVICE		
		EXTRA SKILL	NEW ABILITY	LONG SERVICE		
		EXTRA SKILL	NEW ABILITY	LONG SERVICE		
		EXTRA SKILL	NEW ABILITY	LONG SERVICE		
		EXTRA SKILL	NEW ABILITY	LONG SERVICE		

PERFORMANCE ✓

CHARACTER OF SERVICE	Excel-lent	Good	Fair	Unsatis-factory	Hopeless
QUALITY OF WORK					
PRODUCTION-VOLUME					
ATTITUDE-WORK					
ATTITUDE-ORGANIZATION					
ATTENDANCE-PUNCTUALITY					

GENERAL INFORMATION & REMARKS: —

VACATIONS

DAYS	FROM	TO

ANNUAL EARNINGS

YEAR	AMOUNT
19	$

EMPLOYMENT RELEASE: — DATE LEFT ____

CHECK AND EXPLAIN IN DETAIL UNDER "REMARKS" EXACT REASON FOR LEAVING:

☐ DISCHARGED:
- ☐ MONEY
- ☐ DRINKING
- ☐ INSUBORDINATE
- ☐ INCOMPETENT
- ☐ LAZY — TOO SLOW
- ☐ TROUBLE MAKER
- ☐ OTHER ____

☐ RESIGNED
- ☐ BETTER JOB
- ☐ ILL HEALTH
- ☐ DOESN'T NEED WORK
- ☐ SELF EMPLOYED
- ☐ ATTEND SCHOOL
- ☐ TO MARRY, ☐ PREGNANT
- ☐ TO DRAW UNEMP. INSURANCE

☐ OTHER REASON:
- ☐ ENTER MILITARY SERVICE
- ☐ LIST BRANCH OF SERVICE UNDER "REMARKS"
- ☐ ON STRIKE
- ☐ MOVED AWAY
- ☐ REFUSED TRANSFER
- ☐ VAC. RELIEF WORKER
- ☐ EXTRA WORK ONLY

DID YOU OFFER FURTHER EMPLOYMENT? ____ IF NOT, STATE REASON BELOW:

WOULD YOU REEMPLOY? ____ IF NOT, STATE REASON BELOW:

RECEIVED PAY IN FULL OF ALL DEMANDS SIGNATURE: ____

Fig. 25-5. Other parts of the application form will contain a record of the applicant's test scores, his appearance and personality, and a record of his employment if he is hired.

Aptitude tests are used to measure an inexperienced or untrained person's ability to learn and do a job quickly. The results of these tests help in the selecting of apprentices in the construction trades and for many other kinds of jobs.

Many specific aptitude tests for skilled occupations in the construction industry have been made by the United States Department of Labor, Bureau of Employment Security, United States Employment Service. This Service has also developed a General Aptitude Test Battery. This test gives the applicant a good idea of his ability for a number of different kinds of work. It is used to help an applicant who is not sure of what kind of job he would like. Information about these tests can be found at any State Employment Service office. Preemployment testing is an efficient way of estimating an applicant's ability before he is hired. An hour of testing may tell as much about him as several days on the job, Fig 25-7.

Interviewing is another way of selecting employees. The interview is generally thought of as the most important part of the hiring process. Every job selection procedure includes one or more interviews. *An interview is a talk between an employer and a person who wants a job.* Usually, the employer asks the applicant questions, but the applicant also has a chance to question the employer about the job and the company. Interviews are different depending on the job to be filled. A small building contractor interviewing an applicant for a laborer's job at the building site may spend only a few

Fig. 25-6. The state employment service begins its work by having an applicant fill out an application form.

Fig. 25-7. Next, the applicant is tested.

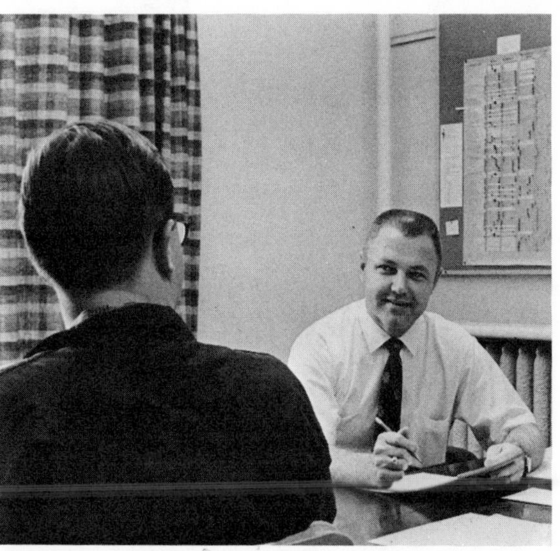

Fig. 25-8. The applicant is interviewed by a staff member.

minutes with him. Interviewing a civil engineer, draftsman, or foreman might take more time. Very often the applicant may be interviewed by more than one person. A foreman, superintendent, or manager may do the final interviewing, Fig. 25-8.

Checking references is another method used to select workers. *A reference is a statement of an applicant's qualifications.* Most application forms ask for the names of persons who may be contacted for references. Sometimes applicants are asked to show letters that recommend them. Usually references are of two kinds: (1) *Character references* are statements from people who have known you for some time and can tell about your reputation and what kind of a person you are. (2) *Former employer references* are statements from former employers about the applicant's previous performance. *For young applicants, school records are almost always checked.*

Final decisions are usually made by personal value judgments. No two employers will look for the same qualities, and no two employees will want the same things in an employer. Employers have different strengths and weaknesses in their capacities to select efficiently; and workers have different strengths and weaknesses in their capacities to do jobs.

Inducting

Induction programs are designed to make the new employee feel that he belongs to the team and to help him learn how to do his job as part of that team. These programs give information about the history of the company, its products, employee benefits and services, company policies and practices, work rules, and the importance of each job for the whole project.

Fig. 25-9. When work is found, the applicant is notified by phone.

Fig. 25-10. On the job, the new worker can now be informed as to his specific duties.

A large industrial manufacturing company may have a formal induction training program with employee handbooks and pamphlets to explain the whole company's operation. A small contractor hiring a building craftsman may assign him to a project superintendent who will in turn assign him to a foreman who will assign him to his job, Fig. 25-10. Before being referred to the job by his union, the building craftsman is expected to know the work and to be qualified to perform the type of work to which he is assigned.

What Applicants Should Do

When applying for a job, it is very important to make a good first impression. It may decide whether or not an applicant is hired. To make a good impression, an applicant should prepare for an interview by gathering facts about the construction industry, the employer, and the job he wants. Also, he should be especially neat and clean when he appears for the interview. He should take care to fill out the application forms neatly and accurately.

Where hiring is done through a hiring hall or referral plan, the applicant should apply to the local office of the union or craft in which he is interested. This office will then provide application forms and arrange interviews.

Summary

There are three major practices in hiring: *recruiting, selecting,* and *inducting.* Recruiting is finding and attracting job applicants. Selecting is choosing the person for the job. Inducting is getting the worker started on the job.

Through collective bargaining, many employers and unions have set up orderly procedures for recruiting, selecting, and inducting skilled production craftsmen. These procedures are known as the hiring hall or referral provisions of a collective bargaining agreement.

A person applying for a job should prepare for the interview by learning about the company and its hiring practices.

Terms to Know

selection
hiring
  a. recruiting
  b. selecting
  c. inducting
personnel man
personnel department
job descriptions
hiring hall
referral provisions
proficiency tests
aptitude tests
applicant
interview
references
  a. character references
  b. former employer references

Think About It!

1. *Recruitment* practices vary for different occupations in construction.
   a. Name several ways in which a construction contractor may *recruit job applicants.*
   b. What is the purpose of a *hiring hall?*
2. To *select* the best person for a job, a contractor needs to know many things about the applicants.
   a. What questions usually are asked on *job application blanks?*
   b. Why does the employer need to know the answers?
3. An *induction* program for new *employees* may be simple or complex.
   a. Why would a contractor want a new worker to know something about the whole project?
   b. What kinds of *rules and policies* does the employee need to know about?

READING 26

Training and Educating for Construction

It takes training to become a good baseball player. You must first learn to hit, field, and run bases. Then you must practice all of those things. In the same way, there are many things a person who works in construction must learn if he is to do his job well. In order to become a good craftsman, a carpenter must learn to saw, assemble, and fit materials. This takes training. A worker also needs training if he is to advance to a better job. If a skilled journeyman carpenter wishes to become a foreman, he must first learn how to supervise the work of others.

Fig. 26-1. American Indians, especially Mohawks, have traditionally become ironworkers and bridgemen, putting up the steel for many of the nation's great structures.

Groups Requiring Training

There are three major groups of workers for the construction industry: (1) those who perform management tasks, (2) those who work on production, and (3) those who perform office tasks. Each group has different training needs.

There are different levels and kinds of *managers*: (1) community planners, (2) draftsmen, (3) estimators, (4) contractors, (5) supervisors and foremen, (6) architects, and (7) engineers. Most of these people complete educational programs beyond high school.

Those who work on *production* carry out the plans of management, Fig. 26-1. They are responsible for doing the on-site work necessary for the successful completion of the construction project. These skilled craftsmen have many different specialties. For example, there are bricklayers, electricians, plumbers, and carpenters. All must first complete high school and then enter apprenticeship programs, but they all work together to complete the construction project.

Those who perform *office tasks* do work which is much like that found in any office. Those doing this work include telephone operators, receptionists, secretaries, and payroll clerks. All these workers keep records and provide the information which is needed to keep construction operations moving smoothly. Office workers usually receive their education and training in programs outside the construction industry, Fig. 26-2.

Educating Architects, Engineers, and Managers

Architects and engineers have the responsibility of: (1) designing, (2) surveying, and (3) engineering the construction project. *Civil engineers, sanitary engineers,* and *architects* work mainly in construction. There are also *aeronautical* and *industrial engineers* who work mainly in manufacturing. *Electrical* and *mechanical engineers* work in both construction and manufacturing, Fig. 26-3.

To gain the knowledge and skills necessary to do designing and engineering work, they all must attend college. Usually they attend college for four or five years. During this time they take courses in mathematics, science, and in areas related to architecture or engineering such as drafting, electrical circuit design, and the designing of foundations. To graduate from an architectural or engineering school, students must generally have a "C" average. Their courses are usually very difficult, and they must study and attend classes regularly.

Fig. 26-2. A high school education may provide you with efficient communication skills which are essential in any office.

To become a successful architect or engineering student, it is not enough to have intelligence and desire. You must also have a good high school background, including high grades in mathematics and science, Fig. 26-4. Without this background your chances of being accepted into a good engineering school, or of doing well in such a school, are slim.

Although each engineering school sets its own background requirements, they all want similar things. A typical engineering school requires that the following subjects be taken in high school: (1) three or four years of mathematics, (2) three or four years of English, (3) one or two years of industrial arts, and (4) two or three years of science. In each of these subjects, the higher number of years is preferred. Usually a "B" grade average is necessary. For more information about these programs and the standards for getting into a particular engineering school, speak to your teacher or guidance counselor.

Many architects and engineers also work as managers or contractors, and many experienced tradesmen become supervisors or contractors. Some managers study professional construction management in college

Fig. 26-3. These civil engineers use construction technology in solving many construction problems.

programs. They are neither engineers nor tradesmen. They are persons who plan, organize, and control the actions of others in the construction industry. These kinds of managers often attend commerce colleges instead of engineering schools. There are other kinds of management personnel who attend special classes to become surveyors or estimators.

Training of Production Workers

The construction industry gets production workers from four main sources: (1) outsiders who have little skill and who come into the industry just when activities are booming and unskilled labor is needed, (2) young workers who come into the trade as helpers or laborers, (3) young men who wish to become skilled craftsmen in one of the building trades, and (4) the pool of skilled workers who are already trained and qualified, but who may have been learning new skills and techniques. Although men from all four sources are often needed as construction workers, it is necessary to become a *skilled craftsman* if you are to find permanent and rewarding work in the building industry.

Skilled tradesmen go through a training period called an *apprenticeship.* During their apprenticeship, the young trainee or apprentice is given: (1) 6,000 to 10,000 hours of training on the job and (2) 144 hours per year of classroom instruction which will help him to become a journeyman or highly skilled building trades worker, Figs. 26-6 and 26-7.

Both labor unions and contractors work together in setting up apprentice-training programs. These programs usually require an apprentice to be between 17 and 25 years of age and to be in good physical condition. It is usually necessary to have a good high school education in mathematics and science. The apprentice should also be handy with tools and have a mechanical aptitude. Each apprentice is graded and advanced on his own progress.

An apprenticeship program is usually supervised by a Joint Apprenticeship Committee made up of representatives of local employers and unions. The committee has many important tasks which include: (1)

Fig. 26-4. These future engineers are gaining knowledge about strength of materials.

Fig. 26-5. Both managers and production workers spend time in independent study to keep abreast of the changing technology.

deciding how many apprentices are needed, (2) deciding what standards for education, training, and experience are to be met, (3) finding out what employers have equipment and other things needed to provide good training, (4) settling disputes between employers and apprentices, and (5) certifying the apprentice as a journeyman upon completion of the course. This committee also registers apprenticeship programs with the state apprenticeship agency and with the United States Department of Labor's Bureau of Apprenticeship and Training.

Where there is no Joint Apprenticeship Committee, the apprentice may make an agreement with the employer or the employer's agent. Although this arrangement may be as good as any, it does have some risks. If there are disputes or differences between the two persons, the apprentice does not have the protection of the committee. Because training and grading depend only on one man, the apprentice's skills may not be up to other contractors' standards.

A young man who is interested in joining a building trade may shorten his period of apprenticeship by preapprenticeship instruction in high school, trade school, or junior college. (This does not apply to all trades.) If he does well in subjects related to his trade, the Joint Committee or his employer may give him credit for this training. This instruction will often enable him to begin his apprenticeship at a higher rate of pay than others who start without this training. If you want to know more about preapprenticeship programs and apprenticeship programs, your teacher or guidance counselor will help you.

Fig. 26-6. These apprentices spend about 144 hours per year in the classroom along with on-the-job training before becoming highly skilled journeymen.

Summary

Training is important in the construction industry. It enables the worker to do his job well and to advance to a better job. There are three main kinds of workers in the construction industry: (1) those who manage the construction project, (2) those who carry out the work on the project, and (3) those who work in the office.

The architect, engineer, and contractor have the joint responsibility of designing, engineering, and completing the construction project. They are usually trained in a college, university, or technical institute.

The production worker is responsible for the actual construction of the project. He is trained under an apprenticeship program.

Fig. 26-7. As part of their on-the-job training, these apprentices are learning how to screed concrete.

This program is from three to five years long and requires on-the-job training and classroom instruction. The program is usually operated by a Joint Apprenticeship Committee made up of representatives of local employers and unions.

Office workers usually receive their training outside of the construction industry. They may take business courses in high school and/or college.

Terms to Know

architect
civil engineer
sanitary engineer
tradesmen
trainee
apprentice
on-the-job training
community planners
draftsmen
estimators
contractors
foremen
supervisors
Joint Apprenticeship Committee

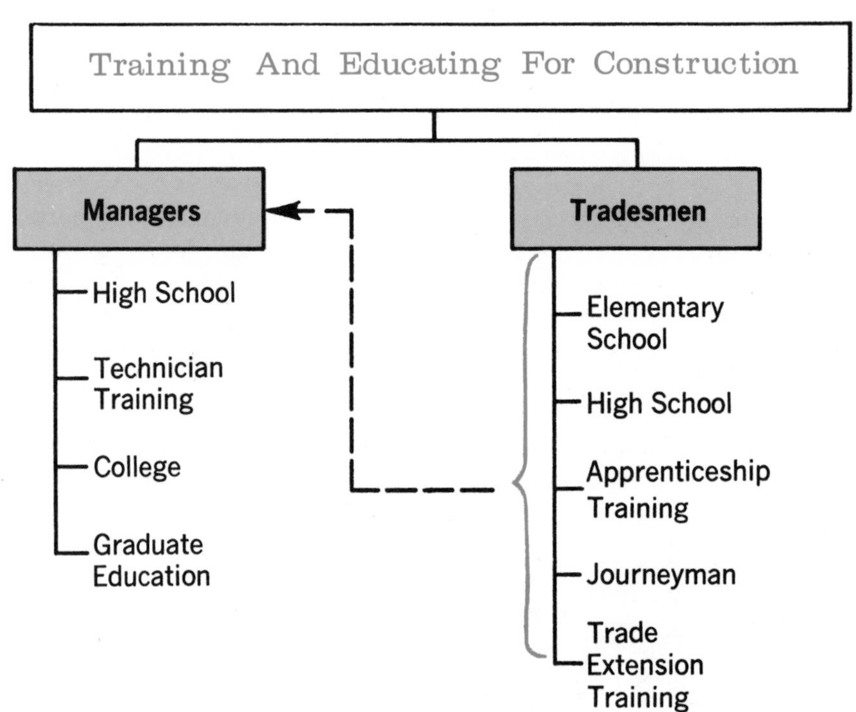

Think About It!

1. Name several *jobs* in each of these groups:
   a. *Managers*
   b. *Production workers*
   c. *Office workers*
2. Which of these people work mainly in *construction*, which work mainly in *manufacturing*, and which work in both?
   a. *Aeronautical* engineers
   b. *Architects*
   c. *Civil* engineers
   d. *Electrical* engineers
   e. *Industrial* engineers
   f. *Mechanical* engineers
   g. *Sanitary* engineers
3. A *skilled craftsman* is trained in an *apprenticeship program*.
   a. Who sets up and runs this kind of training?
   b. What is usually required, if you want to become an *apprentice* in a *construction trade*?
   c. How much and what kinds of training are required to become a *journeyman*?

Working Conditions

How well a coach and a team work together will affect the game. Each member of a football team must do his part. Because the coach pulls together the actions of the team members and tries to put each player in the position where he does his best, the team must also work with the coach. A coach can't win a game without a team, and a team can't go very far without a good coach. Each is important to the success of the other. The employees on a construction job and their employer must work together like a coach and the players. Each one should try to do his own job as best he can, Figs. 27-1 and 27-2.

Working Rules

Each sport has rules which players must follow. It is the same way in the construction industry. There are rules for the workers and for the employer. These rules cover three main areas of work:

1. Physical working environment (where the work is done),
2. Social working environment (the other workers), and
3. Economic rewards (the worker's pay and benefits for the job he does).

Although the *physical working environment* is somewhat determined by the job,

Fig. 27-1. Each member of a football team plays according to rules and game conditions.

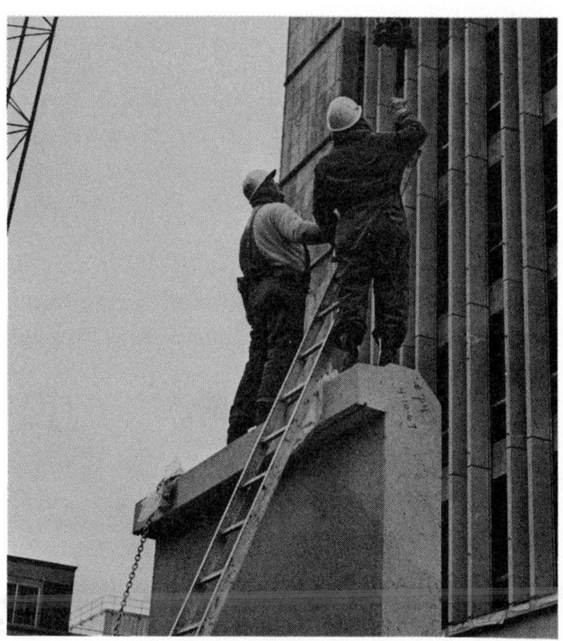

Fig. 27-2. Construction workers also agree to work under certain conditions and according to certain rules.

labor and management may work together to improve such things as the safety equipment, the lighting, or dust conditions. Certain conditions cannot be changed. In construction work, much of the work is done outside or in partly enclosed structures. Thus, exposure to cold, hot, and rainy weather is common. However, many persons prefer construction work because it is out-of-doors.

The *social working environment* refers to many things:

1. The attitude other workers have toward each other and their own job,
2. How many hours a day each worker must work,
3. What after-hours get-togethers there are (such as a company bowling team or Christmas party).

Economic rewards mean more than the money the worker receives. The fringe benefits such as the industry's insurance program and a paid vacation are also economic rewards, Fig. 27-3.

Construction trades offer especially good career opportunities for those who are not planning to go to college, but who are willing to spend several years learning with pay. Well-trained construction craftsmen can find jobs in all parts of the country. Generally, their hourly wage rates are much higher than those for most other *manual workers*. Those with business ability have a greater opportunity to establish their own businesses than do workers in other skilled occupations. Even with advances in technology, employment in most construction trades has expanded during the past 30 years, and it is still growing. See Table 3-2, page 13.

Setting the Rules

The working rules are set by an agreement between the employer and his employees. This may be done on an individual basis or on a group basis. Today most such agreements are put into a formal written contract called a *collective bargaining agreement*. Sometimes workers only have a *spoken agreement*. They may even work under an *assumed agreement*. If an employer does not say a workday is eight hours, and the worker only works eight hours, the agreement is understood or assumed.

If there is a collective bargaining agreement, it should be very specific and cover all items of importance, as the hours of work are in this statement from a typical agreement:

Eight hours shall constitute a day of work and shall be performed between the hours of 7:00 a.m. and 5:00 p.m., local time (8 hours sometime within this 10-hour period) with one-half hour off for lunch between 11:00 a.m. and 12:30 p.m., (one-half hour sometime within this hour and a half period) Monday through Friday.

It is important that each point that might cause a conflict between labor and management is written into the agreement.

Fig. 27-3. Fringe benefits mean such things as vacations which the whole family will enjoy.

Most working conditions are set by *negotiations.* The worker and the employer both compromise (give in) so that both can be satisfied. If an agreement can't be reached this way, an outsider may be called in to help settle the problem.

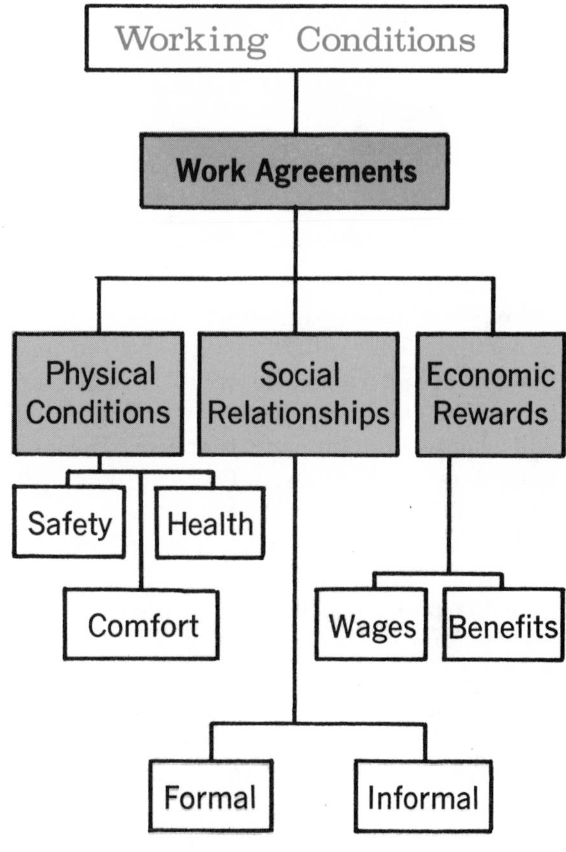

Summary

There are rules for the world of work just as there are for football. The way employees and employers follow the rules helps make construction a success or a failure. Working conditions or rules are agreed to by labor and management. If they cannot agree, an outsider may be called on to help them agree or to settle the problem for them.

Terms to Know

physical working environment
social working environment
economic rewards
fringe benefits
negotiations
collective bargaining agreement
spoken agreement
assumed agreement
compromise

Think About It!

1. Your classroom is your *physical working environment* for many hours each week.
   a. What parts of your *physical environment* in the classroom cannot be changed?
   b. Suggest some ways of improving the *physical environment* in your school.
2. The other students and the activities they share with you are part of your *social working environment.* How do group activities help you with your main job in school—which is getting an education?
3. The main *reward* for working in school is a good education. However, many *fringe benefits* are available to students.
   a. What tickets for sports events or entertainment can you buy at student rates?
   b. Does the school provide equipment for playing after-school sports?

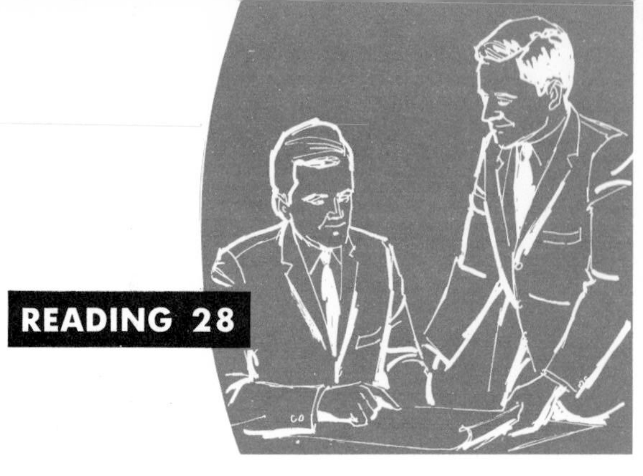

READING 28

Advancing in Construction

Construction advancement practices are important. They affect what kinds of employees are attracted to work in construction. The ambitious person wanting a job will choose the company that uses the best advancement practices. These people will probably be the best workers.

Advancement practices also affect the employers. An employee who is unhappy with his position often has low *morale* and may not do his work as well as if he felt good about his position and his company. If a worker is very unhappy, he may finally quit his job. When a great number of employees are unhappy in an organization, there is usually a high percentage who quit. Poorer quality work will probably result from those who stay. It costs industry money to hire new employees and train them to replace those who quit, Fig. 28-1.

There are many differences in the *advancement practices* of individual employers. These practices also vary in different parts of the country. The amount of money available to pay workers and how many workers need jobs both have an effect on advancement practices. As a result, it is hard to give any common guidelines about general advancement practices. Wherever you are, though, the person with the best

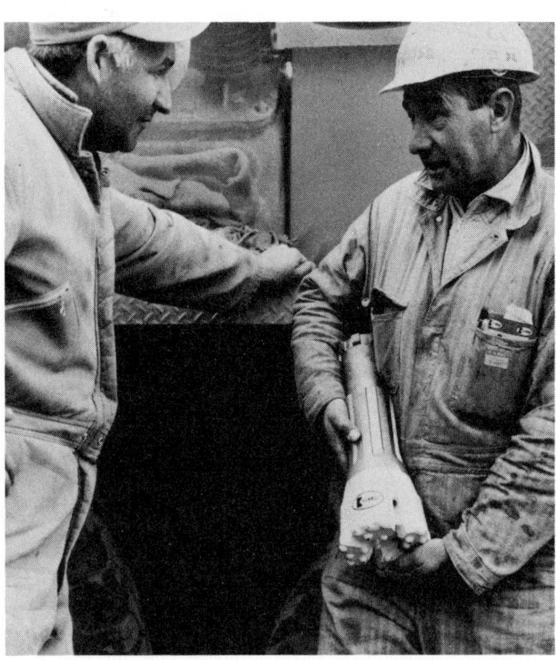

Fig. 28-1. Good employee relationships result in happy, productive employees.

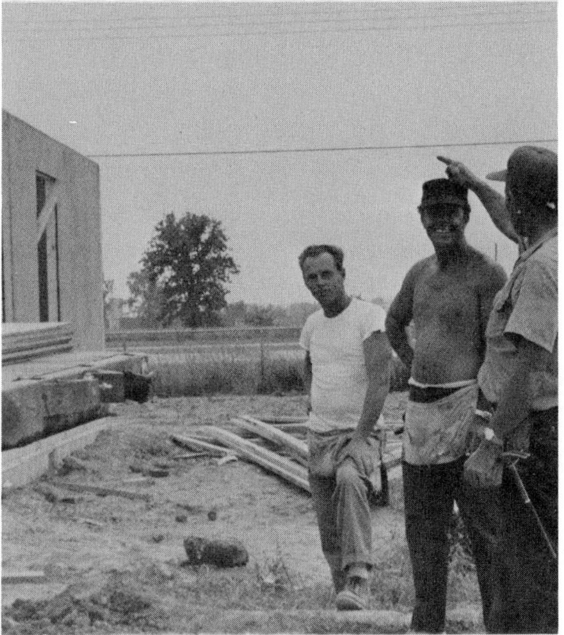

Fig. 28-2. Here is a foreman who is in charge of a construction crew.

training and qualifications has the best chance of advancing.

Career Progression

Career progression is the normal advance because of promotions, special knowledge, or job experience. Job changes are directly related to and depend upon advancement practices. There is both positive and negative career progression. *Positive progression* is movement upward. This means either going up in job position or receiving an increase in wages or both. *Negative progression* is moving downward. This means a lowering of job position or having wages decreased or both. In addition to positive and negative progression, a person may also move along at the same job level and at the same pay. This is called *lateral progression.*

In the construction industry, a person can advance in many ways. A craftsman may become:

1. A foreman in charge of a crew (Fig. 28-2), or
2. An estimator for a contractor, or
3. A project superintendent, or
4. An instructor or teacher of vocational and trade classes, or
5. A salesman for building supply companies, or
6. A contractor.

Career Patterns

There is no way to show all of the opportunities that might be open to you in the construction industry. There are far too many job possibilities to include them all here. You may get a very rough idea of how an individual might move up in a company by studying some of these common progressions:

1. high school graduate / apprentice / journeyman / foreman / job superintendent / general superintendent / estimator
2. technical school graduate / assistant expediter / expediter / purchasing agent / vice president
3. technical school graduate / assistant engineer / job superintendent / general superintendent / vice president
4. college graduate / junior estimator / estimator / engineer / business solicitor / partner
5. college graduate / engineer / job superintendent / vice president / president
6. high school graduate / apprentice / journeyman / grievance man / business agent / union president

Kinds of Advancement Practices

Advancement practices are those which result in worker movement within an organization. There are four major kinds of practices:

1. *Promoting* is moving to a higher job with an increase in responsibility, and

Fig. 28-3. Many small contractors have their own businesses and operate with small crews.

/or knowledge needed, and/or ability needed. The new job may or may not mean more pay.

2. *Demoting* is moving to a lower job with less responsibility, and/or knowledge needed, and/or ability needed. It may or may not mean less pay. It is often only temporary.
3. *Transferring* is moving to another job of the same level and pay. The responsibility, knowledge, and ability needed are much the same as that in the job held before. Transferring happens when an employer has an opening to be filled or when an employee would be happier in a new job.
4. *Separating* is discharging, relocating, laying off, or retiring. *Discharging* means firing. *Relocating* is changing an employee to a work site which is often far away from the place where he has been working. *Laying off* is the temporary release of an employee during a cutback in the number of workers. Lack of work, breakdown of equipment, and bad weather are a few of the many reasons for laying off workers. *Retiring* means that older workers must quit when they reach a certain age. Most companies set an age limit beyond which employees are not permitted to work for the company.

Effects of Advancement

Many things happen as a result of advancing on the job. Promotion usually means more pay. One's income determines the goods, services, and luxuries that an employee and his family can enjoy.

In addition to the economic effects of advancing, there are social effects. People tend to have friends who have jobs at much the same level they do and who earn about the same amount of money. It is often considered to be poor management practice for those in high positions to get together socially with the persons they supervise. Therefore, advancing often causes a change in social status and prestige. For example, a shop worker is made a foreman. He will probably make new friends and give up old ones because of his new job position. When job advancement means moving to a new place, the social effects are even greater. New *community ties* must be made, schools must be changed, and new friendships are made by all family members.

In addition to the economic and social effects of advancement, a person often changes within himself. A promotion, especially when it is given because a person does very good work, gives the person confidence, a sense of accomplishment, and a better feeling about his own worth. Ambition to get ahead and to do the best job possible often develops within a person after he has been promoted. Also, his attitude toward his job may be changed from that of unhappiness to that of satisfaction.

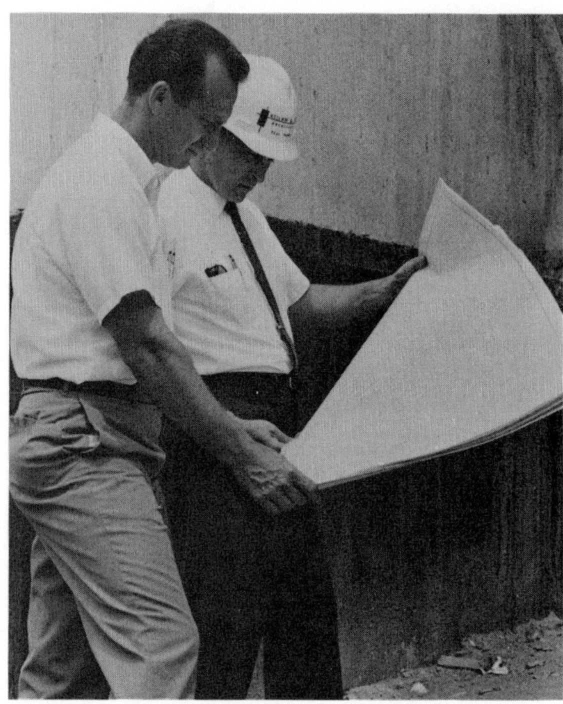

Fig. 28-4. A college graduate engineer discusses plans with a job superintendent.

We have given only a few of the effects of advancement. There are many more possible effects. Advancement concerns not only the employer and the worker, but also the worker's family, the community, and the whole society of which he and his family are a part.

Summary

Advancement practices are very important in industry. They may affect an employer's hiring and recruiting program, because many persons wanting jobs consider an employer's advancement practices when choosing a company for which to work. In addition, an employer must think about what advancement plans he has for a person he hires. Poor advancement practices may lead to poor employee morale and turnover problems.

A worker's career progression depends upon advancement practices. Progression is any movement within a person's work life.

Fig. 28-5. A person's salary determines the goods, services, and luxuries that his family can enjoy.

There are three kinds of progression: (1) positive, (2) negative, and (3) lateral.

There are four kinds of advancement practices: (1) promoting, (2) demoting, (3) transferring, and (4) separating. Retiring may be considered to be a special and permanent form of advancement practice. The advancement of the worker in his job is very important to his satisfaction on the job. In addition, advancement has educational, social, individual, and economic effects, Fig. 28-5.

Terms to Know

advancement
morale
career progression
- a. positive progression
- b. negative progression
- c. lateral progression

turnover
community ties
advancement practices
- a. promoting
- b. demoting
- c. transferring
- d. separating

prestige
competition

Think About It!

1. Compare *promotion* on a job with *promotion* to a higher grade level in school.
   - a. How are ambition and hard work involved in both school and job *advancement*?
   - b. How is promotion to a foreman's job different from promotion to the eighth grade? (Give several differences.)
2. Explain *discharging, relocating,* and *laying off*.
3. What would you want to know about the *advancement practices* of a construction firm if you were looking for a *permanent* job?

Basic Production

Clearing | **Earthmoving** | **Foundations**

The site must be cleared before construction can begin.

Earthmoving is required to prepare the bearing surface for the foundation.

Foundations are prepared to support the superstructure.

Concepts

Superstructures | **Utilities** | **Finished Project**

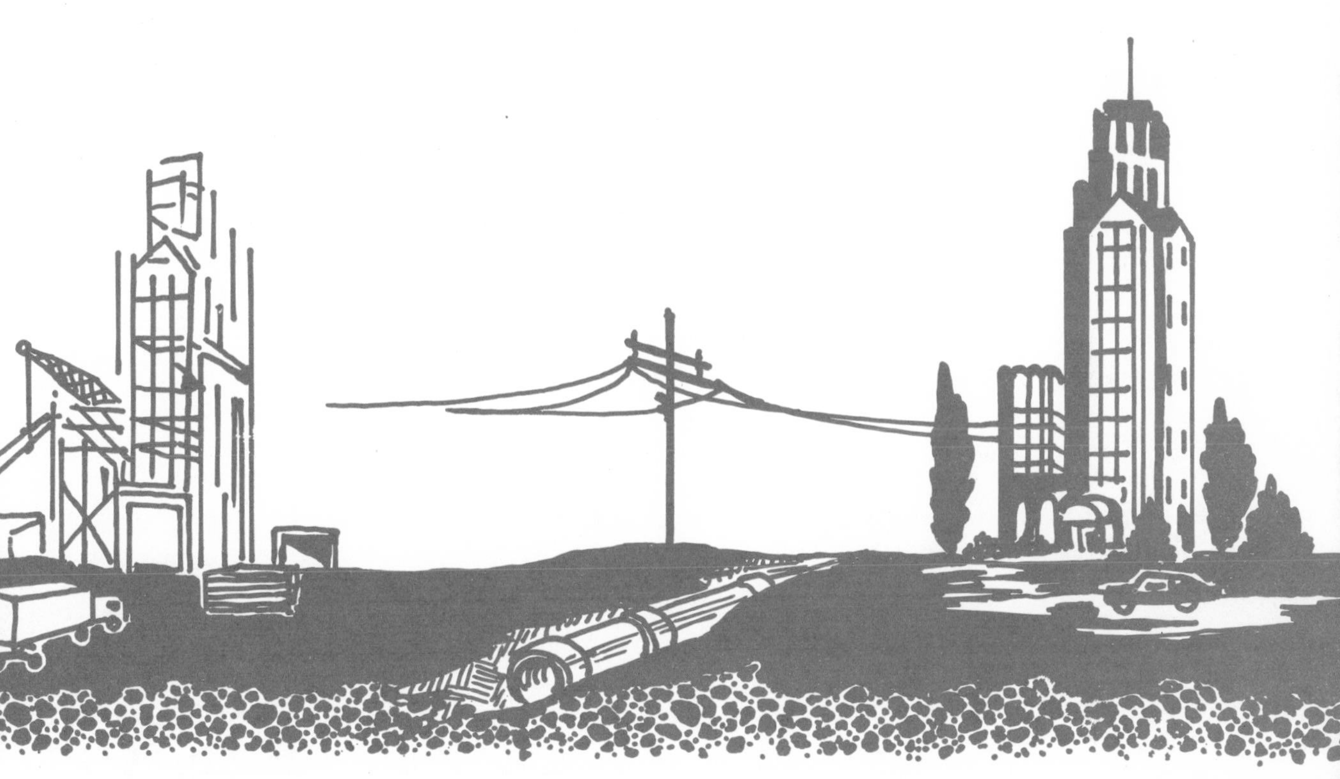

Superstructures
are built upon
the foundation.

Utilities
are installed
to make
the superstructure
more functional.

The finished project
will represent
the thinking
and planning
of the builders.

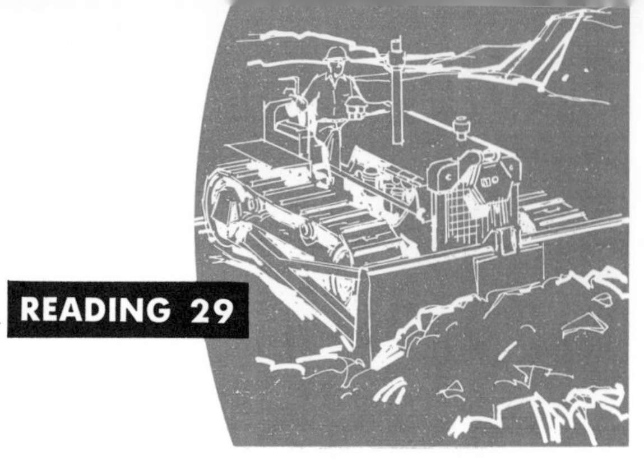

READING 29

Construction Production Technology

You have learned that the construction industry is a managed production system. During the past several weeks,

1. You have been studying the management practices of *planning, organizing,* and *controlling* the work to be done, Fig. 29-1.
2. You have learned that every construction project begins with a want or need. To satisfy this need, certain things must be done:
   a. The goals must be decided upon,
   b. The design must be created,
   c. The organization must be set up, and
   d. Controls must be set up to insure that the goals of the project will be met.
3. You have also learned how bids are prepared and contracts made.
4. Most recently, you have studied the personnel practices used in construction.

It is at this point in the construction story that the *production of the product begins.* Now, and for the next several months, you will be studying the practices of production. During this time, you will take part in many of these practices and develop some beginning skills in the using of tools and materials of construction. As a result, you should have a better understanding of the skill and ability of skilled construction workers. You should be able to understand how your man-made surroundings have been produced on a construction site.

Production

Producing any material object, whether it is done on a site or in a plant, *means to*

Fig. 29-1. This structure could not be erected if it were not for planning, organizing, and controlling.

Fig. 29-2. These men are storing materials on the site to be used when needed.

change the materials to increase their value. All *raw materials* are either grown or are taken from nature. *Industrial production* is the changing of these raw materials into something which has more value for the buyer. One of the reasons why the United States has become the wealthiest nation in the world is that we have had the ability to change the raw materials of the land. These practices of changing materials are called *industrial production technology. Construction production technology* is that group of practices which are used to change materials on a site.

To learn about these production practices, it will be helpful to learn how to classify them. All production practices may be classified into three divisions: preprocessing, processing, and postprocessing. Each of these major divisions of production practices has a more detailed set of classifications within it.

Preprocessing Materials

Producing material goods may be thought of as processing materials. However, before materials can be processed, they have to be prepared. *This preparation* (or getting materials ready for processing) *is called preprocessing.*

Preprocessing involves practices of:

1. Receiving,
2. Handling,
3. Storing, and
4. Protecting.

These practices also go on throughout the production period, Fig. 29-2.

Not all the materials needed to construct a building arrive at the site at the beginning of the project. They arrive at the various times when they are needed. When the materials arrive at the site, they must be received and counted and moved to the exact point where they will be used. Sometimes they need to be stored until they are used. At all times they must be protected from loss or damage.

Processing Materials

Select an object and try to think of what practices were used to produce it. Did the producer have to cut the raw material? If

Fig. 29-3. A piece of wood is changed by separating.

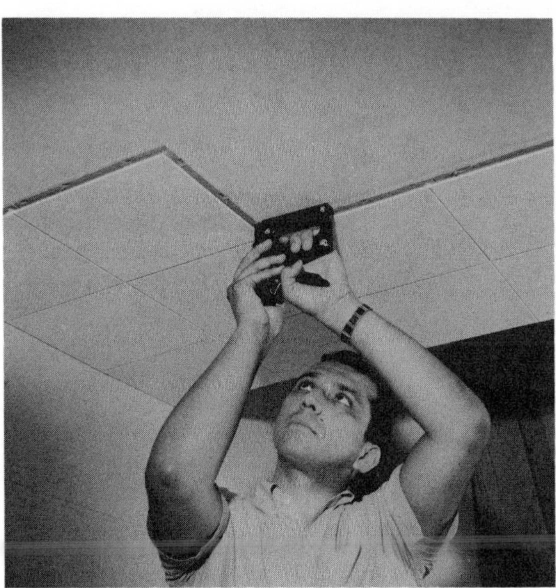

Fig. 29-4. Ceiling tile is installed by combining different materials.

Fig. 29-5. Electrical metallic tubing being formed during installation.

he did, he was *separating* materials. Did the producer have to mix materials together? If so, he was *combining* materials. Did he have to bend the materials? If this is true, he was *forming* the materials. If you take a piece of paper in your hands, what can you do to change it? You can rip (separate) it into pieces. You can also pick up another piece of paper and staple the pieces together (combine). You can fold (form) the paper. Therefore, you can change materials by: (1) *separating* (taking away from the materials), Fig. 29-3; (2) *combining* (adding to the materials), Fig. 29-4; or (3) *forming* (changing the arrangement of the materials), Fig. 29-5.

Often these operations are used in combination. For example, in building forms for concrete, the materials are cut to length (separated), then fastened together (combined), and may be bent to form a rounded shape (formed), Fig. 29-5.

Postprocessing

The life of a product does not end with its processing. Many times a new part has to be installed. Almost always it has to be maintained. Sometimes the product must be repaired, and sometimes it has to be altered. All of the practices of installing, maintaining, repairing, or altering are done after processing. These practices are called *postprocessing*. More commonly, they are called *servicing*.

The servicing of a home is a good example of postprocessing practices. A home has to be maintained in many ways by: (1) periodically washing the windows; (2) mowing the lawn, Fig. 29-6; (3) waxing the floors; (4) repairing parts of the home; or (5) by adding a television antenna or a room. The skill and knowledge needed for postprocessing are much the same as those needed for processing. There is little difference between putting in a window pane the first time the home is built and replacing it a second time. This is also true for adding on a room.

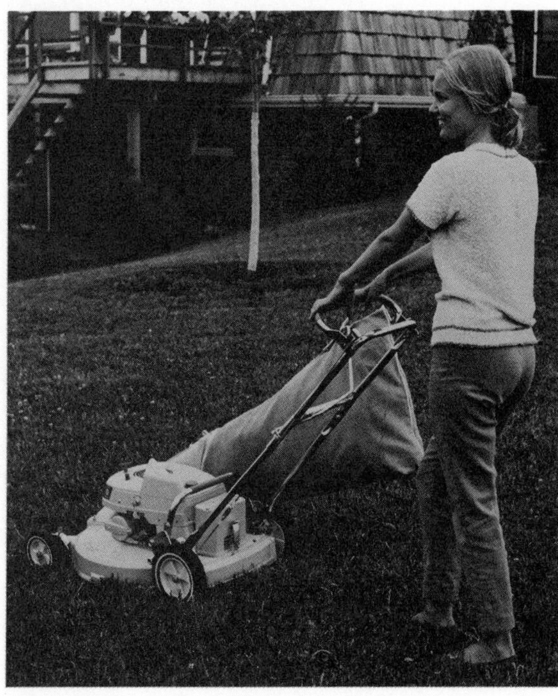

Fig. 29-6. A lawn must be maintained by periodic mowing.

The same practices are used for doing this as were used to build the original structure.

You will recall that manufacturing is done in a plant which is away from the construction site. The product is then taken to the place where it will be used, Fig. 29-7. *Construction* is built and used in the same place. *Construction may even be defined as the assembling of raw materials and manufactured products on a site.* Construction production and manufacturing production are similar in that both involve preprocessing, processing, and postprocessing. However, they do differ in the ways these activities are carried out. For example, earthmoving is a production practice of construction but not of manufacturing. Can you think of other examples? See Figs. 29-8 and 29-9.

The Construction Story

In the construction of any item, there is a series of steps to be followed. During the next few weeks you will be studying and developing skills in the order in which they are used.

Fig. 29-7. Timber has been changed into lumber which is used in making laminated wooden beams.

You should remember that all construction practices follow the same general procedure:

1. The site must be prepared.
2. The foundation is set.
3. The superstructure is built.
4. The plumbing, heating, and air conditioning are installed.

Fig. 29-8. This equipment is manufactured but is used in construction.

Fig. 29-9. Which of the items in this picture are constructed and which are manufactured?

5. The superstructure is enclosed.
6. The surfaces are finished.
7. The grounds are landscaped.

1. **Preparing the site.** To prepare the site, it has to be cleared of all unwanted objects, Fig. 29-10. After the site has been cleared, and sometimes during the time the site is being cleared, *temporary shelters* are built and *temporary utilities* such as water and electricity are installed. Once the site has been cleared and the temporary facilities have been set up, the site is surveyed to locate where the structure will be. *Earthmoving* is the last step in site preparation, Fig. 29-11.
2. **Setting the foundation.** After the site has been prepared, the foundations or *substructures* (part below ground) are set, Fig. 29-12. Substructures are the bearing surfaces, footings, foundation walls, or piers.
3. **Building superstructures.** When the substructures are completed, superstructures (part above ground) are built. Superstructures rest upon the substructures. The skeleton of a superstructure is set up first.
4. **Installing utilities.** Then plumbing, wiring, heating, and cooling systems are installed.
5. **Enclosing the superstructure.** If the structure is a building, the superstructure must then be enclosed. This is usually done by attaching panels of wood, steel, or glass to the skeleton or by enclosing the framing with brick or stone.
6. **Finishing the surfaces.** Next, the surfaces of the structure which need it are finished. This is the attaching of the final surface coatings and trim, and painting and decorating.
7. **Landscaping the site.** Finally, temporary facilities are removed, and the landscaping is completed, Fig. 29-13.

After the constructed product is completed, provisions are made for servicing it. That is, the practices used in constructing

Fig. 29-10. This equipment is preparing the site by removing unnecessary buildings.

Fig. 29-11. This equipment is used to remove earth in site preparation.

Fig. 29-12. This is a substructure showing the foundation wall.

may be used again, when necessary, to keep the structure in good condition. Understanding this general procedure in construction will make it possible for you to understand each construction practice regardless of whether the product is a building, a highway, or a dam.

Summary

Industry changes the form of materials by: (1) combining, (2) forming, and (3) separating them. The knowledge of how to work these changes is called *industrial production technology*. In actual construction and manufacturing, production technology often requires using combinations of these three major ways of changing the form of materials to complete common tasks.

Production often requires combinations of combining, forming, and separating materials in preprocessing (getting ready to produce), processing (producing the materials), and postprocessing (using the materials and servicing them). For the next several weeks, you will be studying and using construction production technology according to the general sequence (order) which is followed in the construction industry.

Fig. 29-13. These men are landscaping a site.

Terms to Know

production
industrial
  production
  technology
construction
  production
  technology
raw materials
preprocessing
  a. receiving
  b. handling
  c. storing
  d. protecting
processing
  a. separating
  b. combining
  c. forming
postprocessing
  a. installing
  b. maintaining
  c. repairing
  d. altering
temporary shelters
temporary utilities
excavated
substructure
superstructure

Think About It!

1. Even before a structure is begun, materials start *arriving* at the construction site. Other materials arrive later.
   a. What kinds of *preprocessing* do these materials go through?
   b. Why does a contractor *not* want all the materials delivered to the site at one time?
2. *Changing* the materials in a factory or at a construction site is called *processing*. Name some materials that are *processed* by:
   a. *Separating* (making smaller pieces from a large piece or taking some away from a piece).
   b. *Combining* (putting together two pieces of the same material or putting one material with another).
   c. *Forming* (changing the shape without adding anything or taking anything away).

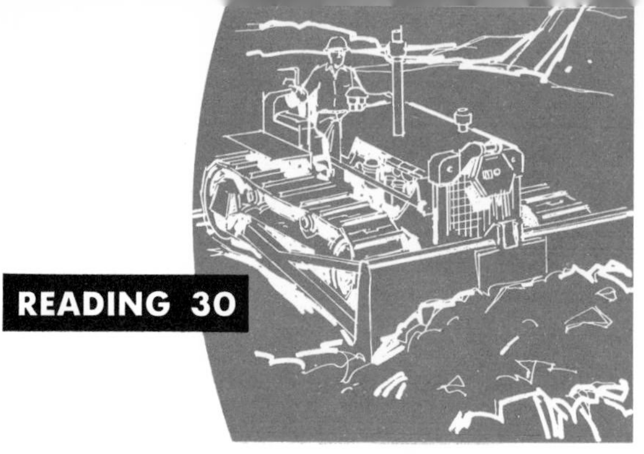

READING 30

Getting Ready to Build

Once the contract is given to the contractor, he must plan to move men, materials, and equipment to the site. This lesson tells about the different steps taken to get the project started on the site.

Following Laws

In most construction areas, there are many laws that a contractor must follow. It is important for him to know these laws before he begins to plan the project. He must follow the laws carefully from the beginning to the end of the project. These laws may be national, state, county, township, or city laws.

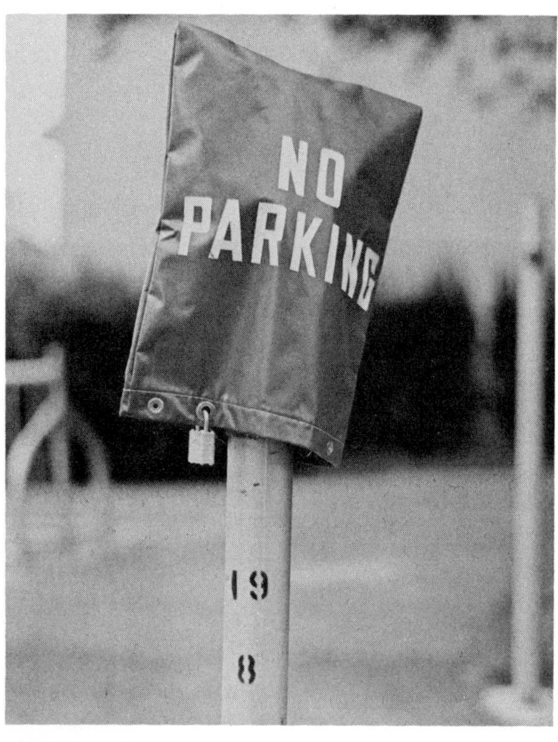

Fig. 30-1. A "No Parking" meter bag is placed over a meter near or at the construction site so that the space can be used for loading and unloading materials.

An example of national laws is one which requires all employers to keep many records on their business operations and on their employees. State projects must follow state laws. For example, states may have laws which say who can and cannot qualify as an engineer, architect, or contractor.

Cities and townships have many regulations and laws that apply to anyone constructing in their areas. For example, often there are *zoning laws* which limit what can be built in each area of the city. The major city zones are: (1) single family housing, (2) multiple family housing (apartment building), (3) general shopping areas, (4) commercial areas, (5) light industrial areas, and (6) heavy industrial areas. Some areas also have added restrictions such as: (1) minimum size of lot, (2) maximum size of building unit per lot, (3) maximum height of building, and (4) minimum floor space.

To make sure that each project follows the laws for a certain site, city laws often require that a *building permit* (license) be obtained for any project costing over $250. This permit must be posted in a place on the site for authorities and the public to see. A building permit is even needed for making additions or alterations to existing projects.

Sometimes large and heavy equipment must be moved to a site. Special plans have to be made with the highway departments or police so that the equipment may travel on the roads. Many streets and highways are limited to certain loads. Only under special agreement is the contractor allowed to move heavy equipment over these.

Many of you may have seen brown bags covering parking meters at construction sites in cities, Fig. 30-1. Local police have given permission for the contractor to use these spaces to unload or load materials at the construction site. This permit must be clearly displayed in the contractor's office.

Keeping Safe and Protected

In all phases of construction, safety and protection are very important. There must be safety and protection of: (1) the general public, Fig. 30-2; (2) workers, Fig. 30-3; (3) property close to the site; (4) the site itself, Fig. 30-4; and (5) equipment and materials. This responsibility is not taken lightly by a contractor. Most contractors have insurance against accidents and other problems which may come about on a construction site. However, they still must rely on their good judgment in seeing that they and their subcontractors take all possible steps to avoid accidents or other safety problems.

The best site, as far as protection is concerned, is a place which is cut off from the outside. At any site there is always the

Fig. 30-2. Pedestrians are protected from falling material by a sidewalk canopy.

Fig. 30-3. A construction worker wears a helmet for protection.

Fig. 30-4. Wire mesh fence is used to control trespassing on the site.

danger of having material and equipment stolen. To keep this from happening and to better control the entry and exit of materials, equipment, and workers to and from the area, walls or fences are put around the site and traffic may move only through certain gates. Then a count can be kept of what goes in or leaves the site. Also, unwanted visitors can be kept from entering the site. At certain sites where workers must wear protective clothing, eye glasses, or helmets, the safety materials can be checked at the gates.

Protecting neighboring property is very important in any project. When structures or valuable natural growth are on property next to the site, steps must be taken so that the project works will not harm them. If digging exposes neighboring walls or soil, they must be protected by shoring or bracing to keep them from sagging or collapsing. If there is any damage to the property around the project, such as the breaking of curbs or sidewalks, this is repaired by the contractor.

Getting to the Site

In most cities, existing streets are used to get to the site. In rural areas, the contractor sometimes must build his own roads to get to the site.

Within the project, sometimes walkways, usually made of wood, are built for the workers and visitors to use. They help because almost all sites are bare earth. Since sites are not protected from rain, persons must walk through mud to their jobs unless these walkways are made.

Providing Temporary Facilities

Depending on the size and kind of a new project, shelters may be made on the site for: (1) construction materials, (2) equipment, (3) offices, (4) sanitary facilities, (5) laboratories, (6) maintenance shops, and (7) many other things. These temporary facilities are required at the sites for large bridges, dams, airports, defense installations, and other projects which take months to build. See Fig. 30-5.

Weather can cause serious problems in any construction project. Protecting workers, materials, and equipment from weather is a must. At most sites, temporary, overhead shelters are built. To protect equipment and materials, tents, canvas, or plastic covers often are used.

Fig. 30-5. The arrows point to shelters used on a construction site.

Fig. 30-6. A truck trailer is used for storing and protecting material.

In most projects of any size, each trade group (heating and ventilating workers, plumbers, electricians, steel workers, carpenters) needs its own office and storage areas. Many of the shelters, especially those for offices, are *prefabricated* (built in sections) and put together at the site. Trailers are very popular because they can be easily taken from site to site. Trailers often house the tools and equipment needed by the different craftsmen. They are brought to the site and put out of the way of the work going on. Then they are jacked up and blocked in place, Fig. 30-6.

The contractor may use a trailer for offices for his superintendents, foremen, engineers, or the supervising architect. The timekeepers and the storekeepers also need places where they can work, Fig. 30-7.

Temporary shelters must all be planned. In cases where the project is in the middle of a city and construction takes most of the site space, the local government or police may be asked to give permits so that parts of the street may be blocked for storage and office space. Where there is little space, some of the craftsmen will not come to the job until the foundations and the basement or first floor are partly completed. They may then use these areas for offices and storage.

Fig. 30-7. A house trailer is used as an office on a construction site.

Providing Utilities

Electricity is needed not only for lights but also to run pumps and shop equipment. To get the needed electricity, power lines are brought into the site, or a generating plant is set up on the site. Usually, power lines are close to any construction area.

Telephones or radios are a must at all projects of any size. These are put at a central location. Portable, two-way radios are a great help on projects. The foreman, the superintendent, project engineers, and the offices can all be connected by radio. Even workers directing heavy equipment can do this by two-way radio, Fig. 30-9.

Water is needed at any project. It is used for sanitation, construction work, and drinking. It is needed for fire protection, mixing, cleaning, water-cooled equipment, and for many other things. Water lines can be brought to the site from nearby water mains. When these are not near, water tanks on trucks can be used. In many remote areas, pumping stations are placed near rivers or lakes to bring water to the project. In other cases, water wells are dug close to the site. When the contractor gets

Fig. 30-8. Utilities and fresh air are needed so that people can work in this tunnel.

drinking water directly from the wells, rivers or lakes, he must use special filters and chemicals to remove impurities.

Summary

In most construction areas, there are many laws that a contractor must follow from the time he moves to the site until the project is finished. These include national, state, county, township, or city laws. Also, in all phases of construction, there must be safety and protection of: (1) the general public, (2) workers, (3) property close to the site, (4) the site itself, and (5) equipment and materials.

Often temporary facilities and utilities are needed at construction sites. These include offices, storage space, electricity, telephones or radios, and water to name a few. Laws, safety and protection, facilities, and utilities must always be considered when getting ready to build.

The next lesson tells about clearing the site before construction begins.

Terms to Know

zoning laws
maximum
minimum
building permit
qualify
trespassing
shoring
temporary facilities
temporary utilities
prefabricated
communication
sanitation

Think About It!

1. *Zoning laws* place *limits* on construction in each area of a city.
   a. Name the major *kinds of zones.*
   b. Describe some other *restrictions* or limits that may apply in some areas.
2. Safety and protection are very important in construction.
   a. At a construction site what and who must be *protected*?
   b. What dangers must they be protected from?
   c. Describe some ways in which the contractor provides for safety.

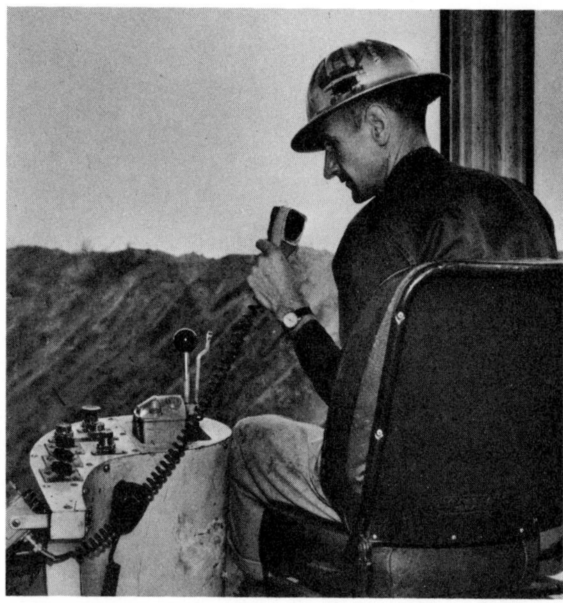

Fig. 30-9. A two-way radio is used for communication in layout work.

Getting Ready To Build

- **Following Laws**
  - Permits
  - Zoning regulations
- **Protecting**
  - Public
  - Workers
  - Adjacent property
  - Building site
  - Equipment and materials
- **Getting to the Site**
  - Roads
  - Walkways
- **Providing Temporary Facilities**
  - Materials
  - Equipment
  - Offices
  - Sanitation
  - Laboratories
  - Maintenance
- **Providing Temporary Utilities**
  - Electrical power
  - Communications
  - Water

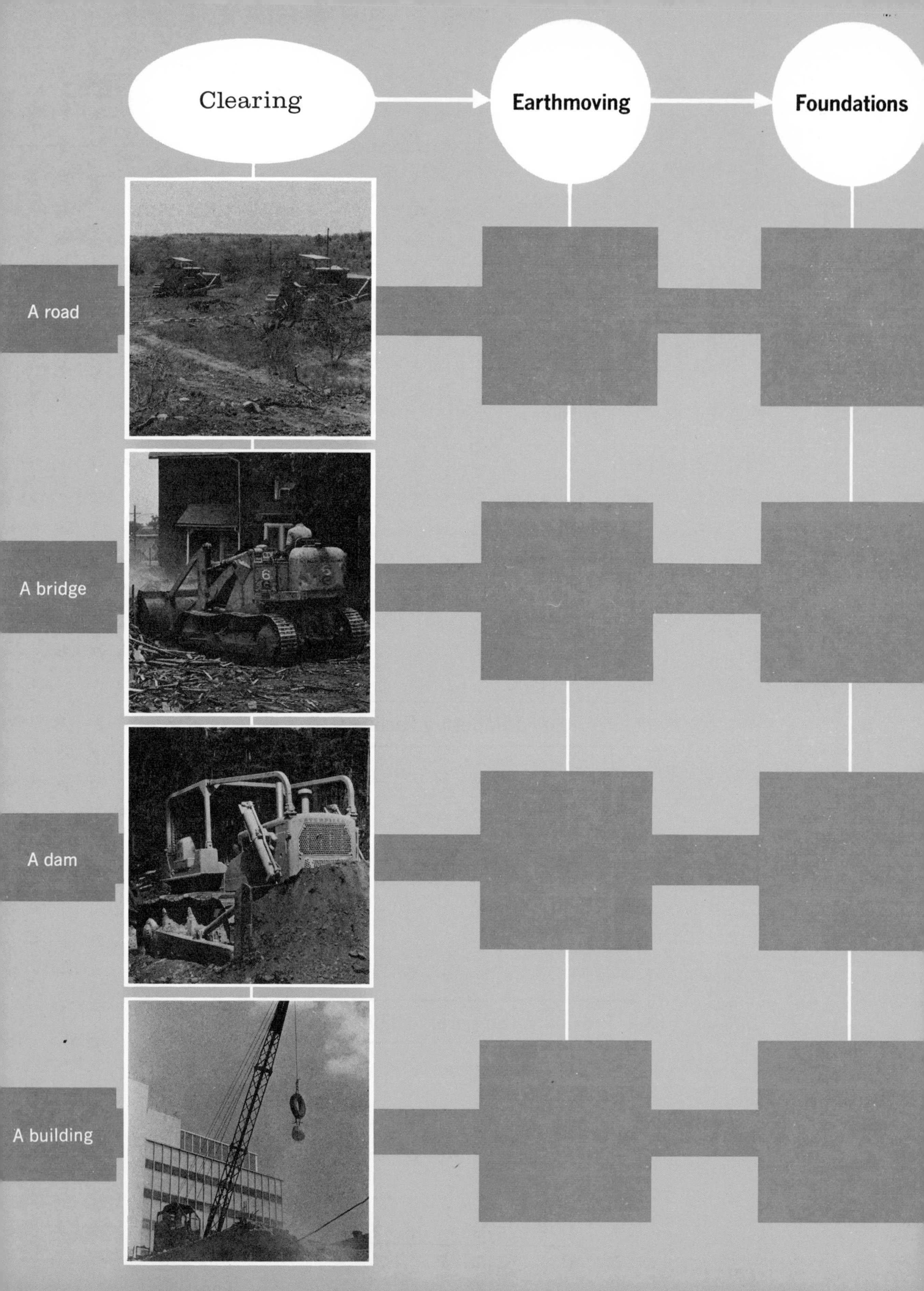
Clearing
Earthmoving
Foundations
A road
A bridge
A dam
A building

Superstructures
Utilities
Finished Project

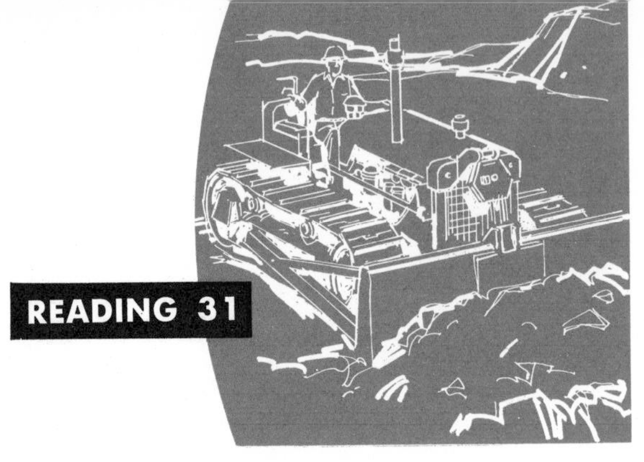

READING 31

Clearing the Site

This lesson tells how a site is prepared and cleared. You will learn some of the terms, problems, and equipment used for preparing and clearing operations.

Site Factors

Site factors (things about the site) are important to those who prepare and clear the site. The size of the site, the amount of natural growth, man-made and natural obstacles (Fig. 31-1), the location of the site, and what is around the site are examples of important site factors.

What site clearing practices are used depend upon the problems found on a particular site. The contractor must know all about the site and about site clearing practices.

The most common site clearing practices are: (1) demolishing, (2) salvaging, (3) cutting, (4) burning, (5) earthmoving, and (6) disposing. We will look at examples of these operations.

Fig. 31-1. Only small equipment is used to clear the man-made obstacles from this site. The workers are using air-powered breakers.

Demolishing

Demolishing means destroying. If we demolish by using high explosives, we call this operation *blasting,* Fig. 31-2. When bulldozers or wrecking balls are used, it is called *wrecking,* Fig. 31-3.

Using *explosives* has become popular for small projects in recent years. The development of safe, *plastic explosives* during World War II brought about a change in the use of blasting techniques. When high chimneys are demolished, properly placed

Fig. 31-2. Blasting, one method of clearing a site, is exciting to watch.

explosives will bring the chimney down into a fairly neat pile of rubble. Plastic explosives are now used for clearing stumps and trees and for breaking up boulders, Fig. 31-4. Experiments with high explosives, even nuclear devices, have been made to make channels for rivers or gravity irrigation systems. Blasting can be used both to create and to destroy.

Fig. 31-3. A wrecking ball is used to demolish this building.

Wrecking can be done with many mechanical devices. A *crowbar* is a hand tool which is often used by men in the wrecking field. A *crawler tractor* with a bulldozer blade is often used. For tall structures, a *crane with a wrecking ball* is used. This heavy steel or metal ball hung on the end of a cable is swung as a *battering ram* against the structure to be wrecked.

Salvaging

There are many times that the things on a site have some value and should be saved for use on another project. Saving things from being demolished (destroyed) is called *salvaging*. This can be done by tearing down, taking apart, or removing the wanted material from the site. When a building is to be demolished, most electrical switchboards, plumbing fixtures, doors, and windows are salvaged. See Fig. 31-5.

Fig. 31-4. Plastic explosives can be easily and safely loaded into a bore hole.

Fig. 31-5. After this disaster, efforts will be made to salvage parts of this house.

Cutting

Cutting has many uses. In wooded areas, cutting means bringing down timber by using axes, explosives, or saws. Cutting also can be done with a torch to cut through pieces of metal. For example, old steel towers or bridges are cut in this way.

Special equipment can be used, Fig. 31-6, when areas are cleared where there is not much timber or brush. Crawler tractors with bulldozer blades can push over trees up to 18″ to 20″ in diameter. When trees are not too large, two crawler tractors with a heavy steel cable connecting the two can be used. Usually a heavy steel ball is placed on the cable halfway between two tractors. The tractors, along parallel lines, pull the cable and the ball. The ball keeps the cable down close to the ground and tramples the small trees. The cable slices through the brush and pushes over small trees. See Figs. 31-7 and 31-8.

Burning

When wood cannot be used or vegetation has to be cleared, one of the best ways of destroying is by *burning*, Fig. 31-9. This

Fig. 31-6. This large area was best cleared by using a large crawler tractor with bulldozer blades.

Fig. 31-7. Heavy equipment using a chain drag to clear a site.

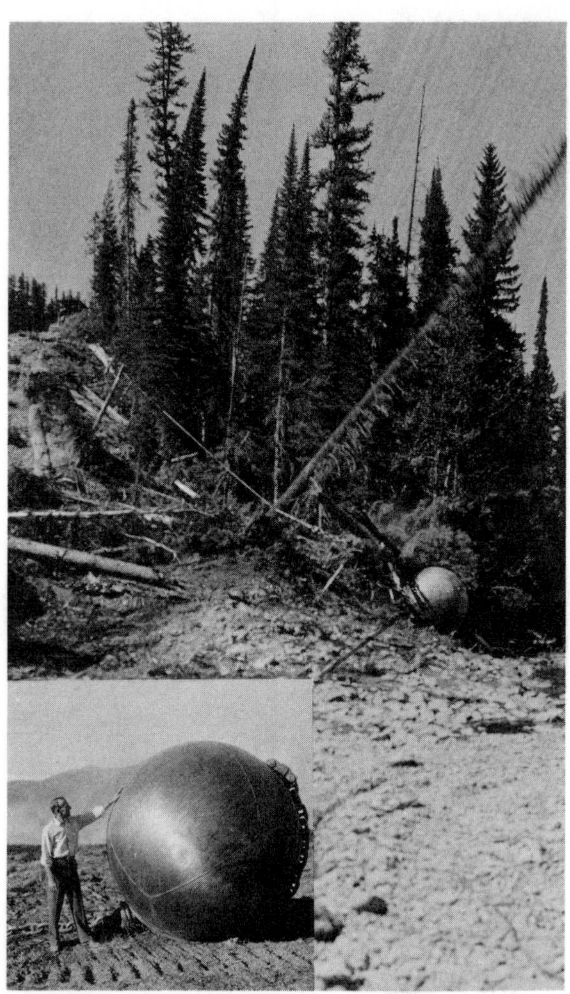

Fig. 31-8. Two crawler tractors are pulling a heavy ball and cable to clear the site.

can be done by setting a fire under controlled conditions. By using special fuels, vegetation—even when green—can be set on fire. Many times jungle sites are set on fire. After the fire has burned everything that it can, bulldozers are used to clean up the site.

Earthmoving

Earthmoving is used in clearing many sites. In addition, earthmoving may be a major part of the construction work on heavy construction projects such as highways, tunnels, and earthen dams. Earthmoving will be studied in a future assignment which is all about earthmoving practices.

Disposing

Disposing means removing from the site materials that are not wanted. Disposing may be done by burying, burning, or hauling away.

Examples of Preparing and Clearing

An important point to remember is that often more than one of the major operations is used to prepare and clear any one site. Sometimes there are also special problems. The following examples will give you a better understanding of the many things involved in preparing and clearing.

Some projects require that the land itself be changed. When a large dam is to be built, part of the preparation of the site might be to change the river flow from the area where the dam is going to be built. This, in itself, is a major engineering project, Fig. 31-10. This means that new channels or tunnels must be dug so that the flow of the river water can *bypass* the site of the dam. Other times, only a small change needs to be made. If a factory needs more space, the site preparation might mean only clearing out the parking lot next to the factory for a construction site.

In some cases, structures that are already there might have to be removed to make space for the new, Fig. 31-11. In urban or city areas this often must be done

Fig. 31-9. Clearing a site can be done by burning materials that have been removed.

Fig. 31-10. To build this dam, the flow of the river must be changed.

when older buildings are on the sites where a new project must be built.

There have been occasional newspaper reports of contractors who began to clear a site and, by mistake, brought down or started to bring down the wrong building. To avoid this, proper engineering preparation must be made so that everyone knows exactly where the site is, what work is to be done, and where it must be done.

To show the many kinds of sites used, we might talk about the modern approach to the erection of transmission line towers at hard-to-reach sites. By using helicopters, men and materials are brought to the site where the towers are to be built. The area is cleared to the shape needed for each tower. The towers are built using helicopters as cranes, Fig. 31-12. Once the towers are finished, helicopters help to string the wire between them. Preparing the site, in this case, is nothing more than clearing an area to build the tower.

At some sites high water level is a problem. In order to have solid ground on which to work, the water level must be lowered

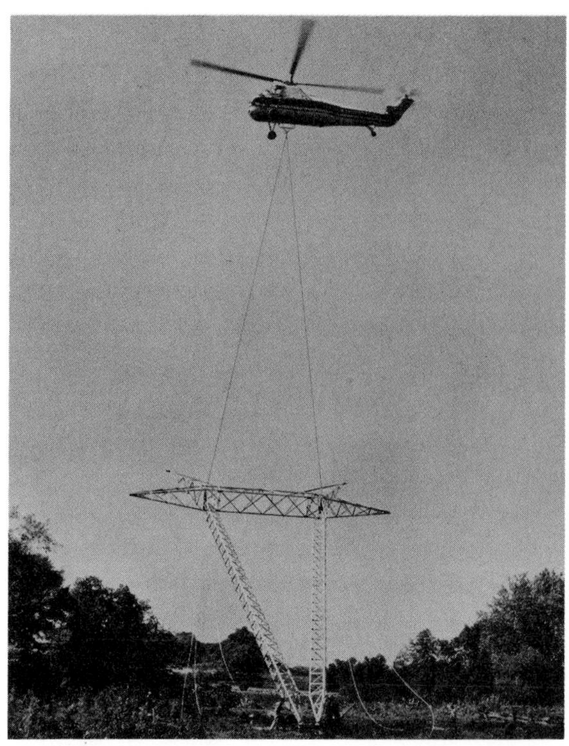

Fig. 31-12. A helicopter is used to transport sections of a metal tower to a site that is hard to reach.

Fig. 31-11. A structure being moved from its old site to a new site.

Fig. 31-13. A cofferdam is used to keep water from the construction site.

by pumping or draining the water to a place where the level is lower.

There are special problems when working in water. Man is not well suited for working under water. Therefore, if he is to work under water, a way must be found to help him. The most popular methods are to provide caissons or cofferdams. *Caissons* are large tubes which are placed through water to solid ground. When the caisson is emptied of water, this gives a dry place for working.

Cofferdams are a series of cells, or units, which sit on the bottom and are filled with soil and rock. These units are placed next to each other to make a wall around the site. The area within the cofferdam is then emptied of water to make a dry area. See Fig. 31-13.

Summary

You have learned in this lesson that many factors are important in preparing and clearing a site. The major operations most often used for clearing the site are: (1) demolishing, (2) salvaging, (3) cutting, (4) burning, (5) earthmoving, and (6) disposing. An important point to remember is that more than one of these operations often must be used to prepare and clear one site.

Terms to Know

- prepare the site
- site clearing operations
  - a. demolishing
    - (1) blasting
    - (2) wrecking
  - b. salvaging
  - c. cutting
  - d. burning
  - e. earthmoving
  - f. disposing
- vegetation
- obstacles
  - a. man-made obstacles
  - b. natural obstacles
- explosives
- plastic explosives
- bulldozer
- bypass
- caissons
- cofferdams

Think About It!

1. Give the name or location of one structure or building in your neighborhood or city that is in the process of being demolished.
2. Where are the unwanted materials from demolished structures in your community placed or disposed? Can some unwanted materials be burned in your community?
3. In your telephone directory find the names of two companies that are involved in practices of "clearing the site."

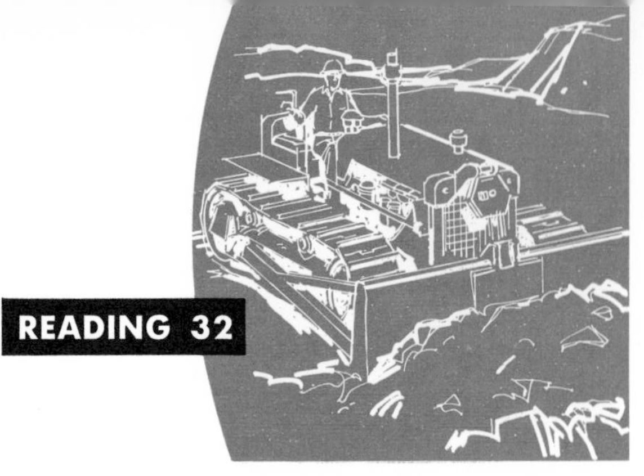

READING 32

Locating the Structure

Earlier in this course you studied how *surveying* and *mapping* practices are used to locate and describe a site. When it is time to begin construction work, surveying practices are used again, this time to locate the structure on the site. The importance of locating the structure and two major ways of doing it are discussed in this lesson. One set of practices is used for locating highways and things like airports. Other practices are used for locating structures such as houses, bridges, and concrete dams.

Importance of Surveying

Once the site has been cleared and temporary facilities have been set up, the workers must know the exact location and size of the structure to be built. The location has been shown on the drawings, but it must be *laid out* on the site. The *surveyor* is the man with the training and equipment needed to do this job. Through his training and experience, and with the help of measuring equipment, he can take dimensions from a set of plans and mark them on the site. See Fig. 32-1.

A surveyor uses a *measuring tape* and *transit* to measure *horizontal distances* and *angles,* Fig. 32-2. To measure *vertical distances,* he uses an engineer's level and a level rod, Fig. 32-3. With surveying equipment, the surveyor shows construction workers the exact location and size of the structure they are to build. The workers then are able to put materials in the right place to construct a building or a highway as it has been shown on the drawings. Even though most people do not see the direct results of the surveyor's work, his job is important and must be done carefully.

Surveying for Highways

The first and most important part of laying out a highway is to find the *correct direction.* The surveyor does this by finding existing highways, trees, survey stakes already set, or other landmarks on the plans. The plans show the exact location of the highway to be built in relation to these landmarks or features.

Fig. 32-1. A surveyor is sighting for a location or a measurement.

Once the surveyor has found these features, he uses them along with a transit and measuring tape to find the *center line* of the proposed highway, Fig. 32-4. Stakes are then set along the whole center line about 50′ to 100′ apart. The most important points along the center line are called *control points*. These usually show where two lines cross or where the center line turns. These control points are well marked with flags and stakes to keep construction equipment from running over or bumping them. All measurements are put in a notebook for future use. After the center line has been found, the surveyor measures horizontally from it to both sides and finds the edges of the pavement. The horizontal measurements needed for earthwork are then complete.

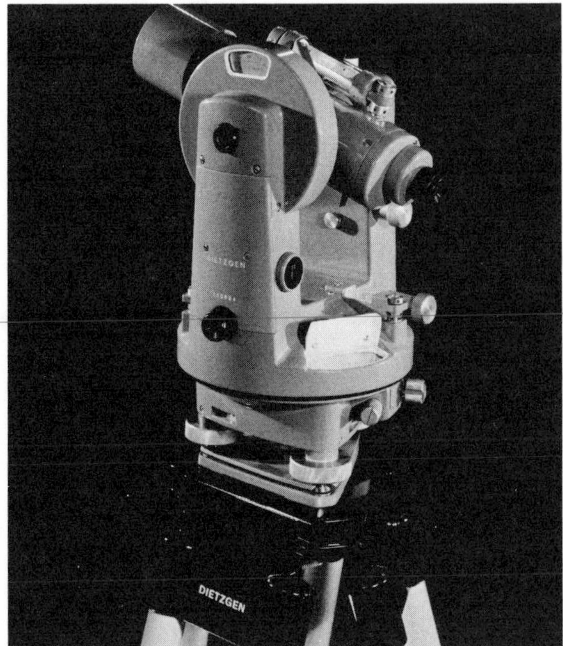

Fig. 32-2. The transit pictured here and a measuring tape are used to measure horizontal distances.

The vertical measurements must then be made. There are also control points for vertical measurements as there are for horizontal measurements. These are called *bench marks. Bench marks are points of known elevation or height above sea level.* The location of several bench marks is shown on the plan. The surveyor uses his level and rod to find the height of the ground at each of the center line stakes.

Then, by comparing the real elevations with those shown on the drawings, he can find how much cut or fill is needed to build according to the plans. The word *cut* means the amount of earth which must be cut away and removed to get the right elevation or height. The word *fill* means the earth which

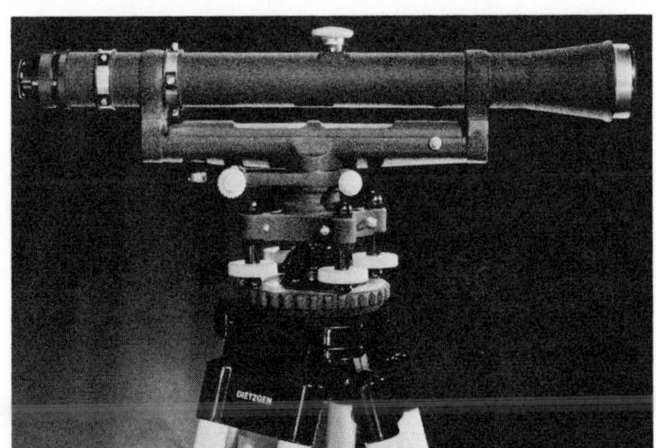

Fig. 32-3. This engineer's level and a level rod are used to measure vertical distances.

Fig. 32-4. The center line of a proposed superhighway is shown on this aerial photo.

must be filled in to get the right height. The surveyor marks the amount of the cut or fill needed on each center line stake. The construction workers will later follow the surveyor's marks when they *grade* the ground.

The surveyor then marks the amount of cut or fill on the stakes at each edge of the proposed pavement. The cut or fill should slope from these stakes to some point on the ground. See Figs. 32-5 and 32-6. Thus, stakes are also set at the place to where the cut or fill is to slope. These stakes are called *slope stakes* because they show the slope of the ground to be constructed. All vertical measurements are then put in a notebook for future use.

When the cut, fill, and other earthwork is done, the surveyor must put up new stakes for the workers to follow while they are constructing the *roadbed,* Fig. 32-7. This is done by beginning with the control points and setting stakes on each side of where the pavement should be. These stakes usually are set about 25′ to 50′ apart and 2′ outside the edge of the proposed pavement. The tops of the stakes are set at the height that the finished pavement will be. The level of pavement will be at the top of the stakes. Other workers will then lay the pavement by following the surveyor's stakes.

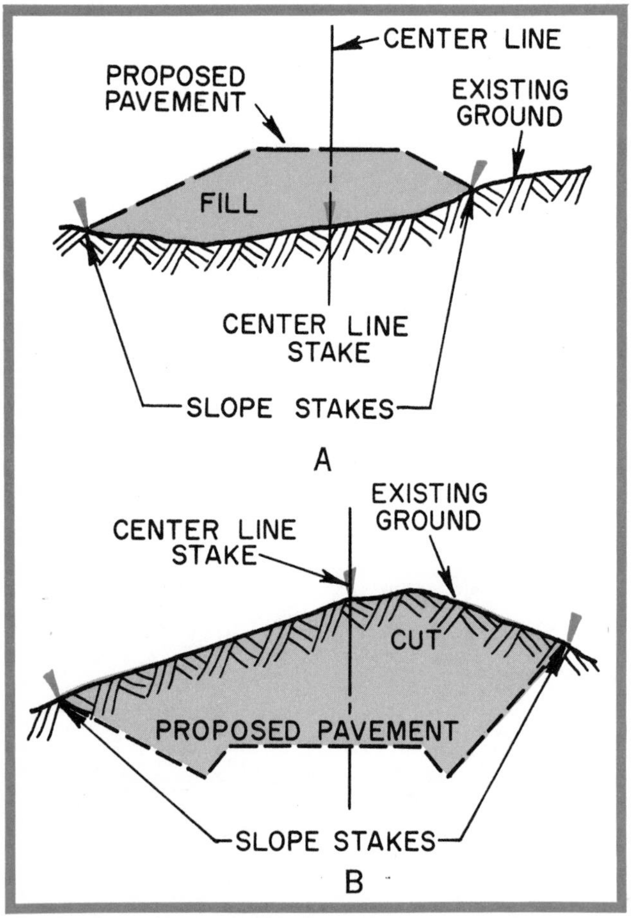

CENTER LINE
PROPOSED PAVEMENT
EXISTING GROUND
FILL
CENTER LINE STAKE
SLOPE STAKES
A
EXISTING GROUND
CENTER LINE STAKE
CUT
PROPOSED PAVEMENT
SLOPE STAKES
B

Fig. 32-5. Slope staking shows where the earth is to be removed or filled when the subsurface of the pavement is prepared.
A. These slope stakes show the area to be filled.
B. These slope stakes show the area to be removed.

Fig. 32-6. Stakes indicate the amount of fill or cut required for the grading.

Fig. 32-7. Heavy equipment is used in grading a roadbed.

All earthwork and highway projects are surveyed in much the same way. Slope stakes are used for the earthwork, and then more stakes are put in to outline the pavement or structure to be built.

Surveying for Buildings

Building plans generally show where the building will be in relation to the *property line* or some other feature, Fig. 32-8. After the surveyor has marked where the structure is to be on the site, he uses these markings to set *control points*. These are points from which to measure both horizontal and vertical distances. Control points are put any place where they will be safe from construction equipment.

The actual layout of the building is done by using *batter boards*. These are made of

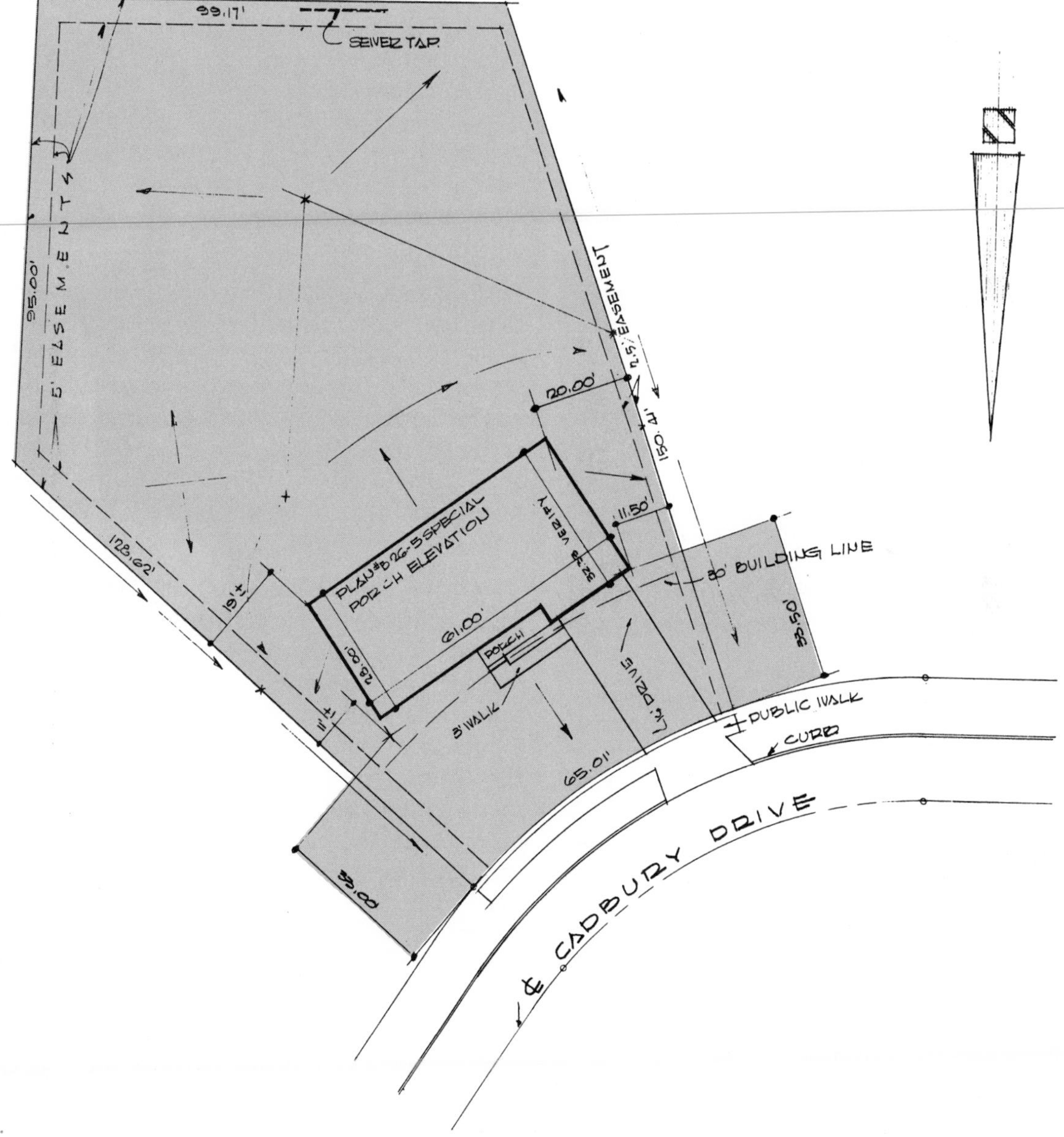

Fig. 32-8. The plot plan shows the relationship of the building to the property lines.

2″ × 4″ stakes driven part way into the ground. A board is fastened to the tops of these stakes. Then a nail is driven into the edge of this board, or a saw cut is made on the line that is being laid out.

To stake a wall of a building, the surveyor locates it on the drawings and then constructs batter boards beyond each end of the wall, Fig. 32-9. The batter boards are placed far enough past the ends of the walls to let construction equipment work without bumping the walls.

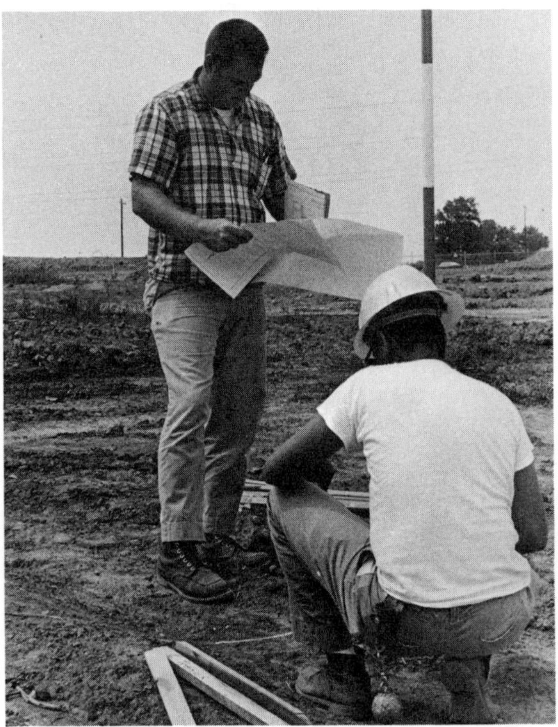

Fig. 32-9. Surveyors locate the walls of a building according to plans.

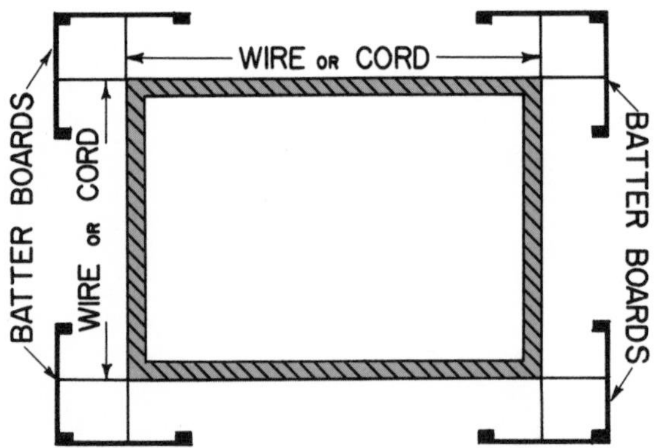

Fig. 32-10. The building layout locates the shape and size of the planned structure.

Nails are driven into each batter board or saw cuts are made where the exact line of the wall should be. Then construction workers stretch a wire or cord between the nails or saw cuts to find the wall line. The surveyor does this for each wall until *the building is located.* See Fig. 32-10. Corners are located by intersecting (crossing) wires. Other marks may be put on the batter boards to mark the wall line, the foundations, or columns. Sometimes separate batter boards are constructed to mark each line. Batter boards and the marks on them must always be clearly titled to avoid confusing one batter board mark for another.

Horizontal measurements and location have been described. Vertical measurements are also needed. Batter boards are usually set with the top board at a known elevation above the ground. A *plumb bob* then is hung from the wire which is stretched between the batter boards, Fig. 32-11. Vertical measurements can be made along the plumb line.

During the construction of large buildings, a surveyor looks through his transit to make sure that correct locations are maintained. The surveyor uses a level and rod to take vertical dimensions. He takes measurements from the plans and the bench mark to the actual building. The surveyor does this many times during construction, especially on multistoried buildings where it is important that each floor be the right height. He may also do this to check how much the structure has *settled* during or after construction.

Concrete dams, bridges, and many other structures are laid out in much the same way as that described for buildings. Often surveying records are kept so they can be used to check how much a project has settled or tilted.

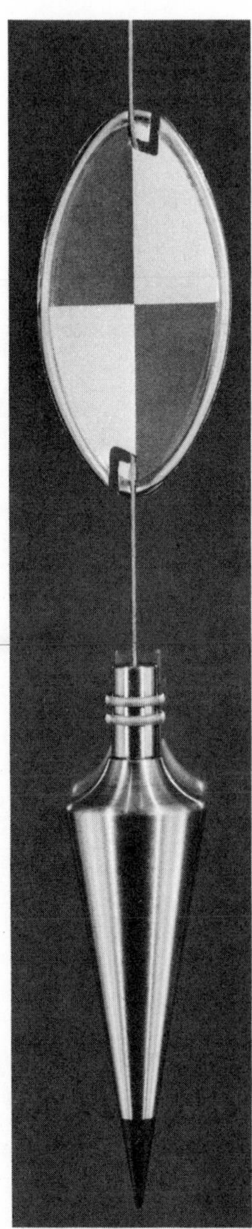

Fig. 32-11. The plumb bob is used to locate vertical points along the wire that forms the building layout.

Summary

Surveying is needed for locating structures on construction sites. This lesson has explained what equipment is needed for surveying and has described how surveying is done for highway and building construction.

Terms to Know

surveying
mapping
surveyor
lay out a site
transit
measuring tape
horizontal distances
vertical distances
engineer's level
level rod
center line
control points
bench mark
elevation
cut
fill
slope stakes
grade a roadbed
roadbed
property line
batter boards
locating a building
plumb
plumb bob
multistoried

Think About It!

1. What do you think would happen if a new home were incorrectly located and built on a portion of someone else's property? Ask your parents if they know of an example.
2. List at least three kinds of construction workers who would use surveying equipment to locate structures on a site.
3. Have you ever seen surveyors working? Could you tell why they were surveying?

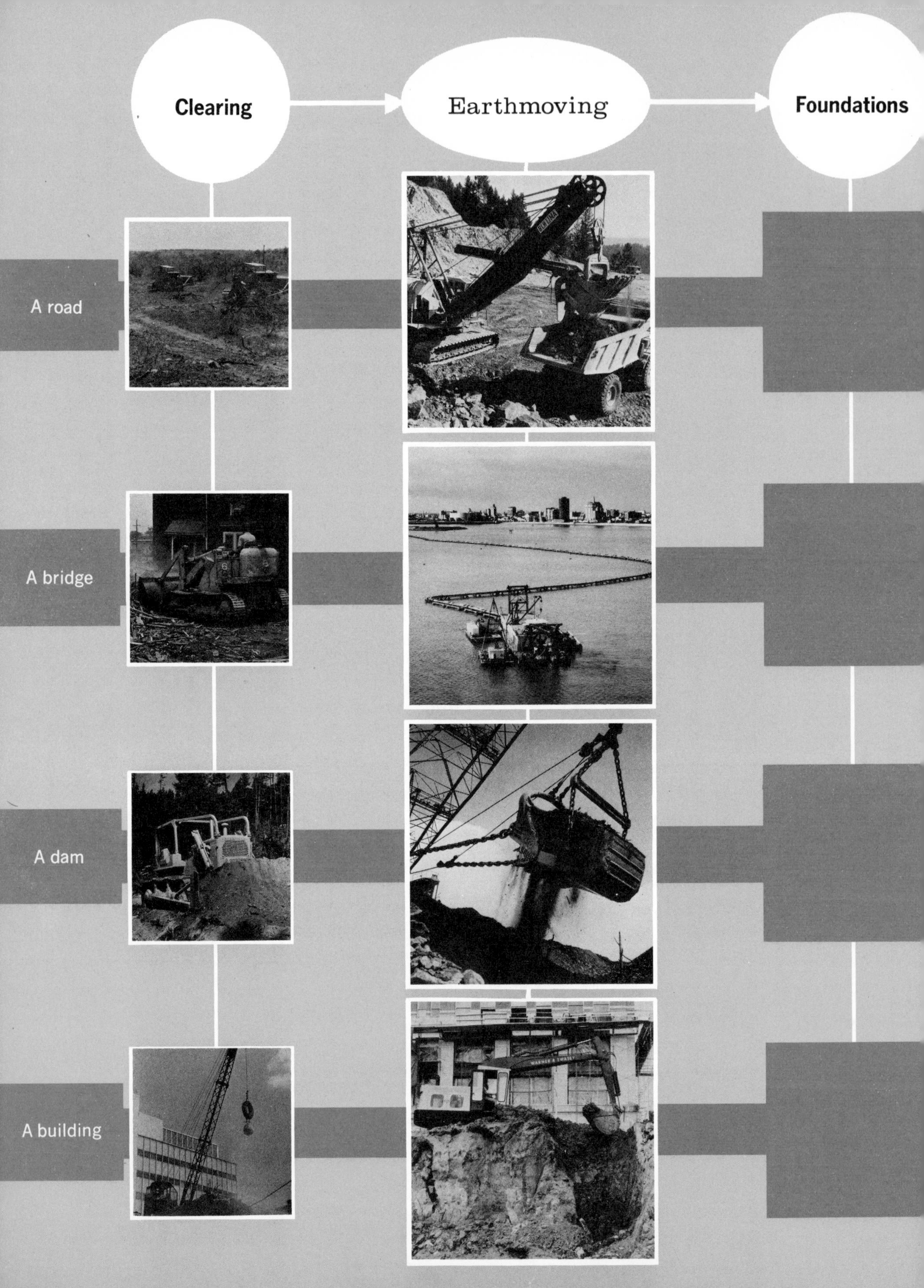

Clearing
Earthmoving
Foundations
A road
A bridge
A dam
A building

Superstructures
Utilities
Finished Project

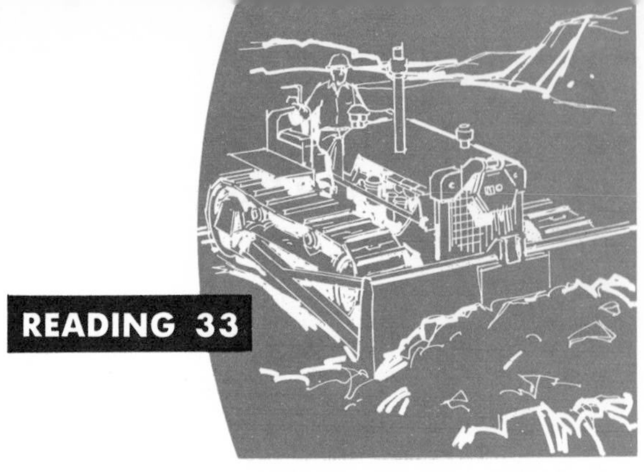

READING 33

Earthmoving

Moving earth, both soil and rock, has always been important to man. Early man was limited in what earthmoving he could do because he relied highly on his muscle. Now man has huge pieces of machinery for earthmoving. It is now possible to do more work than was ever dreamed of by our ancestors.

There are many kinds of earthmoving equipment. See Figs. 33-1 and 33-2. The types range from small farm tractors with earthmoving attachments to large shovels which, in only one *bite,* can carry enough material to fill one railroad car, Fig. 33-3. All this equipment is very expensive to operate and maintain. Much of it is very specialized. The contractor, in many cases, will have only some pieces of basic equipment. When a job calls for special machines, the contractor goes to a sub-contractor or a leasing or rental agency who has them. Charges for the rented machines are based upon the time the equipment is worked and how much it costs to bring the unit to the site and to return it.

Transporting Equipment

Some earthmoving equipment is self-propelled and can be driven to the site, Figs. 33-4 and 33-5. Other units must be hauled to the site on special flatbed trailer trucks. Still other equipment is towed to the site.

The transporting of earthmoving equipment may be complicated by many conditions: (1) the distance to the site, (2) the access routes to the site, (3) the height

Fig. 33-1. This power shovel is loading a truck that will haul earth to another site.

Fig. 33-2. This scraper is moving earth from one place to another.

and width of the equipment, (4) the speed and kind of wheels on the equipment, and (5) the total weight of the equipment. The limits of overhead utility lines, bridges, number of lanes of traffic, and other things to do with the road all have to be considered when moving equipment.

Setting Up Equipment

Before the equipment gets to the site, the contractor decides how he will use the machinery. All needed ramps, mats (which give support on soft soil), assembly areas, and parking aprons (used for servicing and storage) are made ready ahead of time. Once the equipment arrives, work is done very quickly.

Excavating

Earthmoving is usually done by excavating (digging) material in one area and transferring (moving) it to another place where it is either piled up, spread out, or used as fill material (*disposing*).

Fig. 33-4. This dragline and bucket can move large quantities of earth.

Fig. 33-3. Earthmoving equipment comes in many sizes, depending on the job that it has to do. Here just the bucket of a large machine can hold a piece of equipment that is taller than a man.

Fig. 33-5. This hydraulic excavator is self-propelled and can be driven from one job to another by its own power. Here it is placing pieces of rock to protect a river bank from being washed away.

Fig. 33-6. This is a clamshell loading a rock crusher.

Excavating is done (1) to reach a good base for a foundation, (2) to build basements, (3) to make cuts through hilly land for travel routes, and (4) to level uneven ground. Shovels (Fig. 33-1), scrapers (Fig. 33-2), draglines (Fig. 33-4), clamshells (Fig. 33-6), and hoes (Fig. 33-9) are some of the big machines used for this work. Tractors with special attachments, pumps, trenching machines and loaders, are some of the smaller units used.

Excavating is classified seven basic ways:

1. **Bulk pit excavating.** This is the digging up of a wide and deep area. The loose material must be hauled away from the site. Access to this excavation is very limited. An example would be a basement being dug for a downtown building which is between two existing buildings. See Fig. 33-7A.

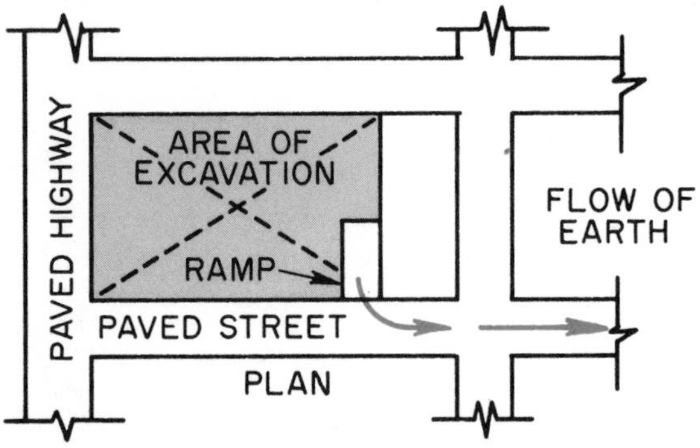

PAVED HIGHWAY
AREA OF EXCAVATION
RAMP
FLOW OF EARTH
PAVED STREET
PLAN

A. Typical bulk pit excavation.

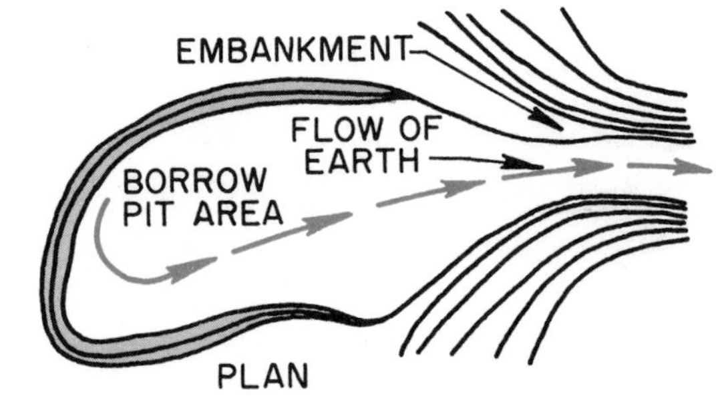

EMBANKMENT
FLOW OF EARTH
BORROW PIT AREA
PLAN

B. Typical bulk wide-area excavation.

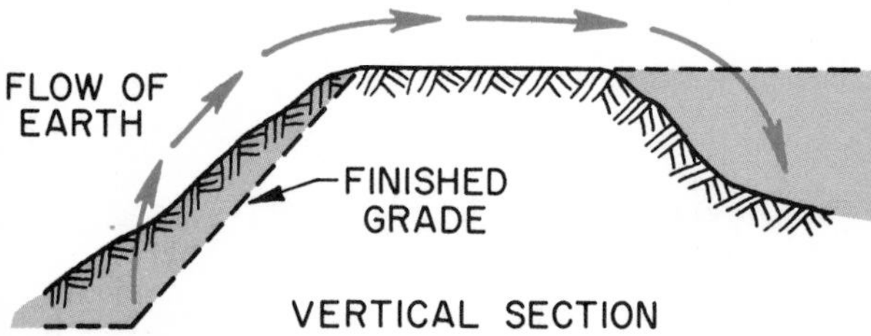

FLOW OF EARTH
FINISHED GRADE
VERTICAL SECTION

C. Typical loose bulk excavation.

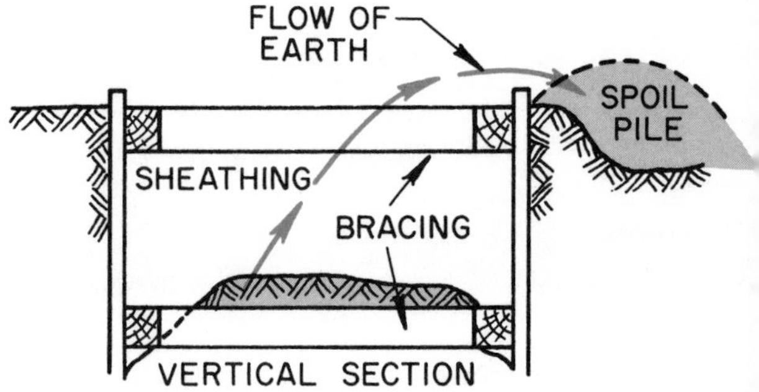

FLOW OF EARTH
SPOIL PILE
SHEATHING
BRACING
VERTICAL SECTION

D. Typical limited-area, vertical excavation.

Fig. 33-7. Four of seven excavation classifications.

2. **Bulk wide-area excavating.** These areas are wide but fairly shallow, and there is easy access to them. The process is mainly one of leveling. An example is the grading for a highway or an airfield. See Fig. 33-7B.
3. **Loose-bulk excavating.** The material is not hauled away, as in the above two, but it is piled into a new position. Wet clay is the type of matter that is moved. An example of this excavating practice is the way in which soil is moved in making dikes in order to form a pond. See Fig. 33-7C.
4. **Limited-area vertical excavating.** This kind of excavation is done mainly by digging vertically. It may be used to dig a basement. The sides of the excavation may be braced or shored. The material is lifted up and over the sides of the excavation. See Fig. 33-7D.
5. **Trenching.** In trenching, the excavation is long and narrow. The trench must be wide enough so that conduits, pipes, and other underground materials can be placed into it. The *spoil* (removed earth) is piled on the surface at the sides of the trench. It is used later to refill the trench. See Figs. 33-8 and 33-9.
6. **Dredging.** This kind of excavation deals with the removal of soil or other materials from under water. It is much the same as loose-bulk excavating. For example, this practice might be used in making harbors or river channels deeper.
7. **Tunnel excavating.** Tunneling is not usually considered under the heading of general excavation, because it is done completely underground. See Fig. 33-10.

Fig. 33-9. A backhoe is used to dig a trench.

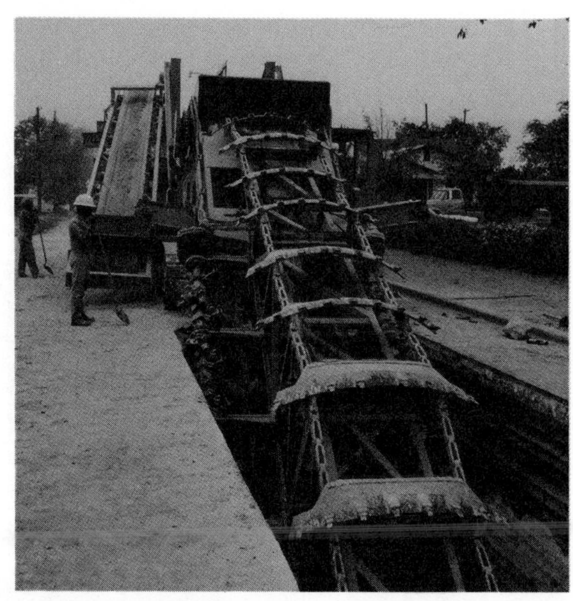

Fig. 33-8. A trencher is used to dig a deep, wide trench below the earth's surface.

Fig. 33-10. An earth auger is used to dig tunnels.

Sometimes tough or dense material must be loosened before it can be excavated. The most common techniques for loosening these materials are: (1) blasting, (2) breaking, (3) scarifying, and (4) ripping.

Blasting is done mostly to rock, Figs. 33-11 and 33-12. An explosion caused by high explosives placed as charges in special places in the material causes the rock to break into pieces.

Fig. 33-11. Rock is being loosened by blasting.

Breaking is the applying of strong blows to tear up hard materials. Air hammers are examples of breaking tools.

In both the *scarifying* and *ripping* process, much tough or dense material is loosened by running blades or teeth through it. This is like plowing. Scarifying is usually done in the upper 18″ of soil. Ripping is done by pulling one or two large teeth with a tractor to loosen material down to depths of 2′ to 3′. Ripping is used instead of blasting wherever ripping equipment can get to the area and where materials are not too hard. New advances in heavy equipment and ripper design are making the ripper very popular in the field. See Fig. 33-13.

Earth that is readily workable or which has been loosened is excavated. Then it is moved out of the way.

Transferring and Disposing

Excavated materials, called *spoil,* are transferred or moved from one place to another, Fig. 33-14. Then, they are disposed of. The spoil may be stored for reuse on the

Fig. 33-12. Blast holes are drilled where rock must be blasted away.

Fig. 33-13. This crawler tractor with ripper attachment loosens the earth.

site or for possible sale and later use on other sites. Spoil may be disposed of by using it for fill or top dressing. *Filling* is the leveling of low spots, while *top dressing* is the spreading of a thin coat over an area. Transferring and disposing are often done at about the same time, and some of the same equipment is used for both operations. See Fig. 33-15.

Transferring liquid waste such as water from a construction site takes different kinds of equipment and operations. Rain may cause problems such as the collapsing of walls and the filling of holes. Equipment may even get stuck in the mud. *Pumping* is a normal way to transfer water from the site. This allows work to continue. Portable *sump pumps*, which are operated by electrical or gasoline power, are easily lowered into the excavation. The water is pumped through lengths of piping to another location away from the working area or directly into storm sewers.

On some construction sites, spoil may only be pushed or moved out of the way of the workers. This is done when the materials are to be used again on the site or when it is to be sold, dumped, or spread. A contractor will sometimes have the spoil arranged in mounds, slopes, or hills around the construction site. Topsoil might be put on it and grass and shrubs might be planted in it to make it attractive, Fig. 33-16.

Spoil also may be used to raise the general level of the construction site. Again, in this case, the topsoil is saved separately and used as the top layer to make landscap-

Fig. 33-15. Spoil is being removed and loaded by a wheel-type excavator.

Fig. 33-14. Dump trucks are used to haul spoil from one place to another.

Fig. 33-16. Crawler tractors with dozer attachments push spoil from one place to another.

ing easier. Spoil may also be used to fill old gravel pits, washed out trenches in the land, and other holes.

Summary

It is often necessary to excavate certain materials so workers may prepare a foundation or install pipe lines or other underground works. Spoil or loose materials must be used on the site or be transferred to some other place.

The equipment and procedures used in excavating and relocating earth materials are similar regardless of the kind of construction. Often the only differences are in the power of the equipment and the number of man-hours needed to do the work.

Terms to Know

ancestors
self-propelled
transporting
flatbed truck
excavating
disposing
transferring
trading
loosening methods
  a. blasting
  b. breaking
  c. scarifying
  d. ripping
chain conveyor

types of excavating
  a. bulk pit
  b. bulk wide area
  c. loose bulk
  d. limited area vertical
  e. trenching
  f. tunneling
  g. dredging
fill
top dressing
pumping
sump pump
man-hour

Think About It!

1. Identify one place in your neighborhood where earthmoving is now going on. Why is it being done?
2. Why do earthmoving contractors like to have their equipment in use as many hours a day as possible?

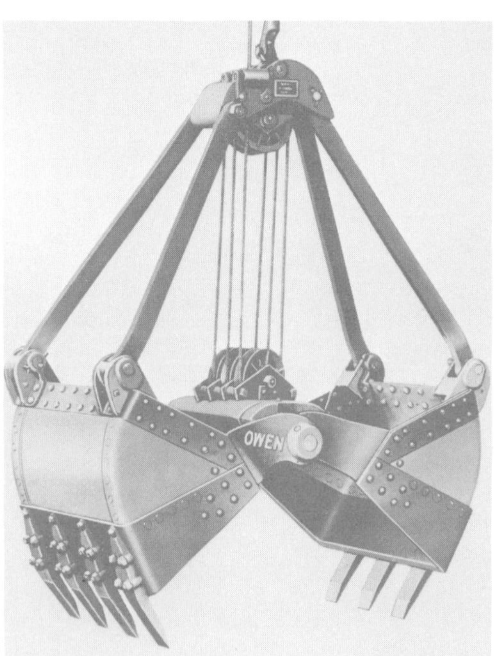

General purpose excavating clamshell.

Handling Grievances

READING 34

You have read that unions and employees negotiate a collective bargaining agreement. One of the important parts of this agreement is a statement of the rules for handling worker complaints which may come up while the agreement is in effect. These rules are called *grievance procedures.* In this lesson you will study: (1) what problems are covered by grievance procedures, (2) why grievance procedures are needed, (3) what grievance procedures are, and (4) the results of poor grievance procedures.

Problems Covered by Grievance Procedures

A person has a *grievance* when he believes that he is not getting the praise, rewards, working conditions, or satisfaction which he deserves. You could be said to have grievances about the way you were treated if, for example,

1. You ask your parents for permission to watch a television show about Abraham Lincoln, and they refuse, or
2. A baseball umpire declares you out when you feel you were safe.

In your own life, a collective bargaining agreement might be compared to the rules of baseball. Before you begin a neighborhood game, you decide on the bases, whether or not you will use an umpire, and which rules you will follow. After you begin the game, other problems may come up. These problems might not be solved through the rules. If your team disagrees with an umpire's ruling, then a discussion between the two teams and the umpire may be necessary. In this case, the discussion could be

Fig. 34-1. The referee in this game represents "management" and the players represent "labor."

Fig. 34-2. Men must be able to work together as a team in order to prevent trouble.

Fig. 34-3. These workers seem very pleased with their working conditions.

Fig. 34-4. In order to keep this job moving along, good working conditions must exist.

compared to the grievance procedure for labor.

For labor, there are two kinds of grievances that are handled by grievance procedures. There are: (1) grievances covered by the collective bargaining agreement and (2) grievances not covered in the collective bargaining agreement.

In general, workers may use grievance procedures for any complaint or grievance. Grievance procedures, however, are not useful for changing what has already been decided in a collective bargaining agreement. For example, if it is written in the collective bargaining agreement that construction laborers should receive $3.50 to $4.50 an hour, a construction laborer could not use grievance procedures to get a higher wage during the term of the agreement. However, he would have a grievance if he were asked to do a cement finisher's work and that salary was higher than that of his classified position.

Most grievances are about working conditions. *Working conditions affect the worker at his job.* The danger involved in a job, the way in which the tools and equipment are maintained, and the foreman's attitude toward his employees may all be thought of as working conditions, Figs. 34-3 and 34-4.

Why Grievance Procedures Are Needed

The grievance procedure is a way of handling problems before they lead to larger problems such as strikes and unhappy workers. Grievance procedures are a way for: (1) making it easy for people to talk to each other, (2) promoting understanding of the way other people feel, and (3) letting the workers know that their employer will listen to their complaints.

No matter how understanding an employer and worker try to be, problems still come up between them. The quickest and best way of preventing trouble is to make sure that the people involved know they can talk over a problem. In order to understand one another's feelings and problems, people must be able to talk with one another, Fig. 34-5. The understanding gained in this way may help solve small problems before they lead to big problems.

If a worker does not feel an employer will listen to a small grievance, he may begin to resent the employer and to believe that the employer cares nothing about his problems. If this situation continues over a long period of time, it may make it impossible for the employer and worker to work out a solution. The worker's resentment (unhappy feelings) about a small matter then may affect the way he feels about the employer, the way he hears what the employer says, how he feels about the business, and how he feels about his own job. When resentment becomes that big, it is hard to change it.

If, however, the worker knows that the employer will listen carefully to his grievance, then a small matter might be easily changed, and the worker will be able to continue on his job feeling good about it and his employer. The worker will know from past experience whether or not the grievance procedures work. If he knows that the grievance procedures have worked before, he will not be so quick to turn to strikes.

Fig. 34-5. A group consisting of labor and management is discussing problems at a contract bargaining session.

Grievance Procedures

Although grievance procedures are different in one part of the country than in another, there are some things that are important to any good grievance procedures. These are:

1. At any grievance discussion, there should always be representatives from both the union and management.
2. Grievance procedures should always begin with the lowest level of management, usually the foreman.
3. Progress should be orderly from one level of authority to the next until a satisfactory solution is found.
4. Management, at all levels, should have the authority to settle the matter without going any further. For example, suppose your teacher rules on a student grievance against school policy. It should be assumed that the ruling will be supported by the principal, superintendent, and board of education. At each level there should be enough authority to settle the issue without going any further.

A set of grievance procedure steps for a large company might be something like that shown in Table 34-1.

As you can see, the first level of the grievance process may be just a discussion between the worker and his foreman. Many times, however, a union representative or union steward takes part in this discussion. This first level is very important. The worker and the foreman are the two who are most directly concerned with the grievance. If they can solve the problem, many delays and difficulties may be avoided.

As the grievance goes on from level to level, misunderstanding of the original problem may occur. Therefore, *the grievance is put into writing to reduce possible misunderstanding of the original or first problem.* Sometimes this is not done at the first level, but it is almost always done after that. Grievances put into writing: (1) provide a record of the case, (2) allow people at each level to read what was said in the levels before, (3) help establish rules for future cases, (4) are more official, (5) cause employees to think carefully before raising an unimportant problem.

Sometimes the employer and the union cannot find a satisfactory solution to the grievance. It is then necessary to use *mediation* and in extreme cases, *arbitration.* Sometimes mediation or arbitration are written into the collective bargaining agreement as final steps in the process.

When mediation is used, a neutral outsider or group of outsiders is brought together with the representatives from the union and the employer. This outsider or group of outsiders may make comments which will help each side understand the other so that they can work out their own solution. *A mediator cannot enforce his decisions. An arbitrator studies the case and makes a ruling which he can enforce.*

Sometimes grievance procedures don't work. If this happens, both the union and management suffer. Poor grievance procedures may lead to unhappy employees. The workers may develop the attitude that they are working against the employer instead

Table 34-1

Grievance Procedure in a Large Company

Step	Worker's Representative	Employer's Representative	Procedure
1	Steward and employee	Foreman	These three parties will probably discuss the problem.
2	Chief steward or business agent	Foreman's supervisor	These two parties may discuss the problem and draw up a written statement of it.
3	Grievance committee	Local management head or representative of industrial relations department	These two parties will discuss the written statement and may draw up a more complete statement.
4	International union officer	National corporation executive	These two parties may attempt to solve the problem, and if no solution can be seen, they may begin steps toward having a neutral observer meet with the group.

	Neutral Party or Parties	
5	A mediator or arbitrator may be called in to hear the problem. Representatives with the most authority, from both labor and management, meet with the neutral party or parties.	They attempt to reach a final solution.

of with him. They may then produce a smaller quantity of work and work of poorer quality. As a result, the employer will not be able to get further contracts, and everyone loses.

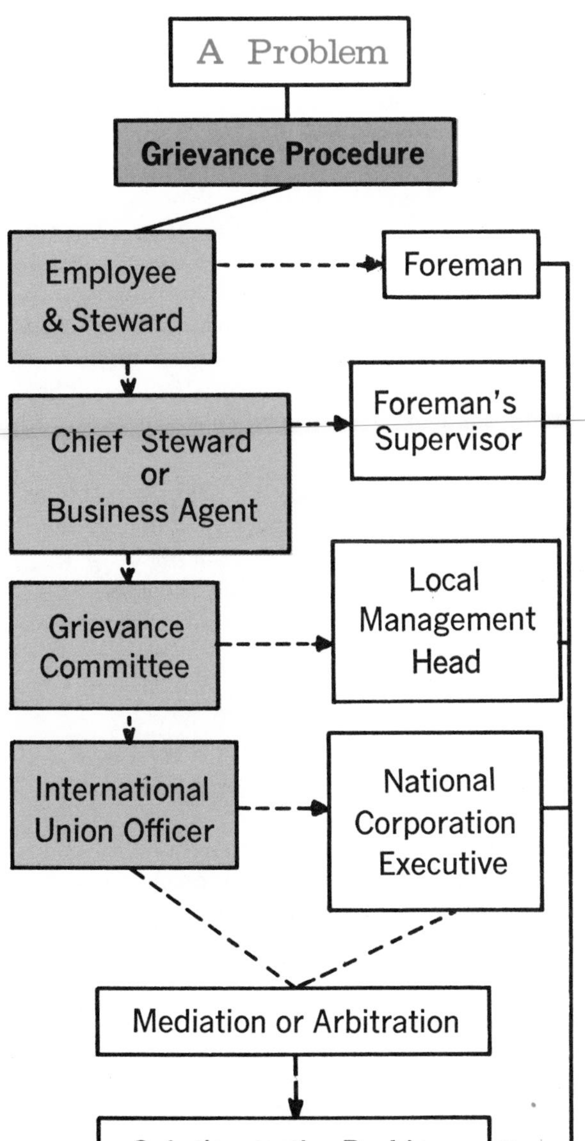

Summary

Grievance procedures are ways for handling worker complaints after the collective bargaining agreement is drawn up. They make it easy for the employer and the worker to talk things over. By working together, the worker and the employer attempt to solve their problems before they get serious. In the construction industry, it is only rarely that it is necessary to call in a neutral outsider to arbitrate or mediate. If the grievance process fails, strikes and unhappy workers and employers may be the result. This is harmful to both sides. Grievance procedures help to build happy relationships between workers and employers.

Terms to Know

grievance
grievance procedure
collective bargaining agreement
working conditions
mediation
arbitration
solution
casual

Think About It!

1. If you want to watch a particular television program, but your parents or brothers and sisters want to watch another, do you have a way (grievance procedure) of settling your differences? If so, what is it?
2. What might happen on a construction project if orderly procedures for handling complaints were not agreed upon before they occur?

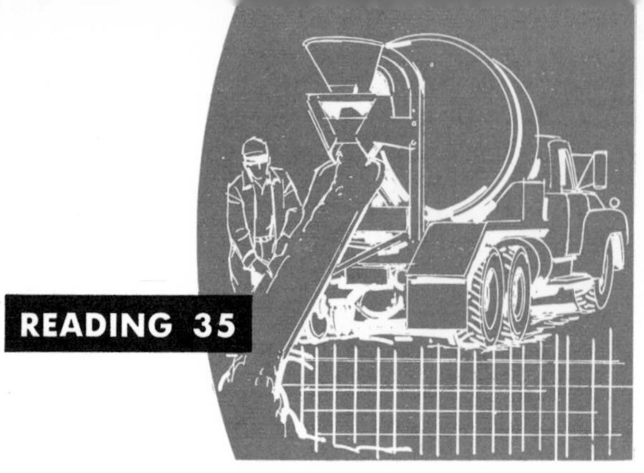

READING 35

Stabilizing Earth and Structures

Rough excavating may leave a crude trench or pit which is unfit for the foundation. It may also weaken the support of structures next to the excavation. *Trimming* and *stabilizing* the bed and walls of the excavation may then be necessary, Fig. 35-1. There are several ways in which trimming and stabilizing are done. In this lesson, you will read why trimming and stabilizing are needed, how they are done, how each works, and when each is done.

Reasons for Trimming and Stabilizing the Bed and Walls of the Excavation

Trimming is done to make the excavation ready for the foundation. Very often the rough excavating does not leave a proper place for the laying of the foundation. In such cases, more exact excavating is done in order to reach the planned bearing surface. Soil which has slid into the open pit from loose sides of the excavation must also be removed, Fig. 35-2. Sometimes the foundation is to be built on bedrock, crushed rock, or gravel. If the rock is covered with mud, this must be removed before there can be a good bond between the concrete of the foundation and the rock.

Fig. 35-1. Heavy equipment, called a "front-end loader," is used to trim and stabilize an excavation pit and to load the material on trucks.

It may be necessary to stabilize the excavation walls. *Stabilizing is done to make the walls hold their form and to keep them from falling in.* Stabilizing protects men, equipment, and structures in or near the excavated area.

Trimming and Shaping the Bed and Walls of the Excavation

There are four major practices used for trimming and shaping the excavation bed and walls: (1) cleaning and washing, (2) grading, (3) sloping, and (4) treating. Which process is to be used depends on such things as the condition of the soil, the kind of excavation, or the weather in the area where the work is to be done.

1. *Cleaning and washing* remove mud from base rock. This is done so there will be a good *bond* between the concrete of the foundation and the base of the excavation. This is done by high pressure water hosing which blasts the mud off the rock and then carries it away through a drainage system. When you wash mud off a sidewalk with a garden hose, you are doing much the same thing.

2. *Grading* makes the bed and walls of the excavation level and firm. It usually means cutting away high parts of the excavation and filling in uneven, low spots. Grading is done by: (1) compacting (packing), (2) grouting (filling with mortar), (3) scaling (scraping), or (4) filling (moving in loose earth). Grading is used in preparing many excavations, especially those for highways. See Fig. 35-3.
3. *Sloping* is another way of trimming and shaping earth. The sides of excavations are sloped to lower the chances of slides. In sloping, the loose soil is usually removed from the sides of the excavation. Sloping is a common way of stabilizing the earthwork in an excavation which covers a large area. Sloping might be used where a large building is to be built or where a dam is to be built, Fig. 35-4.
4. *Treating* is also used for trimming and shaping the excavation bed and walls. In this process, loose soil is filled with a substance that makes it more solid. Sometimes a chemical solution is used. In other cases, water is used. Freezing of the soil may be used when the earth is full of water and hard to drain. This freezing serves two purposes:
   a. It helps to stabilize the soil and keeps the earth from falling in.
   b. It helps control water in the ground.

Fig. 35-2. Soil and rocks that fell into the excavation are being removed.

Stabilizing Earthworks and Structures

There are five main ways of stabilizing earthworks. They are: (1) compacting, (2) sheathing, (3) bracing and shoring, (4) piling, and (5) cofferdamming. Which proc-

Fig. 35-3. A tractor with a bulldozer blade is grading a site for a highway construction job.

Fig. 35-4. Heavy equipment is being used to load spoil after blasting has sloped the sides of an excavation.

ess is used depends on outside conditions such as the state of the soil and the kind of material being excavated.

Compacting is the compressing or packing down of the earth to make it firm. Large rollers pack the earth to make it firmer, Fig. 35-5. For small areas, an air hammer is used to compact the surface.

Sheathing forms walls to keep earth out of the excavated area. All sheathing has some kind of framework which makes it take the shape of the excavation. Common sheathing materials are metal panels and wood planks or panels. These are supported by bracing and shoring.

Bracing and shoring are processes usually used with sheathing. However, each is placed differently. The brace is put in horizontally between the sheathing panels. The shore is placed diagonally against the excavation walls or sheathing panels. It is held by stakes at the bottom. *Bracing is used in narrow excavations,* Fig. 35-6. *Shoring is used in wider excavations* where you cannot brace against the sidewall. The material used for bracing or shoring is usually wood or metal.

Sometimes large concrete, steel, or wooden stakes are driven into the ground to give more stability to a structure, Figs. 35-7 and 35-8. This is called *piling,* and the stakes are called *piles.* This is a construction practice which has been used since prehistoric times. Piling has two main purposes: (1) to improve the load-bearing capacity of the earth and (2) to help guard against uneven settlement of the structure.

There are two kinds of piles: (1) friction piles and (2) end or point support piles. *Friction piles* support a load by the friction developed between the surface of the pile and the soil through which it is driven. The *end* or *point support pile* supports the load by having the structure rest on one end and having the other end rest on a firm layer of rock or earth below ground or water level. A common example of this kind of pile may be found along a waterfront. Piers are supported by piles which are driven into the rocky bottom of a lake, river, or ocean harbor.

Cofferdamming is a popular method used in construction when a structure must be

Fig. 35-5. A compactor-tractor is spreading and compacting a roadbed.

Fig. 35-6. Shoring and bracing are used to keep earth out of an excavation area. They also may stabilize nearby structures which are resting on the excavation sidewalls.

built in water or water-filled soil. It is used to make a dry working area and to keep water out of an area where concrete must be placed and cured. The main parts of the modern cofferdam are sheets of wood, steel, or concrete (may be called sheathing) which are driven into the ground or water to form a watertight wall around the work site. (See Fig. 35-9.) Shores or braces support the sheathing. The water and other materials are removed from this space. This space is then a dry area for construction workers and materials, Fig. 35-10.

Summary

After the major excavation has been made, more work may still be needed before the foundation is laid. It may be necessary to trim the excavation bed and walls to make the excavation ready for the foundation. Trimming and shaping the bed and walls of the excavation are done by one or more of four processes: (1) cleaning and

Fig. 35-8. The round discs are the tops of piles that have been driven into the ground to give better stability to the structure that will be built here. A concrete slab will become the "pile cap."

Fig. 35-7. A pile driver is used to drive steel sheet piles into the ground.

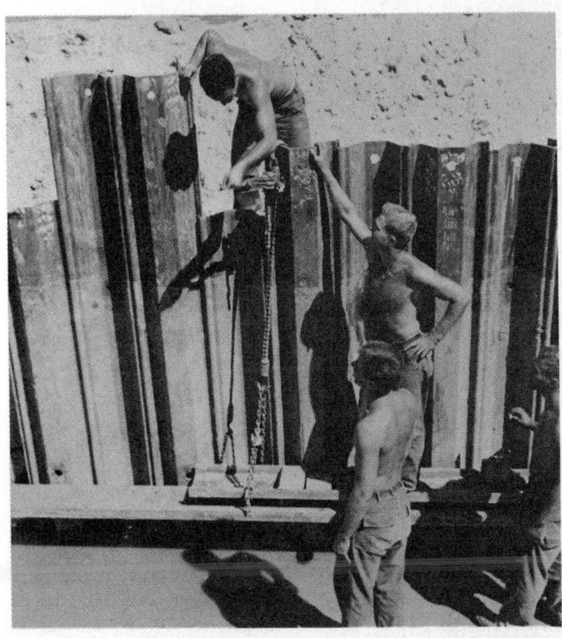

Fig. 35-9. Steel sheet piles are being adjusted for cofferdamming.

Fig. 35-10. The picture shows a finished cofferdam which will keep water out of the working area of this excavation.

washing, (2) grading, (3) sloping, and (4) treating. Which practice is used depends upon such things as soil condition, weather in the area, and the kind of excavation being made. All of these processes are used to make the excavation ready for the foundation.

Stabilizing earthworks and structures is done in five main ways: (1) compacting, (2) sheathing, (3) bracing and shoring, (4) piling, and (5) cofferdamming. These processes have much the same general purpose as those used for trimming and shaping the structure. However, they are used more to steady and support the excavation and any surrounding structures.

Terms to Know

excavation
trimming
stabilizing
foundation
bond
piles
trimming and shaping the excavation
- a. cleaning and washing
- b. grading
- c. sloping
- d. treating

settlement of a building

types of grading
- a. compacting
- b. grouting
- c. scaling
- d. filling

means of stabilizing
- a. compacting
- b. sheathing
- c. bracing and shoring
- d. piling
- e. cofferdamming

Think About It!

1. Sometimes workers are caught in excavations when the sides cave in. Has this ever happened in your community? What should have been done to prevent this?
2. What must be done to support an existing structure if earth is removed very close to its foundation? Have you ever heard of an incident where damage was done to an existing building? If so, when and where?

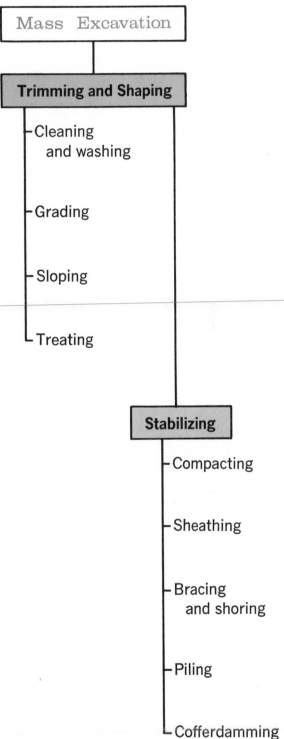

Mass Excavation

Trimming and Shaping

- Cleaning and washing
- Grading
- Sloping
- Treating

Stabilizing

- Compacting
- Sheathing
- Bracing and shoring
- Piling
- Cofferdamming

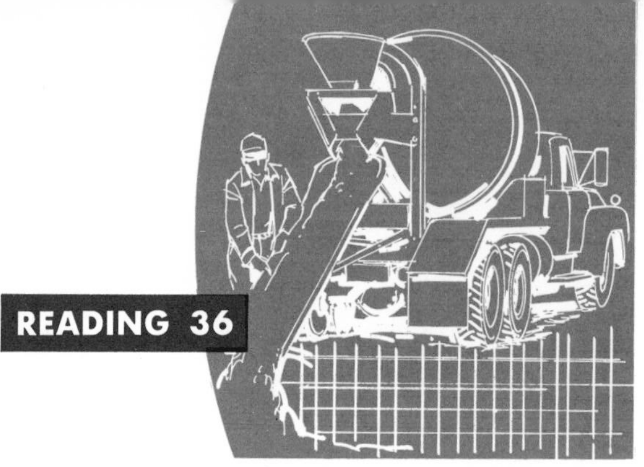

READING 36

Classifying Structures

All constructed works may be thought of as structures. Each has a substructure that rests on some part of the earth called the *bearing surface.* Each has a *superstructure* which rests on the *substructure.* We are most likely to notice only the superstructure, which is *the part above the ground.* The substructure, even though we may not see it, is an important part of the whole structure. In the next series of lessons you will study these main parts of structures and learn how to build them.

Fig. 36-1. Some substructures are very complex. This one is being made of sand pumped from the mainland.

Fig. 36-2. This rockfill dam is a mass superstructure.

A structure is an arrangement of materials that have been put together (constructed). Structures include such things as dams, roads, tunnels, bridges, marine projects, utility networks, towers, monuments, and buildings.

The Substructure

The structure is made up of a *substructure* (a foundation) and a superstructure which rests on it. The foundation supports the weight of the whole superstructure and must also support any load added to the completed structure.

Sometimes the foundation is very complex, such as when it is necessary to build a structure on marshy or wet land (Fig. 36-1) or in cold regions where freezing and thawing conditions break up most of the foundations used in warmer climates. In some cases, the foundation is only compacted natural earth or solid rock.

We usually think of the substructure as that part of the structure below the surface of the ground. However, it is sometimes difficult to decide just which is the foundation, or substructure, and which is the superstructure. In setting a foundation for a building on a steep slope, for example, one foundation wall may rise above the ground surface. The opposite wall may be buried in the hillside. In such cases where part of the foundation wall is buried, we would say that all of the foundation wall, whether buried or not, is the substructure.

In a house, everything below the first floor level is called the foundation, even if part of it can be seen above the ground. *Every part of the house above the foundation is the superstructure.* In a bridge the walls that support the ends of the bridge are part of the foundation, since some of them are buried in the ground. The part of the bridge resting on the walls is the superstructure.

Fig. 36-4. Many of our most modern buildings are bearing wall types which do not have skeletal frames.

Fig. 36-3. The homes of the early cliff dwellers were of the bearing wall type. They can be seen at Mesa Verde National Park, Colorado.

The Superstructure

Most of the structure you can see after the project is complete is the superstructure. There are several major kinds of superstructures. These may be called *mass, bearing wall,* and *framed superstructures. Mass superstructures* use a solid mass of material as in a dam, highway, or monument. (See Fig. 36-2.) *Bearing wall superstructures* have unframed walls such as those in a brick home or a concrete block supermarket, Figs. 36-3 and 36-4. *Framed superstructures* have a skeleton.

Most superstructures fit fairly well into the classes of mass, bearing wall, and framed types, Fig. 36-5. However, there are some exceptions which are hard to classify. Tunnels, underground pipelines, and boat and ship channels are examples of constructed works that do not fit the common types of superstructures. See Fig. 36-6.

Underground projects such as tunnels and pipelines do not show above ground,

Fig. 36-5. Can you identify the substructure and the superstructure?

Fig. 36-6. Railroad tracks (superstructure) and ties (substructure) must be placed on a firm bearing surface to support the weight of the trains.

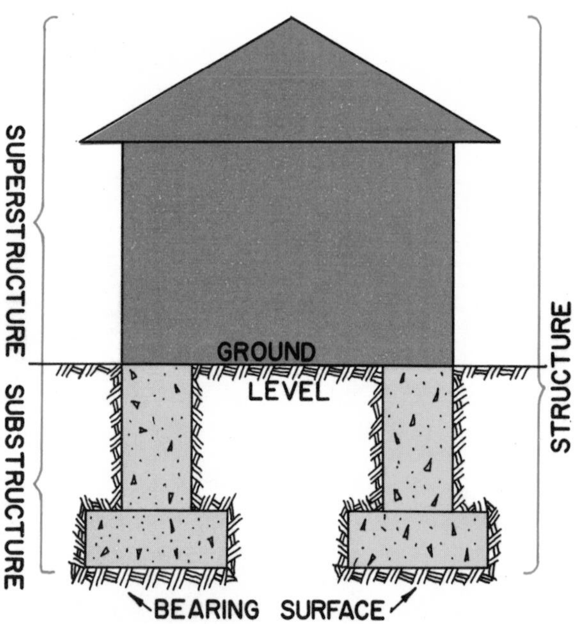

Fig. 36-7. All structures have a superstructure and a substructure.

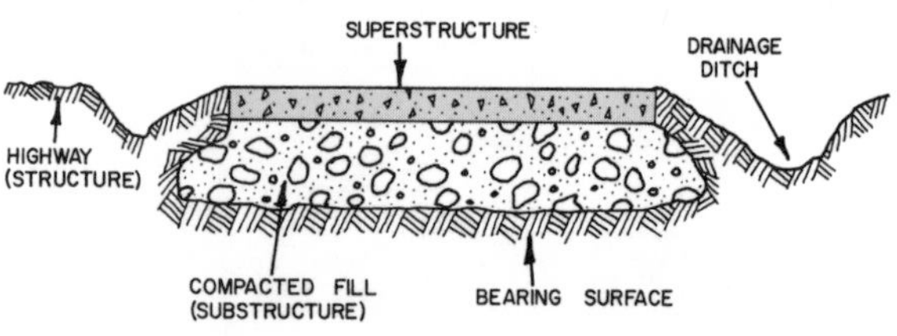

Fig. 36-8. A concrete roadway has a substructure and a superstructure.

just as river and port channels do not show above water. Therefore, they are not normal superstructures. They do have bearing surfaces, but their substructures also are not easily classified.

For the student who is trying to make some order out of all the many kinds of constructed projects, confusion can be avoided by simply noting that some projects do not fit the general substructure-superstructure groups. The projects which do not fit into a group can be accepted as exceptions to a useful way of classifying most projects and parts of projects.

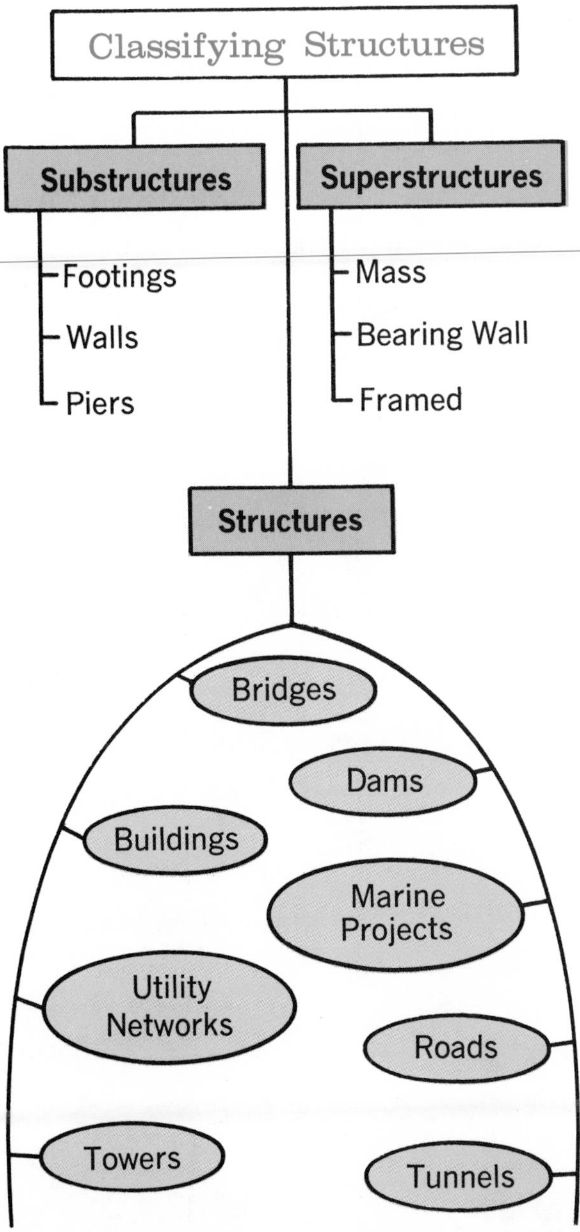

Classifying Structures

Substructures
- Footings
- Walls
- Piers

Superstructures
- Mass
- Bearing Wall
- Framed

Structures

Bridges
Dams
Buildings
Marine Projects
Utility Networks
Roads
Towers
Tunnels

Summary

Structures are made up of a substructure (a foundation) and a superstructure (part resting on the foundation). Man builds many kinds of structures. However, they can be classified as: dams, roads, tunnels, bridges, marine projects, utility networks, towers, monuments, and buildings.

Substructures all rest upon bearing surfaces. In addition, they may have footings, walls, or piers. (Study Figs. 36-7 and 36-8.)

Superstructures may be classed as mass, bearing wall, and framed types. There are some projects which are hard to classify, but most constructed works easily fit into one of the groups.

You will next study how substructures are built. After a study of substructures, a study of superstructures will follow.

Terms to Know

structure
bearing surface
substructure
  a. footings
  b. walls
  c. piers
utility networks
marine projects
superstructures
  a. mass
  b. bearing wall
  c. framed

Think About It!

1. Can you think of structures that do not have substructures? If so, give two examples.
2. List three superstructures within one city block of where you are at this moment. Identify one mass, one bearing wall, and one framed superstructure in your list.

Clearing
Earthmoving
Foundations
A road
A bridge
A dam
A building

Superstructures
Utilities
Finished Project

READING 37

Setting Foundations

The preparations necessary for starting to build a structure have been completed. The site has been cleared. The size and shape of the structure have been laid out on the site by the surveyor. The necessary earth has been removed. Where stabilization of earth or structures was necessary, this has been done. We are now ready to begin building the structure. *The first step is to build the foundation* (substructure).

To understand about foundations, we must know why foundations are needed and what the parts of a foundation are. We must know what types of foundations are used, what materials are used in them, and how they are built.

Fig. 37-1. A sturdy foundation is necessary to support the weight of the superstructure. This foundation, under construction, will support a chimney.

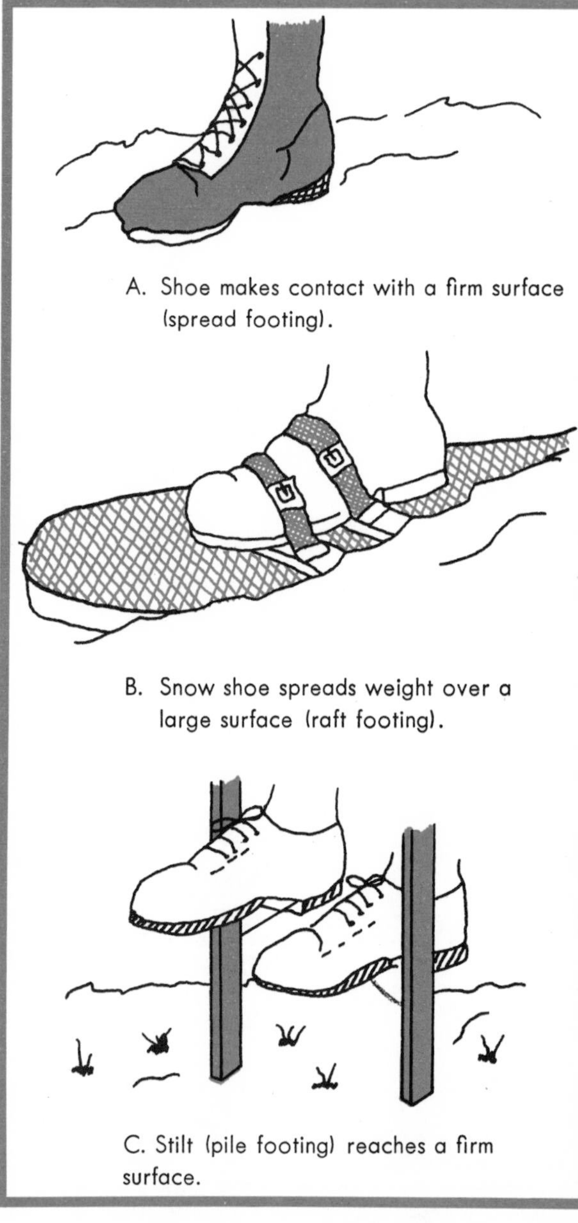

A. Shoe makes contact with a firm surface (spread footing).

B. Snow shoe spreads weight over a large surface (raft footing).

C. Stilt (pile footing) reaches a firm surface.

Fig. 37-2. The foundation of a structure is much like your foot when you are standing.

The Reason for Foundations

The foundation of a structure is the part which supports the weight of the whole structure. It must cover enough area to spread the whole weight of the structure onto the earth on which it is built so that the structure will not sink into the soil. See Fig. 37-1.

What a Foundation Does

The foundation of a structure is much like your foot when you are standing. On hard soil a structure would use a footing that spreads out like your foot. Such a footing is called a *spread footing,* Fig. 37-2A.

If you are standing on loosely packed snow, you would sink part way into it. You could only stay on the surface by using snow shoes which cover a greater area than the sole of your shoe. It is much the same for foundations that must be placed on soft soil. You might use a larger spread footing or you might use a *raft* (slab) *footing* to keep the foundation from sinking, Fig. 37-2B.

When the snow has turned to slush, your foot will sink into it until it reaches a hard surface under the slush. The only way you could walk on the slush would be on stilts which would reach down to a harder surface. For foundations to be placed on wet, marshy soil, something like stilts is used. These are called *piles.* They are driven down to the firm earth below the marsh, Fig. 37-2C.

The foundations for all parts of a structure should be supported on the same kind of soil. If part of a foundation is placed on rock and the other part is placed on marshy soil, the part on the soft soil will sink and tilt the foundation. The result will be to tilt the whole structure very much as the Tower of Pisa is tilted, Fig. 37-3.

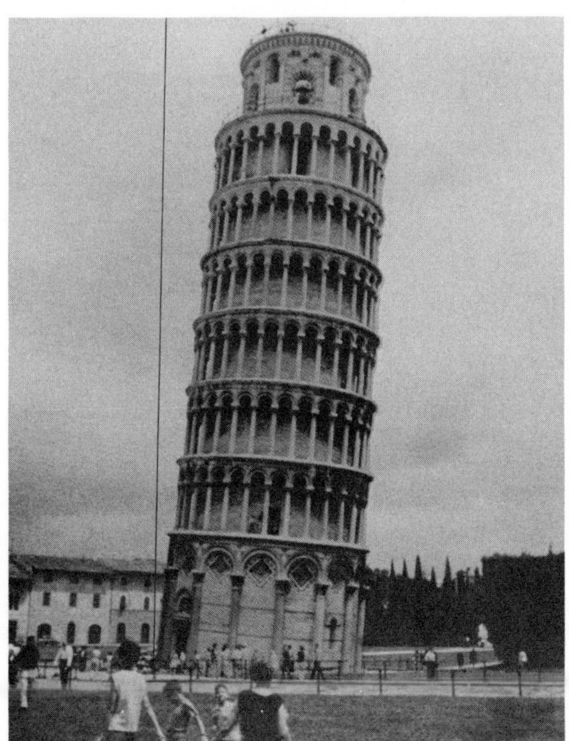

Fig. 37-3. The tower of Pisa leans about 14 feet.

Parts of a Foundation

A foundation (substructure) can be divided into three parts:

1. The *bearing surface* (part of the earth on which the foundation rests),
2. The *footing* (flat part of the foundation which spreads the load of the structure above it), and
3. The *upright supports,* such as walls or piers. The upright supports rise above the footing to form the rest of the substructure, Fig. 37-4.

Types of Footings

Three kinds of footings are used most often. These are: (1) spread footings, (2) raft or slab footings, and (3) pile cap footings.

Spread footings are the simplest kind. They are used on bearing surfaces of rock or of soil that is packed solidly like hard clay. The spread footing is a pad which may be long and rather narrow to go under a wall, or it may be square or rectangular where it is to go under a pier or post, Fig. 37-5.

Where the soil of the bearing surface is soft or where there might be vibration due to an earthquake, a spread footing cannot be used. In such cases a *raft* or slab *footing* may be used. A raft footing spreads the weight of the structure over a very large area. It is used only with small, lightweight structures where the bearing surface is too soft for a spread footing. The raft footing usually covers a larger area than that of the structure it supports. We can say that the structure "floats" on the soil, Fig. 37-6.

When the bearing surface is in marshy land, in sand, or under water as in a river, lake, or along the ocean, we must find a good bearing surface. To do this, *piles* are driven down through the soft or wet soil until a strong supporting layer of hard clay or rock is reached. A footing, like a spread footing, is then built on top of the piles. This footing is called a *pile cap,* Fig. 37-7.

Fig. 37-4. The foundation elements can be seen in this photograph of the substructure construction of a shopping center basement.

Foundation Materials

Different structures need different kinds of bearing surfaces, depending upon how heavy the structures are. The designer

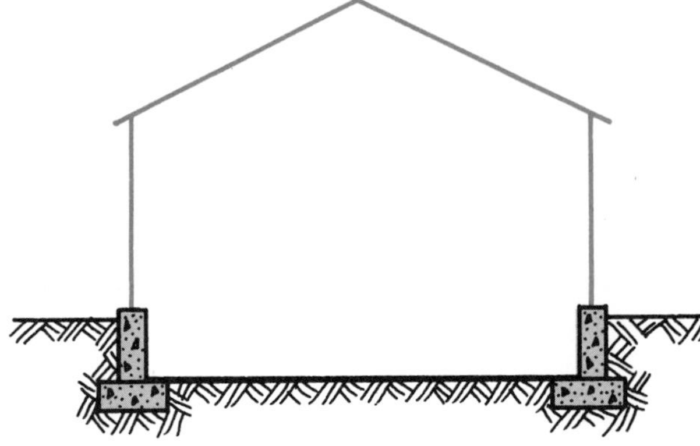
Fig. 37-5. Spread footing.

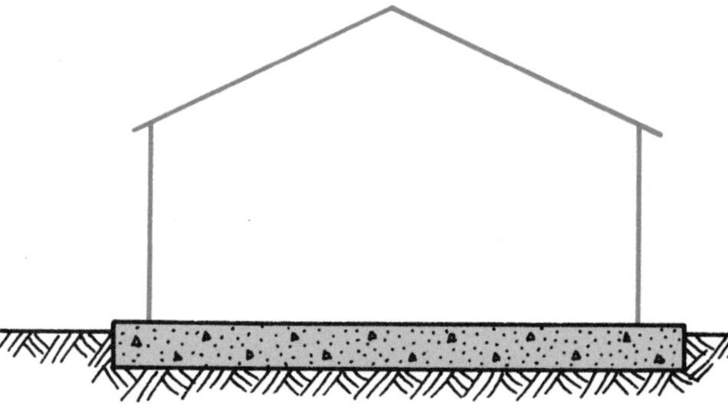
Fig. 37-6. Raft (slab) footing.

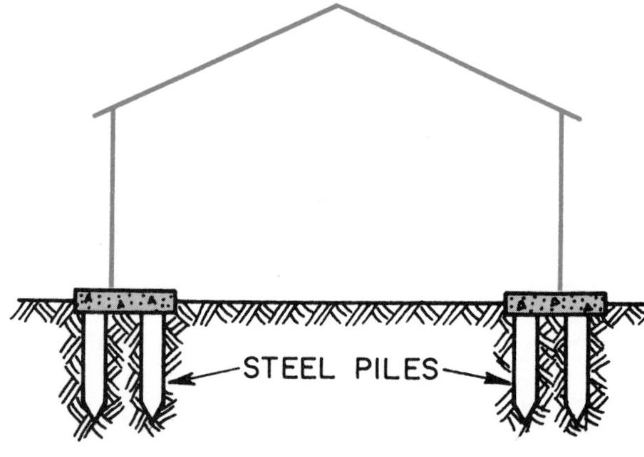

Fig. 37-7. Pile footing.

must decide what kind of bearing surface will support the weight of each structure.

Today, concrete is the most common material used for footings. Sometimes only concrete is used, but it can be made stronger by burying steel rods in it for *reinforcement.* Examples of other footing materials are crushed rock or gravel for highways or airport runways.

Fig. 37-8. Piles are vertical footings. These piles support the Chesapeake Bay Bridge and Tunnel. The men shown here are cutting the concrete piles to the correct length. In completing the substructure, pile caps will be put on top of the piles.

Most footings are horizontal. Sometimes footings are vertical. Driven pilings are an example of vertical footings. (See Fig. 37-8.) Many times vertical piers or walls are added to horizontal footings to build them up to grade level. Piers, piles, or foundation walls may be made of natural materials such as stone or wood. They also may be made of reinforced concrete or steel.

How to Set Foundations

The bearing surface is first prepared to support the footing, Fig. 37-9. When the bearing surface has been prepared, the footing can be placed. Since most footings are made of concrete, let us see how they are made. Concrete footings are made in six steps.

1. Forms or molds are set in place.
2. Rodsetters place steel reinforcement in the forms where it is needed.
3. A mixer operator puts materials into a drum and mixes them to make concrete.

Fig. 37-9. The first step in constructing the foundation is to prepare the bearing surface. This machine prepares the bearing surface for concrete highways.

4. Concrete laborers and cement finishers place the concrete in the form, Fig. 37-10.
5. The cement finishers compact the concrete in the form and finish the surface of the concrete.
6. After the concrete has set, the laborers remove the formwork.

Sometimes, the superstructure rests directly on the footing. An example of this is when a highway surface of concrete is placed over compacted fill. Other times, after the footing has been finished, the next step is to place upright parts of the substructure on the footing.

If the upright parts are to be made of concrete, the six steps used in building the footing will be repeated. If they are to be made of stone, brick, or concrete block, masons will lay the foundation walls or piers on the footing. Also, ironworkers or carpenters may fasten columns to the footing with heavy bolts that were set in the footing while the concrete was wet. These columns usually are capped by beams (horizontal pieces that lay on top of the columns).

Fig. 37-10. Concrete is being placed in a form by concrete laborers. Very strong men are required for this work.

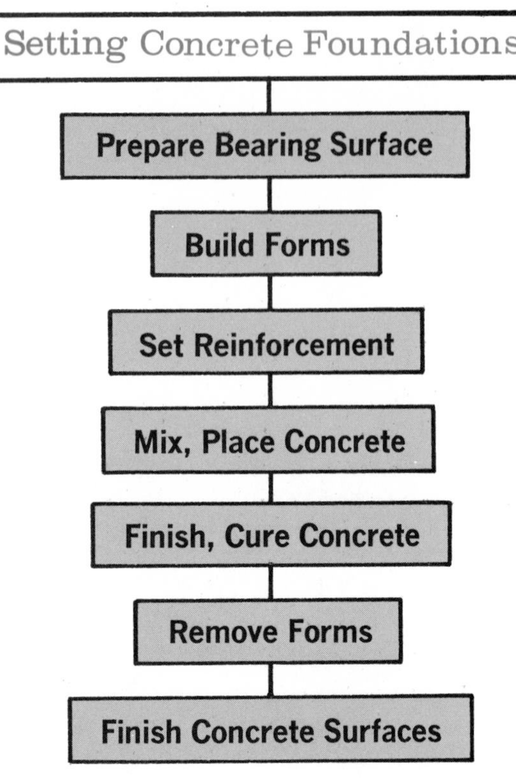

Summary

After the site has been prepared, the next step in building a structure is to set the foundation (substructure). The three parts of most foundations are: (1) a bearing surface, (2) a footing, and, sometimes, (3) a substructure rising above the footing which may be a wall, a pier, or a column.

The *bearing surface* must be solid enough to support the weight of the whole structure. The bearing surface may be rock or soil at the surface of the earth; it may be a few feet below the surface, or it may be many feet under a swamp, a river, or an ocean.

Footings usually are made of concrete. Sometimes, as is the case with highway construction, they are made of compacted fill such as crushed rock. Where firm soil is very deep below the earth's surface, the footing may be piles driven into the soil with a pile cap placed on top of them.

The part of the substructure or foundation rising above the footings may be a wall. The *upright* part of the substructure also may be piers or columns made of concrete, stone, brick, concrete block, steel, or wood. Beams are placed on top of the piers or columns to form the base of the superstructure.

Terms to Know

spread footing	to *finish* concrete
raft footing	to *cure* concrete
pile cap footing	compacted
bearing surface	foundation parts
steel reinforcement	a. bearing surface
forms	b. footing
	c. upright supports

Think About It!

1. What type of footing would you guess is under your home? Your school? The nearest bridge? Do you think they are all the same type?
2. Why has the Tower of Pisa in Italy leaned about 14′? Do you know what can be done to stop it from leaning any farther?

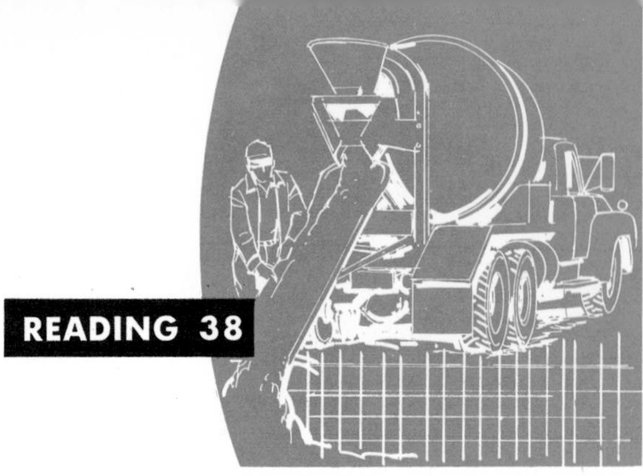

READING 38

Building Forms

In earlier readings you learned that structures are made up of substructures (foundations) and superstructures. You also learned that setting foundations is the first step in building structures. In this reading you will find that *building forms usually is the first step taken in setting foundations,* Fig. 38-1.

Most foundations are made of concrete. Before we can place the concrete, forms must be built. Building foundation forms is only part of the knowledge about building forms. A later reading on erecting concrete superstructures describes building forms above the foundation.

Giving Shape to Concrete

Concrete is made of stone, sand, and water bound together with cement. When concrete has been freshly mixed and is still wet, we can handle it just as we would handle wet mud. Shortly after it has been mixed it begins to set (get stiff). It finally becomes as hard as stone. We can think of concrete as *man-made stone.* In order to get the shape of the slabs, footings, walls, and piers that we need, we must shape the concrete. Concrete is shaped by placing it into forms while it is still wet.

The forms for concrete are something like the molds into which gelatin is poured. When the gelatin is set, it can be dumped out of the mold. It then has the shape of the inside of the mold.

When we are shaping concrete, we do not simply pour it into the form (mold). We do not dump it out after it has become hard. Concrete must be carefully placed in the form. Also, we remove the form, piece by piece, leaving the concrete in the shape of the form. Therefore, the form must be built so that it can be removed easily without damaging the concrete, Fig. 38-2. Also, the form must be strong enough to keep from bulging from the weight of the wet concrete. Since workmen often must stand on the form or climb around on it, the form must be strongly built to protect it from being pushed out of shape before or during the concrete placing operation.

Material for Forms

Concrete foundation forms usually are made of wood. They also can be made of steel, or a combination of wood and steel. Wood is lighter in weight, easier to handle,

Fig. 38-1. Carpenters busily erect forms for a foundation wall, foreground, while another crew places concrete in a completed form, background.

and less expensive than other materials. Also, it is easier to change the size and shape of wood by using hand tools.

Wooden forms are built by carpenters working at the construction site. The carpenters may make every part of the form at the site, or they may assemble forms that have been partly fabricated (made) at a manufacturing plant. The forms that we will discuss here are made entirely at the construction site. See Fig. 38-3.

The wood or lumber used for building forms is of two kinds. First, there is *dimension lumber*. It is called dimension lumber because we speak of the size of the piece by its dimensions. For example, a piece of lumber approximately 2″ thick by 4″ wide is called a "two by four." Dimension lumber comes in even-numbered lengths such as 8′, 10′, or 12′.

The second kind of lumber used for building forms is *plywood*. This comes in large sheets 4′ wide and 8′ to 10′ long. These sheets most commonly are ¼″, ½″, ¾″ or 1″ in thickness. They are used to cover the frame built of dimension lumber. Instead of plywood we may use a kind of dimension lumber called *planking, sheathing,* or *boards*. These usually are 1″ or 2″ thick and may be of different widths from 4″ to 12″. See Fig. 38-4.

Preparing the Materials

The first step in building forms is to prepare the materials. The lengths of the pieces of dimension lumber and the sizes of the

Fig. 38-3. These forms are made of wood and are assembled on the site.

Fig. 38-2. Forms are built in such a way that they may be removed without damaging the freshly set concrete.

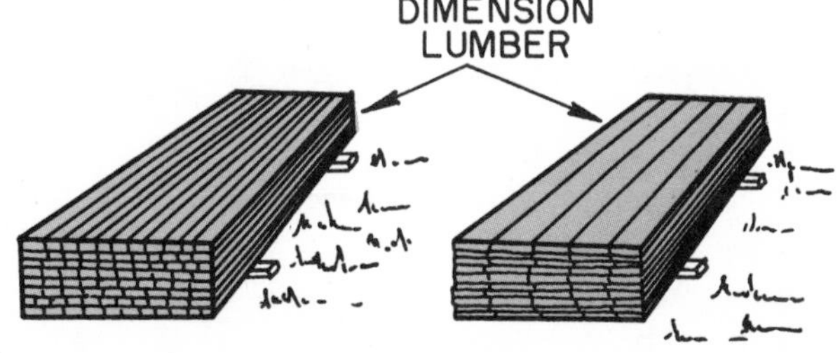

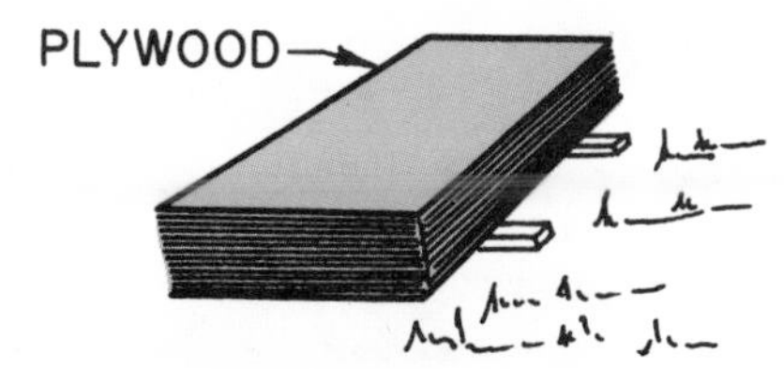

Fig. 38-4. Form materials.

sheets of plywood that will be needed must be measured and cut. Common tools for measuring are carpenter's squares, six-foot folding rules, flexible metal measuring tapes, chalk lines, and carpenters' pencils, Fig. 38-5.

A *chalk line* is a heavy string or cord. For layout work it is covered with colored chalk dust and then is stretched tightly between two points on a line which is to be marked. When the center of the string is lifted straight up from the surface and then re-

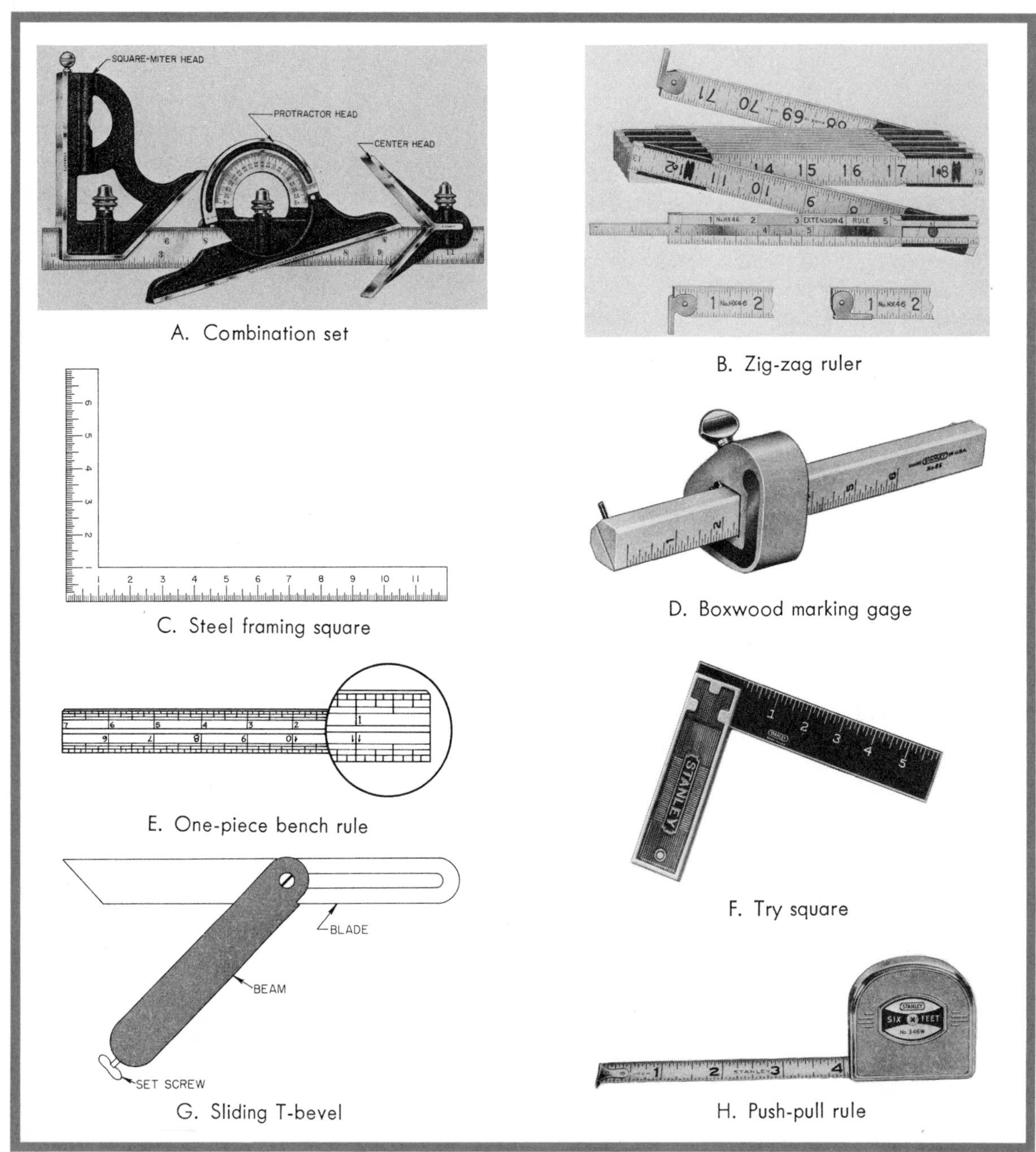

Fig. 38-5. Carpenter's common measuring tools.

Fig. 38-6. This carpenter is cutting "two by four" dimension lumber for a form. How many of his tools can you identify?

leased, like the string of an archer's bow, it snaps back and leaves a faint line of chalk dust.

Carpenters' pencils have a heavy, rectangular-shaped lead in them instead of a round one. Because of their shape, they are easily sharpened with a pocket knife. Also, because of their heavy leads, they do not break as easily as do common lead pencils.

After the wood has been marked to the length or width required, it is cut to the measured size by sawing. Small pieces may be cut with a hand saw. Larger pieces may be sawed with an electric saw. See. Fig. 38-6.

When the pieces required for the forms have been cut to size, they then are assembled and fastened together. Usually the lumber in forms is fastened together with nails, but bolts and nuts or wood screws sometimes are used.

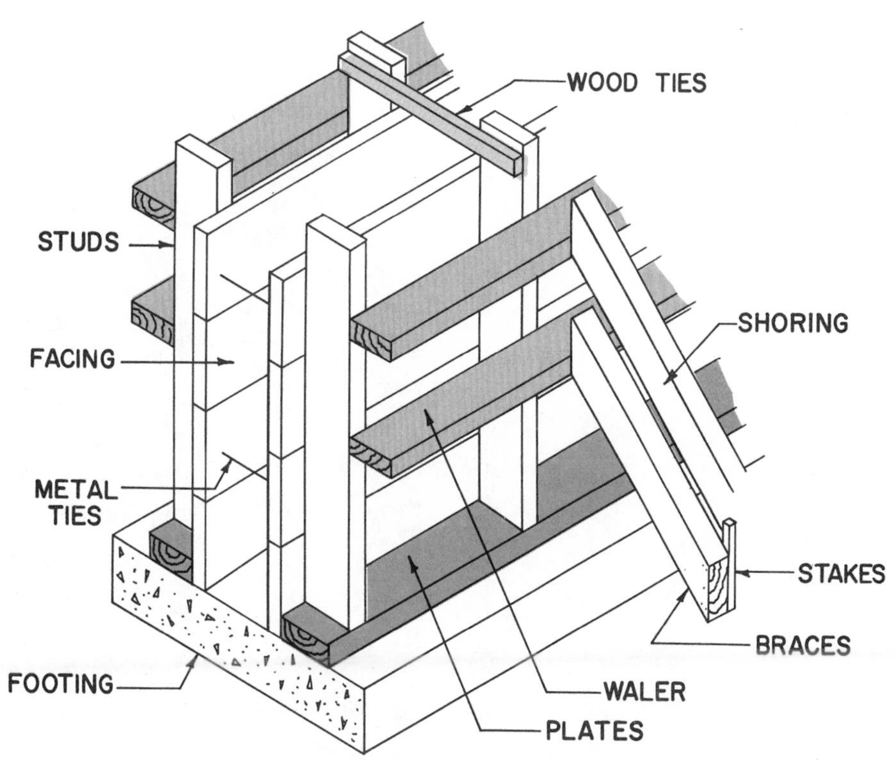

Fig. 38-7. Wood form for a foundation wall.

Form Parts

Wood foundation forms are made up of seven main parts. These are: (1) plates, (2) studs, (3) walers, (4) ties, (5) braces or shores, (6) stakes, and (7) facing, Figs. 38-7 and 38-8. *Plates* are pieces of dimension lumber on which the forms rest. They usually are two by fours. When plates are used as part of a wall or pier form, they are fastened to the footing to hold the form in place.

Techniques in Building Forms

We have said that forms may be made completely at the site or they may be manufactured in pieces or sections and delivered to the site for assembly. When forms are completely made at the site, they may be built in two ways. The first way is to build it piece by piece in place. To do this, we first place the plates in position and then nail the studs to them. After the studs are standing upright, we then nail the facing to the studs, Fig. 38-9. The next step is to set the walers in position and fasten the form ties to the walers.

Another way of completely making the forms at the site is to make up panels and then set the panels in position. A panel is a section of form of a standard size, such as 4′ × 8′. Each panel has a plate at each end with studs nailed in between the plates. The plywood or other form facing is then nailed over the studs. Standard size form panels are also made in manufacturing plants.

Assembling Forms in Place

No matter how the forms are built, the first step in assembling them is to lay out their position on the bearing surface or footing. When getting ready to assemble forms for slabs or spread footings, we mark the position of the inside of the form by stretching a string between two stakes driven into the ground. One edge of the plate then can be set along this line and held in place by small stakes driven along the outside edge of the form, Fig. 38-10. If panels are to be used, the faces of all the panels on one side of the form are set to the string line. Then

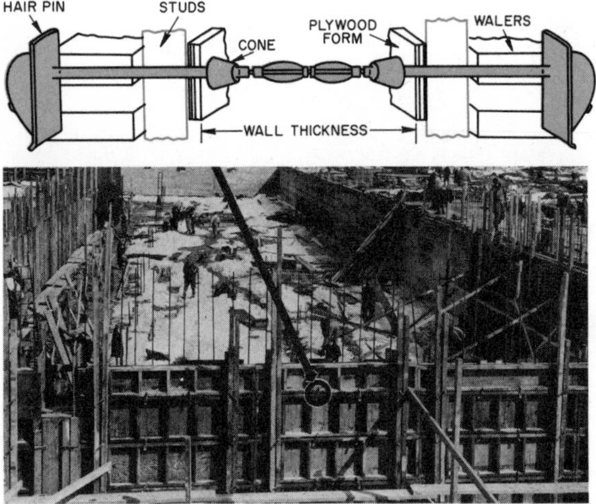

Fig. 38-8. This form is made up of panels which have been set in position.

Fig. 38-9. These men are assembling a form for a thin, slab foundation.

the panels are fastened together by nailing or bolting the stud in one panel to the stud in the next panel.

To set forms for a wall or a pier, there already is a slab or spread footing on which to work. A line can be laid out on the concrete surface. This line then can be used to set the plate or to set the bottom of the panel to be used. The next steps in assembling forms are different for slab or spread footings, for walls, or for piers.

Forms for a Slab Foundation

Forms for large slabs or for smaller spread footings are assembled in the same way, Fig. 38-11. If the slab or footing is less than a foot in thickness, we may need only boards or other facing material, some stakes, and some bracing lumber. If the slab is thick, we will need all, or almost all, of the seven parts of a form.

After we have fixed the position of the form by using a chalk line, we can place a strip of facing upright against it so that the string just touches the facing. We then can drive stakes into the ground tightly against the facing. After the stakes have been solidly driven, the facing is nailed to the stakes. Then we must *plumb* (make vertical) the facing and nail a brace between the top of each stake and another stake driven some distance away to hold the facing upright.

When panels are set for a slab form, we use many of the same steps to set them as we do for setting narrow strips of facing. Stakes are driven behind the panel and are braced to stakes driven into the ground some distance away. Always remember that nothing can be placed in front of the facing because that is where the concrete is to be placed.

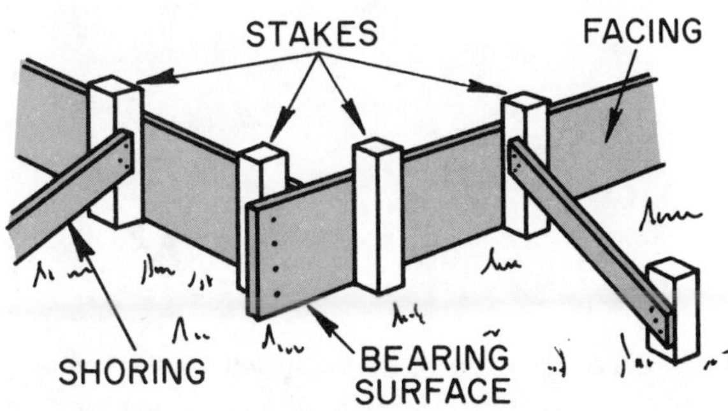

Fig. 38-10. Form for a thin slab foundation.

Forms for a Wall Foundation

A wall almost always has two sides. Therefore, two facings are needed inside a wall form. Sometimes the earth forms one facing.

The line for one side of the wall is marked on the concrete footing. The panels are placed in position along that line. Walers, in pairs, are nailed to the back of all the panels to keep them in line. Bracing and stakes then are put in to hold the wall in an upright position. After this one face of the form is in position, reinforcing steel is set. You will learn how this is done in the next assignment.

The next step is to set the form ties, Fig. 38-8. These are placed in holes in the facing and are pushed back between the pairs of walers. Now the panels for the other side of the wall can be set in position. Holes are drilled in the facing so that the metal tie can be pushed through.

After the second set of panels is in position, first the walers and then the bracing and the stakes are set. One face of the form

Fig. 38-11. A footing is a narrow, thin, slab foundation. This one will support the weight of a single-family home.

is lined up by stretching a string along the top from one end to the other. Then the second face of the form is set parallel to the first one. The distance between the discs on the form ties is used to maintain the wall thickness needed. When one side of the form is straight and the facings on both sides are pressing against the discs, we are ready to place the concrete. See Fig. 38-12.

Forms for a Pier Foundation

Piers may be square, rectangular, or round. Piers that are to be square or rectangular are formed with two short sets of wall forms. The forms may be built in place, or they may be prefabricated panels. See Fig. 38-13. Wall ties may tie the faces of the forms together on opposite sides. They are set and plumbed in the same way as wall forms. When they are finished, the corners must be checked with a carpenter's square to be sure that they are square. Bracing must be used on all four sides to keep the pier forms from moving.

Fig. 38-12. The forms for this retaining wall are the manufactured metal type. They are moved as one unit by a crane. Can you find the marks in the finished wall that are made by the wire ties?

Fig. 38-13. This manufactured form is used to mold square piers.

Fig. 38-14. Fiber form material is used for this round pier. How is the form material removed when the concrete has set?

When a round pier is to be built, sections of metal or fiber tubes are used. These sections are assembled into what looks like a large piece of pipe. They are set in place on the footing and are plumbed so they stand straight. Then braces are used to hold them in position, Fig. 38-14.

Fig. 38-15. Sometimes the earth and a traveling form are used to support the concrete while it is setting. This technique is called "slip form lining."

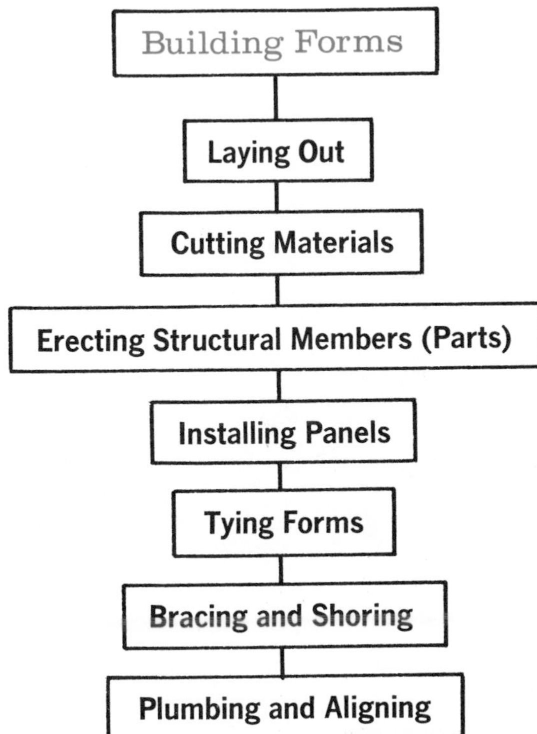

Summary

Concrete is a wet material that can be shaped in forms. Most foundation forms are built of wood. There are seven parts to a form. These are: (1) plates, (2) studs, (3) walers, (4) ties, (5) braces, (6) stakes, and (7) facing.

Forms may be built in place, piece by piece. They also may be made into panels at the site, or they may be manufactured in a plant and then brought to the site.

The position of the form for a foundation is marked on the bearing surface for slabs or footings. The position of the form for a wall or pier is marked on the footing. Wall and pier forms are tied together with form ties. All forms must be carefully set and lined up. They must be plumbed (vertical to the earth) to stand straight and must be well braced to hold them steady while the concrete is placed into them.

Terms to Know

forms	foundation form parts
dimension lumber	a. plates
plywood	b. studs
assemble	c. walers
retaining wall	d. ties
installing	e. braces or shores
plumb	f. stakes
parallel	g. facing

Think About It!

1. Look around you or out the window. Can you identify at least two concrete surfaces that were shaped against forms? Were these forms foundation forms or forms for the superstructure?

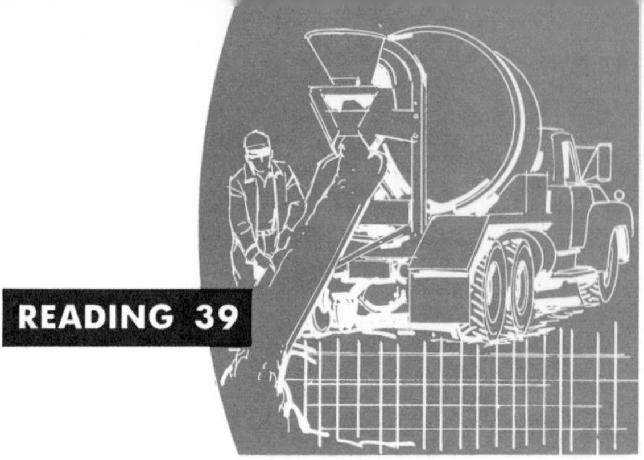

READING 39

Setting Reinforcement

If we take a long thin section of concrete and try to bend it, we find that it will not bend very far before breaking. If all foundations could be built of one large piece of concrete, no reinforcing steel would be needed. This would be very expensive and would take up too much space. Therefore, to use thinner sections of concrete in walls and piers, *reinforcing steel* is buried in them to keep them from cracking or breaking. This reinforcing steel *must be set in the forms before the concrete is placed.*

Kinds of Reinforcing Steel

Reinforcing steel is the name given to round steel rods that may be of any diameter from 1/8″ to 1″ or more. Each size rod has a number starting with No. 1 for a 1/8″ rod, No. 2 for a 1/4″ rod, No. 3 for a 3/8″ rod and so on. These rods are not smooth on the outside. If the outside of the rod were smooth, it might pull out of the concrete. Each rod has been run through a machine at the steel mill that presses ridges into it in different patterns. Because of the ridges, these are called *deformed rods.* When the rods are deformed, the concrete hardens tightly between the ridges and the rods cannot be pulled loose easily. Reinforcing rods are used in all wall, pier, and slab foundations.

Another kind of reinforcement that is used mainly in slab foundations and road slabs is called *reinforcing mesh.* Reinforcing mesh looks somewhat like wire fencing except that it generally is made of heavier wire. These wires cross each other at right angles to form squares. Where the wires cross they are welded together at the steel mill during manufacture. Reinforcing mesh is made in widths that may be 4′, 6′, or wider and in lengths that may be as long as 100′. It is delivered to the construction site in rolls which may be unrolled and spread on the ground to cover the whole area of the slab, Fig. 39-1.

Preparing Reinforcing Steel

The engineer who designed the foundations has shown on his plans where he wants reinforcing rods to be placed, the size of the rods he wants, and how close together the rods are to be placed in the concrete. The contractor who is building the founda-

Fig. 39-1. These men are straightening a roll of reinforcing mesh so that it will lay flat in the form. When the concrete is placed, they will pull the mesh up into the concrete.

tions gives a copy of the engineer's plans to the manufacturing company where he plans to buy the reinforcing steel, Fig. 39-2.

When the reinforcing steel company receives the engineer's plans, it makes up another set of plans showing nothing but lengths, sizes, and bending needed for all the reinforcing rods in the foundations. These new plans are called *shop drawings.* When they have been completed and the

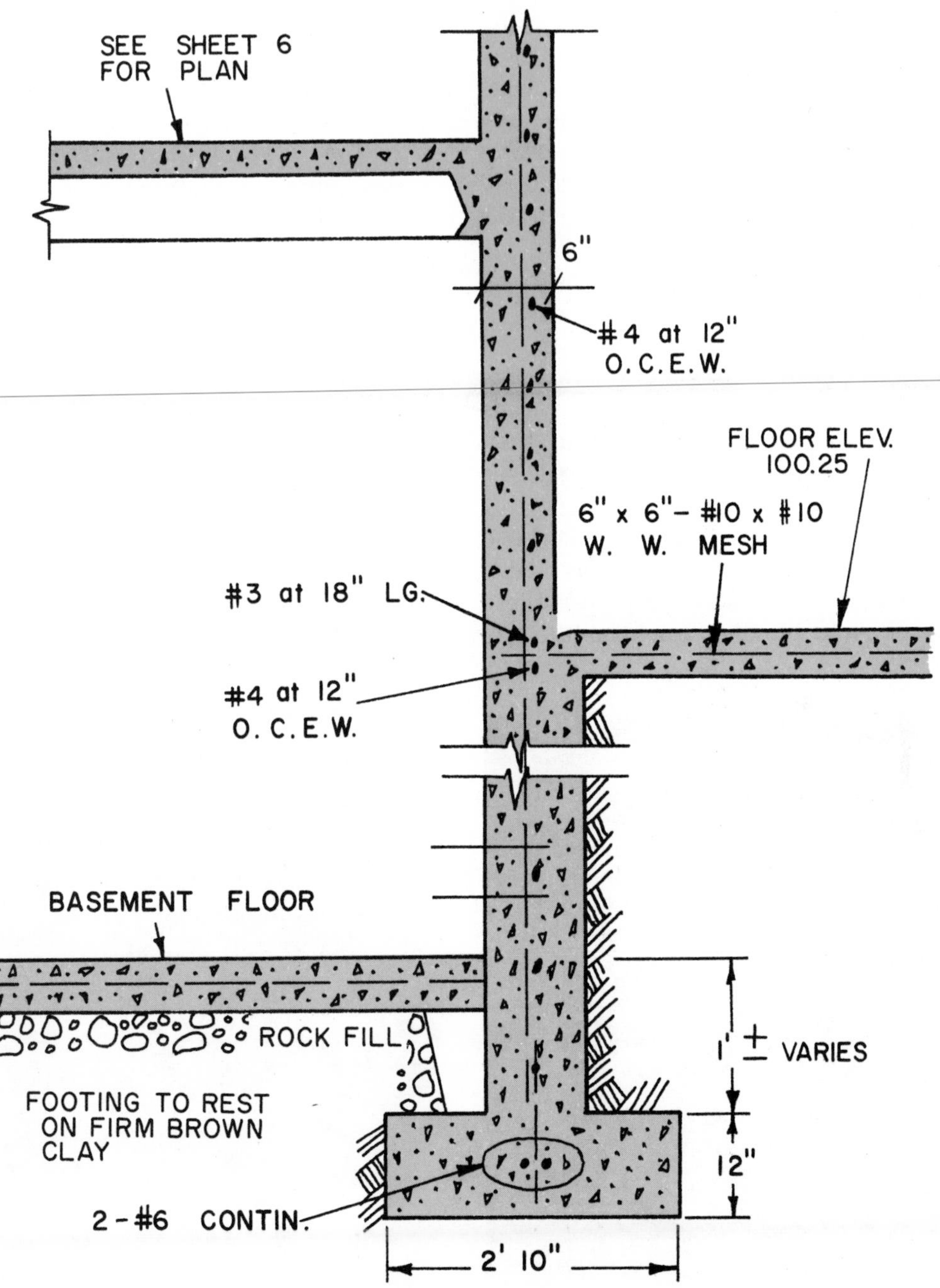

Fig. 39-2. Reinforcing materials are specified in the designer's plans. Shop drawings are prepared from the details found on the designer's plans.

engineer has approved the drawings, the reinforcing steel company gives them to its fabricating shop. The shop workers cut and bend the steel rods as shown on the shop drawings.

The reinforcing steel company buys reinforcing rods from a steel mill in 30′ lengths. The shop drawings sent to the fabricating shop might show that 10 No. 5 rods, each 20′ long, are needed for horizontal placement in one wall. The drawings also may call for 26 No. 6 rods, 10′ long, for vertical placement in the same wall. These and all the other rods are cut to the right lengths by a shearing machine.

Suppose that the shop drawing shows that the vertical rods are to be bent so that 1′ 6″ extends horizontally in the spread footing and 8′ 6″ of the same rod extends vertically up the wall. When these rods have been cut to the length needed, they are taken to a bending machine and are bent as shown on the shop drawing.

When all of the reinforcing rods have been cut to the right lengths and have been bent as shown on the shop drawing, these rods are put into bundles. Each bundle has the same size and length of rod. The bundles are then tied together with a piece of soft wire. One bundle may have 10 pieces of straight No. 5 rod tied together, and another bundle may have 26 pieces of bent No. 6 rod tied together.

The shop drawing has a number assigned to each size, each length, and each kind of bent rod. Each bundle of rods has the same number on a tag tied to that bundle. Then, when the bundles reach the construction site, the location of the rods needed for walls, piers, or slabs can be found easily, Fig. 39-3.

Placing Reinforcing Steel

When a truckload of reinforcing steel reaches the site, it has been cut, bent, bundled, and tagged. Workmen unload the bundles of steel with a power crane if the

Fig. 39-3. Reinforcing rods are delivered to the site in bundles.

Fig. 39-4. The man who places reinforcing steel is called a rodsetter. These steel rods will add strength to the concrete which is placed around them.

bundles are very large. The bundles must be stacked as near as possible to the wall, pier, or slab in which they are to be placed. They should not be in the way of the men working on the forms. They are stacked on boards to keep them clean.

Reinforcing steel is placed in position in the concrete form by workers who are called *rodsetters,* Figs. 39-4 and 39-5. Reinforcing steel is usually placed 1″, 2″, or 3″ from the face of the form so the concrete can pass between the form and the reinforcing steel.

Shop drawings are used by the rodsetters as they set the reinforcement steel in place. In a slab, the plan may show No. 6 rod at 9″ *on center* and show in which direction they are to be placed. A second notation may indicate No. 4 rod at 12″ *on center.* The rodsetter carries the No. 6 rods and lays them one by one on the ground within the form so that there is a space of 9″ from the center of one rod to the center of the next. When these have all been placed, he places the No. 4 rods across them at right angles with 12″ from the center of one rod to the center of the next. Where the top rods cross the bottom rods, he ties the two rods together with a short piece of wire, Fig. 39-6.

The mat of reinforcing steel for a slab must now be raised so that it is not resting on the ground and concrete can be placed

Fig. 39-6. Reinforcing steel for a slab is placed before the concrete is placed. The reinforcing rods protruding at the left of the picture are dowels for a pier.

Fig. 39-5. These rodsetters are placing reinforcing steel at the construction of a hydroelectric dam.

Fig. 39-7. Small blocks of concrete keep this mat of reinforcing steel off the ground.

under it. It must be kept off the ground until all the concrete is placed. There are two common methods of holding the reinforcement off the bottom of the form. Small concrete blocks may be placed under it every few feet. These blocks are the same thickness as the distance the steel is to be off the form bottom. A 3″ block is used if the steel is to be 3″ off the ground, Fig. 39-7.

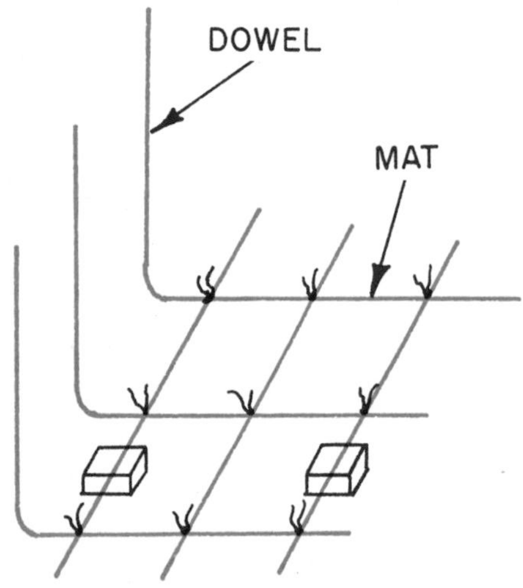

Fig. 39-8. The bent rods form dowels which will help support the wall.

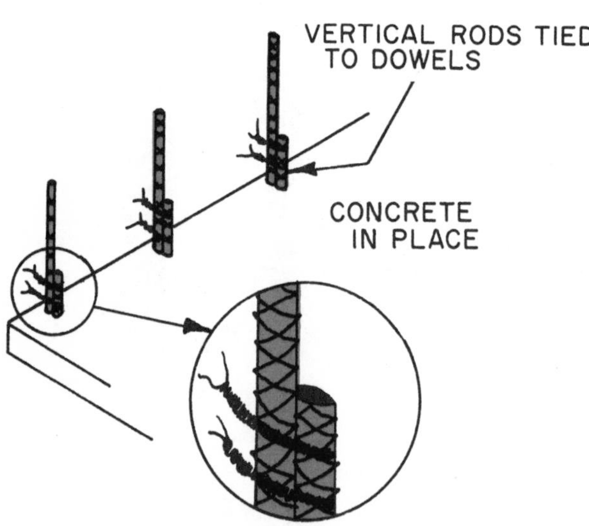

Fig. 39-9. Vertical rods are tied to the dowels after the slab has set.

In addition to concrete block supports, bent pieces of metal, called *chairs,* may be used. *High chairs* are used where there are two levels of reinforcing steel in the same slab. They are used on the level near the top surface. *Low chairs* are used to support the bottom level. Because chairs are made of wire and would be pushed into the ground under the weight of the concrete, they cannot be used for slabs built on the ground. After the reinforcing steel is in place, we are ready to place the concrete in a slab form.

Spread footings for walls and piers have the same kind of mat prepared as that for the slab just described. In addition, we have to provide for bent rods called *dowels* that are to be partly in the footing and partly in the wall or pier, Figs. 39-6 and 39-8.

When the footing has been placed and the concrete has set up or hardened, the braces and stakes used to hold the vertical steel are removed. One face of the wall

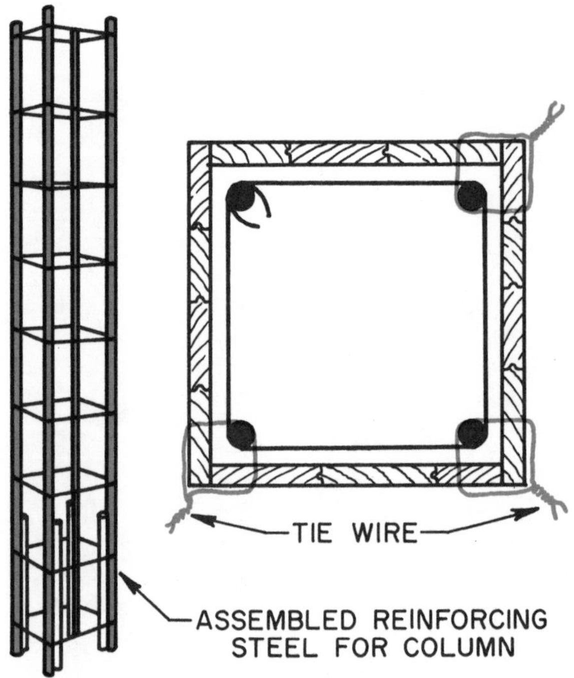

Fig. 39-10. The reinforcing steel in a pier is often set up and then put in place for tying to dowels.

form is now built. The horizontal rods to be used in the wall are tied to the vertical rods, the ends of which are now buried in the footing concrete. See Fig. 39-9.

Walls often have two mats of steel, one near each face of the concrete. Both mats may have vertical rods embedded in the concrete footing, or one may simply start at the top of the footing and go upward. When both mats have been tied in place, the second face of the form is built and tied to the first one with form ties. Before concrete can be placed in this form, the steel must be checked to be sure that it is exactly the right distance from the face of the form. To hold it in position, the two mats either are tied to the form ties or a nail is driven into the form every few feet and the mat of reinforcing steel is tied to the nails.

In setting the reinforcing steel for piers, mats of steel are not generally used unless the piers are very large. In smaller piers, the vertical rods are held in position by a rod that has been bent to the shape of the cross section of the pier. These shaped pieces, called *hoops,* are tied to the vertical rods. They are spaced along the vertical rods according to the specifications on the shop plan. After the pier form is in place, the reinforcement is fastened in position so that it will be the right distance from the faces of the form, Fig. 39-10.

Summary

All foundation walls built of concrete must have reinforcing steel in them. Reinforcing steel may be either deformed steel rods which are set at right angles to each other and tied in place, or it may be reinforcing mesh. Reinforcing steel is set by rodsetters using a shop drawing showing the size, position, and number of reinforcing rods to be used.

In a foundation slab, either reinforcing rods or reinforcing mesh may be used. This is set in place after the forms have been built. Reinforcing steel for walls is set in place after one side of the form has been erected. Reinforcing steel for piers is set in place before any of the forms are erected.

Terms to Know

reinforcing rods
reinforcing mesh
rodsetter
on center
hoops
chairs
  a. high chairs
  b. low chairs
dowels
deformed rods

Think About It!

1. Why do you think reinforcing steel rods are deformed (ridges on the surfaces of the rods)? Would smooth-surfaced reinforcing steel work as well? Why?
2. Does reinforcing steel in concrete allow the solid concrete mass to "bend"? In a dictionary or encyclopedia, look up "tensile" or "tensile strength." Does the meaning of these terms provide a hint?

READING 40

Mixing Concrete

The forms for the concrete foundations have been set, tied together, and braced into position. The reinforcing steel has been set in the forms and tied in place so that it will not move when concrete is placed around it, Fig. 40-1. We are now ready to prepare the concrete to place in the forms.

Concrete is made of crushed rock or gravel that is mixed with sand, portland cement, and water. Each of these must be specially prepared before it can be used in the concrete. In addition to the basic ingredients, most modern concrete contains at least one *admixture* (special additive). These admixtures are used to change the basic nature of concrete. For example, they may speed up or slow down hardening time. This lesson describes how the ingredients used in making concrete are prepared, measured, and mixed.

Preparing Coarse Aggregate

Gravel or crushed rock is used for coarse aggregate. Gravel (small stones) is found in natural deposits on the earth's surface. The stones are various sizes and shapes. Generally they have rounded edges, and most

Fig. 40-1. The form must be ready, including tying reinforcing steel, before concrete can be placed.

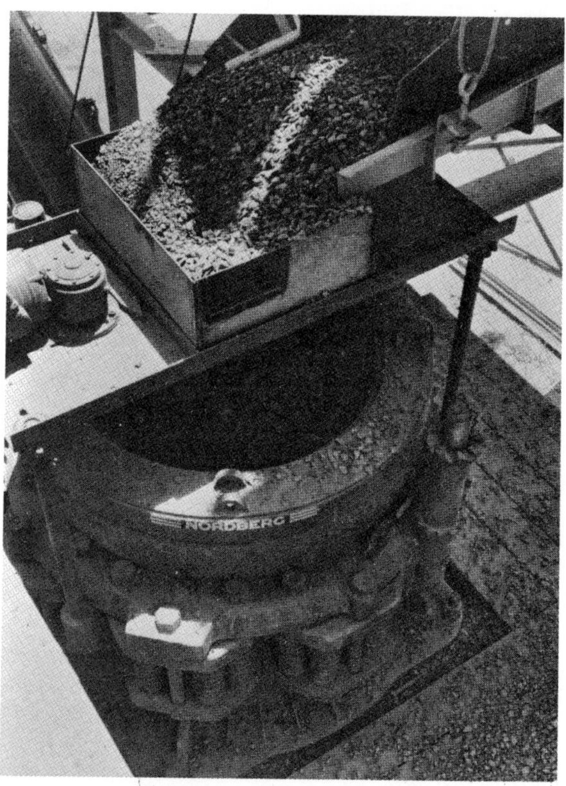

Fig. 40-2. A rock crusher reduces the size of the material.

of them are shaped like balls or spheres. *Crushed rock* is manufactured by breaking rock into pieces in a rock crusher, Fig. 40-2. Pieces of crushed rock have sharp edges and may be shaped much like cubes. This is the best shape for aggregate. If the rock is too soft, it will crush into powder which cannot be used. Some kinds of rock break up into thin, flat pieces which also should not be used for concrete.

The gravel or crushed rock that is used in concrete is called coarse aggregate, Fig. 40-3. The coarse aggregate should not only have most of its pieces either round or square in shape, but these pieces should also be the correct size. To get the sizes which are needed, coarse aggregate is *graded* (sized) from the largest to the smallest sizes used in concrete. The largest size of stone generally used in coarse aggregate is 2½″, and the smallest size is ¼″.

The largest size of coarse aggregate is chosen to suit the position of the reinforcing steel. We have said that reinforcing steel may be placed 1″, 2″, or 3″ from the face of the form. We must be able to get the coarse aggregate between the face of the form and the reinforcing steel. If the distance is 1″, the largest size of coarse aggregate must be only ¾″. If the distance between the steel and the form is 2″, the largest size of coarse aggregate would be 1½″. A second reason for using the largest size aggregate possible is to reduce the amount of cement paste in the total mix. This both saves money and improves the quality of the concrete.

Preparing Fine Aggregate

The sand that is used in concrete is called fine aggregate. Just as with coarse aggregate, fine aggregate has different sizes. It is graded (screened) to get the different sizes used in concrete. See Fig. 40-4.

Generally, both the coarse aggregate and the fine aggregate are washed before being graded (sized). Washing removes particles that are too small. Rock dust or clay often found in stone or sand would be examples of such particles. The prepared aggregate is stockpiled until it is needed, Fig. 40-5.

Fig. 40-3. Coarse aggregate is used in making concrete. This photograph shows the smallest size to the largest size.

Fig. 40-4. Fine aggregate also is graded into various sizes.

Preparing Cement

The cement used in concrete is portland cement. *Portland cement* is made from a certain kind of limestone that is found in deposits below the earth's surface. The limestone is quarried (broken) out of its solid deposit in pieces. Then it is crushed to a fine powder in a crusher. Some clay or shale is also crushed and mixed with the limestone in the right amounts. The mixture of limestone and clay is fed into a rotary kiln, (furnace) and heated at a temperature of 2,700° Fahrenheit. During this process, it forms a porous mass called a *clinker*. The clinker is taken from the kiln and ground to a powder. Then a small amount of *gypsum* much like the lime used in masonry is added to make the portland cement, Figs. 40-6 and 40-7.

When portland cement is mixed with water, it forms a paste that becomes firm or sets in about two hours. After the paste sets up, it slowly becomes much harder. The setting up and the hardening of the cement paste is caused by a chemical reaction between the cement and the water. This is called *hydration*.

Since oil or dirt in concrete will interfere with the hydration of the cement, the water used must be clean. Sea water taken from the ocean has a great amount of salt and cannot be used. It is often said that the water used in concrete should be fit to drink. The water used in concrete is much the same

Fig. 40-5. Stockpiling aggregate to be used in making concrete.

Fig. 40-6. From this control room in a modern cement manufacturing plant, a few operators control and monitor the material.

Fig. 40-7. A cement plant where portland cement is manufactured.

as that which comes from the faucet in your home.

Using Admixtures

Modern concrete technology has been expanded by the use of *admixtures* or *special additives* which are to be found in most of the concrete placed today. Common admixtures are *entraining agents* (substances which hold air bubbles in the concrete), water reducing agents (substances which thicken the mix), retarders (substances which slow the hardening), and accelerators (substances which speed the hardening). Admixtures help make concrete easier to work with and extend its usefulness.

Measuring and Mixing Concrete

When concrete is ordered to fill the forms for foundations, it is ordered by the cubic yard. To find how much is needed, the dimensions or sizes of the space inside the forms are multiplied to get the cubic feet of space in the forms. This number of cubic feet is then divided by 27 to get the number of cubic yards of concrete needed.

When concrete is mixed, each of the ingregredients is measured or weighed in pounds. Even the water is included. The ingredients for concrete are mixed at a concrete mixing plant, Fig. 40-8. There, the workers are able to figure the weight of the materials for any amount or kind of mix.

Mixers are part of the mixing plant or are mounted on trucks. Concrete may be mixed at the mixing plant and only be agitated in a truck, or it may be mixed at the same time that it is being hauled to the construction site. The practice used depends upon the length of the haul, the size of the job, and the concrete requirements. Most of the hauling trucks can be used either as a mixer or an agitator, Fig. 40-9.

Fig. 40-8. In this mixing plant, concrete is made by mixing crushed rock, sand, portland cement, and water.

Summary

In concrete, the stone is called the coarse aggregate, and the sand is called the fine aggregate. Both of these aggregates must be carefully cleaned and graded to size before they can be used. Cement in concrete is manufactured from a special limestone to which clay is added before the two materials are heated into a clinker. The clinker is ground to a fine powder called portland cement.

Fig. 40-9. Ready-mixed concrete is being delivered to the site.

Concrete is mixed from the two aggregates, cement, and water. The amount for each is carefully measured. Admixtures also may be added to the concrete. These are then poured into a mixer. A concrete truck usually hauls the concrete to the construction site where it is placed to become part of a structure.

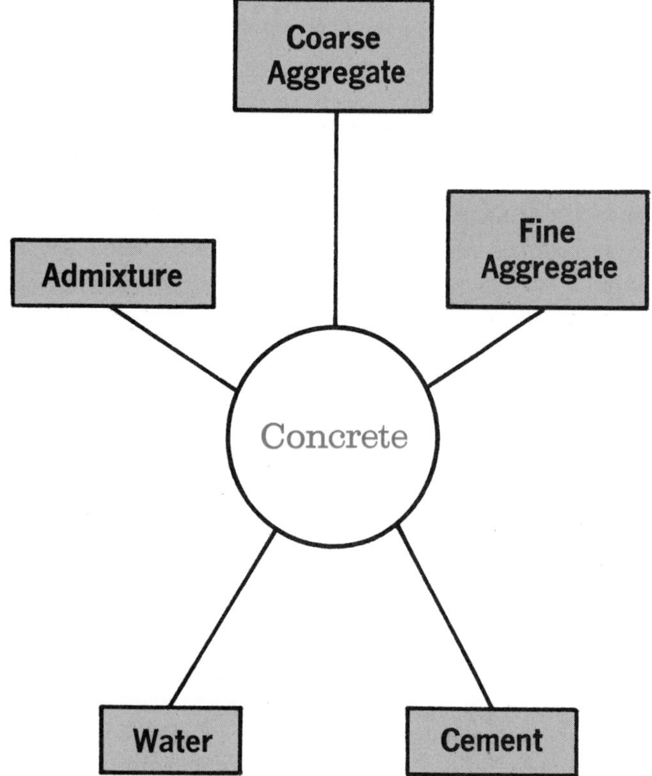

Terms to Know

concrete
admixture
additive
coarse aggregate
fine aggregate
screened
stockpiling
portland cement
kiln
clinker
hydration
mixer
agitator
graded
types of admixtures
- a. entraining agents
- b. water reducing agents
- c. retarders
- d. accelerators

Think About It!

1. What is the difference between cement and concrete?
2. Look in your telephone directory and find out how many "ready-mix" concrete mixing plants are located in your community.

Placing and Finishing Concrete

The forms for the concrete foundation have been completed. The reinforcing steel has been set, tied, and fastened in its position in the forms. The materials for the concrete have been prepared, and the concrete has been mixed. We are now ready to place the concrete in the forms.

Concrete may be mixed on the site, at a batching plant (Fig. 41-1), or may even be mixed on the way to the construction site in a transit mix truck which has a large drum on it. The drum turns slowly during its trip from the batching plant to the construction site to keep the concrete mixed. In unloading the concrete and placing it, every step must be done carefully to keep the heavy particles from separating from the rest of the mixture.

Fig. 41-1. For large jobs, concrete is often mixed at a batching plant.

Unloading and Moving Concrete

When the truck driver is ready to unload the concrete, he reverses the *drum*. This moves the concrete out of a gate that has been opened to let the concrete flow from the truck. The truck also carries a small *chute*, Fig. 41-2. One end of this chute fits under the gate, and the concrete flows into it. The chute slopes down from the gate toward the ground. At the lower end of the chute there must be a container to hold the flowing concrete.

If the concrete has been properly measured and mixed, we should get out of the drum a gray material that flows as slowly as a thick pancake batter. This concrete sets quickly. Because the concrete has been traveling for some time, it must be put into the forms as rapidly as possible, for it must be in the forms in its final position before it sets.

The kind of container into which the concrete is dumped depends on where the concrete is to be used. When the concrete is to be placed near the truck chute, it may be placed directly into the form. Of course, this easy placement of the concrete does not happen often.

If the concrete is to be used quite a distance off the ground, it is often put into a large bucket that is lifted by a crane and swung into position over the form, Fig. 41-3. Each bucket will hold from 1 to 3 cubic yards of concrete. This concrete can be dumped into a form by opening the gate in the bottom of each bucket.

When the concrete must be used on the ground beyond the truck chute, concrete buggies may carry it from the truck to its position. These buggies hold only 6 to 11 cubic feet of concrete. They are small buckets mounted on wheels. Sometimes they are driven by motor and sometimes they are pushed by hand, Fig. 41-4.

Fig. 41-2. The transit-mix truck is often driven onto the construction site to unload the concrete.

Fig. 41-3. Concrete is put into a large bucket to be lifted by a crane.

At very large sites, concrete may be temporarily dumped into steel tanks called *hoppers,* which may be located at various points around the site. From these, it can be dumped into concrete buggies which deliver the concrete to its destination. This is done so that the delivery truck may return to the batching plant. While the truck is gone, each hopper can supply concrete to a number of buggies. Thus, the expensive truck is used more efficiently.

Usually, the concrete is placed by using chutes, buggies, buckets, or hoppers. On large projects, however, placing concrete can be done much faster by using conveyors (endless moving belts) or by pumping it through hoses. Conveyors and pumps place concrete at the rate of at least 30 to 40 cubic yards per hour. Conveyors are the cheapest possible way to place large

Fig. 41-4. When the concrete cannot be placed directly from the chute, it may be carried from the truck in concrete buggies.

amounts of concrete which require intermediate handling between truck and form. Although they work well for most jobs, conveyors are not presently suited to raising concrete straight up. Pumps, however, work well for this.

Placing and Consolidating Concrete

In locations where concrete is to be thick, it is placed in layers about 12″ deep. After each layer is placed into the form, it is agitated (worked) with a rod or shaken by a vibrator to consolidate the concrete, Fig. 41-5. *A vibrator is a tube that is closed at one end.* It is about 12″ in length and 2″ or 3″ in width. A long hose containing a flexible shaft is fastened to the open end and put down into the wet concrete. The shaft in the hose is turned by a gasoline engine or an electric motor which causes the tube or vibrator head to shake. The vibration forces the concrete tightly against the form and gets rid of air bubbles. Vibrating keeps the concrete mixed, levels the top of the layer, and mixes the top layer of concrete with the layer beneath it. For thin layers of concrete, like sidewalks, vibrating is not needed.

Fig. 41-5. A vibrator is used to settle the concrete around the forms and the reinforcement.

If a wall form is very deep, the concrete is dumped from a small hopper that has a chute fastened to it. This chute is made up of short sections of tubing that are loosely fastened together. Because of this, it is sometimes called an *elephant trunk*. Various lengths of chute are needed for filling up a deep form in order to be able to control the placing of the concrete. If the concrete were allowed to fall a long way without being confined by the chute, the heavy pieces in the mixture would plunge to the bottom of the form.

Leveling Concrete

When all the concrete has been placed, the concrete surface should be at the same level as the top of the form. To level the concrete, we use a *straightedge* rested on *screeds* (guides for leveling the surface). The straightedge is a long piece of straight wood or metal. One end of the straightedge rests on the top of one side of the form while the other end rests on the opposite side of the form (also called screeds). Cement fin-

Fig. 41-6. After being placed, the concrete is leveled.

ishers push the board back and forth over the concrete until the surface is level with the screeds or top of the form. See Fig. 41-6.

When a slab is very large, one straightedge may be too short to reach from one side of the form to the other. Then additional screeds must be set in between the form faces. These screeds are pieces of lumber or steel that are set parallel with one face of the form inside the area where the concrete is to be placed. The tops of all of the screeds (both those which are the tops of the forms and those inside the forms) are at the same level.

The bottoms of the screeds inside the form must be kept from touching the top layer of steel used to reinforce the concrete. To keep these screeds in position, they are nailed to stakes driven into the ground between the openings in the rods of the reinforcing steel. Steel pins are sometimes used. Screeds are usually set 6′ apart and parallel to one another so that the straightedge can be pushed back and forth over them to smooth the concrete surface.

After the concrete in the slab has been placed and has been smoothed by this process, the concrete soon *sets up*. When the surface is stiff but not hard, the screeds inside the form are then removed from the concrete, and the grooves they make are patched.

Fig. 41-7. After the surface of the concrete is leveled, it is floated to make sure a smooth mixture of cement, sand, and water is on the surface.

Floating Concrete

There are several surface finishes that can be put on a slab of concrete; but, before we put on the final finish, we must *float* the surface that has been smoothed by using the screeds. After the concrete has stiffened, but before it hardens, *floating* is done by the cement finisher. He uses a tool called a *wood float* which he moves back and forth over the surface until it is level and no coarse particles can be seen. Floating the surface is done to be sure that there is only a smooth mixture of cement, sand, and water on the surface. No coarse particle should show. After the concrete has been floated, a final finish can be put on. Sometimes, however, a float finish is used as the final finish. See Fig. 41-7.

Finishing

Usually a smooth finish like that found on a sidewalk is needed. A smooth finish is called a *steel trowel finish*. The cement finisher makes it by moving a steel trowel back and forth over the surface. A troweled surface can also be made with a finishing machine. The *finishing machine* has an engine or motor that slowly turns a wheel to which three or four steel trowels have been fastened. It can finish a large area in a short amount of time, Fig. 41-8.

The top of a foundation wall may be finished in the same way as a concrete slab. If we plan to put more concrete on top of a foundation wall, it should be left very rough so that the concrete will be able to bond or stick to it. A float finish should be left on top of a wall if masonry, such as stone or brick, is to be laid on it.

For other kinds of walls, we may wish to leave anchor bolts sticking up out of the top of the wall. Steel or wood for the superstructure can then be fastened to the bolts. Bolts must be put in before the concrete is placed for the foundation walls. When bolts are put into the top of a wall in a slab or in the top of a pier, they must be put in very carefully. To do this, a wooden frame is nailed to the top of the form where the bolts are to be placed. Holes are drilled in the frame exactly where the bolts are needed.

Since the bolts are to be anchored in the concrete, the buried part of the bolt has a hook on it. Before the concrete is placed, 2″ or 3″ of the bolt is pushed up through the hole which has been drilled in the frame. This part of the bolt is threaded so a nut may be put on it to hold the bolt to the frame. After the concrete has been placed and has hardened, the bolt cannot move. The nut is then taken off, and the frame is removed just before the wall forms are stripped. Nothing can be done with the other surfaces on the wall or pier until the forms have been removed.

Fig. 41-8. Large surfaces are often troweled with a finishing machine.

Summary

Concrete is moved from mixers or trucks to the forms by chutes, concrete buckets, concrete buggies, hoppers, conveyors, or pumps. While the concrete is being moved, heavy pieces in the mix must be kept from settling. Concrete of any great thickness must be agitated or vibrated when it is placed.

After concrete has been placed, the surface is made level with the top of the form by using a straightedge set on screeds. If the concrete slab is very large, additional screeds must be set in between the ones on the form faces.

Before the final finish is put on concrete, it must be floated. The cement finisher does this by passing a wood float back and forth over the surface until no coarse particle shows.

After a float finish has had several hours to get firm, the final finish can be put on. A smooth finish is called a *steel trowel fin-*

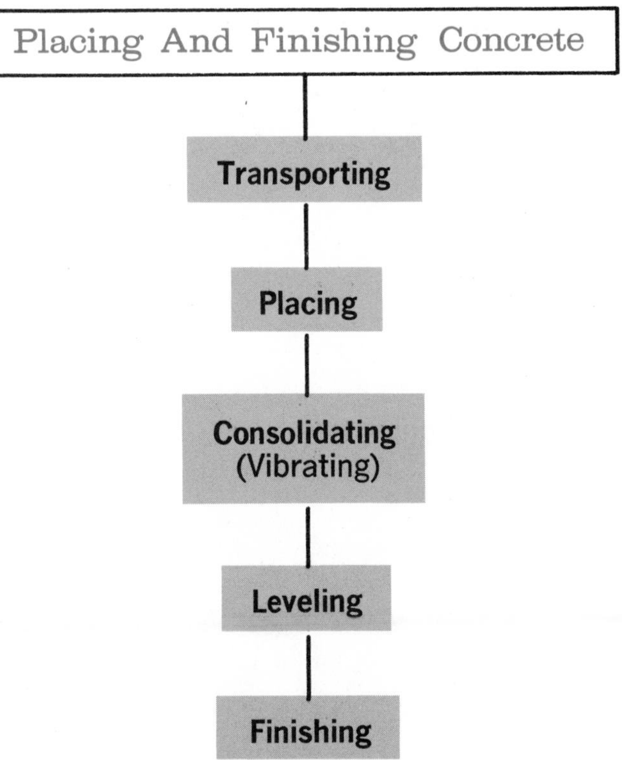

ish. This is done by moving a steel trowel back and forth over the surface.

For some walls, we may wish to leave bolts sticking up out of the top of the wall to use for bolting the superstructure to the foundation or substructure. These bolts must be put in and held in position before the concrete is placed.

Terms to Know

transit mixer truck
  a. drum
  b. gate
  c. chute
pump
leveled
floated
screed
batch
hopper
agitate
vibrate
conveyor
straightedge
sets up
troweled
steel trowel finish

Think About It!

1. Look around your home or school and find several different concrete surfaces. Identify at least one steel trowel finish and one float finish.
2. How does weather affect concrete finishing?

Completing Foundations

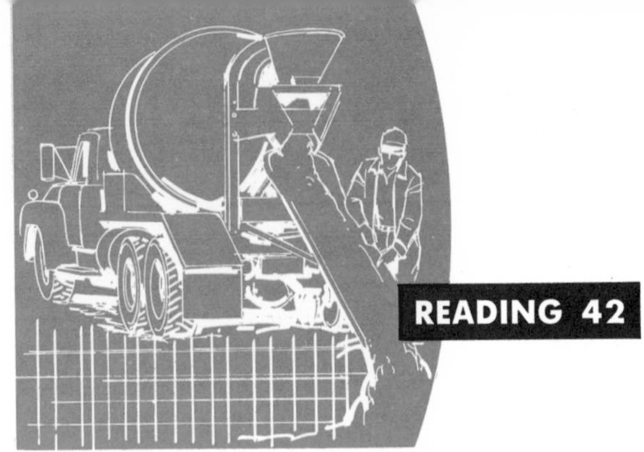

After the concrete has been placed in the forms and the visible surfaces finished, there are still several important steps for the completing of the foundation: (1) allowing the concrete to set, (2) removing the forms, (3) making sure that the concrete is properly cured, and (4) treating the surfaces which were covered by the forms.

Allowing the Concrete to Set

The concrete workers must leave the concrete in the forms until it *sets. Concrete is set when it will retain or hold the shape given to it by its particular form.* Concrete which is set is firm, but it is not hard or strong. The amount of time needed for concrete to set depends upon the kind and amount of concrete used and the temperature and humidity during the time it is in its form. However, concrete will usually set in 12 to 24 hours. It usually takes a much longer period of time for concrete to become hard and strong. The time needed for the concrete to become hard and strong is called the *curing time.* This will be discussed later in this lesson.

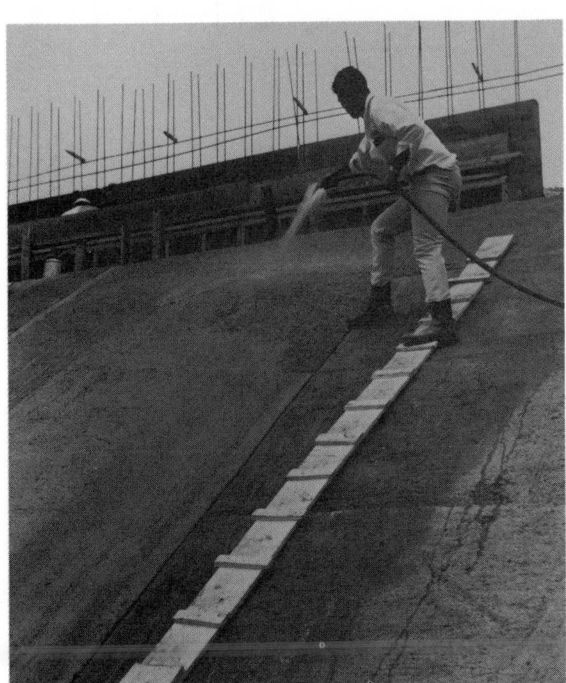

Fig. 42-1. Green concrete is firm, but it is neither hard nor strong.

Removing the Forms

The process of removing the forms from around the concrete is called *stripping the forms.* The workmen must not strip the forms until the concrete has properly set. In some cases, the concrete is allowed to cure before the forms are removed. Concrete which has set but has not cured is called *green concrete.* It is firm but not hard and strong, Fig. 42-1.

To strip the forms, the workers must knock the braces loose and pull out the stakes. Next, they break off the ends of the ties. Then they can separate the forms from the concrete. Using hammers, wrecking bars, nail pullers, pliers, and wrenches, the workmen then remove the walers, studs, plates, and facing material, Fig. 42-2. The men must work carefully when removing the forms so that they do not damage or break the parts. Form materials can be reused, and this reduces or lowers the cost of the foundation. The men must be very careful when they strip forms from green concrete, because green concrete breaks and chips easily.

After all the form parts have been removed, the workers clean and store them for future use. Cleaning form parts includes pulling nails, scraping or knocking off concrete particles, and treating the forms for future use.

Curing is the process through which the concrete becomes hard and strong. Curing is not the result of the concrete's drying out. Rather, it results from a chemical reaction of the elements within the concrete. In fact, curing will not be completed if the concrete dries out too quickly. Therefore, concrete workers take steps to keep the concrete from drying out rapidly.

They may use one of several techniques to keep the moisture in the concrete: (1)

Fig. 42-3. To keep concrete from drying too fast, it may be covered with straw and sprayed with water.

Fig. 42-2. After the surface of this concrete is finished and set, the forms will be removed.

curing with water and (2) curing with sealing membranes. Moist curing is done by spraying the concrete regularly with water or by covering the concrete with earth, sand, straw, or burlap, and then keeping the covering damp, Fig. 42-3. Curing with sealing membranes means that a thin, protective coating is sprayed on the surface of the concrete as soon as the forms are removed, Fig. 42-4. This coating holds moisture in the concrete. Concrete must be kept moist for the first part of the 14 to 28 days it usually takes to properly cure it.

The curing process may be speeded up with accelerators (special admixtures), special grades of improved cements, careful design of the mix, and by steam curing. Modern concrete technology makes it possible to produce in 24 hours or less concrete which will support 3,000 pounds per square inch. Because this can only be done with added expense, these techniques are saved for projects where shortening the curing time is worth the extra cost.

Treating the Formed Surfaces

Formed surfaces are those which touch the forms and can be seen only after the forms have been stripped. The first step that the concrete workers take in treating formed surfaces is patching holes caused by the form ties and any other defects which show in the concrete. The workers put a mixture of sand, portland cement, and water into holes and other chips which show after the forms are removed, Fig. 42-5.

The final treatment depends on the location of the surface. If the surface will touch earth, it may need to be protected from moisture. Concrete is waterproof *if* a perfect job of placing and finishing is done. Usually, however, there are small defects which allow moisture to gradually seep through the concrete. Therefore, workmen waterproof the concrete by putting a layer of asphalt on the surface. The men either brush or spray the asphalt onto the concrete. If a very durable or strong waterproofing

Fig. 42-4. In the process of curing, concrete is sometimes sprayed with a curing compound which holds in the moisture.

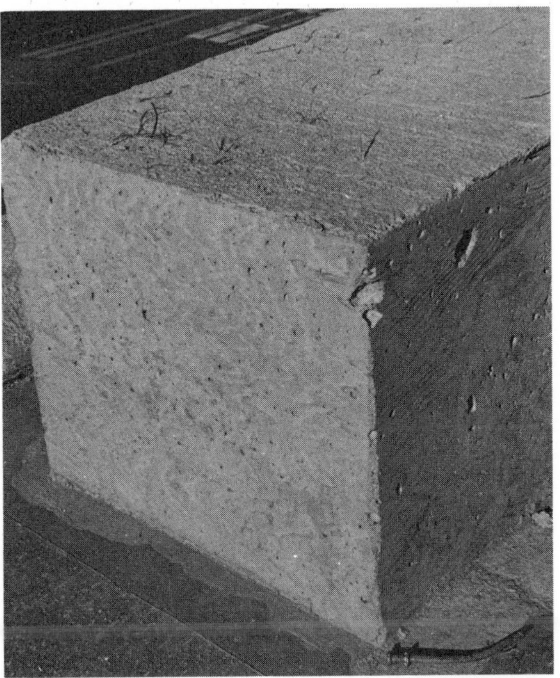

Fig. 42-5. Formed surfaces often have holes and chips in them that need patching.

is needed, the workers put on alternate layers of asphalt and asphalt-saturated paper to build up a thick coating on the concrete surface, Fig. 42-6.

If the surface of the concrete will not be in contact with moisture and will be exposed to view, like the surface of piers which support an elevated highway, it is treated in a different way. The workmen may treat the surface with a stoned finish, a sack-rubbed finish, or a special coating.

To apply a *stoned finish,* the workers wet the concrete surface thoroughly with water and then rub a mixture of sand, portland cement, and water over the surface. Then, the surface is ground with a flat stone until it is smooth and all blemishes are removed.

The concrete finishers apply a *sack-rubbed finish* by wetting the concrete surface, rubbing a thin mixture of sand, portland cement, and water over the surface with a piece of burlap or sponge float, and then rubbing a dry mixture of sand and cement over the same surface. When the finishers have completed the sack-rubbed treatment, the surface has the appearance of sandpaper, but all holes have been removed.

Sometimes concrete surfaces look better when *special coatings,* which are designed to be used on concrete, are put on them. The workers either brush or spray these coatings onto concrete surfaces, Fig. 42-7.

Summary

There are four important steps needed to complete a foundation after the concrete has been placed and the exposed surfaces have been finished. These steps are: (1) allowing the concrete to set, (2) removing the forms, (3) making sure that the concrete is properly cured, and (4) treating the surfaces which were covered by the forms. Concrete which has set but has not cured is called *green concrete.* It is firm but not hard and strong.

Forms are usually removed after the concrete has set. However, in some cases, the

Fig. 42-6. The foundation wall in the center of the picture has been treated with asphalt.

Fig. 42-7. A special finish will be applied to the exposed concrete.

concrete may be allowed to cure before the forms are stripped. Curing results from a chemical reaction within the elements of concrete. Concrete must be kept moist for the first part of the 14 to 28 days it usually takes to properly cure it.

Foundation wall surfaces which are in contact with moisture are usually waterproofed. Wall surfaces which are not in contact with moisture and which show after the structure is complete may be stone finished, sack-rubbed, or coated.

Terms to Know

setting of concrete	green concrete
setting time	waterproof
curing of concrete	asphalt
curing time	stoned finish
stripping the forms	sack-rubbed finish
formed surfaces	special coatings

Think About It!

1. When concrete cures, it becomes hard and strong. Is curing simply the result of the water drying out? Does some other reaction or process take place? If so, what does occur?
2. List two reasons why some hardened concrete surfaces must receive a final surface finish.

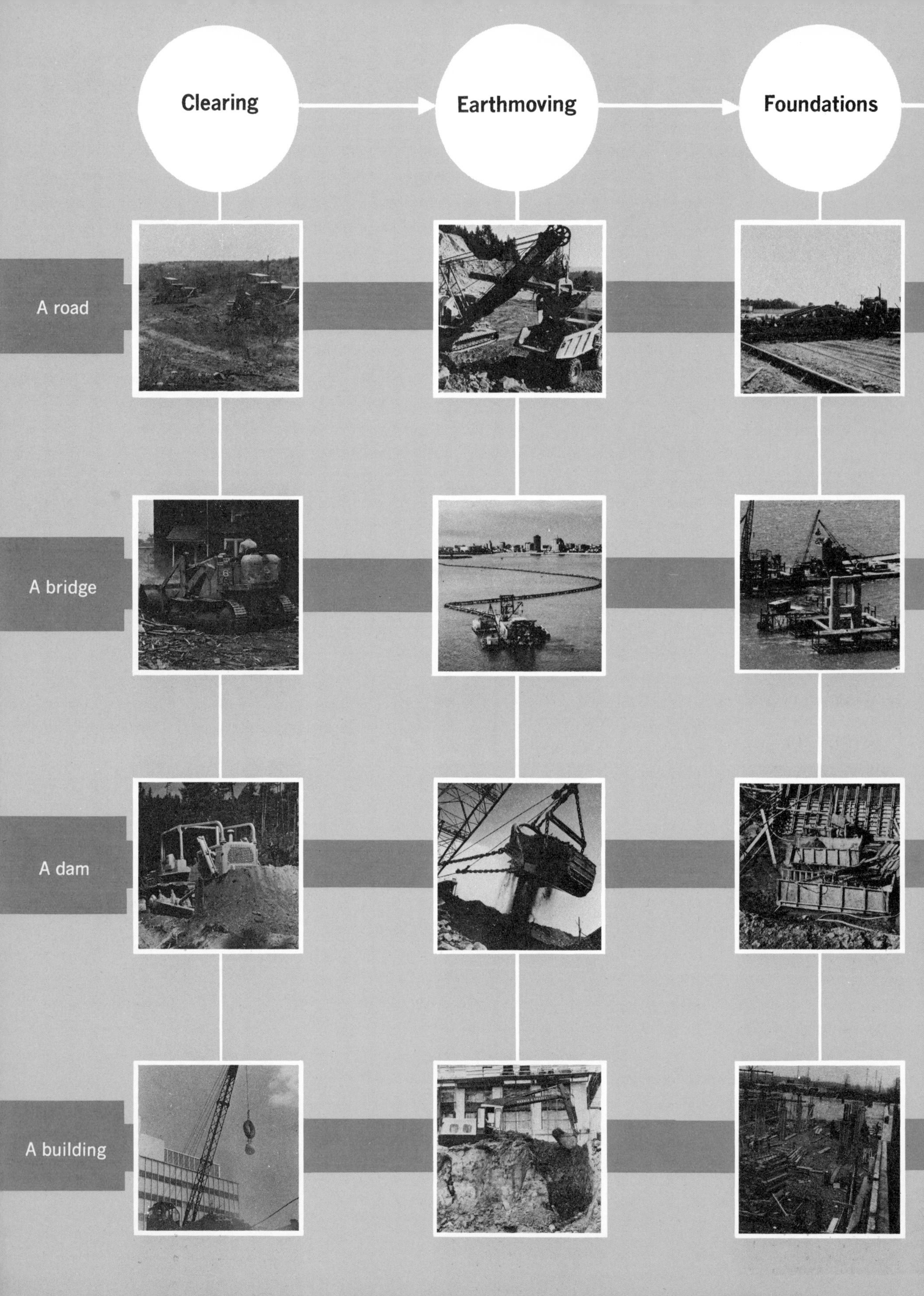

Clearing
Earthmoving
Foundations
A road
A bridge
A dam
A building

Superstructures
Utilities
Finished Project

READING 43

Building Superstructures

You have learned that the first step in building a structure is to set the foundation or substructure. We are now ready to start on the second step of construction, building the superstructure. Later you will study these units: (1) how each major kind of superstructure is built, (2) how framed superstructures are enclosed from the weather, (3) how utility systems are installed, (4) how framed superstructures are enclosed on the inside, (5) how the superstructure is finished, (6) how painting and decorating are done, and (7) how accessories are installed.

Superstructures

When you look at the structures around you, *the part you see rising above ground level is the superstructure.* It is the part of the structure which rests upon the foundation, or substructure. Towers, such as those used for television broadcasting or for transmitting electricity, are mostly superstructure. However, they also have a foundation under them, Fig. 43-1.

The design of a superstructure depends upon the purpose for which the structure will be used. The superstructure of a manufacturing plant is designed so articles may be produced in it. A bridge or highway superstructure is designed to carry traffic. The substructure supports both the weight of the superstructure and the traffic.

In some structures there is no clearly defined superstructure. In a dam, the part which rises above the ground surface and holds back the water may be thought of as the superstructure. That part of the pyramids in Egypt which rises above the surface of the sand is the superstructure.

When we consider a canal, a tunnel, or underground piping, we cannot say that one part of these structures is a foundation and that another part is the superstructure, Fig. 43-2. Railroad tracks usually are not called superstructures. However, they do rest on a foundation and may be classed as superstructures.

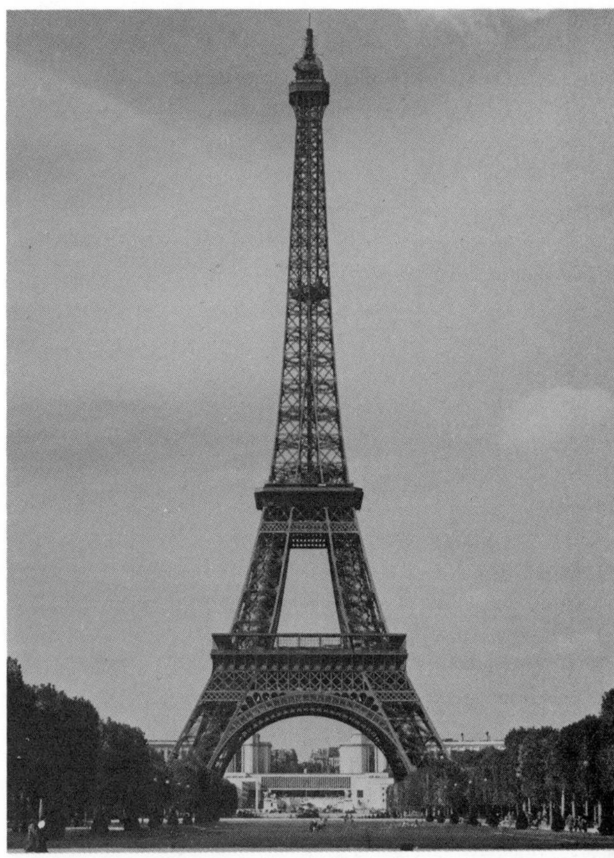

Fig. 43-1. Superstructures serve the purposes for which projects are built.

Kinds of Superstructures

The superstructures you see around you may be divided into three kinds: (1) mass, (2) bearing wall, and (3) framed superstructures.

Mass superstructures are made of large bodies of materials which generally cover large areas. Examples of mass superstructures are earth or concrete dams and cast-in-place concrete retaining walls, Fig. 43-3. Large monuments built of piled up stone, such as the pyramids of Egypt or the Washington Monument, also are mass superstructures, Fig. 43-4. Mass superstructures may have very little or no open space inside the mass of materials.

Bearing wall superstructures are made of masonry or other materials and usually are built as walls, or walls and roofs. Bearing wall superstructures enclose a space. See Fig. 43-5.

Framed superstructures are those such as houses which are built with a frame. The frame is like a skeleton. The parts that make up the frame serve the same purpose as do the bones in your body, Fig. 43-6. Frames for superstructures may be made of steel, reinforced concrete, or wood. The members of a frame are columns or posts with beams connecting one to another. When these members are properly assembled, they provide a rigid form for the superstructure. The frame supports the materials which enclose the space within the superstructure.

Fig. 43-2. Some projects, such as canals, are hard to classify into substructures and superstructures.

Fig. 43-3. San Luis Dam in California is an example of a mass superstructure.

Fig. 43-4. Mass superstructures are among man's oldest constructed works.

The materials used to enclose framework may be steel panels, concrete slabs, wood siding, sheets of plastic or glass, or various kinds of masonry.

Mass Superstructures

Superstructures which are built using a mass of materials are made from bulk materials which are taken from the earth and put into the structure without much processing. Earth dams, for example, are constructed by excavating earth at one location and hauling it to another to be dumped, spread, and compacted without much processing. Embankments built along rivers for flood protection are built in much the same way.

Materials used in mass superstructures also may be made from separate elements of earth that are partially processed and then are cemented together. Concrete is an example of this. You have learned that concrete is a mixture of aggregates taken from the earth combined together with cement and water. Certain structures, such as concrete dams, use solid masses of concrete. Concrete retaining walls or concrete walls used for flood protection also are made of a solid mass of concrete.

Bituminous concrete is made from stone aggregates which are bound together with asphalt. Bituminous concrete is used for surfacing roads, parking lots, and air fields. These surfaces are a kind of mass superstructure.

The Tower of Babel was built using masses of brick bound together. It is an example of a mass superstructure. The brick was placed into solid rectangular layers with each layer smaller than the one below it. This tower was built many centuries ago in Babylon with the hope that the top of it would reach to heaven. The bottom was 300′ square, and the top of it was 325′ above the earth.

Bearing Wall Superstructures

In early times walls were built of stone and were sometimes so thick that they seemed almost like mass construction, Fig. 43-7. Walls might have been 3′ or 4′ thick or more, especially if the superstructure was very tall, such as a cathedral. Today, such walls are not often more than 16″ or 18″ thick even when the building is quite tall.

Fig. 43-5. Load bearing superstructures are enclosures which are not framed. These tanks are examples of this type.

Fig. 43-6. Framed superstructures have skeletons which perform in much the same way as do the skeletons in our bodies.

Brick and concrete block are still much in use today. However, stone is not often used now for masonry superstructures.

Masonry walls enclosing a space to form a superstructure are often called *bearing walls* because they support the weight of the floors and the roof as well as all of the weight of the superstructure above them, Fig. 43-8.

Framed Superstructures

Frameworks of buildings provide the skeletons on which to support the walls that close in the superstructure, the floors that divide it into levels, and the roof over it. When you stand on the floor of a tall building, it is really the framework that supports your weight.

All frames for superstructures are made of individual pieces that are assembled and fastened together. This is true even with concrete framework even though reinforcing steel and formwork are required to produce it.

Frameworks may be built of steel, of reinforced concrete, or of wood. The tallest buildings use frameworks made of steel. The Empire State Building in New York City rises more than 1,200′ into the air. It has a framework made of steel.

Because the individual members of a concrete frame are larger in cross section than those made of steel, concrete frameworks are used for much lower buildings. Concrete frameworks would take up too much of the space inside a very tall building. Generally, they are used in buildings rising only 100′ to 200′ into the air.

Today, many buildings have frameworks made of wood. However, such buildings usually are not more than 30′ or 40′ high. Most of the superstructures framed with wood are the houses in which we live. Wood is used for framing houses because it is easy to work with and inexpensive.

A framed superstructure provides more space inside and is lighter in weight than the mass or bearing wall superstructures. It also provides a superstructure that can be carried many hundreds of feet into the air. A tower is the simplest form of a framed superstructure. Perhaps the best known example of a tower is the Eiffel Tower in Paris, France. The Eiffel Tower was built in 1889 for the Paris Exposition by the man who designed it and for whom

Fig. 43-7. Load bearing superstructures of masonry have been in use for many years.

Fig. 43-8. Some of our newest construction is of load bearing, prestressed concrete sections.

it was named, Alexander Gustave Eiffel. This tower is 984′ high and was built by assembling 12,000 separate pieces of iron. Steel was not yet in use in 1889. The purpose of the tower was to permit sightseers to climb the stairs or be carried to the top in an elevator in order to see Paris from a point high in the sky. Today, almost all the towers are built of steel; but they still are built of many pieces.

Summary

The superstructure is built on top of the foundation or substructure. The superstructure serves the purpose for which the whole structure was built.

Mass superstructures are those built from materials taken directly from the earth. Sometimes these materials are bound together with cement or asphalt. Bearing wall superstructures are those which are made of masonry or other materials which are built into walls around the place to be enclosed. Framed superstructures are made of steel, reinforced concrete, or wood. These are assembled to provide a skeleton upon which the walls, floors, and roof can be constructed.

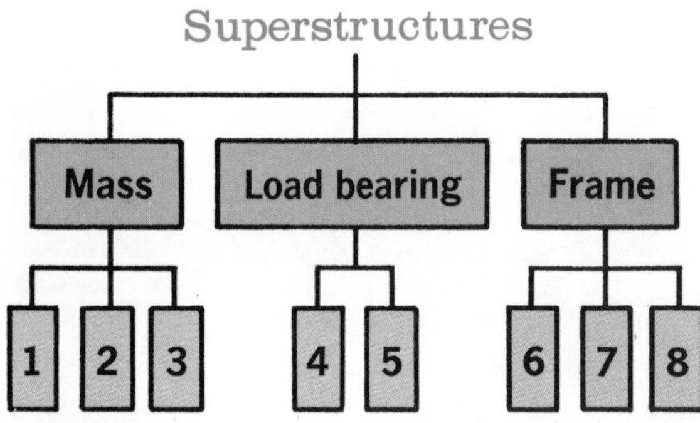

1—Earth
2—Brick and stone
3—Concrete
4—Masonry
5—Other materials
6—Concrete
7—Steel
8—Wood

Terms to Know

superstructure
   a. mass superstructure
   b. bearing wall
   c. framed superstructure

masonry
bituminous concrete
reinforced concrete

Think About It!

1. Classify the following superstructures as (a) mass, (b) bearing wall, or (c) framed:
   a. your home
   b. your school
   c. television tower
   d. highway overpass
   e. earth dam
2. In what way is a framed structure like the human body?

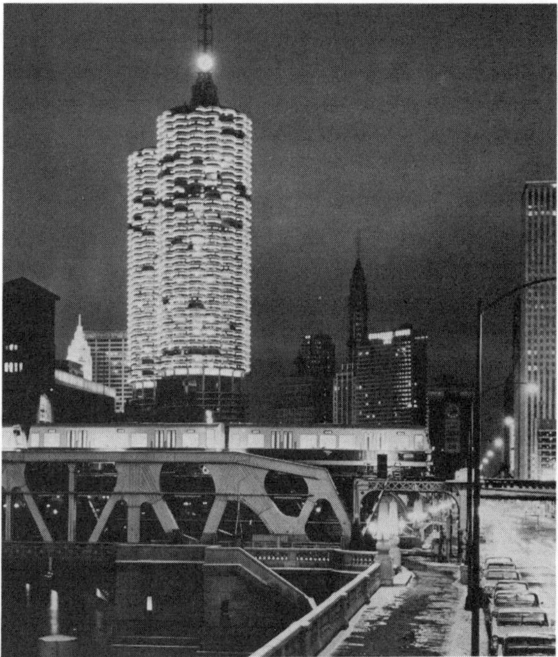

Fig. 43-9. Large superstructures, such as this apartment building, help reduce traffic problems in large cities by locating people near their work.

Building Mass and Masonry Superstructures

READING 44

In the last assignment you learned about superstructures and ways in which they could be built. In this assignment you will study two kinds of superstructures: (1) those which use a mass of materials and (2) those which use a limited mass of materials for walls, combined with a framework for the floors and roofs.

Mass Construction Materials

Soil is a very common and widely used construction material. It is available in large quantities and is not too expensive. Soil is used to build earth dams and other types of earth embankments. It is used to shape our highways and waterways. Even before putting down the substructure of a roadway, soil is moved, placed, and graded to give the correct slope to the road.

Using soil in mass construction usually involves these steps: (1) selecting good soil for the job, (2) excavating, (3) hauling, (4) spreading and mixing, and (5) compacting. Soil must have the proper water content in order to be packed as hard as possible.

Another material taken directly from the earth's surface is rock. *Rock* can be excavated in large blocks or pieces by quarrying. *Quarrying means getting rock out of the earth.* These pieces can be used for massive or very large superstructures. The pyramids of Egypt were built of solid blocks of stone which were carefully quarried and shaped. These blocks were hauled to the site on rollers and then were moved on ramps (inclined planes) using ropes and rollers, to where they were placed.

Many other monuments are built of blocks of stone. An example is the Washington Monument in Washington, D.C., Fig. 44-1. The blocks of stone for this were quarried and hauled to the site on wagons. Each piece was then lifted into place using a derrick resting on the part of the monument that already had been built.

Sometimes large pieces of quarried rock are needed where the shape of the block is not important. *Breakwaters* and *jetties* which slow up the erosion caused by ocean waves are superstructures made of irregular or odd-shaped blocks of stone piled loosely in a long heap. These blocks of stone can be quarried by drilling and blasting.

Mass superstructures also may be built of cemented aggregates. Many kinds of aggregates and ways of cementing them are used for mass superstructures. Concrete is the most common kind of cemented aggregate. In primitive or early construction, mud and clay were held together by mixing them with straw, reeds, and brush.

You have learned something about concrete and how it is made and handled for foundation construction, Fig. 44-2. There are other superstructures built by using concrete as a mass. Many retaining walls, some of which are used to protect the earth along rivers and ocean fronts from being washed away or to provide docks at which ships can unload, are built of concrete.

Highway Superstructures

The surfaces of airports and highways are a kind of mass superstructure. Many of these surfaces are made of concrete, Fig.

Fig. 44-1. Monuments represent one of man's oldest kinds of mass superstructures.

Fig. 44-2. Earthen and concrete dams are examples of mass superstructures.

Fig. 44-3. Highways are the most common type of mass superstructure.

Fig. 44-4. A foundation is carefully prepared for the highway superstructure.

44-3. To build a concrete road, the earth along it is shaped to make a foundation, Fig. 44-4. The soil is compacted or pressed down until it is fairly hard. A substructure of crushed rock or gravel is then placed as a foundation. On this foundation, forms are set along both sides of the strip where concrete is to be placed. These forms are made of heavy steel sheets which are bent so that the top edges are rounded like the rails of a railroad track. They are secured or fastened to the foundation surface with long steel pins driven into the earth.

A concrete mixing unit, usually mounted on crawler treads, sits on the foundation between the forms. Trucks bring coarse aggregate, fine aggregate, and cement in dry batches to the unit and dump them into a ground level hopper. The hopper is tilted to pour its contents into a drum, water is added, and the batch is mixed. The mixed concrete is then spread over the foundation surface between the forms. A mechanical straightedge rides on the forms, as on a pair of rails, to smooth the concrete off and to finish its surface. When the concrete slab has set, the concrete is covered for curing in the same ways as for slab foundations.

Another kind of roadway surface (superstructure) is made with bituminous concrete. This is a kind of cemented aggregate using crushed stone as a coarse aggregate and sand as a fine aggregate. Asphalt is used as a cementing agent instead of portland cement.

Asphalt is a black tarry substance which can be found in pools or lakes on certain parts of the earth's surface. It also can be manufactured from petroleum or from coal.

Bituminous concrete is prepared in mixing plants much like those used for making concrete. The aggregates are weighed and moved into a mixer on a conveyor belt. The asphalt is melted and brought to the right temperature and thickness before it is poured over the aggregates in the mixing tank. When the bituminous concrete has been mixed, it is poured into dump trucks which take the mixture to the paving site.

Bituminous concrete is usually placed in layers. The bottom layer has larger sizes of aggregates, and the top layer is made up of either small aggregates or of fine aggregates. For this reason, steel forms may not be needed along the edges of the paving. The truckload of bituminous concrete is hauled to the site and dumped into a paver. The *paver* spreads the bituminous concrete over the prepared road foundation surface in an even layer. Steel-wheeled rollers follow the paver and compact (pack down) the bituminous concrete while it is still warm. Rolling is continued until the bituminous concrete becomes a hardened mass with a smooth surface. See Fig. 44-5.

Bearing Wall or Masonry Construction

Bricks are used for building many bearing wall superstructures. However, they are

Fig. 44-5. Concrete and asphalt mass superstructures form the surface of modern highways.

not used in a large mass as brick were used in building the Tower of Babel. In bearing walls small bricks are now used and each brick is carefully placed in position by masons or bricklayers, Fig. 44-6. Many kinds of stone, solid concrete, and concrete blocks also are used to construct bearing walls.

Most of the brick used to build bearing walls are 8″ long, 3¾″ wide, and 2¼″ thick. The *mason* stands in front of the wall he is building to spread *mortar* on the lower layer of brick before placing the next brick.

There are six positions in which the bricklayer can place this brick in a wall, and each of these positions has a name. The positions of a brick are those the bricklayer would see looking at the front face of the wall.

Brick is laid in *courses* in a bearing wall. If a brick is laid in a course in the flat position so that the 8″ dimension is along the course and the course is 2¼″ high, the brick is called a *stretcher*. The course is called a *stretcher course*.

If we turn the brick on end so that the 8″ dimension is pointing up and down, the brick is called a *soldier*. If the brick is turned so that the end shows, with the 3¾″ along the course, the brick is called a *header*. If the brick is then turned 90° so that the 2¼″ side lies along the course, it is called a *row-lock*. Two other positions in which a brick may be placed in a wall as a *shiner* or a *sailor* are not often used.

Brick walls are generally built or laid up with stretcher courses. When they are only one brick wide, the walls are 3¾″ thick. This much of a wall is called a *wythe*. Usually, two or three wythes are laid up together to form a bearing wall. However, often only one wythe is used to cover or put a face on a concrete or wood frame wall.

Stone and manufactured block may be used for bearing walls, Fig. 44-7. Some masons lay all kinds of brick, stone, and block. Others specialize in just one kind of material. Brick and block may be set with similar tools. However, the stone mason uses more tools and machines to break, cut, and saw the stone.

Reinforced concrete walls may be used as bearing walls. They are formed and built as upward extensions, above ground, of the reinforced concrete foundations or substructures which were studied earlier. Some of these forms arch over the entire enclosure, forming combined walls and roofs.

Fig. 44-6. Bricks laid one by one for centuries have been used to build load bearing walls.

Fig. 44-7. Concrete block is used to build load bearing walls for many commercial buildings such as supermarkets and bowling alleys.

Fig. 44-8. These bricklayers are working overhand to lay up a 12″ thick wall. The men work in safety from scaffolding *inside* the building.

Bearing walls can be thought of as a kind of brick aggregate cemented together by the mortar between each brick. The mortar, from ¼″ to ½″ thick, provides a bond between bricks and makes them stick together. When two wythes are built side by side to form an 8″ wall, ½″ of mortar is used between them. The mortar bonds (cements) one wythe to the other. See Fig. 44-8.

Summary

Superstructures may be of mass construction or of bearing wall construction. For mass construction we may use earth or rock. The rock may be carefully cut out of a quarry in regular blocks or it may be broken out in oddly shaped pieces. Earth is used for dams and other embankments.

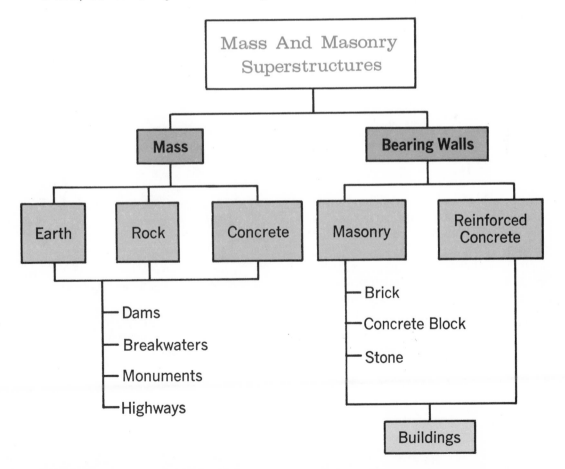

Mass And Masonry Superstructures

- **Mass**
  - Earth
  - Rock
  - Concrete
    - Dams
    - Breakwaters
    - Monuments
    - Highways
- **Bearing Walls**
  - Masonry
    - Brick
    - Concrete Block
    - Stone
  - Reinforced Concrete
    - Buildings

Rock is used for monuments or for ocean breakwaters.

Cemented aggregates such as concrete or bituminous concrete are used for the mass superstructures of highways, airports, and parking lots.

Some bearing walls are made of brick, stone, or concrete blocks. These materials are laid up in courses by masons. Beams, trusses or other framework may be placed in bearing walls to support floors or roofs. Many of the newest bearing walls are made of reinforced concrete. Some of these walls are curved forms which also enclose the roof area.

Terms to Know

quarrying
quarry
foundations
aggregates
batch
drum
hopper
bituminous concrete
paver
mason
mortar
bricklaying courses
  a. stretcher course
  b. soldier
  c. header
  d. rowlock
  e. shiner
  f. sailor
wythe
bearing wall

Think About It!

1. Why is a highway or an airport runway considered a mass superstructure? Can you give reasons why they may be considered substructures?
2. Sometimes brick and stone are used in building construction and they do not make up a load bearing wall superstructure. Give one example of such a structure.

Erecting Steel Frames

Steel frames are generally erected at the construction site one piece at a time, Fig. 45-1. Each piece of steel must be of proper size, and this preparing of each piece is usually done in a *shop* according to the engineer's design drawings, Fig. 45-2.

The steel used in a structural steel framework is made in long pieces called *shapes*. In cross section, common shapes look like the letter "I," the letter "H," the letter "T," the block letter "U," and the letter "L." These long pieces of steel are cut into the lengths by power saws or by heavy shearing machines.

Structural steel is often *assembled* by a subcontractor called a *structural steel erector*. He employs ironworkers to rig, handle, fasten, and plumb and brace the parts of the structural steel frame.

Fig. 45-1. Steel frames form the structural skeleton for many constructed works.

Rigging and Handling Steel Shapes

The columns for the lower levels of a steel frame usually are set in one piece. The beams connecting them are set by using a crane moving on wheels or crawlers. When we have a very tall building or tower to put up, a derrick is used for the higher part of the frame, Fig. 45-3. The derrick is set on a level of framework above the ground level. When all of the framework that can be reached by the boom at that level is finished, the derrick is taken apart and moved up to rest on the steel that has just been set.

The derrick has two main parts, a *mast* and a *boom*. The mast is a tall pole that is held vertically upright by legs or by guy wires. The boom is another long pole that works like the boom on a crane. It is fas-

Fig. 45-2. Steel shapes are made off the site in a shop.

tened to the bottom of the mast on a pivot (movable) joint so that it can move up or down or sideways. A cable fastened from the top of the mast to the outer end of the boom holds the boom in a diagonal position. A second cable that can be moved runs from a winding drum at the bottom of the mast up the side of the mast and then out over the end of the boom. This cable drops down over a grooved wheel at the end of the boom. There is a hook on the lower end of the cable. This hook can be raised by winding the cable on the drum at the bottom of the mast and lowered by unwinding the same cable.

The boom of the derrick is long enough to reach over the side of the steel framework so that the hook can be lowered to the ground. A piece of steel shape or an assembled section is hung from the hook and lifted into place. The steel shapes are hung on the hoisting cable by *riggers* who know how to safely attach the pieces. The rigging

Fig. 45-4. Riggers attach steel shapes to hoisting cables and guide the pieces into place. This welded plate girder section of the new Madison Square Garden floor weighed 96 tons.

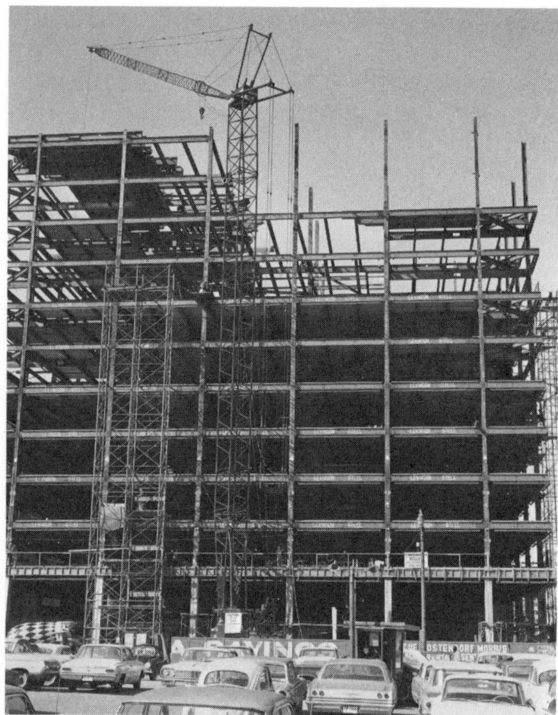

Fig. 45-3. Derricks are used to handle framing members on very tall structures.

Fig. 45-5. Cables often are used by riggers to fasten steel shapes to hoisting cables.

must be done so the piece will be in the correct position so it can be fastened in place, Figs. 45-4 and 45-5. This requires special knowledge about hoisting frames, cables, and ropes, and about hand signals. The hand signals are used to tell the crane operator what to do. Often the crane operator is out of hearing range so hand signals are necessary.

Setting the Supporting Steel

Some parts of a steel frame support other parts of the frame. In a building, the columns support the beams. In a tower, the legs support the bracing that ties them together. In a bridge frame, two or three beams may support all of the other beams or connecting pieces. To set up a steel skeleton, we must first set the bottom pieces of supporting steel.

You have read how anchor bolts are set in the tops of concrete foundations in an earlier assignment. Anchor bolts are used to fasten the structural steel frame to the foundations. Columns for buildings or the legs of towers have a steel plate welded to the bottom of them. This is called a *base plate.* A similar piece of plate may be welded to the bottom of a beam at the end that rests on the foundation. The base plate has holes drilled in it to match the position of the anchor bolts. To set the supporting pieces of steel, each piece is lifted off the truck with a crane. The base plate on the bottom is then set on the foundation so that the anchor bolts stick up through the holes in it.

Base plates must be set at the correct height which may be 1″ or 2″ above the foundation concrete. The plates also must be set so they are level. To set a base plate, shims are placed between the bottom of the base plate and the concrete. *Shims are small square pieces of steel plate or sheet steel.* Each piece may be of a different thickness. A stack of shims is set under each of the four corners of the base plate using the thickness needed to set the base plate level and at the correct height. Then steel nuts are drawn down tightly against the base plate to hold it in place on the shims.

Setting the Connecting Steel

After the supporting members of a structural steel frame are set, the connecting pieces of the frame are placed. All members of the frame, whether partly assembled or not, are delivered to the site by truck or, on bridge construction, by barge. To help identify it, each piece has had a number marked on it at the steel shop. Using the numbers shown on the shop drawing, the foreman of the iron workers selects the right piece of section. A crane with a double sling of wire rope with a hook on each end is used to lift the piece. The two legs of the sling meet in a steel ring at the center. The hook on the lifting line of the crane is hooked into this ring, and the piece is lifted. To guide the piece or section of steel, a length of fiber rope is tied to one end. This is called a *tag line.* As the crane lifts the steel member, one of the iron workers holds the tag line and lets it out slowly to guide the piece of steel into position in the framework.

The columns for the steel frame of a building usually are two stories in height. After they have been set in position, the beams connecting them at the first floor height are placed. An ironworker stands on a ladder that leans against one column. As the end of the beam reaches him, he guides the end into position against the connecting piece fastened to the column. The holes in the end of the beam match those in the connecting piece.

Fastening Steel Shapes

Each ironworker carries a *spud wrench* which is stuck into a holder on a leather belt. The spud wrench has jaws on one end that fit around a nut or the head of a bolt.

The other end is a handle 12″ to 18″ long that tapers down to a rounded point. When one hole in the beam is lined up with the correct hole in the connecting piece, he pushes the point of the wrench handle through the two holes. This also lines up the other holes in the connection. The ironworker then takes bolts from a small pouch hanging from his belt and puts them through all the holes of the connection. He puts nuts on the threaded ends of the bolts and pulls the two pieces of steel together by turning the nut with the jaws of the spud wrench. An ironworker at the other end of the beam does the same thing at the same time.

All connections between parts of a structural steel frame are made in the same way. The bracing pieces between the legs of a tower are connected just as the beams are connected between the columns of a building. Each piece in the frame for a bridge also is placed in this way. When sections have been assembled in a yard and hauled to the site, one section is connected to another in this way.

After the pieces or sections are fastened together with bolts, they must be riveted, bolted, or welded together permanently. When they are to be bolted together permanently, a *torque wrench* must be used. A torque wrench operates something like a very slow electric drill. It turns the nut

Fig. 45-6. Mobile cranes are used to handle steel framework pieces or subassemblies up to the limits of the crane boom.

Fig. 45-7. Helicopters are sometimes used in erecting steel frames.

down hard on the bolt until the two pieces of steel are pressed tightly together. If the frame is to be welded together, welding is done around the edges of the connecting pieces.

Plumbing and Bracing

Before the final riveting, bolting, or welding can be done, the first part of the frame to be braced must be leveled, plumbed, and then held in position with guy wires. *Guy wires are made of steel wire rope.* In a building frame, they may be fastened from the bottom of one column to the top of another column. Guy wires also may be fastened from the upper part of a column to a long iron stake driven into the ground some distance away from the column. The columns are plumbed by hanging a plumb bob from a string beside the column. When the face of the column lines up with the string, the column is plumb. The number or thicknesses of the shims under the base plate may have to be changed to tilt the column until it is plumb. See Fig. 45-8.

The same things may have to be done to level and plumb the steel frame for a bridge. It cannot be braced with guy wires that go down into the water. However, it can be braced behind the shore line either to stakes driven into the ground or to heavy blocks of concrete. Some bridges have towers at the shore line, and guy wires can be stretched from the bridge frame to the top of the tower.

When the first part of the framework has been plumbed, leveled, and temporarily braced with guy wires, *grout* is forced in around the shims between the base plate and the concrete foundation. *Grout is a mixture of sand and cement with very little water added to it.* The grout will set up, like concrete, and hold the base plate in place. Now we can finish putting up the steel frame.

When the steel for the top of the structure has been set in place, the structure is

Fig. 45-8. After the columns and beams are set and partially fastened, they must be plumbed and braced. Then they are rigidly fastened.

Fig. 45-9. The "topping out" celebration marks the placement of the highest framing.

said to be "topped out." An American flag on a pole often is fastened to the highest part of the frame to celebrate the occasion, Fig. 45-9.

Summary

Steel frames are assembled by ironworkers who use shop drawings. A crane is used to set each piece in place. Riggers attach the pieces to the lifting cable. Steel shapes may be connected by bolting, riveting, or welding. After the lower part of a structure has been erected, the steel frame is plumbed and braced with guy wires.

For tall structures, steel for the upper levels is set with a derrick. The derrick is placed at the level of the last steel erected. The derrick is moved up, level by level, until the steel frame is "topped out."

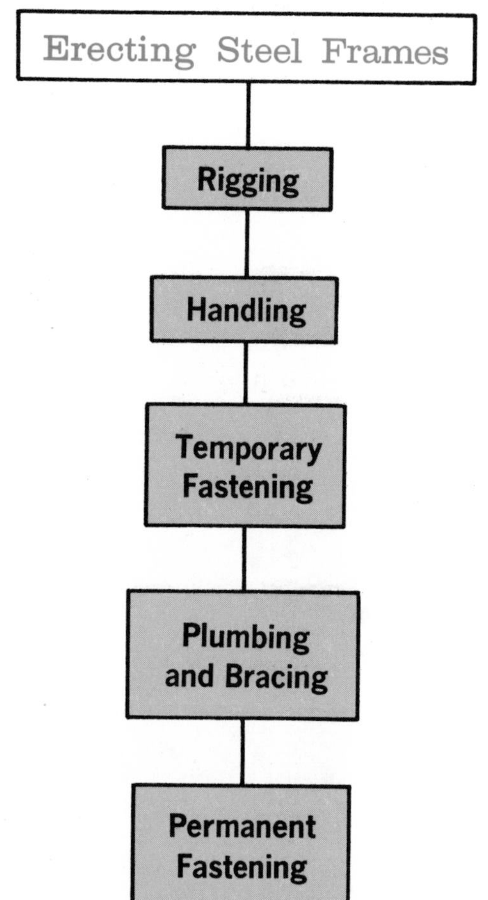

Terms to Know

shop	ironworker
shapes	torque wrench
assembled	plumb bob
derrick	grout
guy wires	plumbing
cable	bracing
rigger	fastening
shims	welding
tag line	riveting
steel member	bolting
spud wrench	structural steel erector

Think About It!

1. Is there a steel framed building being erected near your home or school? If so, is it tall enough so that a derrick is being used? If not, how are the steel shapes hoisted into place?
2. What advantages do steel-framed superstructures have over mass superstructures? Over bearing wall superstructures?

READING 46

Erecting Concrete Frames

You have studied how steel frames for superstructures are put together at the building site. You have read that this is done with lengths of steel called *steel shapes*. In this assignment you will study how concrete frames are built. Some parts of concrete frames may be manufactured in a plant and then hauled to the site where they are lifted into place with a crane. This is much the same way that steel frames are prepared and put up. Heavy beams for highway bridges, sections of concrete floor slabs, or T-beams for a roof may be put up in this way. However, most concrete frames are built at the site, Fig. 46-1. Concrete is placed into position in forms which are built with the inside surface in the shape of the finished frame, Fig 46-2. After the concrete hardens, the forms are removed.

Fig. 46-1. Complex forms must be built to give shape to cast-in-place concrete frames.

Materials for a Concrete Frame

Concrete for the frames of superstructures is made in the same way as the concrete used in foundations. The only difference is that *stronger concrete is needed.* The strength of concrete is measured by how heavy a load it can support after it has hardened for 28 days. Concrete used

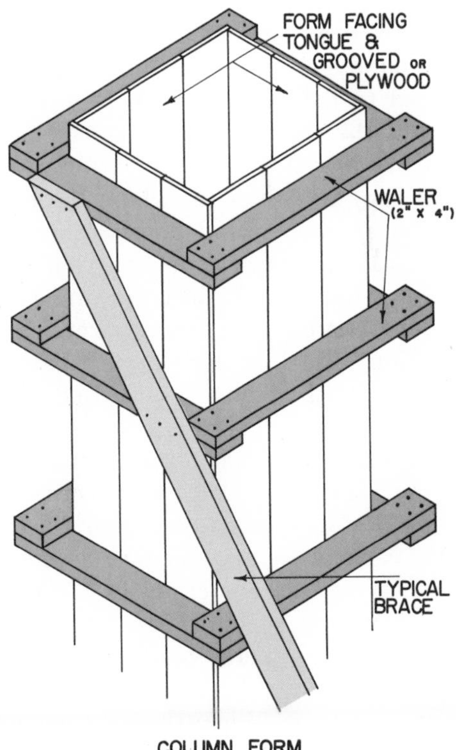

Fig. 46-2. Some forms are made on the site. This column form shows the typical assembly of the form facing, walers, and bracing.

in foundations is strong enough if it can support a weight of 2,000 pounds on each square inch of its surface. The concrete used in frames may need to support 3,000 pounds per square inch. This stronger concrete is made by putting more cement into the same quantity of sand and gravel.

For foundations, we used large masses of concrete. For concrete frames, we use beams, columns, and thin slabs which are much smaller in size. To keep these from cracking we need to use more reinforcing steel than we used in the foundations. For the concrete forms we may use the same materials that were used to build the forms for the foundation, but these materials will have to be used in a different way.

Concrete Columns and Walls

You will remember that when steel columns were set on concrete foundations we used anchor bolts to fasten the columns to the foundation. Concrete columns are also anchored to the foundation but in a different way. Pieces of reinforcing steel called *dowels* are placed in the foundation concrete so that they will stick up where the column is to be built. Around these dowels, the surface of the foundation concrete is left rough so that the concrete in the column will *bond* (stick to) the concrete in the foundation. The long reinforcing bars that are used in the column are tied to the dowels with wire. These long bars are then held in place with hoops of smaller steel bars the same way that they were in the building of foundation piers. See Fig. 46-3.

The vertical supports for a concrete frame may be columns or walls. If they are walls, they will be built just as the walls for foundations were built. If they are columns, they may be square, rectangular, or round in shape. When they are square or rectangular, the forms for the sides of the column are made up in panels. The panels are stood up to match lines which have been marked on the top of the foundation wall. The panels are fastened together with short pieces of waler that are overlapped at the corners and nailed to each other. Panels also may be fastened together with metal bars called *column clamps*. Sometimes form ties may be used. The forms are plumbed and braced just as the pier forms were. Round columns use curved metal forms like those used for piers.

Concrete Beams

The connecting pieces for a concrete frame may be of any size or shape but they are all called *beams*. They may connect two columns, two pieces of wall, or a column and a piece of wall. Column or wall forms are built up to the level of the beams, and then the beam forms are built before any concrete is placed. The concrete is placed into the columns and the beams at the same time so they will be formed together.

All of the concrete that was placed for the foundations was supported on a bearing

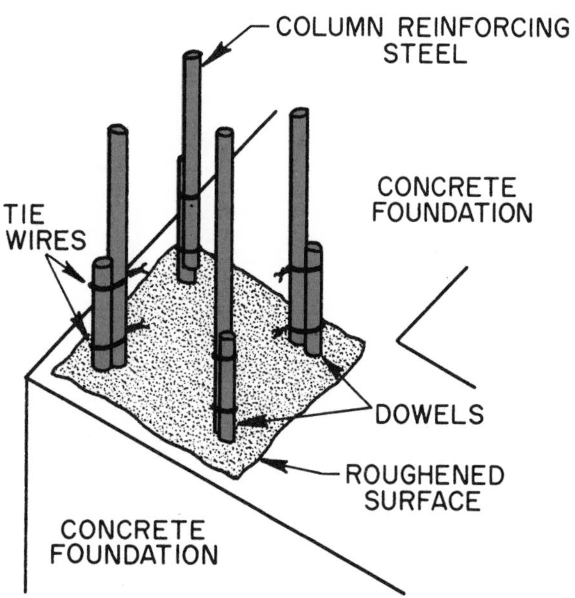

Fig. 46-3. Vertical reinforcing steel for concrete columns is tied to exposed dowels in the foundation.

surface or on a footing. Concrete beams are suspended in the air. The forms for the beams and the concrete in them must be supported until the concrete has hardened and can support itself. You learned earlier that shores are diagonal supports (Reading 38). In addition, they are vertical supports. *Shores* are used for supporting overhead concrete forms. *This kind of a shore is a post made of a piece of dimension lumber such as a 4″ x 4″ or a 4″ x 6″.* Metal shores are made from pieces of pipe with a long threaded bolt at one end so that the length can be adjusted. Shores are set in a straight line under the center of the beam form. They are spaced so as to support the load of the form and the concrete. The bottom of the shore may rest on the ground, on foundation concrete, or on another beam below.

Across the top of each shore is nailed or fastened a piece of lumber at right angles to the line of the beam. This piece is 24″ to 30″ longer than the width of the bottom of the beam. It is braced to the shore underneath with diagonal braces. (Carefully study Fig. 46-4.)

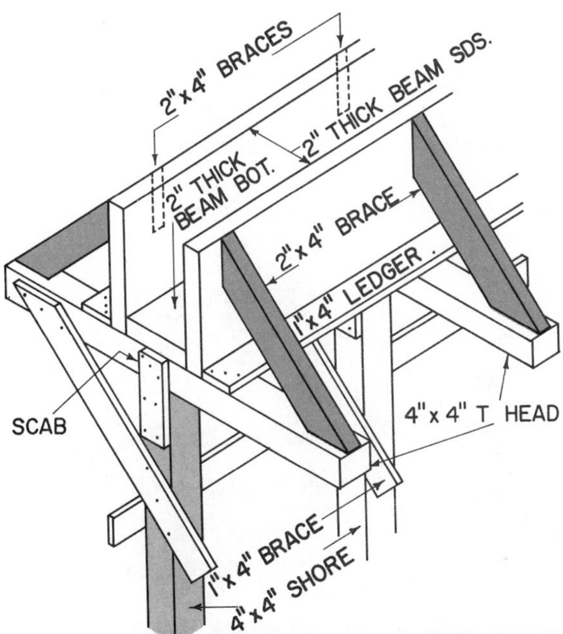

Fig. 46-4. Horizontal concrete beam forms require bracing and shoring to support the heavy mass of concrete until it cures. Notice how the form is constructed.

Fabricating the Beam Form

The form for a concrete beam is made with a beam bottom and two beam side pieces. These are made from 2″ thick dimension lumber and are cut to the necessary width or height. The line of the beam has been marked on top of each 4″ x 4″ that rests on the shores. The beam bottom is nailed to the top of each 4″ x 4″ along that line. Then the beam sides are nailed to the beam bottom on each side. Each 4″ x 4″ will stick out beyond the beam sides about 12″ or 15″. The beam side is then braced with a diagonal brace to the outside of the 4″ x 4″.

After the beam is formed, the reinforcing steel is set. The reinforcing steel bars in beams are called *trussed bars*. The same bar is bent so that the central part of it is close to the bottom of the beam. Toward the ends the bar bends up on a 45° angle so that the ends are near the top of the beam. On the end of each bar, there is a large hook that hooks into the steel in the column. These bars may be fastened together with smaller bars like the hoops in a column, Fig. 46-5.

Fabricating Suspended Slab Forms

Using only columns and beams, we may build a concrete frame for a structure. In that case, when the beam forms were finished, we could pour concrete into the column and beam forms. But very often we will want to pour a concrete floor slab as part of the concrete beam. For this, we must build in between the beam forms a supported form for the slab, Fig. 46-6.

To build a slab form, we will start by placing shores every 4′ in rows, and place a 4″ x 4″ on top of each row of shores. The 4″ x 4″ is called a *stringer*. At right angles to the 4″ x 4″, we will place a 2″ x 4″ or 2″ x 6″ every 16″ from one end of the slab to the other. These will be stood on edge and nailed to the stringers. These pieces are called *joists*. Over the joists, we will nail sheets of plywood to form the facing for the underside of the concrete slab. Where the slab meets the beam, the beam side is cut down so that the plywood can be nailed to the top of it.

The reinforcing steel for the slab is set on the plywood. These are straight bars set at intervals of 4″, 6″, or 8″ in both directions. The bars are fastened together where they cross. To keep them above the bottom of the concrete slab, they are set on small wire supports, called *chairs*, that rest on the plywood surface.

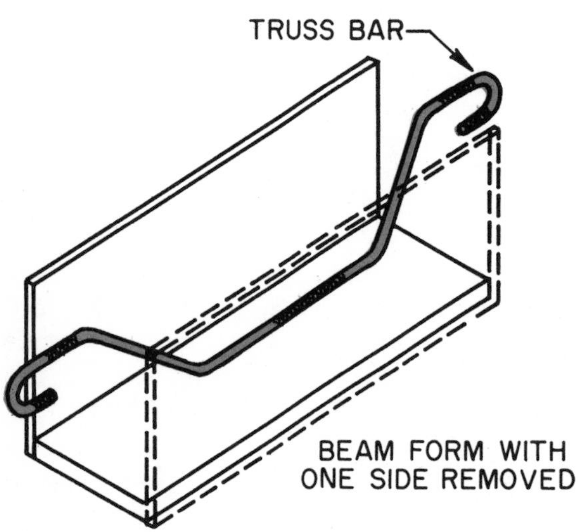

Fig. 46-5. The hooks on the ends of beam trussed bars will hook into the column reinforcing.

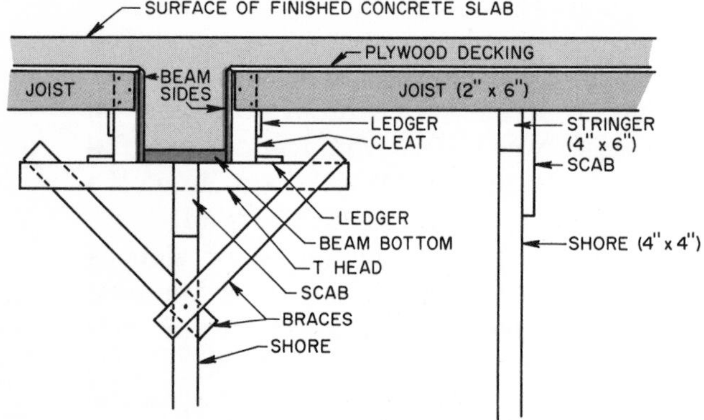

Fig. 46-6. Here is a typical beam and slab form. Notice that the beam is cast in place along with the concrete slab.

Placing the Concrete

Concrete is placed in forms for the frame of a structure in much the same way it was placed in the foundation. The concrete is placed in the column forms a short time before the concrete is placed in the forms for the beams and slabs. Concrete shrinks a little as it sets up. We let this shrinkage take place before the other concrete is placed.

If the structure is not very high, we may place the concrete by using a crane with a long boom. A concrete bucket is hung from the hook on the lifting cable. For taller structures, we may have to use a hoist. *A hoist is like an elevator in a tall building.* It is a steel framework that is set against the side of the structure in which an enclosed platform is raised or lowered by cables. The hoist can be stopped at any level of the structure. A concrete buggy full of concrete is pushed into the hoist cage at ground level and then raised to the height needed. There the buggy is taken out and pushed over runways to reach the point where it is to be dumped, Fig. 46-7.

Fig. 46-7. Concrete buggies may be used to haul concrete from hoppers to the forms.

In the building of foundations, the forms may be removed from the concrete within a day or two. With beams and slabs, there is nothing to support the concrete if the forms and shores are removed. So, to be sure the concrete for the beams and slabs is strong enough to support its own weight, we must leave the forms in place for one or two weeks.

Finishing Concrete Frames

Some of the concrete surfaces in a structural concrete frame may be left exposed when the structure is finished. These surfaces will be finished in the same ways that were described for foundation concrete. The top surfaces of concrete slabs will usually be given a smooth, steel trowelled finish so that tile or other flooring can be put over them. Generally, the columns, the underside of concrete slabs, and many of the beams will be covered by other surfacing materials and will not need to be finished by rubbing or trowelling.

Precast Concrete Shapes

Some parts of a concrete frame can be made in a manufacturing plant and hauled to the site for erection. These pieces are called *precast concrete shapes.* They are made of the same kind of concrete, but instead of using wood for the forms, metal is used, Fig. 46-8. Concrete placed in foundations or in concrete frames is cured by wetting it or coating it with curing compounds. Precast concrete is cured at the manufacturing plant with steam.

Some precast concrete shapes are called *prestressed concrete.* Prestressed concrete is not reinforced with reinforcing rods such as those used in other kinds of concrete. Prestressed concrete uses wires for reinforcing the concrete. Like the wires on a violin, these wires are stretched very tightly and then the concrete is poured in the forms around them. Prestressed concrete is stronger than concrete reinforced with rods, but it is more expensive.

Precast or prestressed concrete beams often are used for highway bridges. These beams are set in place side by side on the foundation, and the road paving is placed over the top of them.

Instead of making a concrete slab when the concrete is placed, precast or prestressed concrete slabs or planks in 2′ or 3′ widths can be used. The ends of these planks are supported on the concrete beams. The beams in a structural steel frame or masonry walls can also be used to support precast concrete slabs.

Summary

Concrete frames for superstructures are usually built on the site, although some parts may be manufactured in a plant. The materials used for making concrete frames are the same as those used for foundations except that the concrete is stronger.

Supports for concrete frames are usually columns connected by beams. The beams rest on top of the columns. Columns are

Fig. 46-8. Steel domes are being removed without damaging the concrete surfaces.

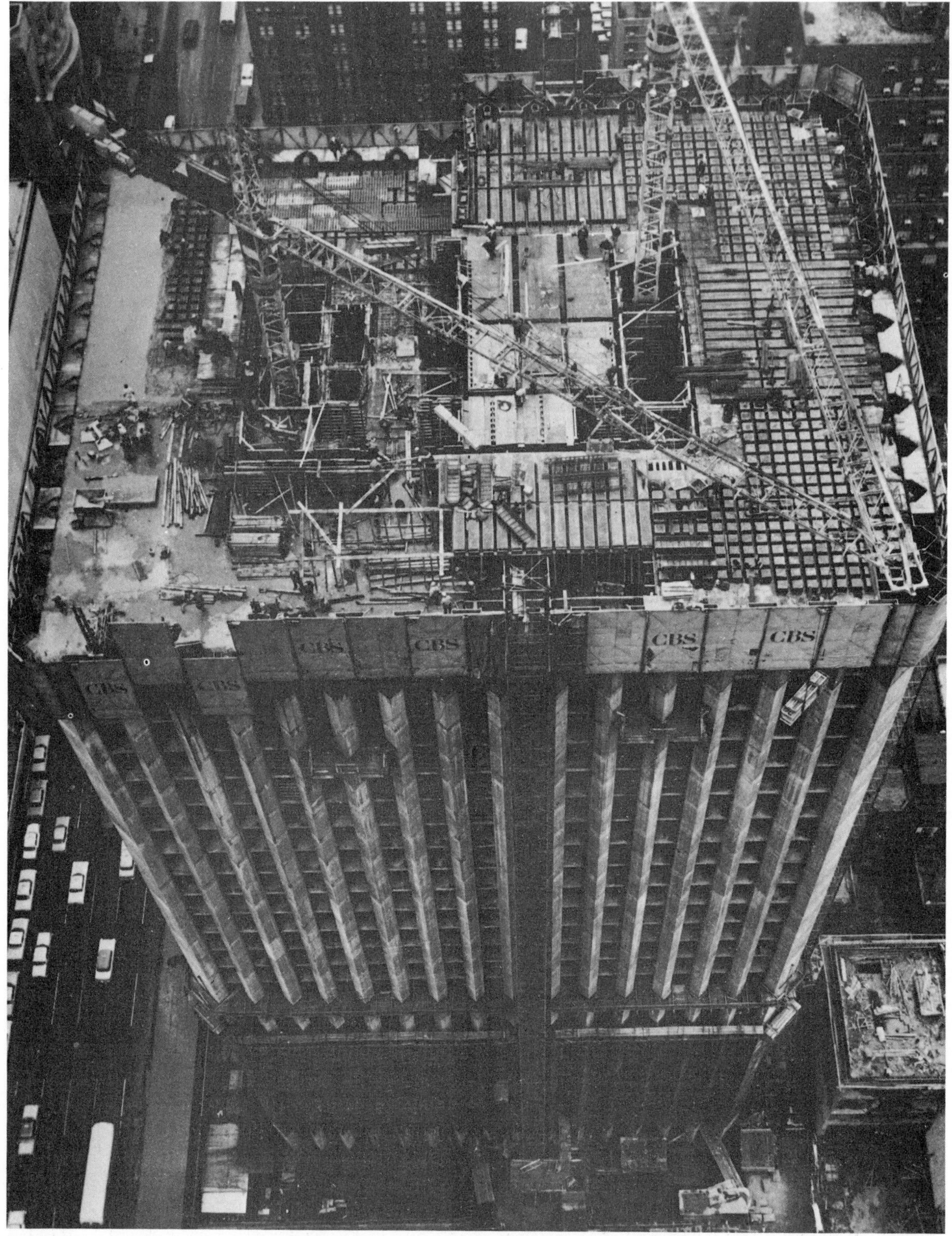

Fig. 46-9. Here some workmen are assembling forms while others are placing and finishing concrete. Note the small square sections in the form. One of these can be seen in detail in Fig. 46-8.

made in the same way as foundation piers. Forms for concrete beams and slabs must be supported on posts called *shores*. The shores support the forms and the concrete until the concrete hardens.

A concrete bucket lifted by a crane or concrete buggies lifted by a hoist may be used to place concrete in forms. Forms cannot be removed from structural frames for one or two weeks after the concrete is placed.

Precast concrete shapes may be beams for highway bridges, slabs for steel or concrete frames, or T-beams for roofs or structures. Some precast concrete is prestressed.

Terms to Know

concrete columns	trussed bars
concrete beams	stringer
column clamp	joists
shores	hoist
forms	precast concrete
bond	prestressed concrete

Fig. 46-10. This hyperbolic paraboloid roof form is typical of new uses of concrete.

Think About It!

1. Why must the concrete used in concrete-formed superstructures be stronger than the concrete used in foundations?
2. What are some advantages of using precast concrete shapes? In the future, do you think more or less precast structural members will be used?

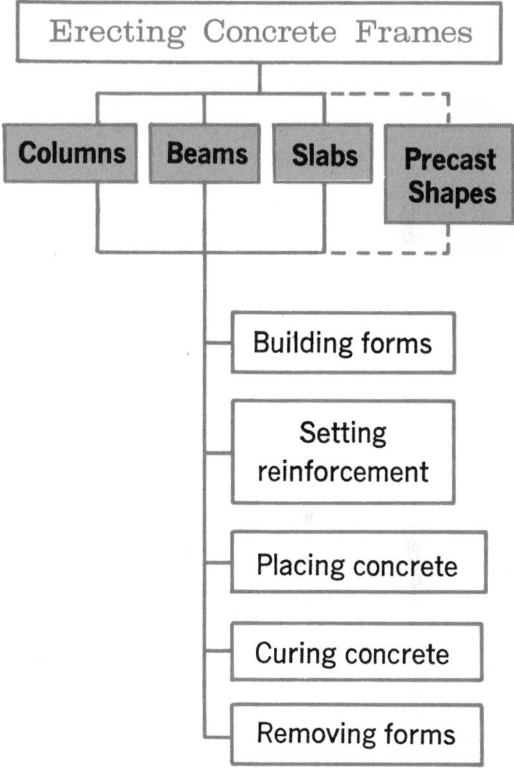

READING 47

Building Wood Frames

Generally wood frames are used for small buildings such as houses. The frames (skeletons) for these buildings may be subdivided into three major parts: (1) floor framing, (2) wall framing, and (3) roof framing. Most floor framing is made up of horizontal members which are called *joists*. Most wall framing is made up of vertical members which are called *studs*. Most roof framing is made up of sloped members which are called *rafters*.

In the days when nails were scarce and labor and lumber were plentiful, most builders used heavy timbers for framing (4″ x 4″, 6″ x 6″, 8″ x 8″). These large pieces of timber were joined with wood pins, Fig. 47-1. Now, labor and lumber are more expensive, and nails have become cheaper. As a result, framing members are now pieces of small dimensional lumber (usually 2″ x 4″, 6″, 8″, 10″ or 12″) joined with nails.

The major steps in erecting wood frames at the site are:

1. Laying out and marking the locations and positions of the framing members according to the blueprint,
2. Marking off the lengths of lumber,
3. Sawing the lumber,
4. Assembling the parts, and
5. Leveling and plumbing the frame.

Setting Sills

To secure and hold the wood framing to the foundation, an anchor bolt is first set every 5′ or 6′ along the center of the top of the footing or wall. The threaded end of the bolt is pointing up, Fig. 47-2.

Fig. 47-1. Before metal nails were invented, heavy timbers were fastened together with wood pins.

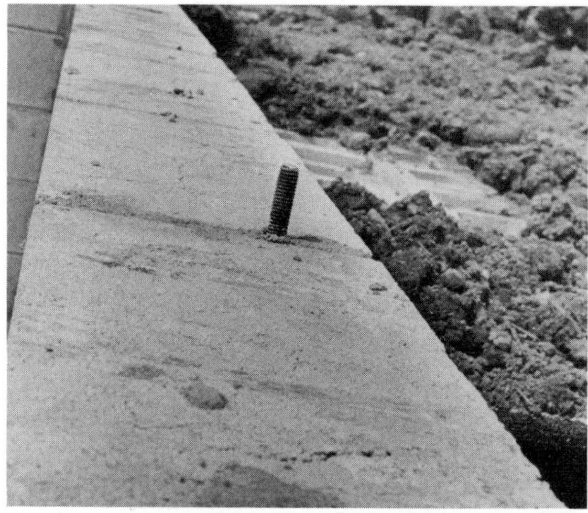

Fig. 47-2. An anchor bolt has been installed in the top of a foundation wall.

To begin construction of the frame, a sill is laid on top of the foundation. *The sill is a horizontal piece of lumber and is the bottom piece of the frame.* Holes are marked and drilled in the sill so that the sill can drop down over the anchor bolts. A thin layer of grout, which is a mixture of sand, cement, and water, may be placed under the sill to help level it. After the sill is leveled, it is held in place by tightening nuts down on the threads of the anchor bolts, Fig. 47-3.

Fig. 47-3. A sill plate is being fastened with anchor bolts.

Fig. 47-4. Floor joists have been nailed in place with solid bridging between them.

In some areas of the United States, *termites* (wood-eating insects) are a problem. Termites can eat their way through framing and make tunnels which weaken the structure. The repair of termite-weakened framing members can be very costly.

In areas where there are termite problems, a *termite shield* made from a strip of sheet copper is placed under the sill. The shield stretches along the full length of the sill and extends on either side. This shield helps to keep the ground-dwelling termites from burrowing through holes or cracks in the foundation into the wood frame.

Assembling Joists

Joists are planks set on edge. They are placed to give a base on which the flooring materials can rest. Joists rest on sills and extend from one foundation wall to the foundation wall on the other side, Fig. 47-4. We may think of joists as floor beams, but they are laid much closer together than are

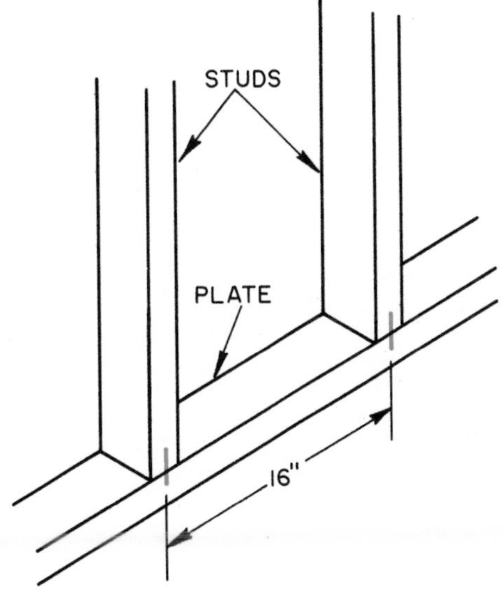

Fig. 47-5. Carpenters measure and locate the wood frame on 16″ or 24″ centers.

beams. Generally joists are set 16″ *on center*. See Fig. 47-5.

The ends of joists are held in place by nailing them to a header, Fig. 47-6. *A header is a piece of lumber of the same dimensions as the joists.* Headers are set flush to the outside edge of the sill. *Bridging* is used to hold the center of the joists firm and to keep them from bending or twisting. Bridging also helps to transfer a heavy load above one joist to an adjoining one. Bridging is made from 1″ x 4″ boards, short lengths of joists, or specially made pieces of metal.

Assembling Girders

When the distance between two foundation walls is great, a girder may be used to support the joists. *A girder is stronger than the joists used in a frame.* In a wood frame, the girder may be a piece of steel I-beam. It might also be three or four pieces of planking nailed or bolted together. Because they are stronger than joists, girders can span more distance than can joists.

Girders may rest on sills, foundation piers, or steel columns, Fig. 47-7. Joists may rest on a girder as they do on a sill. Sometimes a girder is placed at the same level as the joists. Then the joists are butted against the girder. When wooden girders are used, the joists rest on a *ledger* which is a strip of wood nailed to the side of the girder, or they rest in special metal hangers. The joists are *toenailed* to the girder. When steel girders are used, the joists may rest

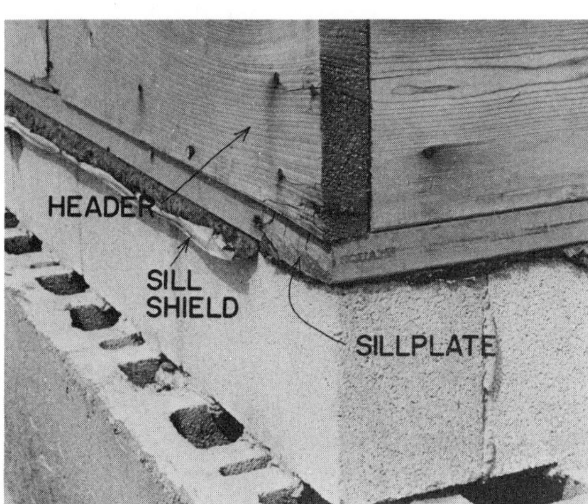

Fig. 47-6. Shown here is a box sill with header, sill plate, and sill shield.

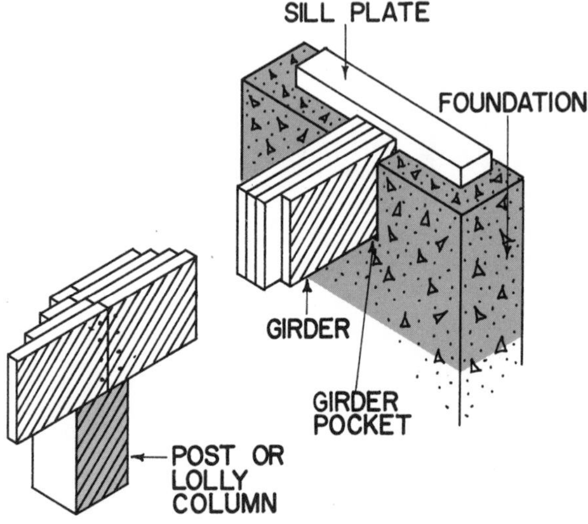

Fig. 47-7. A girder is supported by the foundation wall and post or lolly column.

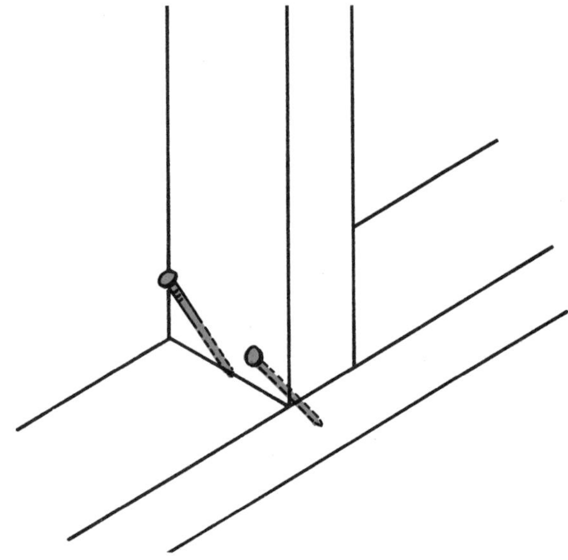

Fig. 47-8. The technique of toenailing is used when a carpenter cannot drive the nail into the end of the wood.

on and be toenailed to a piece of planking which is fastened to the top of the I-beam. If the joists are butted to the beam, they are notched to fit the beam and a ledger which is bolted to the face of the beam. The joists are then toenailed to the wood ledger. See Fig. 47-8.

Laying Subflooring

A *subfloor* is nailed to the top of the joists. Because a second floor is always placed on top of it, this floor is called the rough flooring or subflooring. Boards or pieces of plywood are used for the subflooring. The boards have *tongues and grooves. The tongue of one board fits into the groove of the next board.* This keeps the boards from twisting and makes a tighter floor. The subflooring boards are not laid straight across the joists. They are slanted, Fig. 47-9. When sheets of plywood are used, they are laid perpendicular to the joists.

Assembling Wall Frames

When the subflooring has been placed, the walls for the first floor of the building are laid out. The exterior walls are directly over the outside foundation walls. The interior (partition) walls are usually over an inside foundation wall or over a girder. The walls of the first floor usually are framed with 2″ x 4″ lumber. A piece of 2″ x 4″ lumber, laid flat, is nailed to the subflooring exactly where the wall is to be. This piece of lumber is called the *sole plate.*

Fig. 47-9. The subfloor has been nailed in place.

To complete the wall framing, pieces of 2″ x 4″ lumber are cut to the length needed and are stood on end 16″ *on center* along the sole plate. They are toenailed in place. Across their top is placed a *top plate* of 2″ x 4″ lumber nailed to the top of the *studs.* A second top plate is nailed over the first. The end joints in the two plates are staggered to make the top plate more like one continuous piece.

Another way of building a wall is to first assemble it on the floor. The wall is then tilted up and nailed into position. The second top plate is nailed on, overlapping where walls join, to tie the walls together and to stiffen them.

There are two common ways of bracing studs to keep them from bending or twisting. One way is to place short lengths of 2″ x 4″ lumber, called fire blocks, horizontally between the studs. These fire blocks serve as braces as well as draft stops to prevent the spread of fire in a building. These blocks are nailed in line, or they may be staggered above and below a line for ease in nailing. Another common way to brace studs is to use diagonal let-in braces. A brace is set to run from one top corner of the frame down to some point on the sole plate at an angle of approximately 45°. This makes a triangular frame within the wall section and makes the frame rigid and solid. In the studs, notches are cut to the thickness of the diagonal brace so that they do not interfere with the installation of the sheathing material. (Study Fig. 47-10.)

Additional Stories

After one story of the frame is completed, a second story may be built in the same way. Joists and headers are placed on the top plate of the first story and covered with a subflooring. Walls are built on top of this to form the second story. Additional floors may be added in this same way.

Exterior wall frames are covered with sheathing. Sheathing makes the frame more rigid and makes a surface to which the finished siding material can be attached. Boards or manufactured sheet materials are used for sheathing. They are nailed to the wall studs.

Assembling Roof Frames

Most wood-framed buildings have sloped roofs. The top of the slope is called the *ridge.* The bottom of the slope is called the *eave.* To frame the roof, rafters are used. The rafters rest on the top plates and meet at the ridge. *Rafters* are pieces of lumber set on edge, Fig. 47-11. Where the lower end of the rafter rests on the top plate, a notch is cut so that there will be a flat edge resting on the top plate. Usually the rafter goes a foot or more past the face of the wall. This holds the roofing that goes beyond the outside wall. Rafters are set in pairs sloping down each side of the roof. These pairs of rafters meet at a ridge board along the top. The ridge board gives a straight line on which the rafters can meet and helps to brace the rafters at the top. If the rafters are very long, a *collar beam* is used to brace them, Fig. 47-12. This

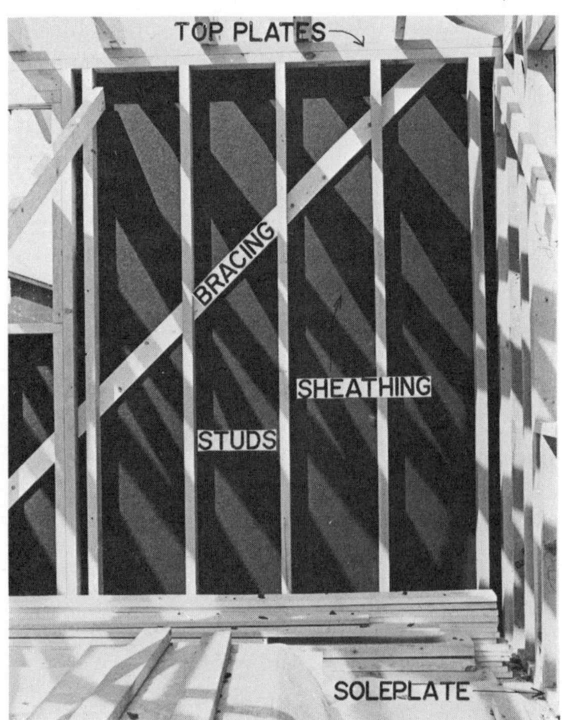

Fig. 47-10. This wall section shows the sole plate, studs, bracing, sheathing, and top plates.

Fig. 47-11. This carpenter is fastening rafters to the rafter plate.

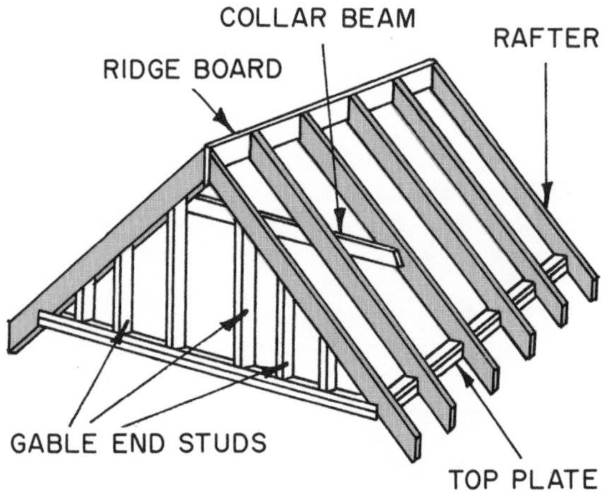

Fig. 47-12. The illustration shows a sloped roof and its framing members.

is a piece of lumber nailed to each of the two rafters facing each other. The collar beam is placed about half-way down the rafters.

Trussed roof members may be used in place of the conventional rafters. Trusses may be made on the site, or they may be manufactured off the site. *Trusses usually combine the rafters and ceiling joists into one triangular piece.* The truss is then installed as a unit, Figs. 47-13 and 47-14.

Roof frames are covered with *roof decking* which serves the same purpose as sheathing and subflooring, Fig. 47-15. Boards or sheet material are nailed over the rafters. The rafters are usually covered over completely. Sometimes, when wood shingles are used, spaces are left between roof decking to save material and to allow better air circulation to dry the shingles after wet weather.

Summary

Wood framing is used for small buildings such as houses. Precut dimensional lumber or manufactured sections are brought to the site and are used as framing materials. The main framing members are called joists, studs, and rafters.

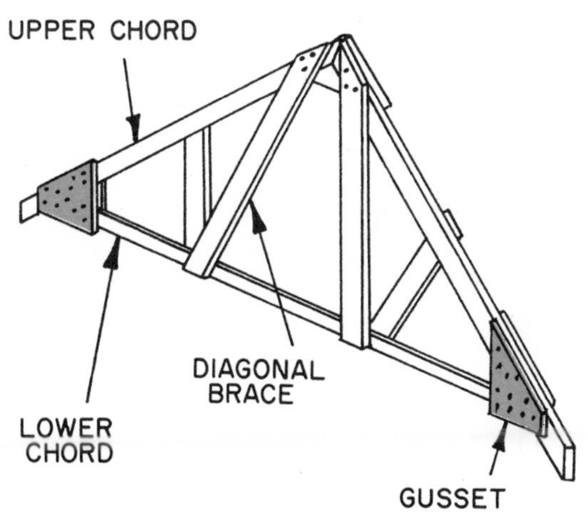

Fig. 47-13. This illustration shows the parts of a roof truss.

To begin the framing, sills are laid over anchor bolts on top of the foundation wall. Floor joists are laid on sills to cross the space between the walls and are then braced with bridging. Girders make it possible to use shorter joists where the distance between walls is too long to be spanned by one-piece joists. A subflooring is placed over the joists.

The framing for the walls is laid on a sole plate and nailed to the subfloor. Studs (vertical pieces) are used in the walls.

Fig. 47-14. Roof trusses manufactured off the site will be installed on top of the structure.

Fig. 47-15. Sheathing, or roof decking, is used to cover a roof.

They are nailed to the sole plate. Then a top plate is nailed on top of the studs. Studs may be braced by fire blocks or by diagonal bracing. Exterior walls are made rigid by covering them with sheathing material.

Roofs are framed with rafters or trusses. Roof decking is nailed over the roof framing to serve the same purposes as sheathing on walls and subflooring on joists.

Terms to Know

joists
studs
rafters
sill
termites
subfloor
tongues
grooves
exterior wall
interior wall
on center
assembling
header
bridging
toenailed
girder
ledger
sole plate
top plate
ridge
eaves
collar beam
trusses

Think About It!

1. Why is wood framing used for structures such as houses? Are wood-framed structures common in your neighborhood? If not, why?
2. In the future, wood-framed structures may be built completely in a factory and transported to the site. Can you see any advantage in such a plan? Any disadvantages?

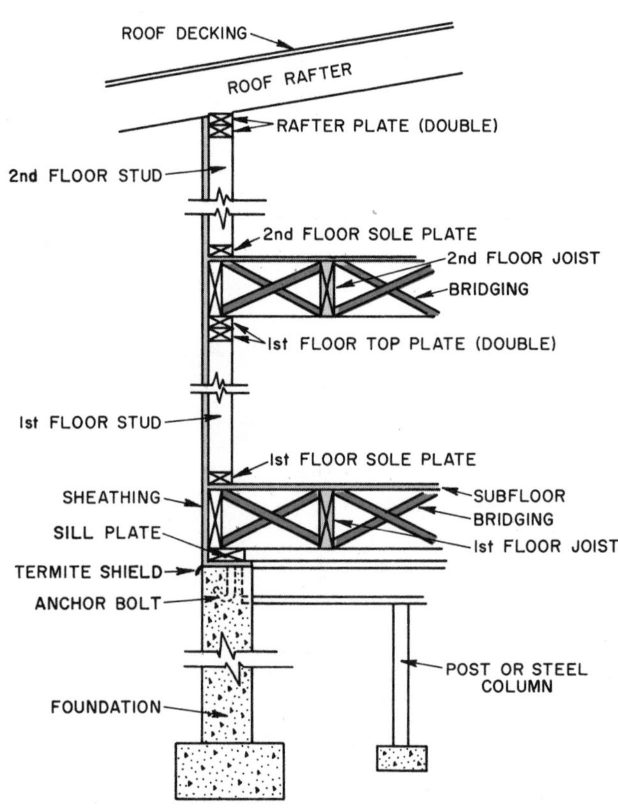

Fig. 47-16. Shown here is a cross section of a house and its composite framing members.

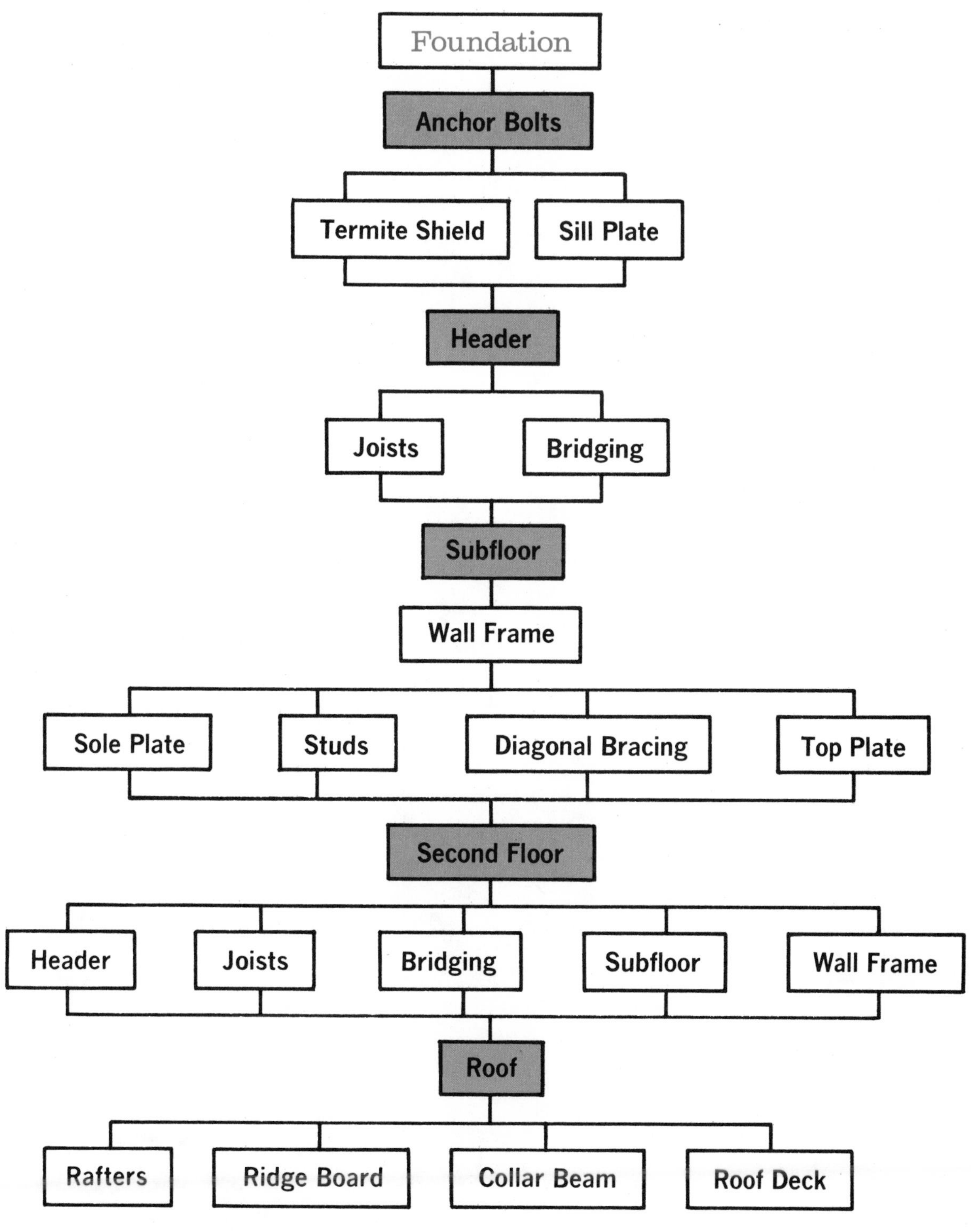
Foundation
Anchor Bolts
Termite Shield
Sill Plate
Header
Joists
Bridging
Subfloor
Wall Frame
Sole Plate
Studs
Diagonal Bracing
Top Plate
Second Floor
Header
Joists
Bridging
Subfloor
Wall Frame
Roof
Rafters
Ridge Board
Collar Beam
Roof Deck

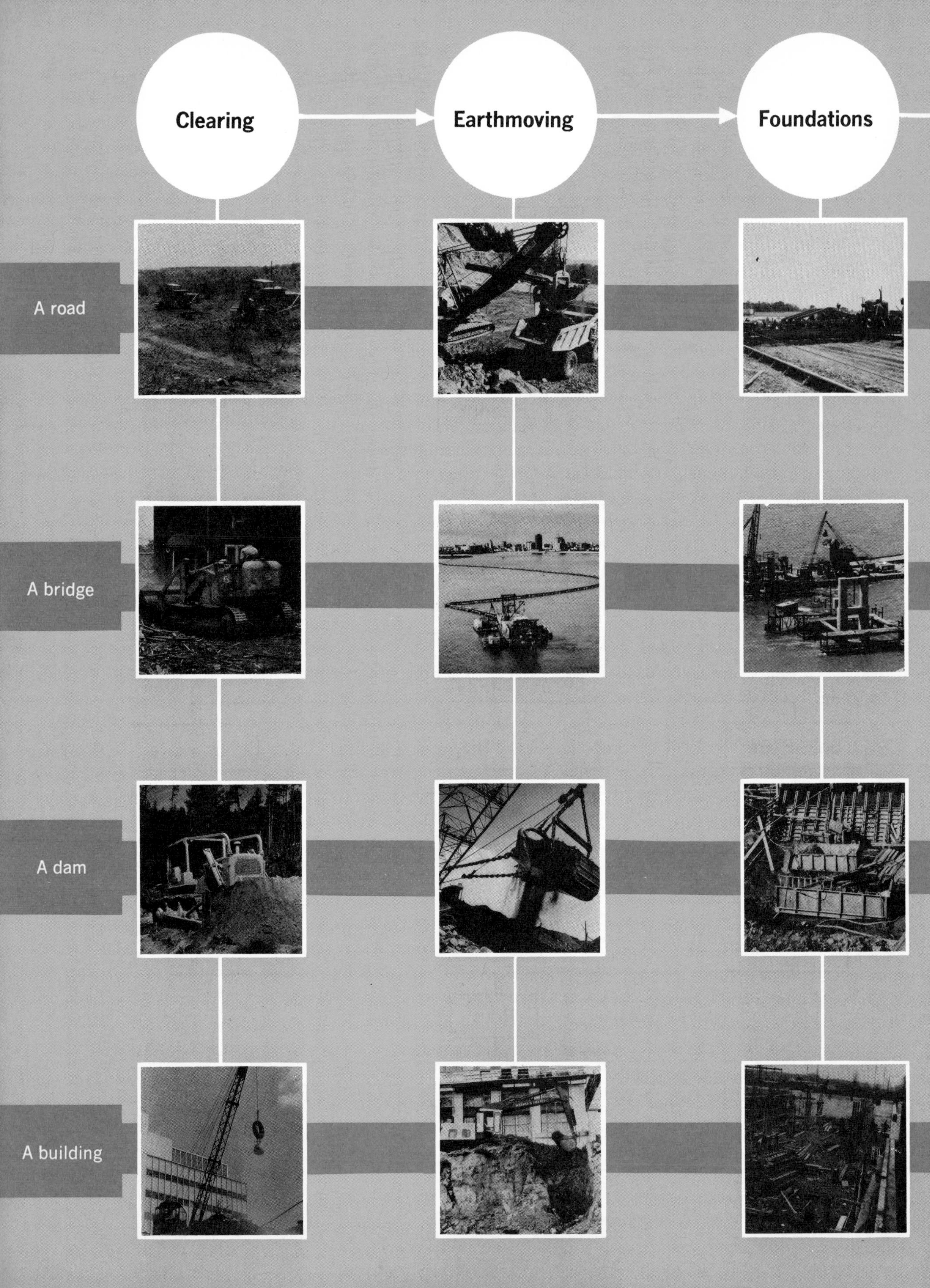
Clearing
Earthmoving
Foundations
A road
A bridge
A dam
A building

Superstructures
Utilities
Finished Project

READING 48

Installing Utilities

Utilities are services such as water, waste disposal, electricity, gas, and communications. Utilities need to be installed in many structures in order for them to serve the purpose for which they were constructed. The utility systems which provide the services also require much construction, Fig. 48-1.

Utilities are a part of and service almost all constructed works. For example:

1. Tunnels must be lighted and ventilated.
2. Highways need traffic controls and drainage.
3. Bridges may need lighting and controls for raising or opening them.

Most utility installation work is in connection with buildings. In many modern buildings, the cost of installing the utilities is more than the cost of the rest of the building. The rest of this reading will be about installing utilities in buildings and about the construction of the systems which bring the utilities to the buildings, Fig. 48-2.

Utilities are installed both inside and outside buildings. For instance, all the electric power equipment which is outside a building is considered an "outside utility." The wiring system within the building is an "inside utility." Usually the electric power company provides the outside electrical system. The building owner, through the general con-

Fig. 48-1. Some pipelines that carry water to treatment plants are so large that they must be constructed on the site.

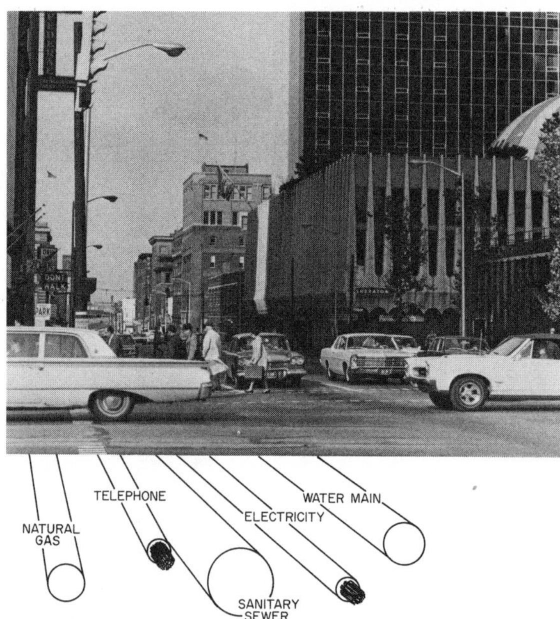

Fig. 48-2. A city cannot operate without the services of utilities. Many utility lines (pipes, wires) are hidden between walls or are underground.

tractor and the electrical subcontractor, provides the inside wiring system.

In describing utilities, we shall assume that we have an office building provided with:

1. A water and a waste disposal system,
2. Electricity for lighting and air conditioning,
3. Gas to heat the building and to heat water, and
4. Telephone service.

The equipment, supplies, and labor for these utilities may be from one-third to two-thirds of the entire cost of a building, Fig. 48-2. Thus, the architect or engineer designing the utilities systems has a job almost as big as the task of designing the rest of the structure.

Water

A city usually draws its water from a river, a reservoir, or a system of wells. The water is pumped through an underground pipeline (a pipe of large diameter), Fig. 48-1. After being purified, it is piped throughout the city in pipes of various sizes. These pipes, called *water mains,* usually are laid beneath the streets.

While our building is being built, the water main at the edge of the property is *tapped.* That is, a hole is bored in the main, and a small diameter entrance pipe is placed, leading from the tap to the building. Usually a meter and a shutoff valve are placed in the entrance line. To distribute water throughout the building, *craftsmen* install smaller pipes which connect to each plumbing fixture. Sometimes, the smaller pipes also connect to a fire-protection system of sprinklers or hydrants. The water flows into and through the building as the result of pressure from gravity or pumps.

Sewerage

A system of pipes which carries off excess or waste water is called a *sewerage.* One branch of the system is called a *sewer.* There are two types: (1) sanitary sewers and (2) storm sewers. Sanitary sewers carry waste water (sewage) away from plumbing fixtures and into a sewer pipe leading from *our imaginary* building. This pipe is "tapped" into a *city sewer main* which usually lies under or close to a street, Fig. 48-3. The sewer mains lead to a city sewage treatment plant. There the waste water is purified and discharged, usually into a stream.

Water falling as rain or snow on the roof of our building runs into gutters and downspouts. It is carried into a system of storm sewers which also drain water from the streets. You have probably seen the drains at street corners, where water passes from the streets to the storm sewer.

Storm sewage, unlike sanitary sewage, usually is not *treated* (cleaned) before it is discharged into natural drainage systems. Both kinds of sewage usually flow as a result of gravity, although sometimes they must be pumped.

Electricity

Electricity is a form of energy. It involves the movement of *electrons.* Ordinary electric

Fig. 48-3. These workers are preparing to lay a small plastic sewerage pipeline.

current is a controlled flow of electrons through a wire or other conductor. Power plants generate electric current by converting the energy of falling water, atomic fission, Fig. 48-4, or fossil fuels to electrical energy, or electricity. The *fossil fuels* include coal, petroleum, and natural gas.

Fig. 48-4. In this power plant, atomic fission supplies heat energy which is converted to electrical energy.

Voltage is a measure of the electrical force needed to push electric current through wires. Electric current is transmitted from a power plant at high voltage, in wires held up by high steel towers such as you may have seen out in the country. When the electricity reaches the city, a transformer reduces the voltage. A *transformer reduces the electrical force* in the line. See Fig. 48-5. The electric power is then distributed throughout the city in wires strung on poles or buried underground. Underground wires usually are placed in a *duct* or *conduit.* Conduit is a metal, plastic, or tile pipe. The conduit protects the wires.

Just before the power reaches *our imaginary* building, it goes through another transformer to lower the voltage to 240 volts. The utility company installs a *drop* (made up of 3 wires) leading from the transformer

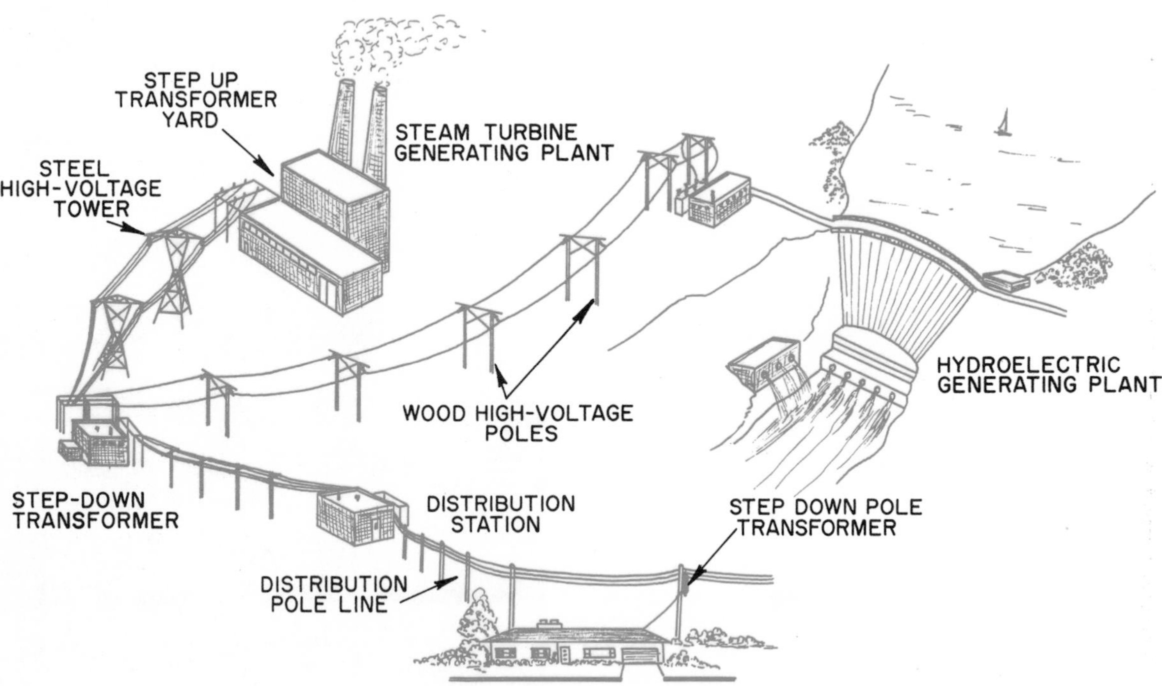

Fig. 48-5. Electricity is produced near a source of power and then is transmitted from the power plant on high-voltage transmission lines to the cities. In cities the high voltage is reduced in transformer stations so that the electricity can be used in homes and industry. Note the pole transformer where voltage is again reduced before entering the home.

to the building, Fig. 48-6. Upon reaching the building, the wires are pulled through a metal conduit (pipe) to a meter. From the meter, the wires are connected to a fuse (circuit breaker) box.

Workmen employed by the electrical subcontractors install the "inside utility." From the fuse box, they put wires in conduit or use flexible cable to distribute the power to all lighting fixtures, to air conditioning and heating equipment, and to all floor and wall outlets. See Fig. 48-7.

Gas

Some fuel gas is manufactured, but a great deal exists in a natural form underground. Most gas used today is natural gas produced by wells in certain parts of the country. From the gas fields, high-pressure pumps force the gas through large diameter pipelines to distant cities, Fig. 48-8. There the pressure is reduced (lowered) and the

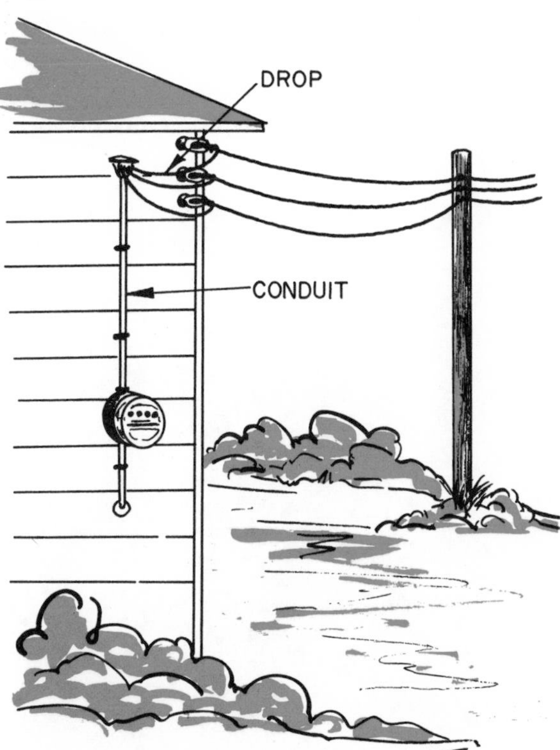

Fig. 48-6. Before electricity reaches a building, it enters a transformer where voltage is further reduced. A "drop" made up of three wires leads from the transformer to the building.

Fig. 48-7. Inside a building, electricity is distributed to light fixtures and other electrical equipment by wires in conduit or flexible cable. Conduits protect the wires.

Fig. 48-8. Underground pipes may have a fiber glass reinforced asphaltic coating such as the one being put on this transcontinental pipeline.

gas is distributed throughout the city in pipes (called *gas mains*) under the streets, similar to water mains. To serve our building, the gas company "taps" the main and lays an underground line about 2″ in diameter. As the gas line enters the building, the pressure is again reduced, and a meter is installed in the line. Through pipes installed by a subcontractor's men, the gas is piped to the gas burning appliances.

Heating and Air Conditioning

The furnace and the air conditioner may be separate units. Usually they are parts of the same unit. The burning of gas supplies heat, and compressors operated by electricity supply the cooled or "chilled" air. Both the furnace and the compressors may be controlled by setting a *thermostat.* The thermostat is a *control device* by which the temperature in the building may be kept constant.

The heated or chilled air is carried about the building in sheet metal ducts, Fig. 48-9. These ducts are rectangular or square and may vary in size from 4″ x 10″ to much larger. The air, at low pressure, moves slowly through these ducts from the furnace or air conditioner to the various rooms. The air enters through a grill device called a *register.*

There are also other registers, either in each room or in the halls, through which the air returns to the furnace and the air conditioning unit. There it is filtered (to remove dirt and dust) and again heated or cooled and circulated throughout the building. These ducts are called *return air ducts.*

Communications

From each telephone in our building, wires lead to one central point where they enter an equipment cabinet. The wires are connected to relays (used for switching) in the cabinet. The wires from the cabinet leave the building bound into a cable containing many individual wires. Outside, this

Fig. 48-9. Ductwork circulates fresh, hot, and cold air. Insulation may be used to prevent heat loss.

Fig. 48-10. Some communications systems have an air gap in the circuit. This microwave tower is used by the Union Pacific Railroad to send traffic control signals through the air.

joins a larger cable running on poles or in underground ducts. Many cables lead to a central telephone office where there are operators and dialing equipment.

Central telephone offices may communicate with each other either through cables or by means of special radio broadcasting and receiving equipment. *Relay stations* receive and retransmit radio messages. Some relay stations are located in high, steel towers, with disk-shaped antennas, Fig. 48-10. Others are man-made satellites circling the earth at great heights.

Other Utilities

A building may include many other utility systems such as:

1. Steam,
2. Chilled water, Fig. 48-11,
3. Compressed air,
4. Oxygen,
5. Teletype and telegraph communications, and
6. Built-in television and radio cables.

Fig. 48-11. Pipe fitting technology is required to install this 180-ton water chilling plant.

Networks of Utilities

It should be easy to see why the utility lines within a building are a large part of the cost of the structure, sometimes the largest part. Utility lines must:

1. Operate satisfactorily and safely,
2. Not interfere with each other, and
3. Generally be hidden or blended into the floors, walls, and ceilings.

The architects and engineers who design them, and the craftsmen who install them, must remember all of these requirements.

Outside our building, the average city street covers a complicated web of water lines, sewer lines, gas mains, and sometimes electric power and communication cables. In large cities these are so numerous that several or all of the utility lines sometimes pass together through concrete-lined tunnels. In any case, each utility company's engineers must keep careful records and drawings of the locations of all lines, along with valves, manholes, and junctions.

Summary

The utilities—water, sewerage, electricity, gas, communications, and others—provide

Fig. 48-12. A modern building requires a complex network of utilities. What distribution lines for utilities are shown?

essential services to structures and the people who use them. The electrical and mechanical work (both equipment and labor) may be a large part of the cost of any structure. Most permanent structures require one or more utilities, Fig. 48-12.

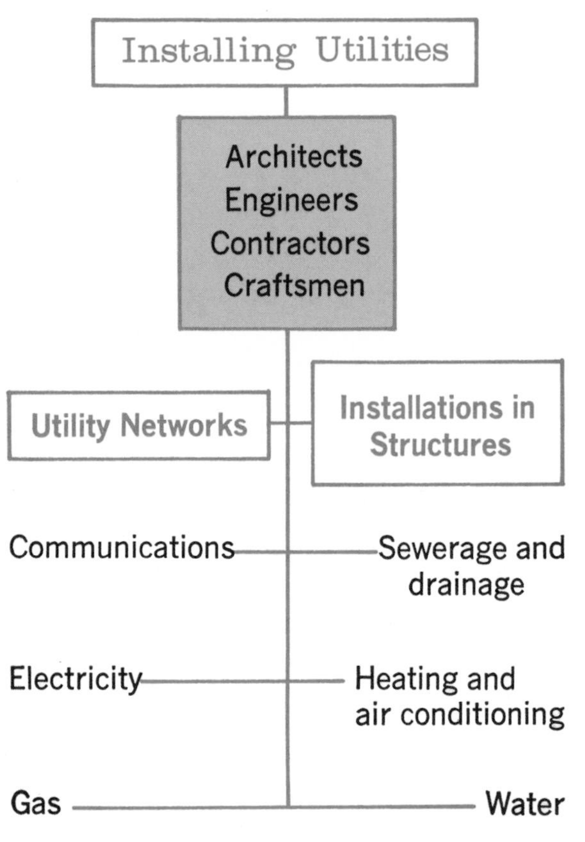

Terms to Know

utilities	electricity
a. inside utilities	electrons
b. outside utilities	generate
communications	converting
distribute	voltage
reservoir	transformer
water mains	duct
sewage	conduit
sewerage	gas mains
a. sanitary sewers	thermostat
b. storm sewers	return air ducts
treated sewage	"tap" a main

Think About It!

1. What utilities service your home? Can you think of others which are used in your community?
2. What are some of the problems you would have if all the utilities you use were suddenly shut off?
3. Describe some utility construction now going on near your home or school.

Installing Heating, Cooling, and Ventilating Systems

This lesson introduces what is done to the air in a structure so that the people inside are comfortable and so that whatever activity is to take place can proceed. For example, in a greenhouse where flowers are raised, the air temperature must be kept well above freezing. We shall describe ways in which air is treated and how treated air can be moved throughout the structure, Fig. 49-1.

Methods of Treating Air

Air is heated either by a centrally located furnace or by separate heating units. Gas, oil, coal, or electricity may provide the heat source. Gas is now the most commonly used fuel.

Fig. 49-1. Sheet metal ducts are installed to send treated air to various points within a structure.

Air is cooled either in centrally located air-conditioning units or in electric window units. Central units run on gas or, more often, electricity. Some electric air conditioning units can also provide heating. These are called *heat pumps* or *reverse-cycle* units.

Fresh air for ventilating is drawn in from outdoors. Some outdoor air has too much water vapor (called *humidity*) for comfort. Humidity may cause you to feel quite uncomfortable on a cloudy, damp day, even when it is not especially hot. Humidity may be taken away from the air by a *dehumidifier* which may work with heat and fans or with chemicals.

Some air has too little water vapor for comfort. You may not feel comfortable in a warm, dry room without some moisture in the air. Humidity is added to the air by a *humidifier,* which may work by spraying fine drops of water or by evaporating water into the air.

One other way to treat air is to pass it through filters. A filter is usually a fine screen of fiber, metal, or plastic which removes dust and dirt, in much the same way that window screens keep insects from passing through. Some filters are permanent and require periodic cleaning. Other filters are disposable. They are thrown away when dirty, and new ones are installed. There are also filters which use electronics or sound to collect unwanted particles from the air.

Distribution

Sometimes air is not heated directly. Instead, the burning fuel heats water to a high temperature or even until it evaporates into steam. The hot water or steam is then sent through the building in a system of pipes. In each room there is a *radiator* to heat the air. In some cases wires, pipes, or tubing are hidden in the floor or ceiling and these serve as radiators.

Usually, the fuel heats the air itself and the air is sent through the building in a system of ducts. Ducts are thin-walled pipes which may be circular or rectangular in cross section.

A fan or blower in a duct, near the heating source, creates a slight pressure which forces the warm air slowly through the duct. The air must not be moved rapidly. A noticeable breeze or *draft* in a room would not be desirable. Often high-pressure duct systems are used in large buildings so that smaller ducts can be used, thereby using less space. In these systems, the speed of the air must be reduced (to prevent a draft) before it enters each room.

Air from the duct system enters each room through a register. The same ductwork which delivers warm air in winter can also carry cool air in summer, if an air-cooling unit is built into the system.

Fig. 49-2. The pneumatic conveying equipment shown here transports flour to various points in the flour mill.

The Air Return System

Removing used or polluted air from structures is just as necessary as introducing treated air. For this purpose, *return air* (exhaust) registers open into a second set of ducts. A slight vacuum, created by fans, pulls the stale air slowly through the return air ducts. This used air may be exhausted to the outdoors, or it may be refiltered, reheated, or recooled, and then recirculated.

Pneumatic Conveying and Recovery Systems

The primary concern in this reading is with the use of *sheet metal ductwork* as it is used in the controlling of the climate inside a structure. Sheet metal ducts have another major use which will only be brought to your attention here. Many of the same techniques used to fabricate and install air distribution and return systems also are used in industry to move materials as well as air. These are called *pneumatic conveying and recovery systems.*

Pneumatic conveying is used to carry materials such as grain, flour, and even bolts and nuts from receiving or storage areas to where they are needed, Fig. 49-2. A stream of air is used to carry the materials inside a duct instead of using more complicated conveyor belts or containers.

Pneumatic recovery systems may be compared with a home vacuum sweeper. In these, waste materials such as wood shavings are drawn up and carried to a collection point. There they are settled or filtered out of the air stream.

Pneumatic conveying and recovery systems are designed, engineered, fabricated, and installed in much the same way as are ductwork systems which carry only air. One major difference is that pneumatic systems seldom require a source of heat or cold. The rest of the systems have much in common because they include the blowers, ducts, filters, humidity regulators, and controls.

Who Installs the Ducts

The duct system is carefully planned by a mechanical engineer. He determines the size of the ducts based on the amount of air per minute that should move through each duct.

The general contractor usually subcontracts the ductwork either to a sheet metal subcontractor or to a mechanical subcontractor who does both sheet metal work and plumbing. The subcontractor prepares detailed shop drawings which show how each part is to be made. After the engineer approves the shop drawings, sections of ductwork are made up in the subcontractor's shop, Figs. 49-3 and 49-4. The ductwork is then installed.

Fig. 49-3. This forming machine produces ducting.

Fig. 49-4. These sheet metal mechanics are operating a power press, forming the sheet metal into the shape required.

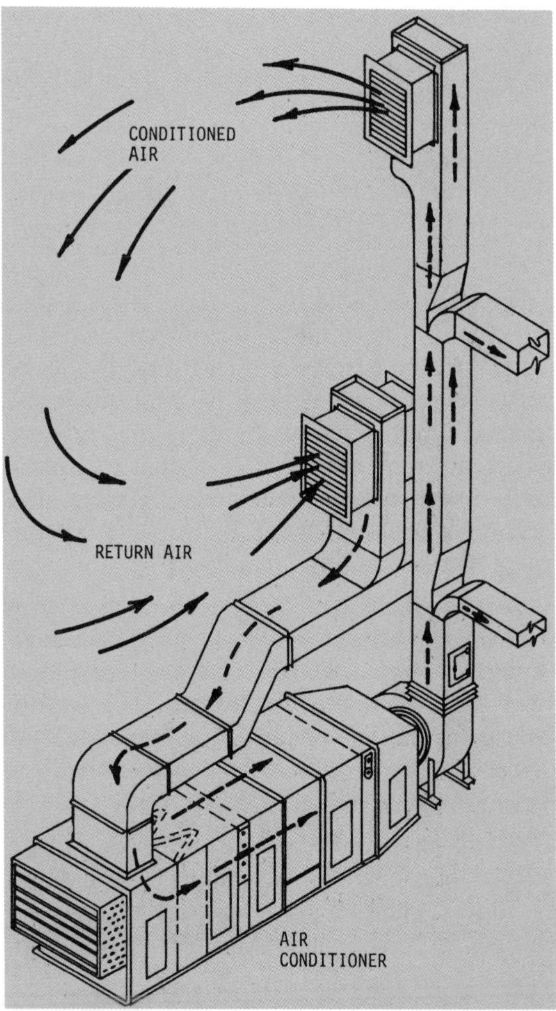

Fig. 49-5. Can you trace the flow of return air through the air conditioner and back into the room?

The people who *fabricate* (make) and install the ducts are skilled craftsmen called *sheet metal workers*. They also perform many other tasks involving sheet metal work in construction.

Installing Ducts

Sheet metal ducts are larger near the furnace or air conditioning unit. They become smaller and smaller as they deliver the air to the rooms. This gradual reduction of the duct size helps keep the pressure about the same throughout the duct, Fig. 49-5.

Ducts are hung in place by straps or *rods* and *angles*, Fig. 49-6. Joints between sections of duct are usually made by slipping one section inside another, with a sealer. Sometimes metal bands are placed across the junction of two sections to form a joint, Fig. 49-7.

Ducts must be so located that they do not interfere with other utility lines, such as water or sewer pipes and electrical conduits. This is true when all utilities must be crammed into openings (called *chases*) between different parts of a structure. Often main sheet metal ducts run between the ceiling of one story and the floor of the story above, usually in a hallway.

Because ductwork is often hidden within the finished structure, it is hard to make changes or repairs after it is once in place. Therefore, it must be installed skillfully. Particular skill is required to fabricate and install ductwork when the ducts change direction, size, or shape.

As sheet metal ducts usually carry air that is warmer or cooler than the air outside the ducts, some type of insulation may be needed to reduce heat loss. Mats of fiberglass or plastic foams are used to cover ducts. The insulation mats may be fastened in place with *adhesives* or *metal fasteners*. Occasionally the insulation is built into the duct as a lining.

Controls

Not only must heat, cold, and humidity be provided, but they must also be controlled so that a building does not get too hot, too cold, too damp, or too dry. Also, the speed of the air in the ducts must be controlled to prevent drafts and yet provide enough ventilation, Fig. 49-8.

The air temperature in a building is controlled by an electrical device called a *thermostat*. It combines a thermometer with a control switch which may be set at a desired temperature. The thermostat automatically turns on the furnace or air conditioner when the temperature varies from the set figure by a small amount.

A *humidity regulator* (called a *humidistat*) automatically controls the amount of water vapor added to the air by a humidifier or taken out of the air by a dehumidifier. This keeps the desired amount of water vapor in the air at all times.

The flow of air into a room may be controlled by a *damper*, either at the register or in the duct, Fig. 49-9. The damper is made of one or more pieces of metal which can be moved to block the air flow. It serves

Fig. 49-6. These sheet metal workers are installing hangers to concrete with a .22 caliber stub gun.

the same purpose in ducting that a faucet serves in piping. The damper can be set so that very little, some, or nearly all the air can pass around it.

Summary

Heating, cooling, and ventilating systems provide a comfortable climate within structures. This climate is an atmosphere of clean, pure air at the correct temperature and humidity without excessive drafts. Usually central units treat the air, which then flows through ductwork to where it is needed. Air is also exhausted and either discharged to the outside or retreated. Proper controls of heat, cooling, humidity, and air flow are necessary to providing a pleasant indoor climate.

Fig. 49-8. The air conditioning of an entire structure is controlled at this panel.

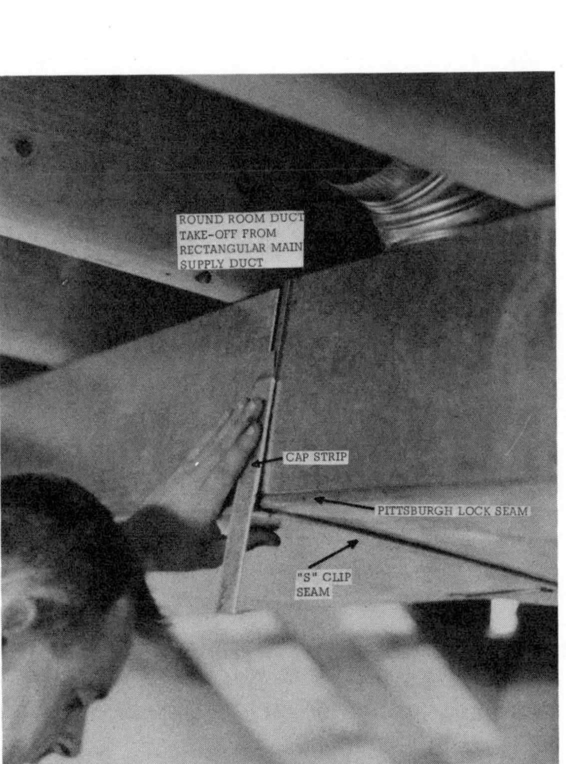

Fig. 49-7. Two sections of a duct are locked together with a cap strip which completes a cap-strip seam.

Fig. 49-9. Sometimes the flow of air is regulated by a mechanical control called a "damper."

Terms to Know

ventilating
air conditioning
humidity
dehumidifier
humidifier
treated air
draft
polluted air
ductwork
radiator
exhaust
pneumatic conveying system
pneumatic recovery system
fabricate
ducts
perimeter heating
adhesives
metal fastener
humidity regulator
damper
filtered
circulated
thermostats
purifying

Think About It!

1. State four ways in which air can be changed or "treated".
2. What are the names of several devices that control temperature, humidity, or the flow of air in a room?
3. Why might it be easiest to install ductwork before plumbing or wiring?

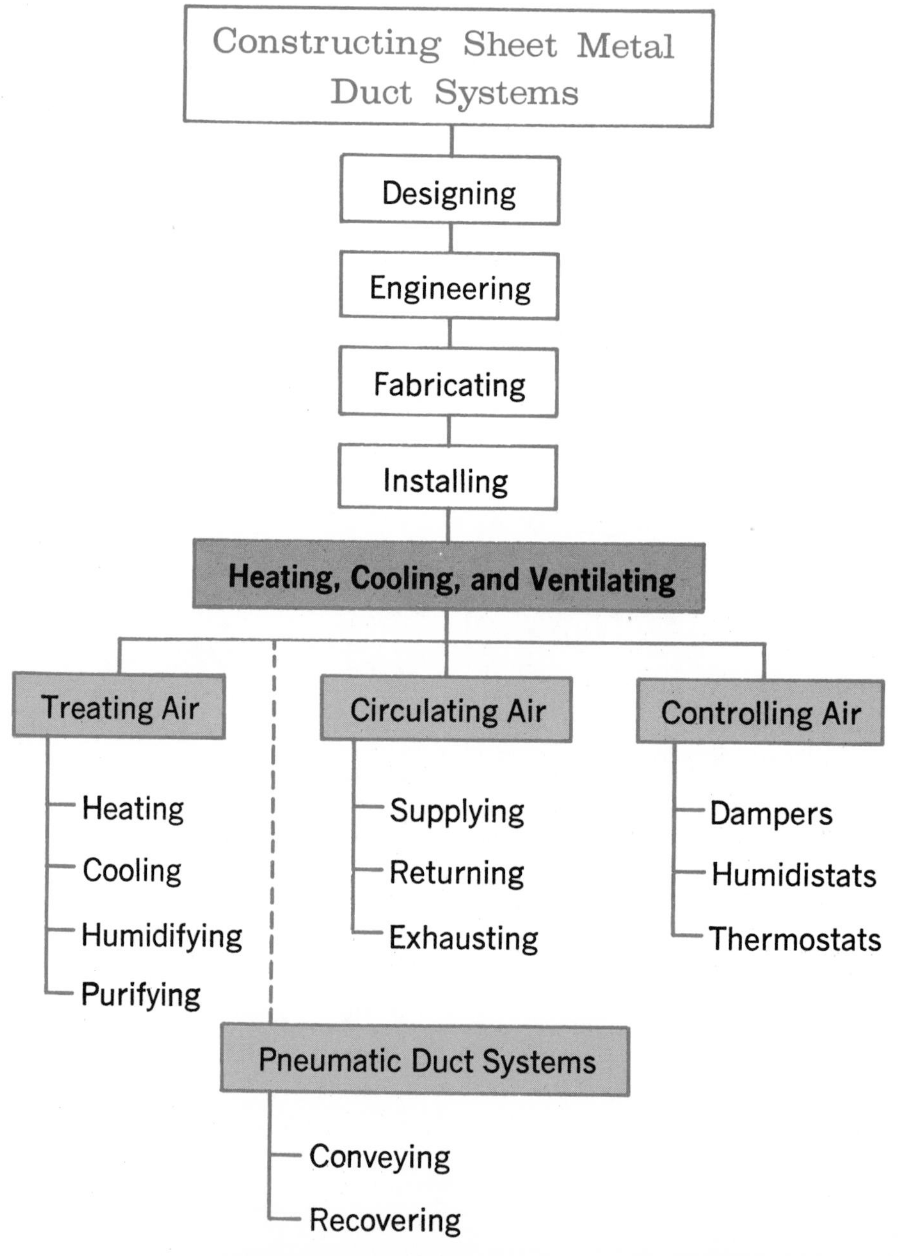

Installing Plumbing Systems

This lesson describes plumbing systems inside buildings, and the next lesson covers piping systems outside of buildings. Outside systems are built chiefly of rigid pipe. Plumbing in a building may use rigid pipe, flexible tubing, or both. A previous reading described sheet metal duct systems through which air moves slowly, under very slight pressures. Plumbing systems carry gases and liquids which move rapidly at pressures varying from the weight of the gas or liquid (gravity) to extremely high pressures. Sometimes the pressure is 5,000 pounds upon each square inch of pipe. All plumbing and piping systems must be tight enough to prevent any leakage, Fig. 50-1.

Fig. 50-1. The boilermaker installs thousands of pipes to make up this large boiler.

Major Kinds of Plumbing Systems

Plumbing systems are used to move the following:

1. Fresh water,
2. Hot water or steam,
3. Water for fire protection,
4. Gases,
5. Other fluids, and
6. Sewage.

The piping material used depends upon (1) the type of plumbing system, (2) the designer of the system, and (3) local building codes and standard practices.

Who Does the Plumbing

The number, type, and location of plumbing fixtures, appliances, and equipment are determined by the architect, Figs. 50-2 and 50-3. The piping needed to serve them is designed by an engineer who makes sure that building codes and good practice are followed. The general contractor usually subcontracts the plumbing to a plumbing subcontractor or a mechanical subcontractor, who also may do the sheet metal work. The subcontractor prepares detailed shop drawings of the plumbing. After the engineer approves his drawings, the plumbing subcontractor begins the installation. He directs the work of plumbers who install water, gas, and sewerage lines. He also employs steam fitters for putting in steam or hot-water lines used for heating or industrial uses, Fig. 50-4. Both plumbers and steam fitters are highly skilled craftsmen.

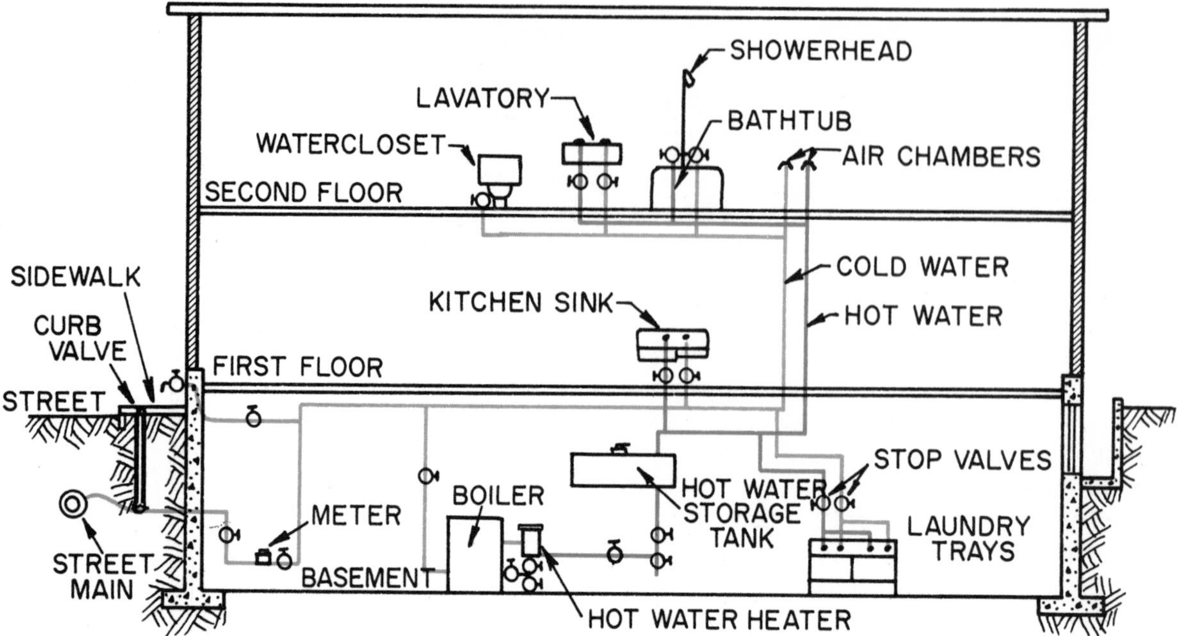

Fig. 50-2. The fresh water piping system within a building is shown. Can you trace the fresh water flow from the street main to the shower head?

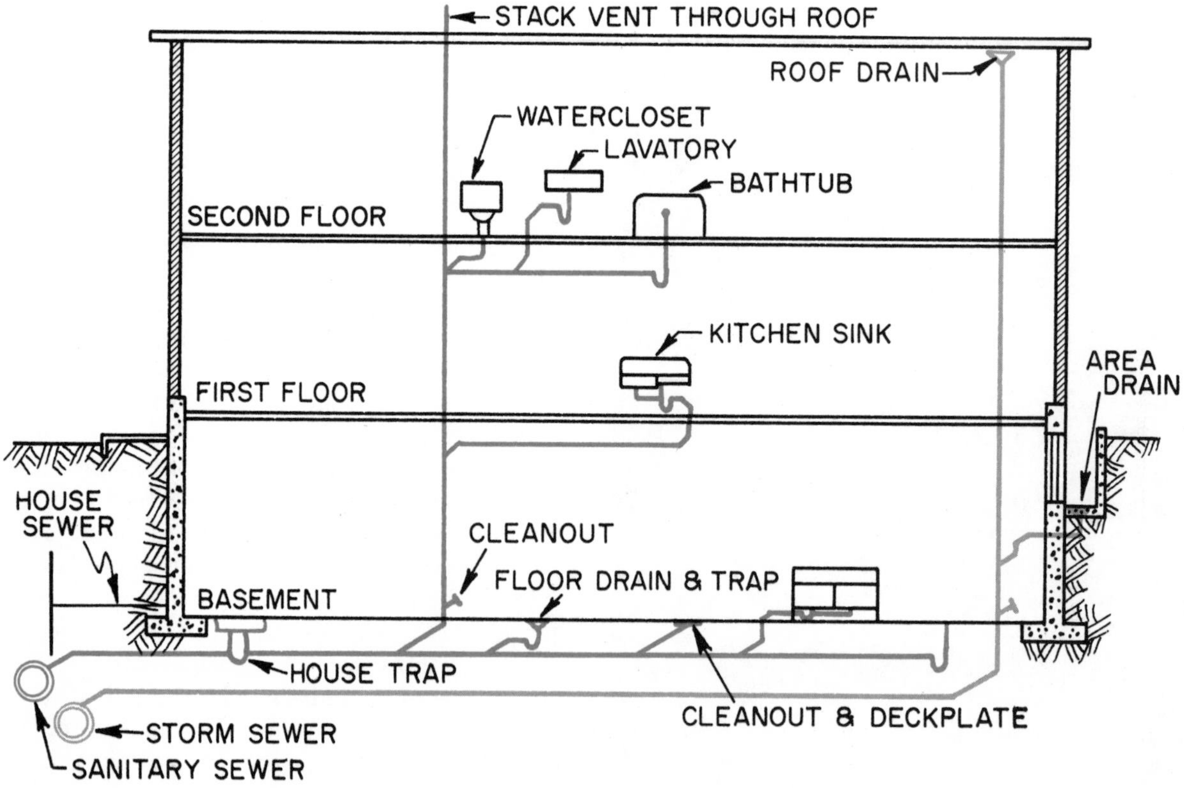

Fig. 50-3. The building sanitary and storm sewer piping systems are shown. Can you trace the drainage from the bathtub to the sanitary sewer?

Piping

Piping is used to make a plumbing system. Piping consists of (1) rigid straight lengths, (2) curved lengths of flexible tubing, and (3) fittings such as couplings, tees, ells (elbows) at various angles, Y's, crosses, reducers, and unions. See Fig. 50-5. A *reducer* connects a pipe of one size to a pipe of a smaller size. A *union* is placed into a system of piping so that it can be taken apart, at that point, for repairs. Where a piping system is under pressure, *valves* are placed in the lines to shut off or turn on a part of the system. Valves are not used in sewerage systems because the lines must be open to perform their functions at all times.

Pipe size is specified by a number which is called the *nominal size.* It is related to the pipe diameter, but for many kinds of pipe and tubing, it is neither the inside nor the outside diameter. For example, ½″ galvanized iron pipe has an *inside diameter* of about ⅝″ and an *outside diameter* of about 13⁄16″.

All pipe fittings which are made to be used together are standardized. Threaded ½″ galvanized pipe will fit together with standard elbows and tees specified as ½″ *threaded.* A pipe die which will cut a standard thread on this pipe is called a ½″ pipe die. None of these items actually has a ½″ diameter, but they are all designed for use together.

Some copper piping is purchased in the form of flexible tubing in rolls up to 100′ long. The *nominal diameter* ranges from ¼″ to 12″. (The true outside diameter of copper tubing is slightly larger than its nominal size.) Rigid copper pipe is also available in standard lengths. Copper pipe can be obtained in nominal sizes of ⅛″ to 12″. It is more expensive, per foot, than flexible copper tubing of the same nominal size.

Installing Piping

At the building site, copper tubing is cut to the lengths needed. Lengths of copper

Fig. 50-4. Many pipes are needed to distribute liquids and gases in manufacturing plants.

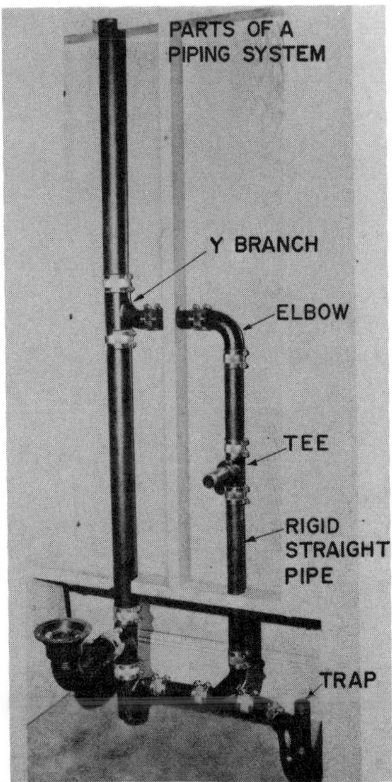

Fig. 50-5. These are typical pipe sections and fittings.

tubing are joined with *couplings, tees,* or *ells* at bends in the lines. All these fittings are made to slide over the end of the piping very tightly. Then they are sealed by a thin film of solder, Fig 50-6. This is called a *sweated joint.* The soldering metal is called *lead solder,* but it is actually an alloy of lead and tin.

Black steel or galvanized steel piping systems are assembled at the site from 20′ lengths of pipe that are cut to the length needed. They are assembled with fittings such as couplings, ells, or tees. Steel pipe is harder than copper tubing, and can be threaded. Therefore, steel pipe of small diameter is assembled using threaded joints. After the pipe has been cut to length, the proper thread size is set up in a threading machine, and a thread is cut into the end of the pipe.

All pipe fittings are threaded by the manufacturer. A compound, often called *pipe dope,* is smeared on the pipe thread before the fitting is screwed onto it. When this pipe dope hardens, it seals the threads and prevents leaks.

As the piping must be adjusted or tailored to each particular building, most pipe of less than 4″ diameter is cut, fitted, and threaded at the site. Often, when the same pattern of piping is used over and over as in a multistory building, parts of it may be prefabricated in a shop. Pipe of 4″ or larger size is hard to handle and to thread on the job. It is often put together in a pipe shop and taken to the site.

Pipe systems using pipe larger than 4″ diameter can be assembled by welding two lengths together at their ends (Fig. 50-7) or by welding *flanges* to the ends of two pieces of pipe. The flanged pieces of pipe are bolted together and can be taken apart.

Cast-iron soil pipe systems are assembled using lead joints. Each length of cast iron soil pipe has a flared end called the *bell end.* The other end of the pipe is called the *spigot end.* The spigot end of one pipe or fitting is placed in the bell of the adjoining pipe or fitting. The space around the spigot end is packed with *oakum* (a greasy packing) for an inch or so. The rest of the bell is poured full of hot lead.

Clay pipe used for storm drainage is also of the bell and spigot type, but the joints

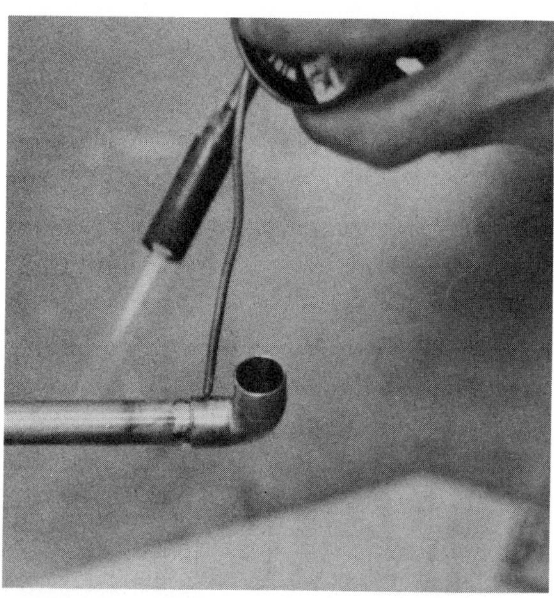

Fig. 50-6. Copper pipe fittings are fastened together by soldering.

Fig. 50-7. These large diameter pipes have been joined by welding.

Fig. 50-8. Plastic pipe is joined by using a special solvent cement.

Fig. 50-9. This plumber is tightening a joint in a pipe network. Did the plumber design the network?

are filled with a *cement grout* (a mixture of cement, sand, and water).

Plastic pipe is now used in many applications. It has the advantages of flexibility and of not being affected by corrosive liquids or gases. Special techniques are required to assemble and install plastic pipe. *Mastics* or cements often are used to join plastic pipe, Fig. 50-8. Also, the pieces may be clamped together, Fig. 50-9. These practices are not commonly used with other kinds of piping.

If a structure is to be built on a slab, some piping is installed before the concrete for the slab is placed. The parts of the piping which extend above the slab are called *risers.*

The horizontal part of piping systems is hung from the underside of floor slabs or from ceilings, using a *pipe hanger.* Where pipe runs vertically up a building, special hangers are used to fasten it to the wall. *Piping systems must be fastened to the structure to prevent strains in the piping which can cause it to leak.* All plumbing must be carefully installed. People and property may be harmed by plumbing failures. For example, leaks may cause fires (from gas), expensive repairs (replacing water-damaged plaster), and even death (being overcome by sewer gas).

Summary

Plumbing systems distribute liquids and gases throughout a building, in pipes of various sizes and materials. Special compressed-air piping systems can carry solid substances.

Architects determine the number, type, and location of plumbing fixtures, appliances, and equipment. An engineer determines what piping should be used to service them. The actual plumbing work is usually directed by a subcontractor who employs skilled craftsmen. All the personnel involved with plumbing must work carefully to make sure that the plumbing does not leak and that materials can flow freely through the pipes.

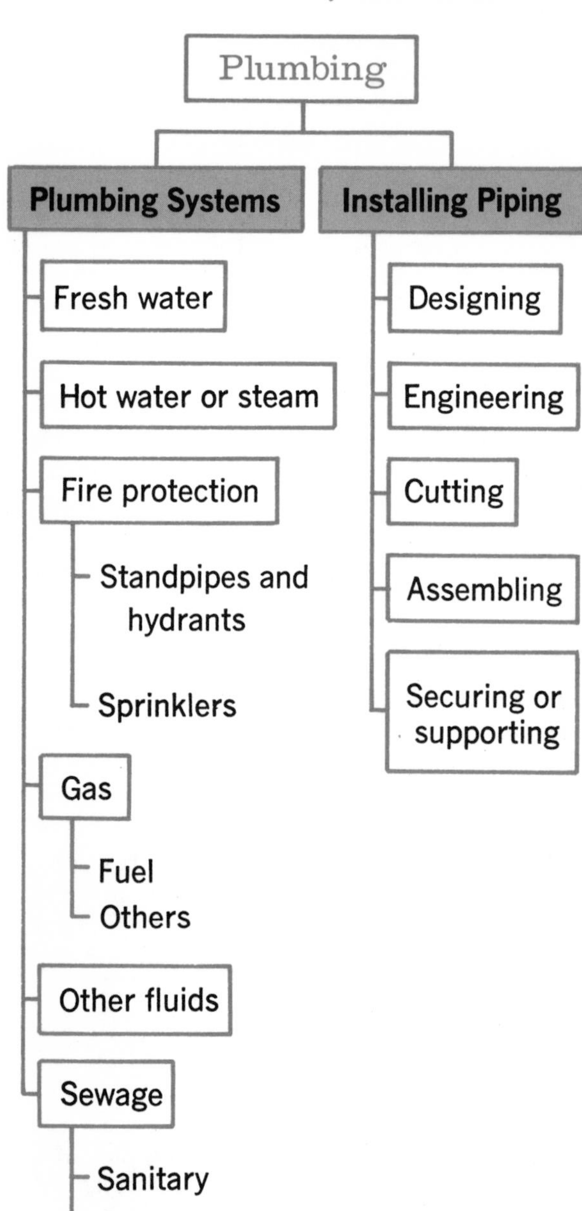

Terms to Know

flexible
reducer
joints
union
valves
nominal size
couplings
threaded
solder
tees
ells
pipe dope
pipe die
welding
flanges
bell end
spigot end
soil pipe systems
risers
mastic
pipe hanger
diameter
vent
standard thread
grout

Think About It!

1. Two separate piping systems are required for most structures. What are they?
2. List four materials carried through plumbing systems.
3. What is the name given to the person whose trade or craft has prepared him to install piping systems in your home?

Installing Piping Systems

READING 51

In the previous lesson you read about *plumbing*. It is piping *inside* a building. This lesson is about *pipelines*. They are piping systems *outside* of buildings.

Pipelines are generally of larger diameter than the pipes within a building. One pipeline may serve several buildings, a whole city, or even a group of cities. Pipelines usually have thick walls to resist heavy internal (inside) pressures and to prevent damage from the outside, Fig. 51-1.

Trenching

A few pipelines are placed on or above ground, but most pipelines are laid in trenches beneath the surface of the earth. There they are less likely to be damaged and are not exposed to severe changes in temperature.

Two types of construction equipment are used to dig trenches for pipelines: the *backhoe* and the *trencher*. The backhoe has a long, jointed arm with a bucket on the end. The edge of the bucket is lined with teeth. In digging, the arm of the backhoe is first stretched out, and the bucket is dropped into the ground to rest on its teeth. The arm then is pulled in toward the machine to dig the trench, Fig. 51-2.

The trencher has a large wheel to which small buckets are attached. As the wheel revolves, the buckets dig into the ground and pick up earth which is then thrown into

Fig. 51-1. Pipelines are generally larger than pipes within a building.

Fig. 51-2. This backhoe operator is digging the trench in which the pipe on the right will be laid.

piles along the sides of the trench. As the trench is dug, bracing sometimes has to be placed between the sides of the trench to keep them from caving in.

Laying Pipe

Pipe usually is laid with a crane. It must be placed in the trench at exactly the correct height and slope, Figs. 51-3 and 51-4. This is most important, particularly in sewer lines. Sewer pipes are laid at a slight slope so that the waste water will flow down toward the sewage treatment plant, Fig. 51-5. Sometimes sewage has to be pumped, but this is avoided whenever possible.

After the pipe has been placed in the trench, the trench is *backfilled.* This can be done with a bulldozer by pushing the earth, a little at a time, into the trench. It also may be done with a crane which has a clamshell bucket hanging from the end of its boom. This bucket picks up a load of earth and drops it into the trench. The earth around the pipe is pounded down, or *tamped,* by a hand operated or a power driven tamper, Figs. 51-6 and 51-7. Filling and tamping continue until the surface is level. Above the pipe, at grade level, the earth is also pushed together (compressed) by a roller or by the treads or wheels of a heavy tractor. Tamping and rolling prevent the surface of the earth around the pipe from settling later.

Fig. 51-3. This excavating machine is performing the "cradling" operation, preparing the foundation for a pipeline.

Fig. 51-4. Each of these concrete pipe sections weighs 24 tons. They are carefully laid in place by the crane.

Fig. 51-5. Some pipes run over the land and obstacles. This sewer pipe is supported on piers.

Who Installs Pipelines

Pipelines are carefully designed by civil engineers. When designing piping systems, civil engineers will:

1. Lay out the route,
2. Specify pipe sizes,
3. Choose locations for pumping, processing, or treatment plants, and
4. Select equipment for these plants.

Pipelines are usually installed by mechanical contractors, some of whom specialize in pipeline construction. Often an owner will install a pipeline with his own employees. The craftsmen involved are the operating engineers who operate the construction machinery (backhoes, trenchers, bulldozers, and cranes) and the pipe layers, who may also be plumbers, pipe fitters, steam fitters, or boilermakers.

Water flows through a pipeline from a river, a reservoir, or a well to a water treatment plant near the city. The water is then distributed throughout the city by a connected series of pipelines. Every effort is made to have the water flow by gravity whenever possible. Sometimes it is necessary to use pumps.

Water systems usually use cast iron or concrete pipe, although steel, asbestos, cement, copper, or plastic pipe is sometimes used. Cast iron pipe has an extremely long life. Some which were installed over 150 years ago are still in use.

Joints in cast iron pipe may be of three types: lead, mechanical, and compression. Lead joints are similar to those on cast iron soil pipe inside a building. Lead is poured into a space (formed by the opening between a *bell* and a *spigot*) between pipes to seal them together. On mechanical joint pipe, bolts hold the two pieces of pipe together. A gasket, or piece of pliable material, seals the joint against leakage.

A *compression joint* (connection) is made by forcing the plain end of one pipe into the bell of the adjoining pipe in which a rubber gasket has been placed. The gasket clamps tightly around the plain end and fits tightly into the bell to seal the joint.

Concrete pipe usually has steel reinforcement placed inside to increase its strength.

Fig. 51-6. This tamping operation is being performed by a multiwheel pneumatic compactor. It can do the work of many men.

Fig. 51-7. Smaller pipelines are usually tamped by men using pneumatic tampers.

To make joints, the smaller end of one pipe is pushed into the bell of the next pipe. Grout (mixture of cement and sand) is used to fill the bell. There are also many types of rubber gaskets for joints.

Water pipelines have all types of fittings (tees, ells, and others, as described in the last lesson). Quite a number of valves are used so that the water in any one part of the city (sometimes a single block) may be shut off for repairs or for new construction. Also, city water distribution systems include a large number of fire hydrants.

Sewerage

A piping system which collects sanitary sewage or storm drainage (or both) is called a sewerage. The piping material is usually *vitrified clay.* The clay, which must be of a certain type, is mixed with salt. After shaping, it is fired (heated in a kiln to a high temperature). This process gives the pipe a hard, *vitreous* (glass-like) surface which cannot be corroded by most waste materials. It is a bell and spigot type of pipe. A joint is made by caulking or by inserting a gasket, and then filling the bell with grout, asphalt, or tar.

Sewers, which must always be ready for use, generally do not include valves. As it is not easy to tap into the brittle vitrified clay pipe, Y-connections are often inserted, usually one for each lot in a residential district. One arm of the Y is along the sewer, while the other arm projects out at an angle. It has a plug which can be removed and replaced by a drain pipe from a building. Plugs can also be removed for cleaning.

Usually sewers are laid in a straight line from manhole to manhole. *Manholes* are placed at street corners and intermediate points, usually between 200′ and 300′ apart. They are made of brick, vitrified clay, or concrete pipe and are about 4′ in diameter. Each manhole has a channel in the middle through which the sewage flows. If a sewer becomes clogged, men can climb into the manholes. Standing on the bottom of the manholes, men can push rods through the sewer to clear out any obstruction. A flexible steel wire (called a *snake*), turned by a slow speed electric motor, also can be used to clear a clogged line.

Storm sewers eventually carry water to a lake or river. Sanitary sewers carry waste into a sewage treatment plant where the solids settle to the bottom of large tanks and are removed. The water is *purified* by filtering, by spraying it into the air, and by chemicals. This treated water (effluent) is then discharged in pipes to an outlet (outfall) where it runs into a lake or a river, Fig. 51-8. A modern sewage treatment plant can purify water so that it is clean enough to drink or to use in industry. However, if the capacity of a plant is not large enough to handle all the sewage which flows to the plant, or if the equipment is old, the effluent will not be clean, pure water.

Steam Lines

Above ground and underground piping systems are used to move steam or hot water from a central heating plant to other buildings. These piping systems may require many valves and controls to maintain the desired pressures and volume.

Generally, steam lines are made of black pipe. Joints are usually made by welding together the ends of two pieces of pipe, but sometimes flanges placed at the ends of pipe are bolted together. Fittings are likewise welded.

Steam lines must be insulated to prevent the heat in the water from being lost, or to prevent the steam from cooling and turning to water. The pipe may be wrapped with insulation which is then covered to protect it underground. Or the pipe may be set in various insulating materials which look like concrete and are made of lightweight aggregates. Often steam lines are placed in a concrete tunnel which sometimes includes other utility lines such as water and electrical conduit.

Petroleum and Natural Gas

Pipelines many hundreds of miles long are built to transport *petroleum* from its place of origin to a *refinery*. Similar pipelines carry natural gas to cities where it will be used. These pipelines are made of black steel pipe in 30′ lengths that are welded together. Oil or gas will not ordinarily corrode the inside of these pipes. However, the earth in which they are buried can cause corrosion. Therefore, the outside

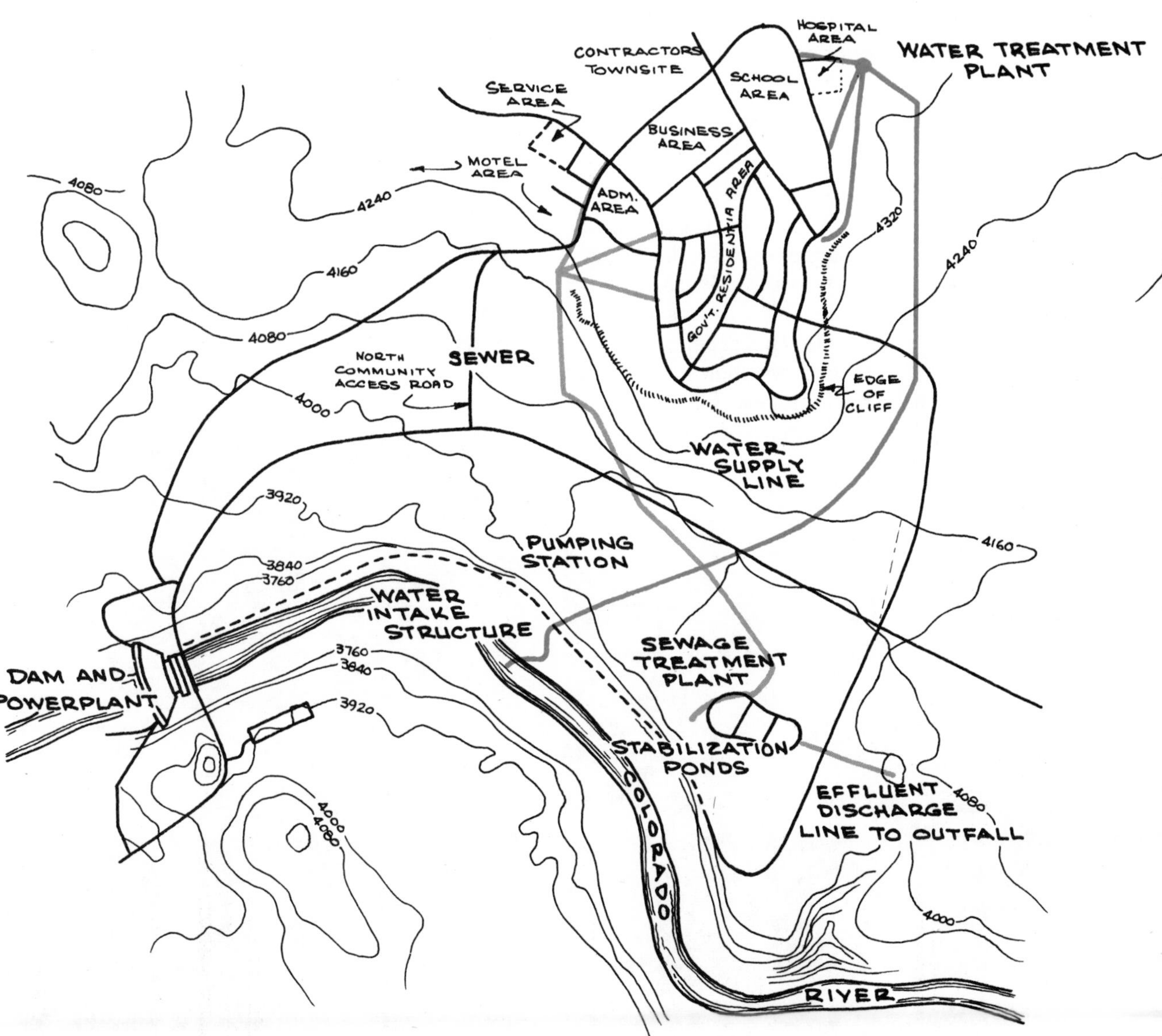

Fig. 51-8. This is the water supply and sewerage system for a small community. Notice that the effluent discharge line is at a lower elevation than is the community. How will the water be raised from the river to the water treatement plant?

of a black steel pipeline is wrapped with fabric and painted with an asphaltic material, Fig. 51-9.

The same pipeline often carries several kinds of oil. When the pipeline operators have finished pumping one kind of oil through the lines, a *go-devil* (like a bottle brush) is forced through the pipeline with a volume of water behind it. The go-devil cleans the inside walls of the pipeline, and the water flushes the pipe. The operators then can deliver another kind of oil through the line.

Records

A great many pipelines (as well as electrical and telephone cables) lie underneath the ground in cities and in some rural areas, Fig. 51-10. Accurate records must be kept showing not only the pipelines themselves, but all valves, manholes, pumping stations, and other features. These records are usually in the form of drawings kept at one of the company's offices. Often the locations of pipelines are *monumented.* Monumented means that permanent marks are placed on the ground itself. This procedure is described in the lesson on surveying and mapping. Any architect or engineer planning new construction must check with the various utility companies to see if the new structure being planned will bother pipelines already underground.

Summary

On the outside of buildings, piping systems or pipelines bring such things as water, steam, and gas from a source of supply to buildings. Piping systems called *sewerages* remove waste water and excess rainfall from buildings and streets.

Most pipelines are laid underground in trenches. The pipe used may be cast iron,

Fig. 51-9. Workers wrap thick insulation around this pipeline to protect it from corrosion.

Fig. 51-10. Here a small plastic sewage disposal line is being laid.

concrete, steel, vitrified clay, or plastic. Each kind requires a special technology for its installation.

Terms to Know

exterior
interior
trenching
backhoe
backfilled
tamped
compressed
manhole
purified
effluent
outfall
insulated
petroleum
refinery
vitrified clay
kiln
corrode
caulking
welded
go-devil
monumented

Think About It!

1. What are the differences between *plumbing* systems and *pipeline* systems?
2. Can you identify a pipeline system in your community that is above ground? Below ground? What is the purpose of each?

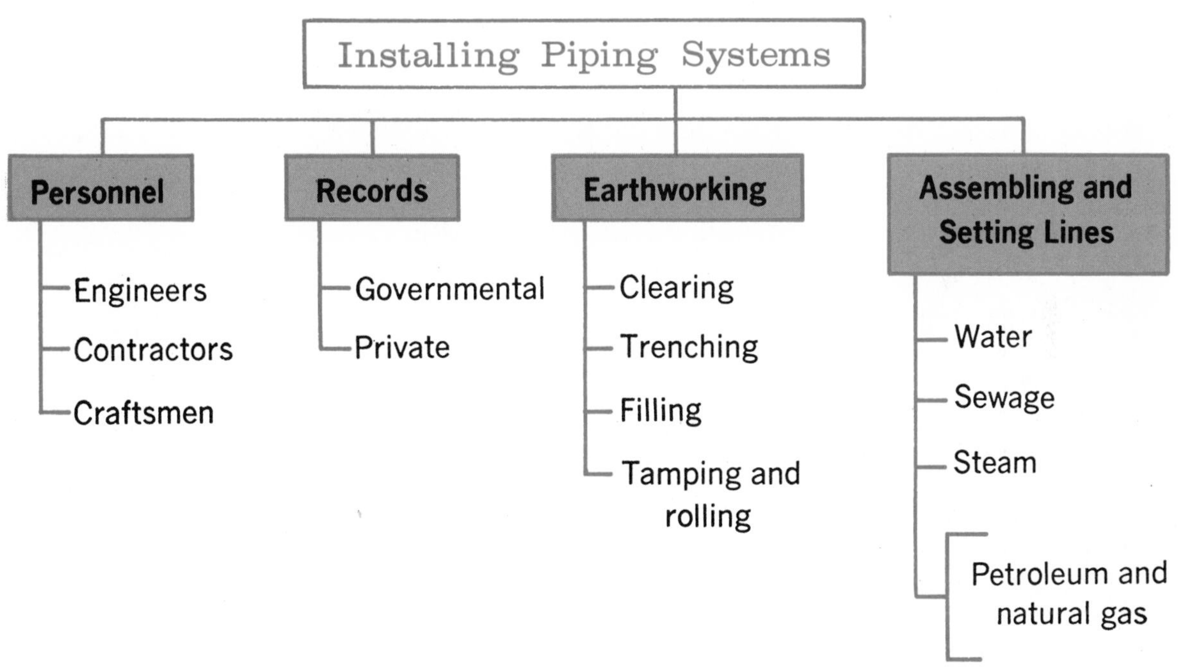

READING 52

Installing Electrical Power Systems

This lesson is about how electrical power is supplied to users and how it is distributed within a structure. A system which brings the power from the generating plant is called *outside electrical construction.* A system which carries the power within a structure is *inside electrical construction.*

Who Designs Electric Power Systems

First, you should understand that electricity can be very dangerous. For this reason, everyone concerned with the design and installation of electric power must be fully qualified by both education and experience.

Fig. 52-1. Electrical transformer stations such as this are designed by a team of engineers.

Usually they must have a license which is granted only after passing a test.

Electrical work is designed by an *electrical engineer.* He often works with a civil engineer when major structures, such as powerhouses or towers, are involved, Fig 52-1. The electrical engineer works with mechanical engineers in designing steam-generating plants and with nuclear engineers in designing atomic power plants. Each of the engineers must either be a registered professional engineer or must work under the close supervision of one. To be registered, an engineer must show to a state examining board that his education and experience qualify him for his profession.

Ownership

Usually an electric utility company owns the power plant and all the outdoor distribution system, up to the place where the electricity enters a structure. The electric utility company usually owns the meter which shows how much electricity each customer uses. The owner of a building owns the electrical system within the structure, except for the meter.

Construction Personnel

The electric utility company usually hires a general contractor to build a power plant. This general contractor usually subcontracts the electrical construction inside the power plant to an electrical subcontractor.

An outdoor distribution system, between the power plant and the building, may be constructed either by employees of the electric utility company or by an electrical contractor hired by the utility company. Some electrical contractors specialize in outdoor or *line work.* Many electric utility companies contract for major construction jobs but do the smaller ones (and all maintenance) with their own employees.

The owner of a proposed structure usually hires a general contractor for its construction. This general contractor may do the inside electrical work with his own employees. More often, however, the general contractor hires an electrical subcontractor to do the inside or *wire work.* In most regions all contractors who do electrical work must be licensed by a state, county, or city before they are permitted to work. This license is given only after the contractor passes an examination. Also, most owners or general contractors, when they hire electrical contractors or subcontractors, check on the qualifications of the electrical firm which is to do the work.

The craftsmen who do electrical work are called *electricians.* There are two groups of electricians. *Linemen* do outside construction, and *wiremen* work inside, Figs. 52-2 and 52-3. Electrical work can be very dangerous. Even 100 volts can kill a man. But some electricians must work with voltage of 1,000,000 volts or more. Thus, the electrical worker must be very well trained. His technical knowledge and practical ability are carefully tested before he is given a license by state, county, or city authority. Most building codes provide that electrical work may be done only by a licensed electrician.

Outside Construction

Electric current, measured in *amperes,* flows great distances to reach its consumers. *Voltage* is a measure of the force which causes the current to flow. Electricity is usually generated at moderate voltages (for example, 13,000 volts). But the cheapest way to send electric power is at a high voltage. Thus, besides a generating plant, there is usually a switchyard equipped with transformers to increase or decrease voltage. The switchyard transformers usually increase (step up) the voltage to 138,000 volts. Sometimes it is increased to 1,000,000 volts.

Power lines, called *transmission lines,* run from the switchyard transformers to cities or industrial areas where the power will be used. These lines are built across great distances, sometimes across several states, Fig. 52-4. Transmission lines are a series of wires made of a metal which readily carries or *conducts* electricity. They are supported by *insulators* (devices made of a material through which electricity cannot pass). The

Fig. 52-2. Electricans who install electrical wiring outside a structure are known as linemen.

Fig. 52-3. The electricians who install electrical wiring inside a structure are known as wiremen.

insulators are fastened to wood, concrete, or metal poles or towers, spaced along the line.

Transmission lines are built by teams of skilled workers according to plans and specifications set up by engineers. First the *right-of-way* is purchased from the various landowners. Usually this is merely an *easement* (right to install and service the power line), as described in Reading 7.

Then the route for the transmission lines is cleared. This means that all trees and other obstructions must be cleared from the path the lines are to follow across the country. Usually this path is as straight as possible. Specialized tools and equipment are used to dig footing trenches for towers or holes for poles. After the footings are placed and the towers or poles are set, special anchors and guys may be used to hold the towers and poles firmly in place. In mountainous country, helicopters are sometimes used to put sections of towers into place.

Electricity at very high voltages is extremely dangerous and hard to handle. Thus, at various points along the transmission system where the power is to be used (for instance, a city), substations are built, Fig. 52-5. Substations use transformers to lower the voltage to 13,000 volts. There are also (1) switches or *disconnects* so that the current may be cut off as desired and (2) circuit breakers which automatically cut off the flow of electric current when it becomes too heavy in the substation, Fig 52-6.

Distribution lines from substations generally are strung on poles, but sometimes they are placed underground. They carry the electrical energy throughout cities, industrial areas, suburbs, and rural areas.

There are two (sometimes more) voltages in a distribution system:

1. The *primary voltage* of 13,000 volts.
2. The *secondary voltage* of 120 or 240 volts.

The primary system carries the power to the vicinity of the owner's property. The primary voltage is much too high to be safe or suitable for most uses. It must be transformed (changed). The transformer is located on an overhead pole, or in a vault where underground cable is used. It reduces the primary voltage to 120 or 240 volts for most residential and commercial uses.

In industrial plants, large machines or other heavy electrical equipment, such as an oven for drying paint, may need 440 volts and higher to operate properly. From the transformer, a set of three wires (called a *drop*) is connected to a meter in the building. This completes the *outside construction.*

Fig. 52-4. These linemen are using "hotsticks" to work on an energized (hot) transmission line.

Fig. 52-5. The electric substation is often called the "crossroads of power." Both switching and reducing of voltage are done here.

Inside Construction

In the building, the inside wiremen connect a cable or large pipe with wires in it to the *meter* The meter *measures the amount of electric current the customer uses.* This part of the project is called the *service entrance.* The meter is connected with wire to the distribution panel. This panel contains fuses or circuit breakers which protect the electrical equipment and the building from electrical damage. Fuses and circuit breakers automatically *break* or open a circuit if an electrical *overload* occurs. A heavy current overload can overheat a line and damage equipment or start a fire.

From the panel, *branch circuits* are installed according to any one of several wiring methods. In a home the two common kinds of wiring are (1) *nonmetallic-sheathed cable* and (2) *armored cable,* both of which are flexible, Fig. 52-7. The *armor* which encloses armored cable is flexible steel. The two wires in the cable are separately insulated and then bound together with additional insulation. This kind of cable is sometimes called *BX.* The other common type of cable, which is not armored, is protected by a heavy, nonmetallic sheath.

Fig. 52-6. This substation is part of the distribution system of an electric utility company.

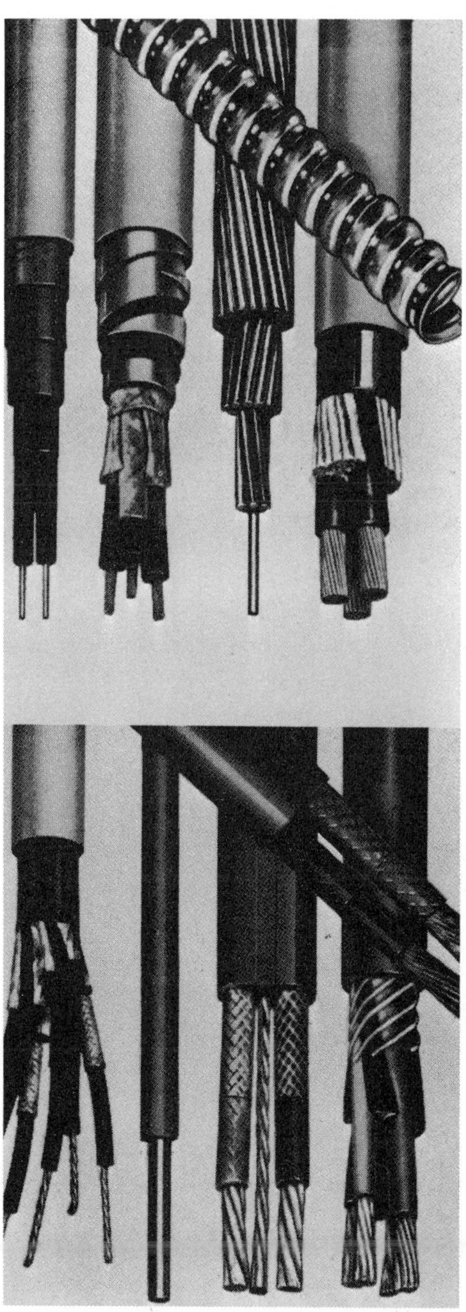

Fig. 52-7. Electricians learn to install many types and sizes of wire.

Flexible cables can be bent or shaped easily by hand to fit inside the walls, ceilings, and floors of the average home. If these cables are properly connected to junction boxes, switch boxes, and other outlets, the distribution panel can supply electrical energy to any point where it may be needed inside or outside the home. Branch circuits may serve special purpose outlets for ranges, dryers, air conditioners, motors, and other electrical appliances.

In commercial buildings and industrial plants, electrical wires are usually protected from damage by being enclosed in conduit (thin-walled tubing of galvanized steel or aluminum), Fig. 52-8. In buildings which rest on *slabs,* this conduit is installed before the concrete for the slab is placed. In buildings that have the walls finished, the conduit runs inside the walls, the ceiling, and the floor. Both rigid and flexible conduit are used. To get the wire into the conduits, a thin flexible strip of metal, called a *fish tape,* is either installed in the conduit as it is put together or pushed through after the conduit is assembled. Then the electrical wires are attached to the end of the fish tape and

Fig. 52-8. In commercial construction, wiring often is run through pipes called conduit.

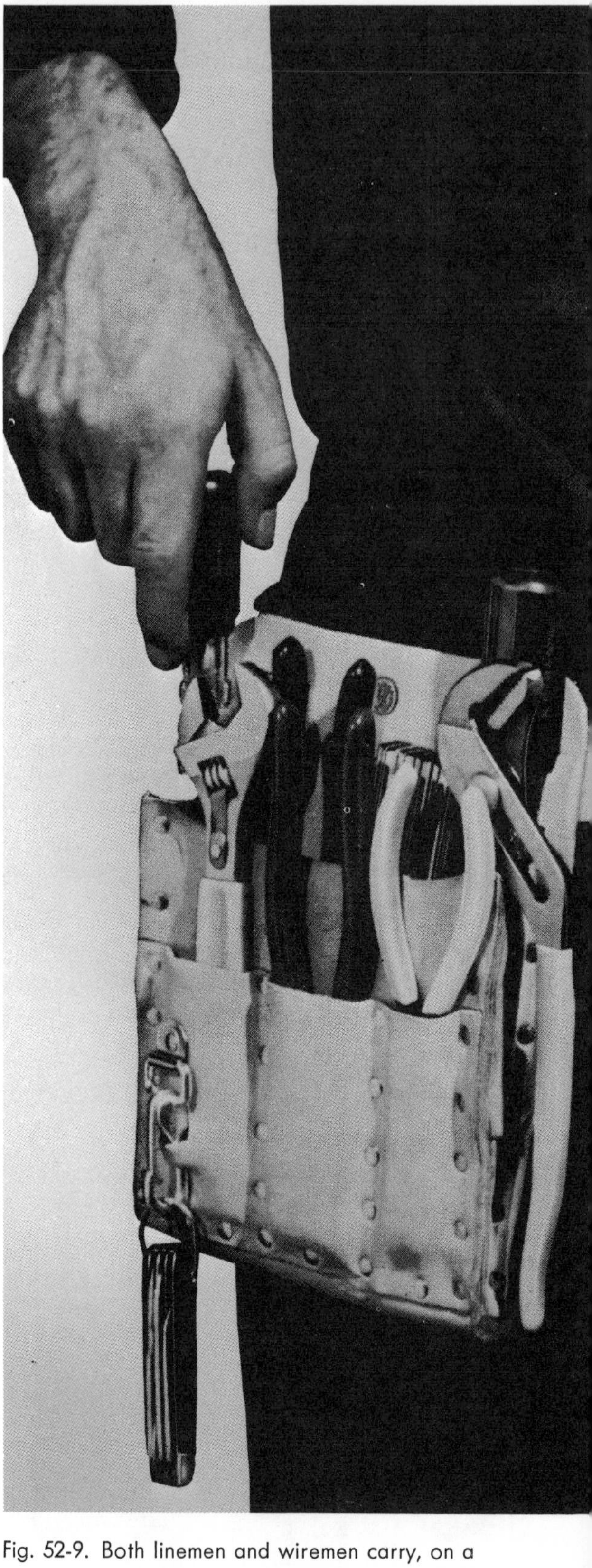

Fig. 52-9. Both linemen and wiremen carry, on a special belt (tool pocket), the tools they use often.

pulled through the conduit. After this, the wires are connected to electrical outlets, appliances, motors, and lighting fixtures.

The location of electric wiring must be planned so as not to interfere with sheet metal ductwork, plumbing systems, or other utilities.

Summary

Electricity is generated in a power plant. From there, outside electrical construction distributes it to various buildings and other structures through overhead wires or underground cables. Within a building or structure inside wiring takes the electric current to fixtures, appliances, equipment, and outlets as needed.

Electrical work can be very dangerous. It must be carefully planned and completed by skilled personnel.

Terms to Know

distributed	wiremen
generating plant	qualifications
voltage	electricians
current	substation
amperage	consumers
amperes	transmission lines
circuits	conduct electricity
generators	primary voltage
transformers	secondary voltage
qualify	electrical overload
line work	meter
linemen	flexible
wire work	inside construction
	outside construction

Think About It!

1. What is the source of the electrical power used in your home? Can you trace the *outside electrical construction*: power plant, transformers, distribution lines, and drop line?
2. Can you locate the three main elements of *inside electrical construction* in your home: entrance, distribution panel, and branch circuits?

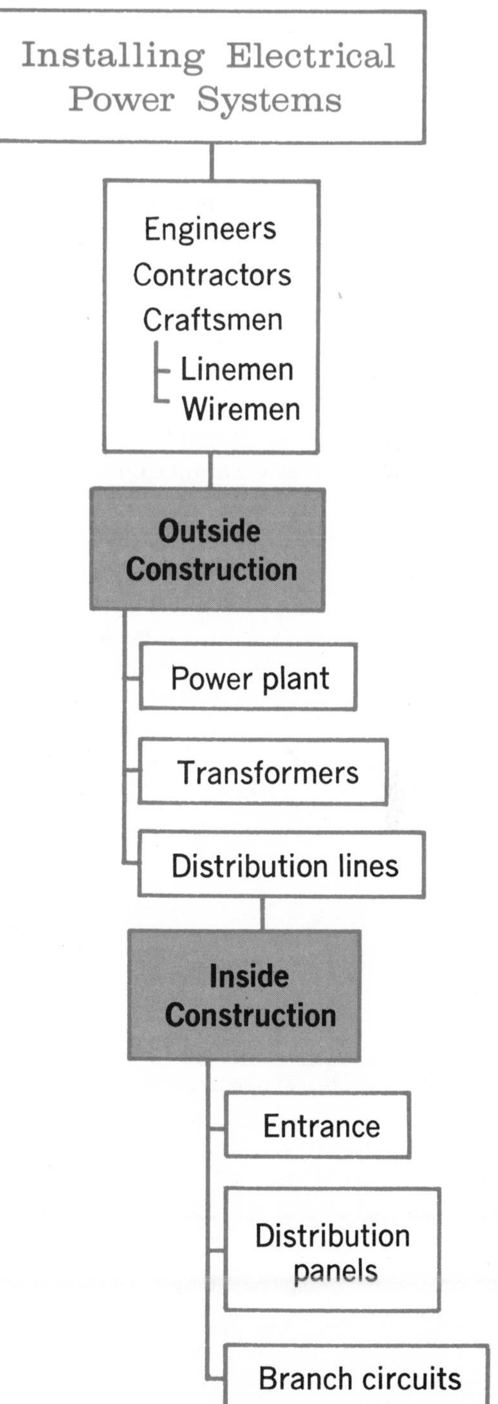

READING 53

Installing Electrical Communications Systems

The last reading described how electrical power systems are installed. This reading describes installation of electrical communications systems: telephone, telegraph, radio, television, and navigational systems.

The electrical work performed in installing communications systems is somewhat the same as that in installing electric power. There are important differences in the systems and in the equipment involved. The voltages and current (amperage) for communications are usually much smaller, although not always. Generally, communications installations and equipment are harder to understand than those for power. Also, the electrical energy is often converted into radio waves which can transmit a message through space without wires. These waves are received elsewhere, amplified (increased), and changed back into electric current. Radio transmitters and receivers are parts of many communications systems, Fig. 53-1.

Who Installs Electrical Communications

Electrical communications systems are designed by electrical engineers who specialize in communications and electronics, rather than in power. These engineers may work for the *operator* of the communications system; for example, a telephone company, telegraph company, or television station. Sometimes they work for the *manufacturer* of the equipment and sometimes for an electrical engineering firm which specializes in the design of communications systems.

The communications company may do all of its construction with its own labor force. It may contract for the work, either with an electrical contractor specializing in communications or with a general contractor who usually does work related to communications. Sometimes there is a combination of the two. A television station may hire a general contractor to erect a transmitting tower, but employees of the station will install the antennas and all of the wiring and equipment. Sometimes equipment manufacturers do the installation.

Fig. 53-1. This microwave "dish" is part of Western Union's transcontinental communications system.

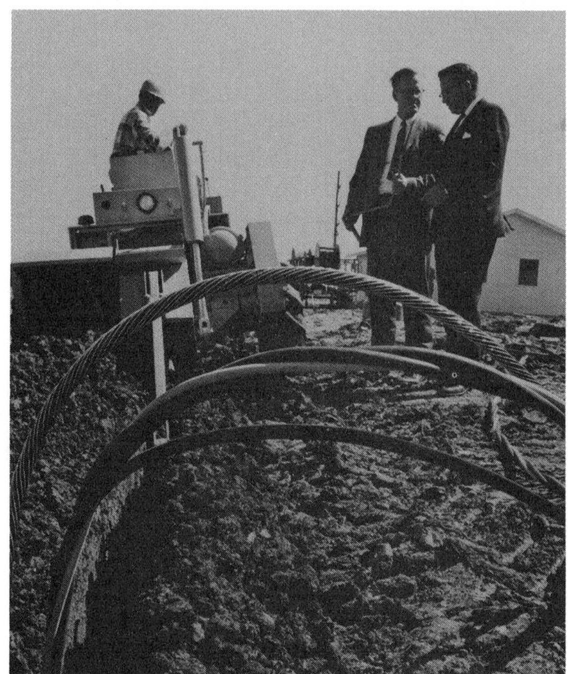

Fig. 53-2. Engineers design communications systems and here are inspecting a buried cable project.

Craftsmen employed are of many types. There are *operating engineers* who operate the construction equipment needed to dig trenches for communication lines, Fig. 53-2. There are *telephone linemen* who work on outside and inside lines. *Installers* hook up equipment, Fig. 53-3. *Electricians* handle the power supply. There are also many *technicians* who build, install, operate, and maintain complicated equipment, Fig. 53-4.

Installing Telephone Systems

When a person talks into a telephone transmitter, the sound of his voice *modulates* (shapes) an electric current. The current changes from moment to moment in a way that exactly matches the sounds of speech. A telephone communications system can be constructed so that modulated electric currents carry their messages great dis-

Fig. 53-3. An installer connects your telephone to a drop line.

Fig. 53-4. Although you seldom see them on television programs, craftsmen and technicians construct and operate the systems that produce the program.

tances. A telephone receiver "undoes" the work of a telephone transmitter. The receiver changes the modulated current back into *sound waves.*

When telephone service is requested, a telephone installer runs a wire from the telephone pole to the building. This wire is called a *drop wire,* Fig. 53-5. In it are a number of pairs of wires all bound together in a single cable. At the building, the drop wire is firmly attached to a solid part of the structure to provide a *service entrance.* From the service entrance, the wires are run through the building to connector boxes of *jacks* for each telephone. Each telephone is served by two pairs of wires which are connected to a jack.

The drop wire is connected to a cable, which may lead to a larger cable. The cable ends at a telephone exchange. To serve a customer far away, it may be necessary to string a single set of wires along poles for some distance before they join a cable.

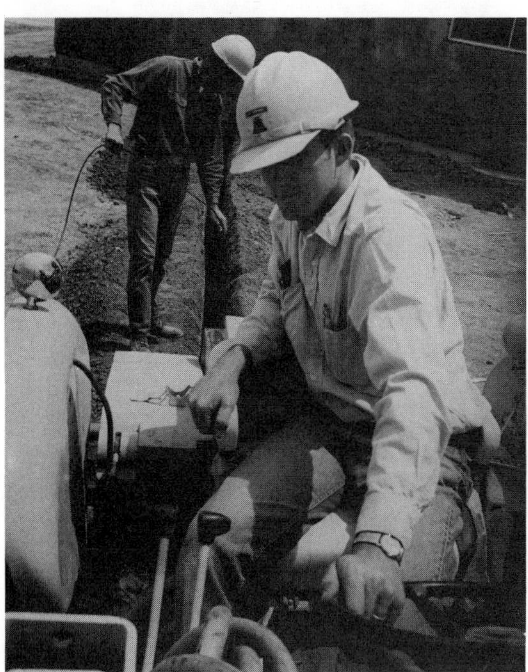

Fig. 53-5. Sometimes a drop wire is buried underground to improve the appearance of the property and to safeguard the installation.

Cables consist of a large number of pairs of wires and are named by the number of pairs they hold. For instance, a *250-pair cable* has 250 pairs of wires in it. No matter how many pairs of wires are bound together, they are insulated so that messages do not "mix" or spread from wire to wire. However, there are methods by which one set of wires can carry more than one telephone conversation and, therefore, can serve more than one telephone.

When a large building is to be built, the telephone installation is carefully designed in advance by telephone engineers. The installation of telephone outlets and wires (often in conduits) goes along with the installation of other utilities. Usually the lines from each telephone lead to a central terminal strip in a cabinet. After passing through relays, they are formed into a cable which goes to the telephone exchange, Fig. 53-6. In some cases, telephone linemen hang the cable from telephone poles or from electric power poles. In other cases telephone cables are buried underground, sometimes passing through conduits.

Fig. 53-6. The switching equipment within a telephone exchange building requires maintenance, following installation.

The building which houses a telephone exchange is constructed in much the same way as other buildings. However, inside this building many highly skilled construction communications workers put in huge metal racks and trays on which they install thousands of miles of electrical conductors or cables. Many of these cables contain hundreds of individual pairs of wires. There are hundreds, sometimes even thousands, of such cables in even the small telephone exchanges. These, in turn, are connected to many switches, relays, and electronically controlled devices which also are mounted on huge racks.

After this equipment goes into operation, it must be maintained and repaired. Sometimes the original equipment must be altered. Telephone company employees who do parts of this work include plant electricians, central office equipment installers, central maintenance men, and troubleshooters. These men are trained in the use of specialized tools, such as measuring instruments and gauges which are very delicate and sensitive. To describe the many tools they use would fill a book as large as this one.

Central offices can be connected with each other by overhead lines, by underground cables, by radio microwave transmission, and by combinations of these methods. Originally, telephone exchanges in different cities communicated through overhead lines on telephone or telegraph poles beside railroad tracks. Although many of those lines are still in use, in recent years underground cables have been laid in trenches in much the same way that electric power lines are placed in the ground. Overseas telephone communications (those which cross an ocean) have used underwater cables, enclosed in a heavy lead armor, and space satellites.

Still more recently, radio broadcasting and receiving equipment has been installed in many regions to connect central offices. The modulated current in telephone wires is changed into radio waves of very short wavelength, called *microwaves.* Microwave towers are erected about 30 to 50 miles apart, because the radio waves cannot bend to follow the earth's curving surface. Each tower receives the radio signal and sends it to the next tower or telephone exchange, Fig. 53-7. Finally the microwave message is changed back into a modulated electric current and then into sound waves.

The industry has tested many other ideas. Radio waves of long wavelength (which are subject to interruption) have been tried. Communications satellites, orbiting several hundred miles in space, are one of the newest devices in the industry. They function as microwave relay stations for some long-distance telephone communications, Fig. 53-8.

In your lifetime you will see many new developments in telephone service. Soon you will be able to dial almost any telephone in

Fig. 53-7. Microwaves have a range of only 30 to 50 miles because they cannot bend around the earth's surface. These men are installing a microwave horn. It will gather microwaves that are being transmitted toward it.

the world. A touch-tone dial phone is already coming into use. For dialing, it has buttons like the keys on an adding machine. And telephones with a small television screen so that you can see the person to whom you are talking are now available in some areas, Fig. 53-9. Laser and maser systems may replace many existing wire lines in the more distant future.

Installing Telegraph Systems

A *telegram* is a message typed onto a special keyboard, sent by electric current through a wire for some distance, and automatically retyped by a special typewriter. Telegraph companies operate the special equipment which sends and receives messages. Most telegraph companies make use of existing telephone lines within the United States to link their transmitting and receiving equipment. (The telegraph companies still operate some undersea cables.)

Telegraph systems are designed, engineered, and installed in much the same way as are telephone systems. As mentioned above, they even use some of the same cross-country lines.

Telegraph sending and receiving equipment operates differently than does telephone equipment. When a message is typed onto a telegraph keyboard, transmitting equipment changes each letter into a code or modulation on an electric current. The receiving equipment "reads" each bit of coded information and changes it back into the correct letter typed on paper. Sound waves are not involved.

By the process called *facsimile* photographs also can be transmitted across great distances and reproduced at the receiving point, Fig. 53-10. The transmitting equipment scans the photograph, "looking" at thousands of individual, tiny areas, one by one. As it "sees" light or dark areas, it changes each bit of information into code on the electric current. Receiving equipment changes each bit of information back into a

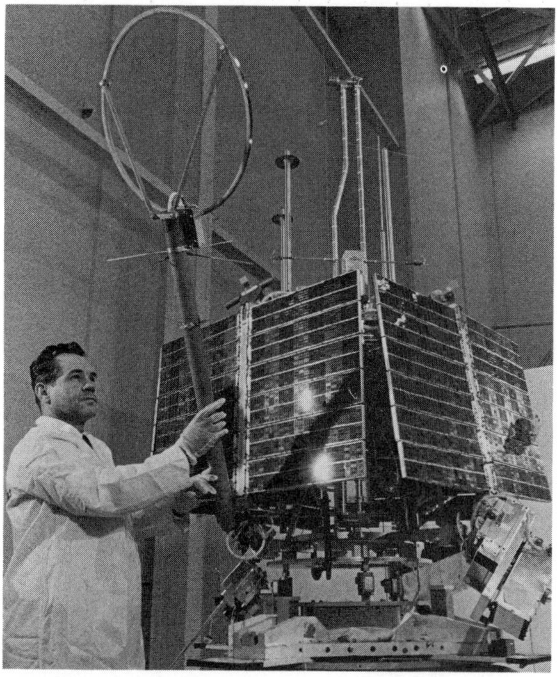

Fig. 53-8. Communications satellites are extending the range of communications systems.

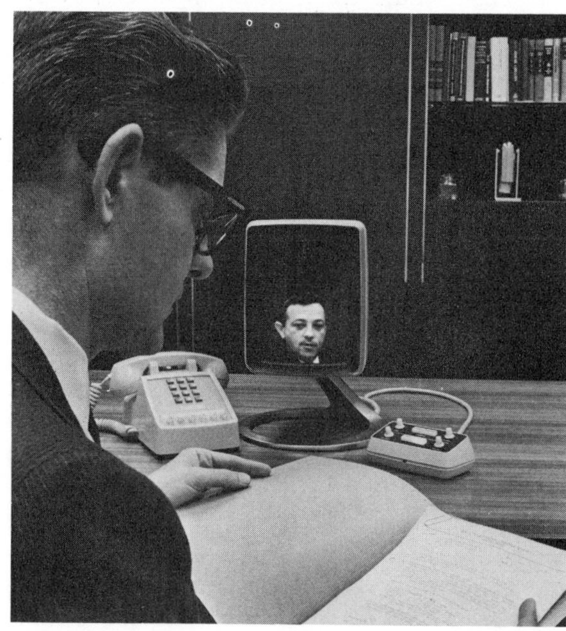

Fig. 53-9. This telephone has a small television screen that enables one to see the person with whom he is speaking.

tiny light or dark area on paper by highly specialized photographic processes. Newspapers are important customers for this kind of telegraph service. The facsimile process supplies them with pictures of an important event occurring thousands of miles away within a few hours after the event takes place.

Installing Radio and Television Systems

A television or radio studio houses a mass of power and communications lines. Electrical communications workers install these lines when the studios are built. Afterwards, they continue to move or change them according to program needs. *Mobile units* (trucks fitted with communications equipment) are sometimes used when a broadcast takes place outside of studios. The communication workers lay temporary lines and set up cameras and microphones at a location, before the broadcast. Their work may begin several days before a large, important event.

Sound and pictures are converted into modulated electrical currents which travel, usually through telephone company facilities, to transmitters. A single transmitter may be involved if the program is broadcast over just one station. Several hundred radio or television stations may pick up a program carried by a network such as NBC, CBS, or ABC, and each station will have its own transmitter, Figs. 53-11 and 53-12.

Fig. 53-10. This receiving equipment reproduces the facsimile photograph.

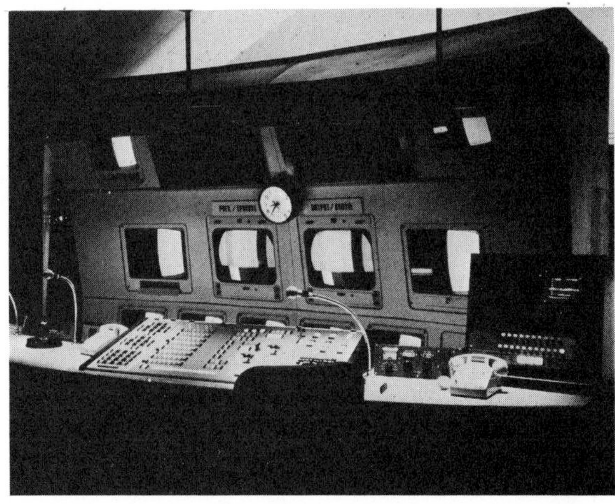

Fig. 53-11. At the television station's control room, engineers monitor various transmissions and select the one which is sent to the transmitter to be broadcast.

Fig. 53-12. Nearly everywhere you look, you can see various communications systems.

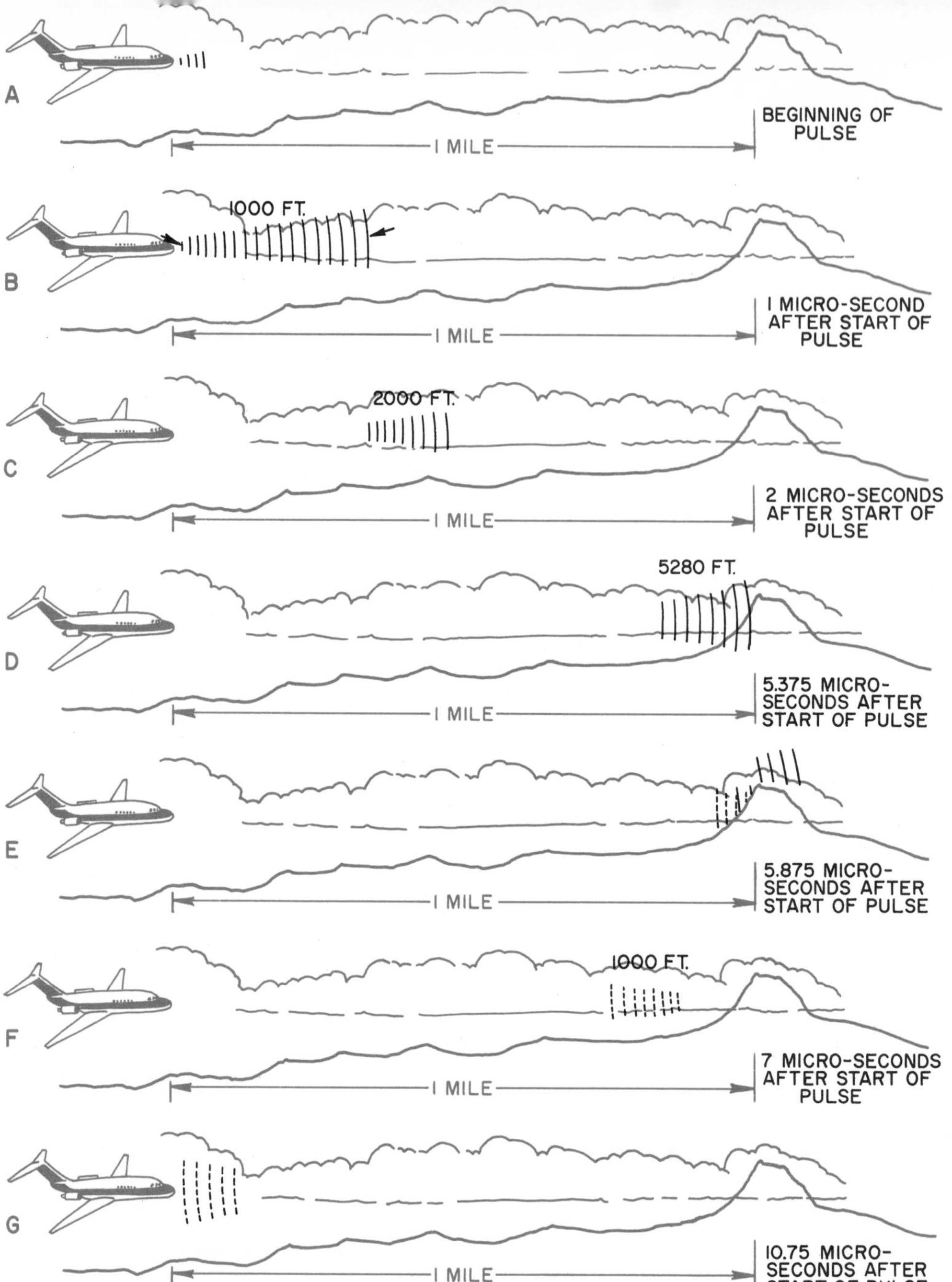

Fig. 53-13. The radar navigational system permits the pilot to "see" through clouds, darkness, and over long distances.

A. The radar signal leaves the airplane's antenna at a radiated speed of 1000′ per microsecond.

B. In one microsecond, the beam has traveled 1000′.

C. In two microseconds, the beam has traveled 2000′.

D. In 5.375 microseconds, the beam has traveled one mile.

E. After the beam has reached the object, it begins to return, in the form of an echo, to the airplane's antenna.

F. Seven microseconds have passed since the beam was transmitted.

G. The plane's antenna receives the beam and the travel time of the beam is recorded (in this example it is 10.75 microseconds). To determine the distance of the object from the plane, the travel time is divided by two.

At the transmitter, the electric currents are changed to radio waves which are broadcast from antennas on top of very high towers. These towers are sometimes as high as 1,500′ and are the tallest man-made structures. The towers are constructed by ironworkers. Communications workers install the antennas and the necessary wiring.

Installing Navigational Systems

There are two types of constructed communications systems for aircraft and ships which permit them to navigate safely in almost all kinds of weather. One type sends a radio signal from a land-based station to instruments which tell each pilot or captain his exact location, Fig. 53-13. A second type is a radar system which also sends an electronic signal from a transmitter, Fig. 53-14. This signal is reflected back to a TV picture tube-like scope which shows where the aircraft or ship is located. Radar sets are used by controllers at busy ports to control the movements of traffic.

Large numbers of electrical workers with many job titles and classifications work to install and service navigational systems. These systems provide control of traffic in shipping lanes (sea lanes) across our lakes and oceans and in skyways (air lanes) in our skies, Fig. 53-15.

Private Communication Systems

In addition to the large public communications systems, many closed or private systems are installed as a part of constructed works. These range from built-in home communications systems to large industrial systems of closed-circuit television, radio, and telephone. These private systems

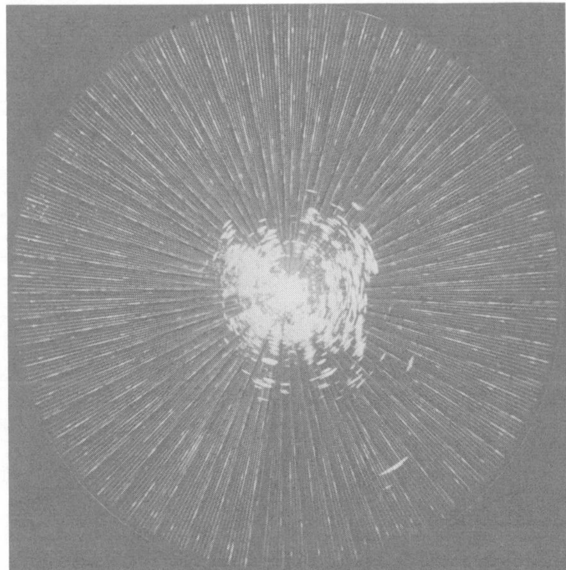

Fig. 53-14. This is a radar screen which indicates the height of a reflecting object. Another kind of radar screen indicates position of the reflecting object.

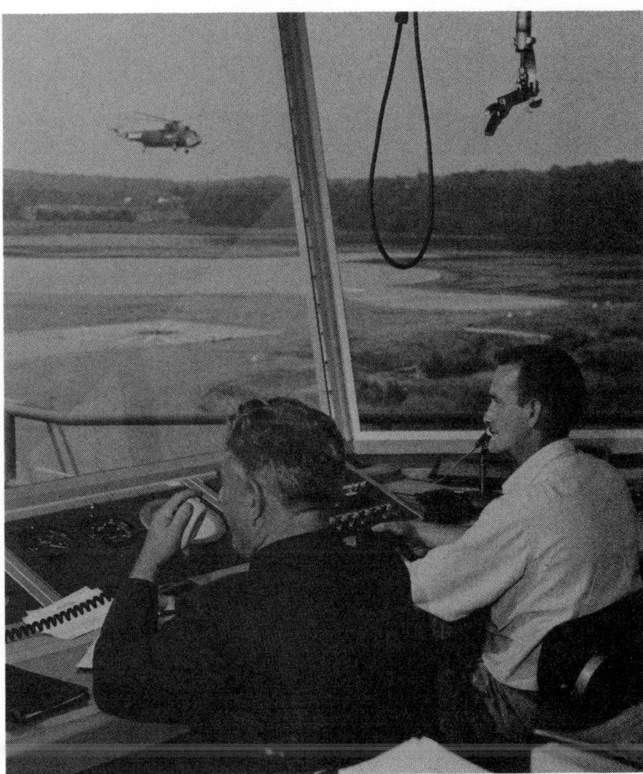

Fig. 53-15. Navigational and control systems for ships and aircraft have made travel reliable and safe.

are used to *monitor* (watch over) traffic flow of men and materials, Fig. 53-16. They also are used to enable people to communicate with other people or groups. Police, businesses, and hospitals already are making increasing use of private communications systems to make their work more efficient. The design of a structure must make provision for these private communications systems, along with other utilities. Installation follows the same pattern as for other communications systems.

Communications in Space

Special electronic equipment enables us to talk with spacemen in satellites and to control unmanned satellites from the ground. There are also major structures, such as the station at Arecibo, Puerto Rico, which can bounce radio waves off stars at almost limitless distances from earth. See Fig. 53-17.

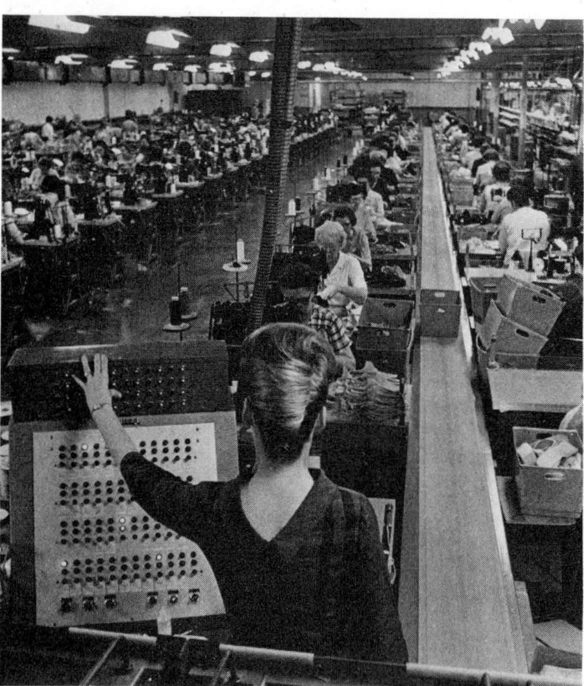

Fig. 53-16. Private or closed communications systems are growing in popularity in office, factory, and home.

Summary

This reading has described the practices of installing electrical communications systems such as telephone, telegraph, radio, television, and navigational systems. Generally, communications installations and equipment are more complicated than those for power.

Transmitting and receiving devices must be installed. Connecting facilities involving wire, cables, and antennas must be constructed. To design and install such systems, many engineers, technicians, and skilled craftsmen are required.

Without such communications systems, man would be very limited in his ability to communicate quickly over long distances. A fast-changing technology is improving the communications process almost daily.

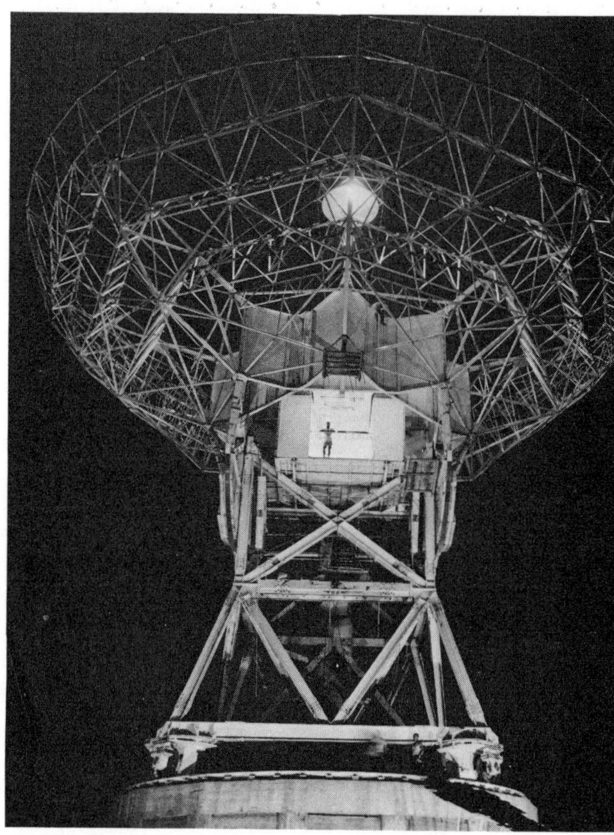

Fig. 53-17. This large antenna will enable scientists to communicate with satellites and astronauts.

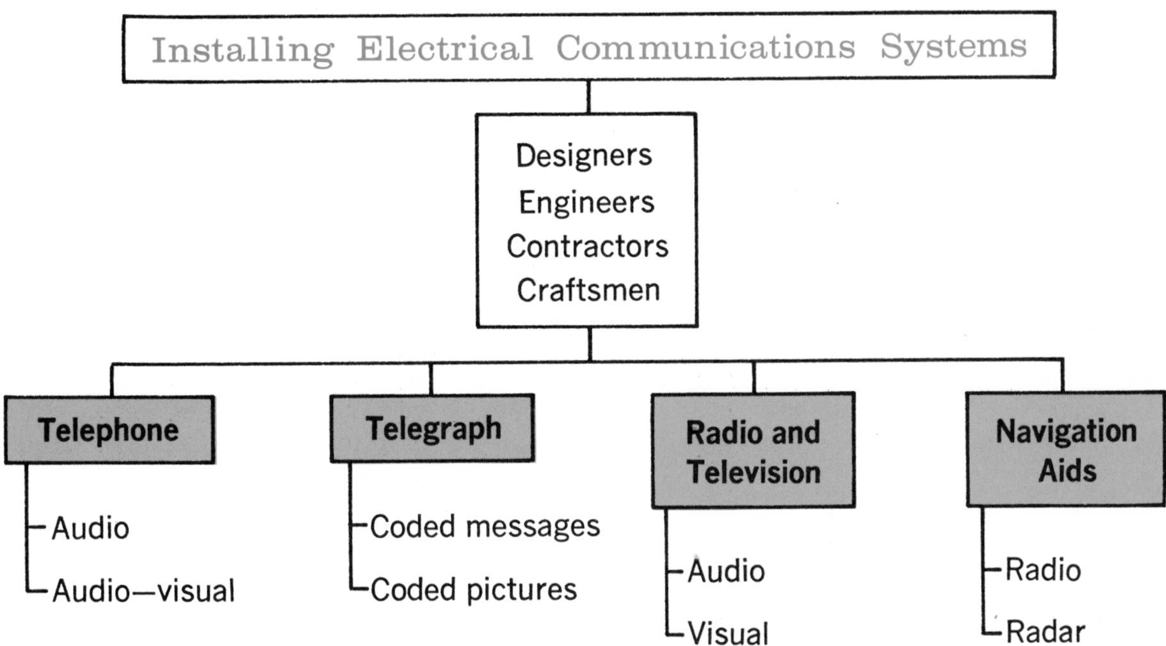

Terms to Know

communications system
radio transmitter
radio receiver
transcontinental
modulates
drop wire
service entrance
jack
maintenance
microwaves
communications satellites
telegram
facsimile
mobile unit
navigate
sea lanes
air lanes
monitor

Think About It!

1. What communications systems do you have in your home? Do you have both transmitting and receiving devices?

2. How far away from your home is the nearest television station? Is the transmitter located at the station or is it elsewhere? Ask your parents if you do not know.

READING 54

Making Inspections

Inspecting is part of the *management function of controlling*. Controlling includes directing, monitoring (inspecting), reporting and correcting. Construction work is directed by people with authority. Inspecting, along with the reporting of the results of the inspection, is done to make sure that the construction work meets minimum requirements. As a result of the inspection report, the work is accepted or corrections are required to be made. When corrections are finished the work is inspected again. Then a final inspection report is made to the authority which asked that the inspection be made.

Inspections are made on construction work from the time the drawings are begun in the architect's or engineer's office until the job is finished. A dictionary definition of *inspect* is "to look at carefully" or "to examine officially." Usually the person who does this "official looking" is called an *inspector*. Inspection may be a person's full-time job, or it may be only one of his duties. People other than the inspector also may inspect (monitor) and report corrections which are needed.

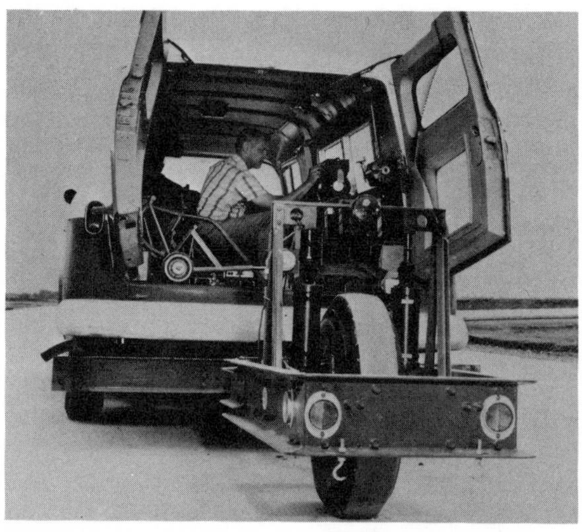

Fig. 54-1. Inspections are sometimes made by people who do not work for the contractor. These state inspectors are checking the smoothness of a newly built highway.

Who Makes the Inspections

This reading will describe three types of inspections: (1) those made during the design stage, (2) those made by the contractor's (or subcontractor's) employees, and (3) those made by people who do not work for the contractor, Fig 54-1.

During all steps of the development of the plans and specifications by the architect or engineer, the designer and his supervisors carefully review their work. In the case of private work, these plans must be given to

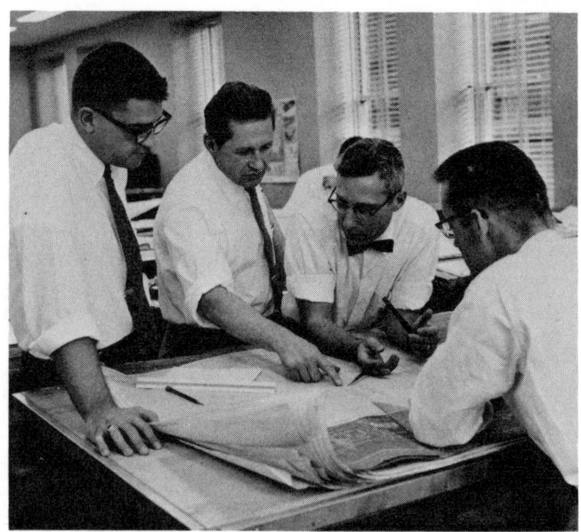

Fig. 54-2. Here inspections are being made during the design stage.

state, county, or city building departments. The departments go over the plans very carefully to make sure that the plans follow the local building codes, Fig. 54-2.

Inspections made by the employees of a contractor or subcontractor are for the purpose of *quality control*: that is, to see that the job is being done in a professional manner. For example, an ironworker fastening two pieces of structural steel will check to see that the bolts are tight, Fig 54-3. A foreman will make sure that beams are level and columns are plumb. A superintendent will constantly watch all details of a job to make sure that his crews are turning out a high quality product.

Fig. 54-3. At the site, men inspect their work as they proceed.

Fig. 54-4. This inspector is checking to see if plans and specifications are being followed.

Many inspections are made by persons not employed by the contractor. The owner may have inspections made by his own employees. Or the owner may hire the architect-engineer who designed the structure to inspect the work. The reason that the owner asks for inspections is to insure that the work carefully follows the plans and specifications, Fig. 54-4. In other words, the owner wants to be sure he is getting what he is paying for under the terms of the contract.

Inspections also are made by people from some level of government. These inspections usually take place where health or safety is important. Examples of work which might be inspected by a city building inspector are structural supports, wiring, plumbing, and heating. These are inspected to see if they have been installed following local building codes and plans previously approved by the building department.

If money has been lent for construction, the loan agency or bank lending the money usually will send out inspectors to look at the work as it is being done. This is to protect their interest in lending the money. Also, agencies of the federal government which guarantee home mortages (such as the Federal Housing Administration and the Veterans' Administration) conduct inspections.

Insurance companies may send their own inspectors to a construction site to see if the work is being done properly and safely. The insurance company might be providing construction insurance for the contractor. If an insurance company is to provide boiler insurance after a building is completed, it probably will insist on inspecting the steam plant installation.

The inspector himself must be completely familiar with the activity which he is inspecting. Often he has a trade background in this activity. For instance, an electrical inspector may be a journeyman electrician.

Chief inspectors may have a background in architecture or engineering.

Duties of the Inspector

The duties of the inspector usually may be divided into three parts. One of these duties has to do with inspecting the materials used in the job. To pass inspection, materials must be at least as good as those called for by the specifications. Sometimes materials are inspected before they reach the job, either by the manufacturer or a member of the inspection organization. For example, lumber is graded and marked before being shipped to the job site. It carries labeling such as "No. 2 Common." The inspector merely has to check the marking against the specifications. Sometimes the inspecting organization runs extensive laboratory tests on materials. This is the case with soils and concrete aggregates. The inspector rejects defective materials and requires the contractor to remove them from the job site.

The second duty of the inspector is to see if the correct methods are being used in preparing the materials. For this kind of inspection, he must watch the men on the job. He checks (monitors) to see if the materials are prepared right, to see if the right amounts of materials are used, and to see if the sizes are correct according to the specifications, Fig. 54-5. For example, before a concrete wall is placed, an inspector may check the reinforcing steel to see if it meets the requirements of the plans and specifications. These requirements may read somewhat as follows:

> All reinforcing steel shall be wire-brushed or otherwise cleaned to remove all loose rust and scale. . . . Vertical reinforcement shall be No. 6 (3/4" diameter) bars spaced on 12" centers . . .

The third duty of the inspector is to make sure the quality of the work is good. Often this can be done by watching each detail carefully to see that the plans and specifications are being followed. The inspector may examine the job while it is in progress. For example, usually an inspector will watch concrete being placed. Corrective action can be started if the cement and aggregates should become separated, if the concrete is too wet or too dry, or if the concrete fails to

Fig. 54-5. To inspect the concrete used on this job, a sample is taken and checked in a laboratory.

Fig. 54-6. Quality inspection is carried out by this tuboscope. Its LINALOG travels through pipelines to electronically inspect and record the condition of the pipe.

flow around the reinforcing steel (so that there is a good bond between the concrete and the steel). The inspector may also examine completed work. For example, he may apply a pressure test to an installed water line to see if there are any leaks, Fig. 54-6.

What Needs to Be Inspected

Inspection covers nearly all materials and workmanship on a construction site. Materials include soils, aggregates, cements, asphalts, brick, tile, lumber, metals, roofing materials, glass, ornamental ironwork, flooring and everything else that goes into the structure. Also included in an inspection will be the equipment, such as furnaces, air conditioners, thermostats, fuse boxes, lighting fixtures, cabinet work, plumbing fixtures, and built-in kitchen appliances. Workmanship is examined on foundations and footings, in steelwork, framing, carpentry, exterior siding, interior walls, roofing, plumbing, paving, and interior finishes such as painting. All of the materials and equipment and the way they are placed in the structure come under the inspector's watchful eye, Fig. 54-7.

Summary

Inspection is a necessary part of construction. It is a continuous process which starts at the beginning of design and continues until

Fig. 54-7. Throughout construction, inspections are made to make sure that the correct techniques and procedures are being used.

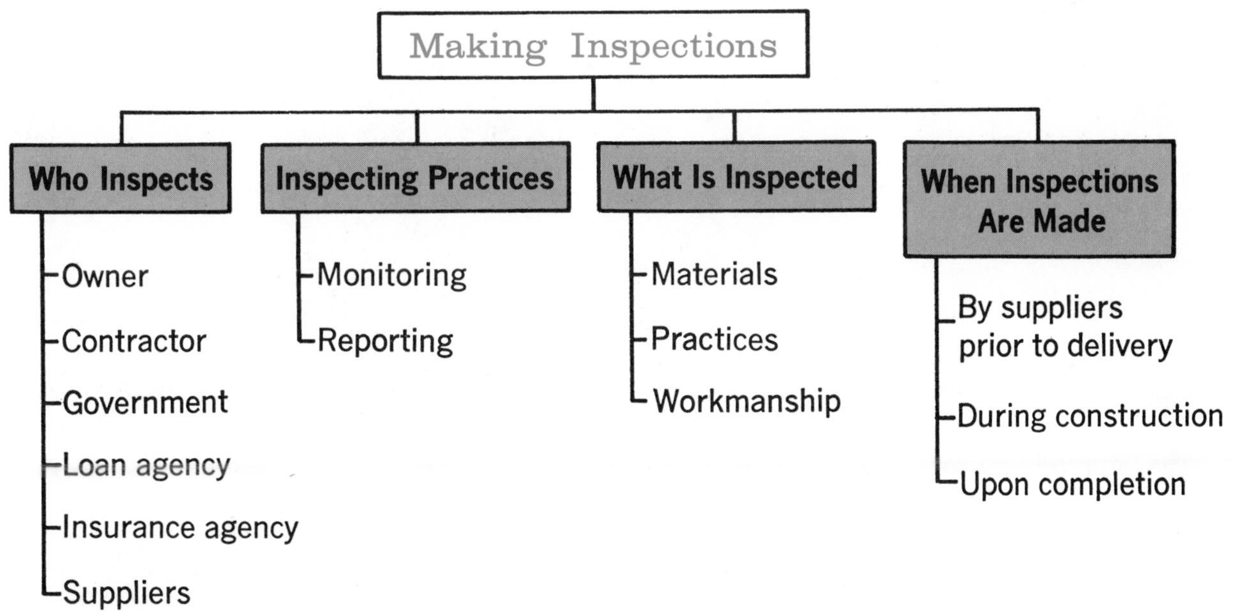

the contractor completes his work. Employees of the contractor are constantly inspecting their own work to control its quality. Inspectors of the owner insure that the job is built according to the contract. State, county, or city government inspectors check the structure for the health and safety of the public.

Terms to Know

monitoring
inspecting
insure
aggregates
inspector
quality control
specifications

Think About It!

1. Why do inspections need to be made at the construction site? When are they made?
2. How important are the local building codes to the inspector? Should he be familiar with these codes?

READING 55

Mediating and Arbitrating

Earlier this year you learned how unions and contractors (or employers) negotiate *collective bargaining* agreements and how the *grievance* process works. Unions and employers settle most disputes in one of two ways. They negotiate agreements on wages, hours, working conditions, and fringe benefits, or they resort to the grievance procedure. When no agreement can be reached by either method, the next event is usually a *work stoppage* (workers leave the job) or a *lockout* (management stops the job). Work stoppages and lockouts are very unpopular with unions, employers, and the general public. Everyone loses money, and many people may suffer, Fig. 55-1.

Accordingly, two other processes to prevent work stoppages and lockouts are employed: *mediation* and *arbitration.* In both of these processes, one or more *neutral* outsiders are brought into the dispute to attempt to settle it. The neutral outsider looks at both sides of the issues separating labor and management. He works for neither side. Normally he has no business interest in either the union or in the company.

Difference Between Mediation and Arbitration

Both mediators and arbitrators bring labor and management representatives together again after negotiations between them have broken down. Both try to resolve the disagreement. The difference is that the mediator has no power to resolve the dispute. He can only help both sides come to an agreement. The arbitrator, however, has the power to make final decisions that must be followed by both parties.

Fig. 55-1. If mediation efforts break down, the result could be a work stoppage.

Fig. 55-2. Here labor and management are discussing contract terms in a bargaining session.

Mediation is used frequently in major disputes. Neither management nor labor is very anxious to accept arbitration because it means surrendering their own right to the authority of the arbitrator.

Who Mediates and Arbitrates

Qualifications for mediators and arbitrators are very much the same: neutrality, a reputation for fairness, knowledge of the construction industry, importance in the industry or the community, knowledge of labor legislation and practices, and experience in labor negotiations.

Sometimes mediators are selected by the federal government to mediate a dispute. These usually come from the Department of Labor, the Federal Mediation and Conciliation Service, or the National Mediation Board. Sometimes state governors appoint mediators from a similar state agency. Many times labor and the employers themselves agree on the appointment of a mediator. He may come from one of the agencies named or he may be a person whose knowledge, wisdom, judgment, and fairness have the respect of both management and labor.

Arbitrators usually are selected from one of the sources named in the preceding paragraph or from the American Arbitration Association, a nonprofit organization which provides arbitrators for labor and other types of disputes.

The Mediation Process

The role of the mediator is to bring labor and management together. He tries to get them to resolve the dispute. He may make suggestions. He may even propose a final solution, Fig. 55-3. But the mediator has no power to make final decisions binding on both parties. Nevertheless, he can be a great help by clarifying or outlining the disagreements, by finding out just how much each side is willing to give in, by coming up with possible new solutions, by advising both

Fig. 55-3. Mediators meet with labor and management to promote discussion and to suggest solutions to problems.

Fig. 55-4. Arbitration may be used to force a settlement to keep the workers on the job.

sides, and by keeping them talking. Sometimes mediation is quite successful, and other times it is not.

Arbitration

Arbitration may be voluntary or compulsory. In *voluntary arbitration,* both sides agree on the selection of an arbitrator and agree to accept his decision. Voluntary arbitration is rarely used in the construction industry except in the settlement of grievances and in jurisdictional disputes which are mentioned in a special section below. Neither side likes to give up its rights, even to an independent arbitrator.

Compulsory arbitration, imposed by the government in a major dispute, is even more unpopular than voluntary arbitration. An arbitrator's decision as to how long a man must work, for what pay, and under what conditions is very close to "slave labor," which workers have been trying to eliminate for thousands of years. Also, management wants no one to decide how it shall use its own employees and how much it shall pay them. In general, compulsory arbitration is not the law of the land. Members of state and national legislatures stay away from it except in the gravest national emergencies, few of which involve the construction industry, Fig. 55-4.

Jurisdictional Disputes

As you know, construction involves members of various crafts who may be working on a job at the same time. Disputes sometimes come up between crafts over which should perform a certain task. For example, when a steam boiler was to be hooked up to operate a pile driver, the steam fitters declared that it was their job because it involved the piping of steam. The operating engineers declared that it was their job because they operate the boiler and the pile driver.

Where more than one craft claims that a task should be assigned to it, the result is called a *jurisdictional dispute.* Several contractors' associations, including the Associated General Contractors of America, and the construction unions of the AFL-CIO, have agreed to arbitrate jurisdictional disputes.

Matters Referred to Arbitration

The arbitration process is usually employed in the construction industry on matters other than wages. It may be used as the last step of the grievance procedure. In either case, arbitration deals with two major problems: (1) disputes over the meaning of the collective bargaining agreement and (2) disputes over matters which are not covered in the agreement.

Disputes over the meaning of the collective bargaining agreement often happen *when labor and management do not agree on the meaning of words or sections in the agreement.* In this case, the job of the arbitrator is to decide what these words or sections really mean. They can mean different things to different people. It is hard to see the meaning of a statement such as "The contractor shall provide for reasonable safety." For example, is "reasonable safety" provided by an elevated walkway with a handrail on only one side? The words "reasonable safety" do not have a definite meaning until they are applied to a job. When a dispute comes up, the arbitrator must give an exact and specific meaning to these words. He must decide what the collective bargaining agreement means.

An example of a *matter not covered by the agreement,* would be the case of a contractor who is building a road leading 15 miles from the town where most workers live. The collective bargaining agreement does not provide for travel pay to and from the job. The contractor receives a change order extending the road 10 miles. The workmen wish to be paid, at the rate of 5 cents a mile, for travel from the city to their place of employment and return. The company's position is that the original agreement included no mileage pay. The arbitrator's job here is to decide if the workers are entitled to additional money for their travel and, if so, whether five cents a mile is the proper rate. The arbitrator must find a way of deciding what is fair for both parties.

The Arbitration Process

After the arbitrator is selected, both labor and management furnish him with written statements of their separate positions in the dispute. Each statement includes a list of the issues or disagreements and offers evidence and argument in favor of one side. The arbitrator studies the two written statements carefully. He then holds a meeting or "hearing" which representatives of both sides attend. He asks questions and discusses the case, Fig. 55-5.

After the hearing, the arbitrator makes his decision and writes it out in the form of an *arbitration award.* The award follows certain rules. First, nothing should be said about issues not at stake. Next, all issues under question must be in the award. Then, the award must be enforceable. (There must be some way to make sure that the decisions are followed.) Facts, figures, and dates named in the award should be correct.

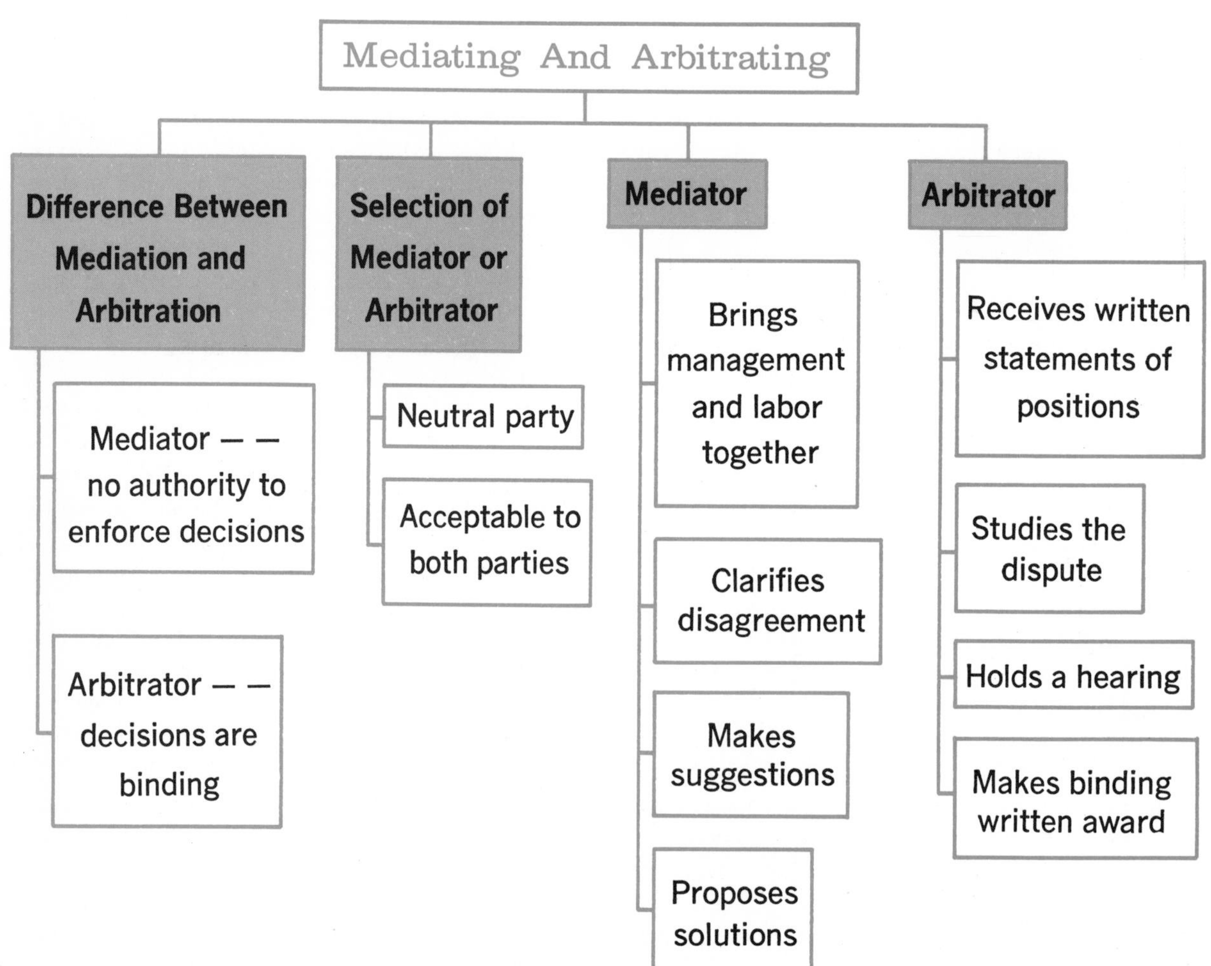
Mediating And Arbitrating
Difference Between Mediation and Arbitration
Mediator — — no authority to enforce decisions
Arbitrator — — decisions are binding
Selection of Mediator or Arbitrator
Neutral party
Acceptable to both parties
Mediator
Brings management and labor together
Clarifies disagreement
Makes suggestions
Proposes solutions
Arbitrator
Receives written statements of positions
Studies the dispute
Holds a hearing
Makes binding written award

Finally, the arbitration award must not go against any provisions of the basic collective bargaining agreement.

Summary

Arbitration or mediation is used when the parties involved in a dispute cannot settle it by themselves. An arbitrator has the power to make final decisions that both parties must follow. A mediator may make suggestions, but his decisions are not binding on either party.

Arbitrators and mediators should always be neutral outsiders who have the confidence of both sides in a dispute. Arbitration is rarely used in construction, except in grievances and jurisdictional disputes.

Terms to Know

mediation	resolve
arbitration	voluntary arbitration
grievance	compulsory arbitration
work stoppage	jurisdictional disputes
lockout	hearing
neutral	collective bargaining
dispute	arbitration award

Think About It!

1. What is the difference between mediating and arbitrating?
2. Why is the process of arbitration rarely used in the construction industry?

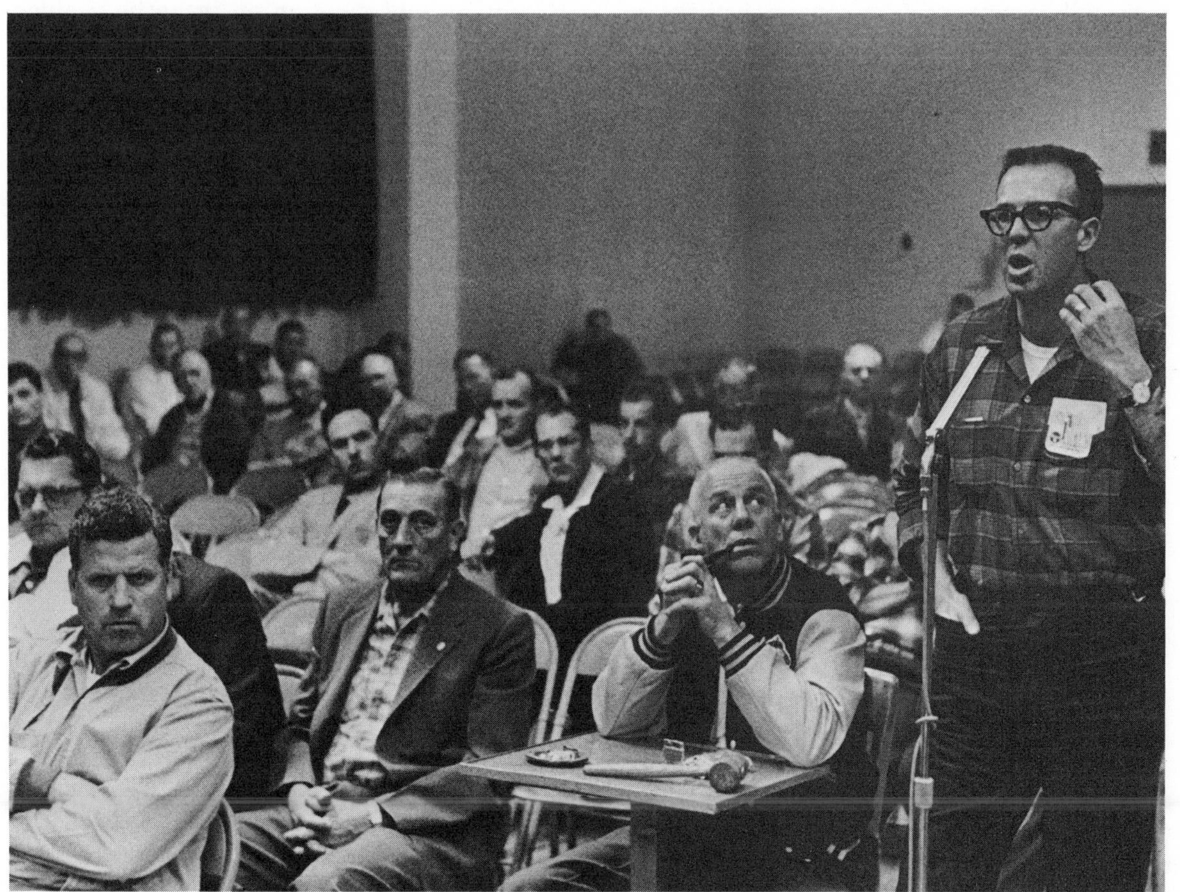

Fig. 55-5. A local union member expresses his opinion at a meeting where an agreement is being discussed.

READING 56

Enclosing Framed Superstructures

Some kinds of structures are usually left uncovered. Bridges, roads, dams, and the towers used for utilities are examples. Most buildings, and some towers, are wholly or partly enclosed. You have studied a number of production practices which apply equally to open and enclosed structures. This reading concerns only enclosed structures. It refers chiefly to buildings which have a framed or *skeleton* type of superstructure. However, many of the practices described here will apply also to superstructures of the load bearing type.

Why the Framework Is Enclosed

Our starting point is a building framework of wood, steel, or concrete. The framework by itself is of very little value. It needs to be enclosed with an *exterior* (outside) skin that will keep out sun, rain, snow, wind, heat, cold, and air pollutants such as dust and smoke. This skin consists of a roof on top of the building and exterior walls (sometimes called *curtain walls*) on the sides. Another need is for one or more floors for the use of people, equipment, and materials. For certain buildings, such as warehouses and some factories, only the *outside* of the superstructure needs to be enclosed. So only a roof, exterior walls, and a bottom floor are needed for enclosure, Fig. 56-1.

But let us assume that we are designing a house, a school, or an office building. These three types of buildings will require some additional features to make them useful and attractive, Fig. 56-2. The features which enclose the *inside* of the building are floors, ceilings, partitions, and the insides of exterior walls. These features permit control of the temperature, humidity, light, and noise inside the building. They also improve the appearance by hiding utility lines and by providing attractive textures, colors, and decorative details.

Accordingly, this lesson will describe briefly roofs, outside walls, floors, ceilings, partitions, and interior surfaces. It will tell briefly what materials are used for each. It will include mention of *insulation* which may be built into any of these six. The next several readings will describe more of the details of each item.

Fig. 56-1. The framework of this building is made of steel.

Who Encloses the Framework

The architect usually selects the methods and materials for enclosing the framework of a building, Fig. 56-3. He makes selections based upon appearance, economy, and the purposes for which the rooms will be used, and upon the recommendations of a structural engineer who may design the frame in a large building.

The general contractor is responsible for enclosing the building although he may subcontract parts of the job such as roofing, tilework, and painting to specialty subcontractors.

Many different types of craftsmen are employed. There are carpenters, masons, roofers, sheet metal workers, glaziers (who install glass), laborers, painters, tile setters, cement finishers, paperhangers, ironworkers, and sometimes men from all 18 of the organized craft groups.

Roofs

A roof is a watertight skin which covers the top of a building. The roof is usually put on before exterior walls are started and before floors are laid. There are many exceptions to this, particularly in the case of a high rise building where exterior walls and floors are sometimes placed before the framework is "topped out" (reaches the roof). Roofs may be flat or sloped (slanted). Flat roofs may be made of metal or plastic, but they are usually "built up" of alternate layers of roofing felt (which you may call *tar paper*) and a black, gummy asphalt or tar. A sloped roof may be made of metals or of rolled asphalt roofing, but the most common roofing materials are shingles of asphalt, asbestos, slate, tile, or wood. The next reading discusses roofing in more detail, Fig. 56-4.

Exterior Walls

Curtain walls enclose the exteriors of framed superstructures, Fig. 56-5. They include windows and doors. These walls always include a surfacing material. They

Fig. 56-2. Frameworks are enclosed on the interior to hide utilities. The enclosing materials also provide a functional and attractive surface.

Fig. 56-3. The architect or engineer selects the materials, and the contractor hires craftsmen to install them. This enclosing material is marble.

usually include insulation to prevent the passage of heat and sound, and a thin vapor barrier to prevent the passage of water vapor in the air.

Exterior walls may be built of wood, aluminum, enameled or stainless steel, concrete, stucco, plastic, glass, or masonry materials such as brick, clay tile, concrete block, and facing stone. Combinations may be used, such as stone backed up with concrete block or stucco (a rough plaster of cement, sand, and water) applied over masonry.

Floors

Most floors are made of at least two layers, a *rough floor* and a *finished floor.* For instance, in a wall-to-wall carpeted house that sits on a concrete slab, the slab is the rough floor and the carpeting is the finished floor. To provide walking surfaces for workmen and a place for storing construction materials, rough floors are usually installed as soon as possible. (In some reinforced concrete buildings, floor slabs are part of the framework.) Finished floors are usually one of the last things placed in a building. Often they are not laid until all interior (inside) painting is complete.

Flooring materials include concrete, steel, wood, ceramic, asphalt vinyl (plastic), linoleum, carpeting, and terrazo (a stone and cement mixture). Floors sometimes include a vapor barrier but rarely do they include insulation, Fig. **56-6.**

Fig. 56-4. This aerial picture shows workmen installing corrugated metal roofing to furring strips on roof rafters.

Ceilings

Sometimes the underside of a floor system serves as a ceiling for the rooms beneath. Usually beneath a subfloor there is an ugly, dust-catching tangle of pipes, wires, and ducts. Also an exposed subfloor reflects sound, resulting in a noisy atmosphere. To prevent these situations, a ceiling is placed at the bottom of the overhead floor system, or hung from it on wires or small steel angles. (The latter is called a *suspended*

Fig. 56-5. Glaziers have enclosed this curtain wall office building with over 1,000 glass panels.

ceiling.) The "dead air" (space above the ceiling) serves as an insulator, making the room easier to heat and cool. A finished ceiling greatly improves the appearance of a room. The ceiling can be made of acoustical (sound deadening) materials to cut down noise. Ceiling materials are lath and plaster, gypsum board, plywood, accoustical or fibrous tile, metal, and plastics, Fig. 56-7.

Partitions

Partitions are walls which divide the space inside a building. They provide privacy and they separate the various functions or activities within the building. Load bearing partitions support part of the structure. Nonload bearing partitions support only their own weight. Some partitions, such as sliding doors and heavy drapes, are easily movable. Your school or Sunday School building may have movable partitions. There are other partitions that can easily be moved by craftsmen. They are useful in commercial buildings where activities change from year to year, and the division of interior space needs to be changed. Partitions may be built of wood or steel framing, covered either with lath and plaster or gypsum board. Other partitions are made of steel, of masonry (usually lightweight concrete block or clay tile), of glass, or of plastics.

Interior Surfaces of Exterior Walls

Interior surfaces hide utility lines and improve inside appearance. They usually have two layers: a subsurface material and a finish or surface layer. Subsurface materials, which are attached to the framework, may be of lath and plaster, glass, wood, plywood, metal, gypsum wallboard, plastic, or masonry, Fig. 56-8. Finishes may be paint, wallpaper, cloth, wood, cellulose or fiberboard products, ceramic tile, or plastics.

Fig. 56-6. The workman is cementing a finished vinyl floor to the subflooring. Notice the chalk lines on the floor. The tiles are laid from the center of the room to the walls.

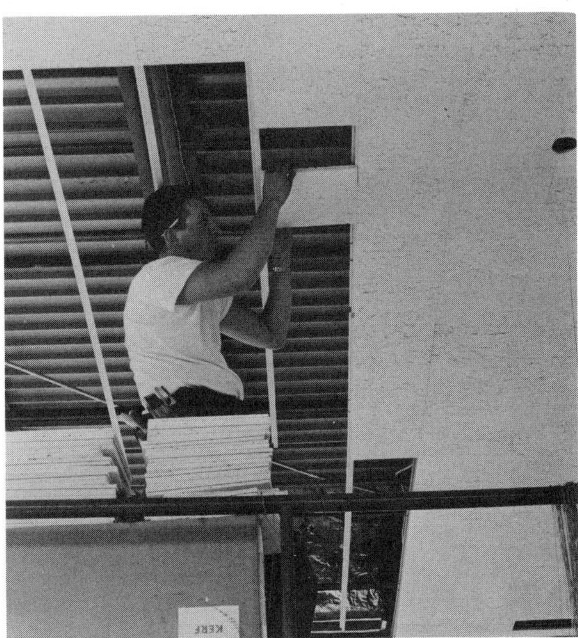

Fig. 56-7. A workman is installing acoustical tile on furring strips which are attached to the ceiling. What are some purposes of the tile?

Insulation

One main reason for insulating is to help keep the temperature inside a structure from changing as the outside temperature changes. Insulation also reduces the passage of noise, and some insulation acts as a vapor barrier, Fig. 56-9.

Just as the insulation is installed to prevent the passage of heat, so a *vapor barrier* is installed to prevent the passage of moisture. The vapor barrier may be the insulation itself, as in the case of aluminum foil sheets. It also may be a part of the insulation, as when asphalt-treated felt is attached to insulating batts. A vapor barrier also may be separate sheets of moisture-resistant material such as a film of plastic or a layer of asphalt-treated felt. In any case, the barrier is installed to keep out unwanted moisture or water vapor. It is usually installed along with the insulation.

Buildings which are to be heated or cooled are insulated with materials which are poor conductors of heat. Some insulation materials also absorb sound waves. These are used where soundproofing is needed.

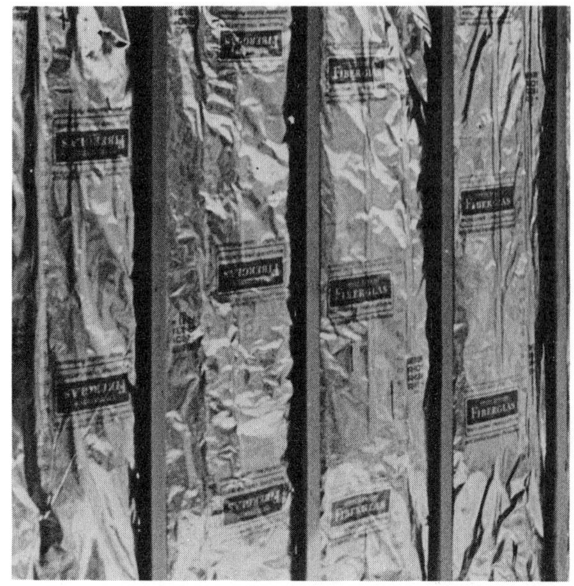

Fig. 56-9. Insulating batts have been installed between the studs of this building.

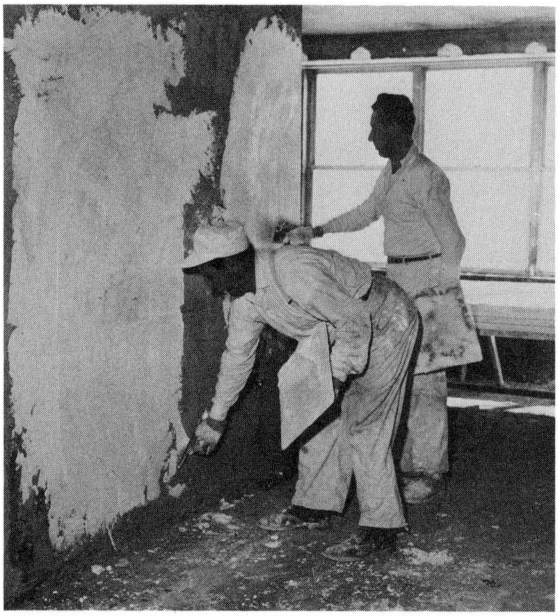

Fig. 56-8. The plasterers here are applying a "brown coat" of plaster over a "scratch coat" to enclose this interior wall.

Fig. 56-10. Shown here are some of the layers of materials which are used to enclose exteriors: plywood, waterproof paper, and shingles.

Insulation may either be placed in the spaces between framing members in the roof and walls or may be applied across the outer surfaces of the frame. Insulation comes as loose materials which are poured or blown in place, flexible batts, or rigid panels. Materials used as insulation include asbestos, spun glass, shredded paper, fiberboard, and plastic foams and crumbs.

Summary

The framework of a building is enclosed on the outside to keep out the weather, Fig. 56-10. It is enclosed on the inside by floors, ceilings, partitions, and interior wall surfaces. Insulation to prevent the passage of heat and sound forms part of the enclosure of a building. A vapor barrier, either separate or included in the insulation, also may form a part of the flooring and exterior walls.

Terms to Know

enclosed structures	rough floor
air pollutants	finished floor
exterior	furring strips
functional	suspended ceiling
glaziers	dead air
insulation	partitions
"topped out"	acoustical tile
corrugated	vapor barrier

Think About It!

1. What kinds of exterior materials enclose your school?
2. Identify the materials that enclose the frame or bearing wall in your industrial arts laboratory.

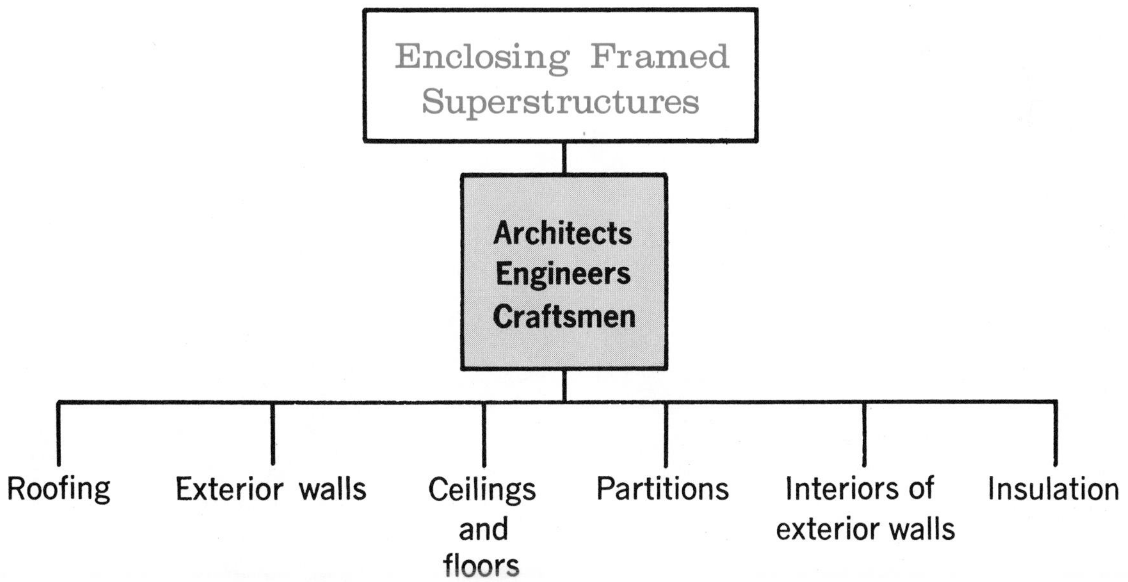

READING 57

Roofing

This reading is about roofs. In a one-or two-story building, the roof is generally one of the first parts of the framework to be enclosed. On high rise construction, much of the structure may be enclosed before it rises to the roof level.

As the top cover for a building, the roof protects the inside from damage by wind, rain, and snow. A roof may also add to the appearance or character of a building. Fig. 57-1.

Types of Roofs

There are two general types of roofs: flat and pitched, Fig. 57-2. A *flat roof* is seldom really level. Usually it has a very slight slope or slant. It is used mostly in commercial or industrial construction.

A *pitched roof* has a much greater slant or slope than a flat roof. It is most often used for houses, but it may be applied to other structures to achieve a pleasing architectural effect. Also, some buildings have a straight or curved sloping roof. An example might be a church or a large auditorium.

You will learn more about pitched roofs used in houses when you design your dream home. The rest of this reading will be about flat or curved roofs as they are built on homes and business places.

Advantages of Flat Roofs

The biggest advantage of a flat roof is that the space directly underneath is completely usable, Fig. 57-3. The slanted ceiling of an attic under a pitched roof can be used only in limited ways. A room with a slanted

Fig. 57-1. The purpose of the roof is to protect the interior of a building from the weather. The roof also can be a major factor in the appearance of a building.

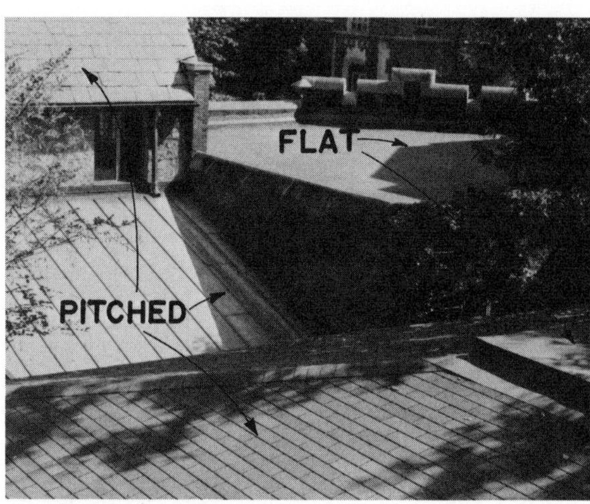

Fig. 57-2. Roofs are either pitched or flat.

ceiling is also difficult to heat and air-condition. Getting the most space for the least money is important in most industrial and commercial structures. Therefore, these buildings generally have a flat roof.

A flat roof offers several cost advantages. It has the least area of roofing for the amount of floor space covered. It uses the cheapest materials. The roofing operation can be done by the most modern mechanized equipment.

Sometimes a flat roof requires a heavier framework than does a pitched roof. However, the cost advantages of a flat roof nearly always outweigh this disadvantage. Accordingly, flat roofs are most common for large buildings unless a specific architectural effect is desired for the sake of appearance or utility.

Fig. 57-3. When a flat roof is used, all the space underneath is usable.

Fig. 57-4. Here steel roof deck is being hoisted into place on top of a framework.

Supporting Framework

A roof is supported by the framework of the building. The part of the framework that lies directly under the roof is a system of concrete, steel, or wooden rafters, beams, trusses, or reinforced concrete slabs. The building of this framework has been studied in earlier lessons.

Deck

On top of the supporting framework, the *roof deck* is laid. The deck supports many things:

1. Weight of the roof,
2. The snow or rain,
3. Roof-top equipment such as air conditioning units, and
4. Equipment used by the roofer.

The deck may be made of steel, prestressed concrete slabs, ordinary reinforced concrete, plywood, gypsum, vermiculite, shredded wood fibers, or fiberboard. Roofs usually cover large areas and are subject to wide variations in temperature (from below zero to above 150 degrees). Therefore, roof decks are constructed with *expansion joints.* The decking is laid by a roof-deck contractor or by a general contractor.

Insulation

The outside surface of a building consists of the exterior walls and the roof. On a modern one-story factory, the roof area may be as much as 95% of the total surface. It is important that the roof be properly insulated to prevent the loss of heat in the winter and of cooled air in the summer.

Some types of roof decking (fiberboard, gypsum, or lightweight concrete) themselves provide enough insulation. These materials, however, cannot be used for decking if great structural strength is needed.

Steel, ordinary concrete, and wood decking provide more structural strength but are poor insulators, Fig. 57-4. Extra insulation is needed with these materials if the temperature inside the structure is to be controlled.

Insulation consists of sheets of wood or plant fiber, fiberglass, cork, or foamed plastic, Fig. 57-5. All of these are excellent insulators when dry, but not when wet. If the building will have high humidity in it, a *vapor barrier* is placed on top of the deck. The vapor barrier will keep the insulation from becoming soaked with water. The vapor barrier is a very thin layer (membrane) through which moisture cannot pass. It may consist of a plastic sheet, cemented to the deck with an adhesive, or of roofing felt and a layer of bitumen. The vapor barrier and the insulation are laid by the roofers.

Built-Up Roofing Materials

Although other materials such as metal and plastics are used, over 90% of all flat roofs are of the *built-up* type. Three kinds of material are combined in a built-up roof: roofing felt, bitumen (asphalt or tar), and gravel (or slag). See Fig. 57-6.

Roofing felt is a mat of fiber which has been soaked (at the factory) in bitumen. It comes in rolls 36″ wide and in a number of weights (for example, 15 pounds per 100 square feet and 30 pounds per 100 square feet).

The bitumen is a thin liquid when heated, and it is easy to apply, Fig. 57-7. However, when it cools, it becomes a soft and flexible solid. It seals against the passage of water.

The *gravel or slag* consists of pieces about the size of a pea. It has many uses:

1. To protect the roof against foot traffic,
2. To help the roof resist uplift (blowing off by wind),
3. To protect the bitumen from the direct rays of the sun, and
4. To reflect and absorb the heat of the sun, thus keeping the roof cooler.

All of these roofing materials are relatively low in cost. The fibers are by-products of the food industry. The bitumen is a by-product of producing gasoline. Slag is a by-product of steelmaking. Gravel is produced by crushing natural rock.

Fig. 57-5. Here foam plastic insulating panels are being installed on the deck.

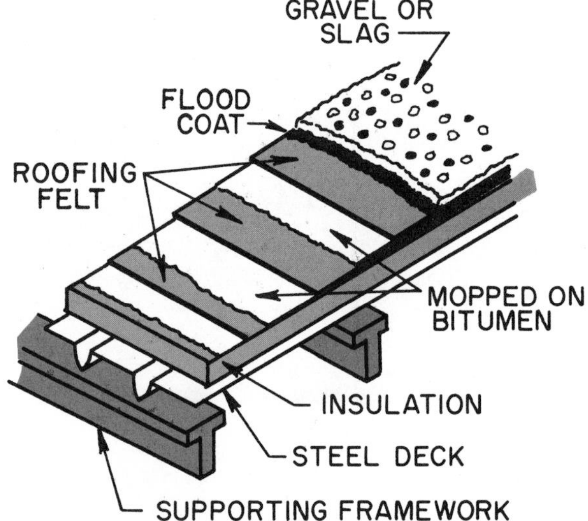

Fig. 57-6. Several materials are combined in a built-up roof.

Laying a Built-Up Roof

In laying a built-up roof, the bitumen is heated and spread, or "mopped," on top of the insulation. A roll of felt is laid in the hot bitumen, and more bitumen is mopped over three-fourths of its width. On top of the bitumen, another strip of felt is laid so that it laps over three-fourths of the width of the previous strip of felt. Another coat of bitumen is then applied on top of this roll of felt.

Fig. 57-7. This man is spreading bitumen on a roof.

The process of building up alternate layers of roofing felt and bitumen is repeated until the desired number of layers (called *plies*) is in place. Fig. 57-8. The number of plies may vary from three to seven, depending upon the climate and the number of years of life expected from the roof. Good workmanship and quality materials are also important in producing a durable roof.

On top of the last layer of felt is spread a heavier layer of bitumen called a *flood coat*. The gravel or slag is spread evenly and embedded in the flood coat while it is still hot, Fig. 57-9. A smooth surface on a roof is simply finished with a flood coat. No gravel or slag is used.

Flashings

Flashings are strips of material which seal the joints between roofing and anything else that projects or rises above it, Fig. 57-10. Flashings are needed at the edges of built-up roofing; around pipes, vents, and chimneys; and at expansion joints. Flashings can be formed from sheet metal (cop-

Fig. 57-8. Roofing felt is applied on top of the bitumen.

Fig. 57-9. The final layer of a built-up roof may be gravel or slag.

per, galvanized steel, aluminum, stainless steel, or lead). Also asphalt felt, rubber, and plastics are used. There are many types of flashings to take care of many different types of joints. All must be carefully installed because a roof is more likely to leak at joints than anywhere else.

New Types of Flat Roofing Materials

Conventional built-up roofs of felt and bitumen have been used for many years and still comprise over 90% of the flat roofing put on each year. Recently some new products and techniques have been introduced. These fall into two basic groups: liquid-applied systems and one-ply systems.

The *liquid-applied systems* may be sprayed or applied with a paint roller. Typical liquid systems may be made of silicone rubber or plastics, Fig. 57-11.

One-ply systems are applied in a manner very much like conventional built-up roofing. There are two differences: (1) these systems are only one layer thick and (2) they are not made of conventional roofing felt. The materials used are synthetic rubber or various types of plastics. The membrane is attached to the deck with special adhesives.

Fig. 57-10. This roofer is installing a metal flashing.

These new materials are attractive in appearance and are durable. The main drawback to them is their cost. They are not made from waste products, as most of the traditional materials are. Thus, they cost more. In most cases the savings in labor costs when a single layer is put on helps to offset the high cost of the materials.

Roofing Bonds

Many times the architect-engineer will specify a *bonded* roof. The bond is a limited guarantee by the company which installs

Fig. 57-11. Silicone is one of the newest roofing materials. Note that the roof is irregular in shape rather than flat.

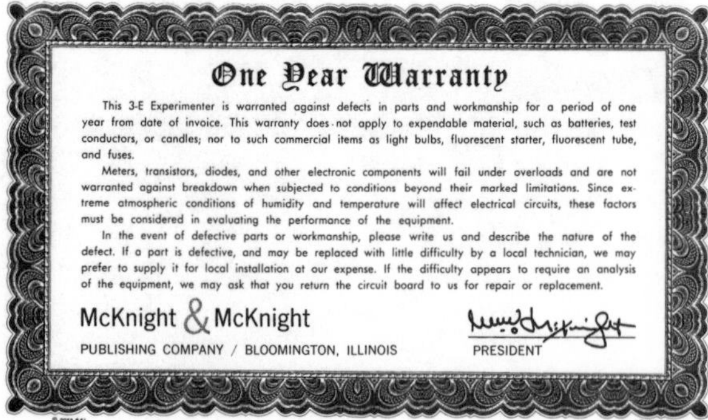

One Year Warranty

This 3-E Experimenter is warranted against defects in parts and workmanship for a period of one year from date of invoice. This warranty does not apply to expendable material, such as batteries, test conductors, or candles; nor to such commercial items as light bulbs, fluorescent starter, fluorescent tube, and fuses.

Meters, transistors, diodes, and other electronic components will fail under overloads and are not warranted against breakdown when subjected to conditions beyond their marked limitations. Since extreme atmospheric conditions of humidity and temperature will affect electrical circuits, these factors must be considered in evaluating the performance of the equipment.

In the event of defective parts or workmanship, please write us and describe the nature of the defect. If a part is defective, and may be replaced with little difficulty by a local technician, we may prefer to supply it for local installation at our expense. If the difficulty appears to require an analysis of the equipment, we may ask that you return the circuit board to us for repair or replacement.

McKnight & McKnight
PUBLISHING COMPANY / BLOOMINGTON, ILLINOIS

PRESIDENT

Fig. 57-12. Manufacturers issue warranty agreements to guarantee their products to the purchaser.

the roofing materials. The contractor guarantees to pay for any necessary repairs to the roof for a certain period of time, usually ten or twenty years. When a bonded roof is specified, details as to the number of plies and the flashing are usually left to the roofing material manufacturer and the roofing contractor.

Summary

A roof encloses the top of a structure. Roofs may be flat or pitched. Flat roofs are watertight skins usually built up from alternate layers of roofing felt and bitumen. Joints between the roofing and objects, such as chimneys which extend above the roof, are made watertight with flashings. New liquid and one-layer roofing materials show much promise in reducing labor costs and extending roof life.

Terms to Know

alternate	built-up roof
flat roof	roofing felt
pitched roof	gravel
slope	slag
roof deck	plies
bitumen	flashings
membrane	bonded
horizontal gutters	expansion joints
vertical downspouts	insulation
adhesives	vapor barrier

Think About It!

1. In your part of the United States, are there more flat or pitched roofs? Why?
2. Look at the ceiling in the room in which you are sitting. Is there evidence of a leaking roof? If so, why? If not, why?

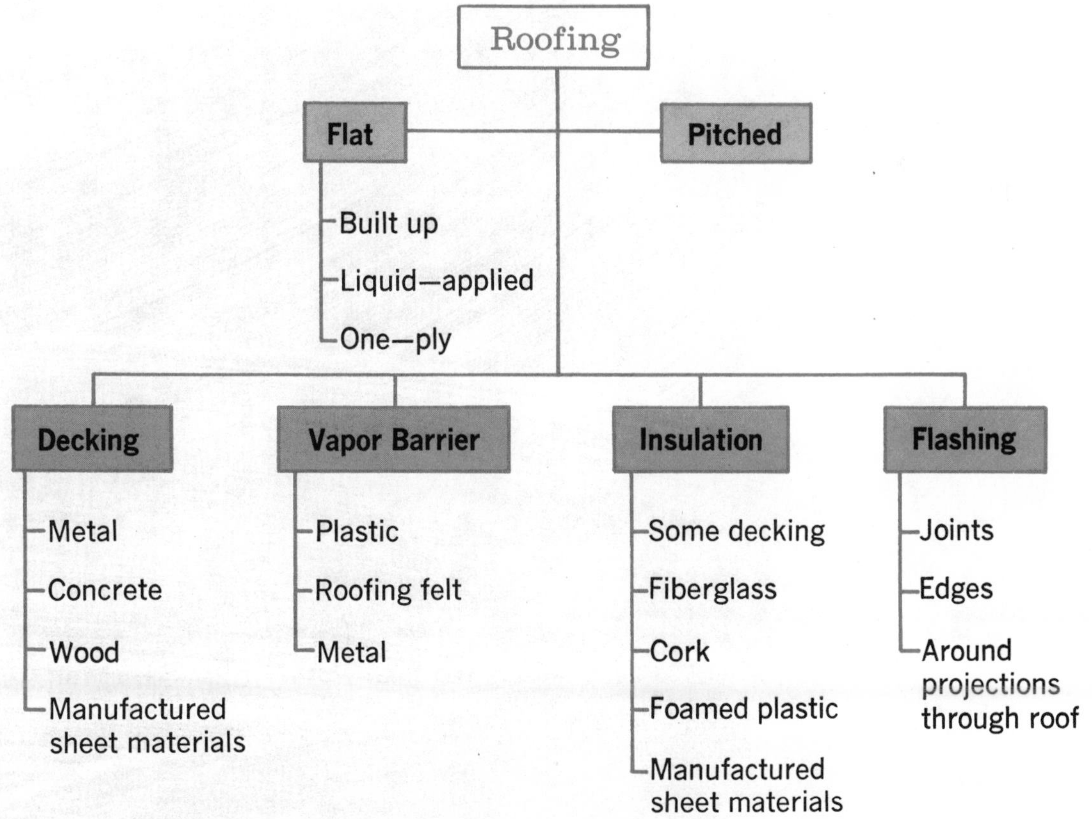

READING 58

Enclosing Exterior Walls

The outside walls of a building are of two types: load bearing and nonload bearing. Many one-story buildings have no framework. The entire load is carried on the wall. Buildings constructed hundreds of years ago used load bearing walls, Fig. 58-1. For buildings more than two stories high, walls had to be quite thick at the bottom to support the heavy loads. Men finally found that it was far more economical to erect framed buildings with nonload bearing or *curtain walls,* Fig. 58-2. Very recently, new techniques of using reinforced concrete have made possible a return to load bearing walls even on high rise buildings. This lesson relates to nonload bearing or curtain walls which form an exterior skin around the sides of buildings.

Who Installs Exterior Walls

The architect chooses the materials and the type of exterior walls for a planned building. If the structure will be large, he consults first with a structural (civil) engineer. The architect must give many kinds of important information. For example, in the

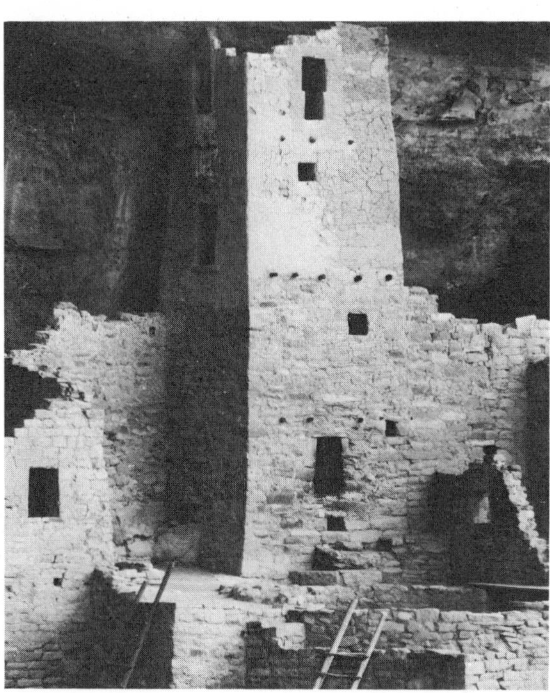

Fig. 58-1. Old buildings were constructed mainly with load bearing walls. This structure in Mesa Verde National Park is hundreds of years old.

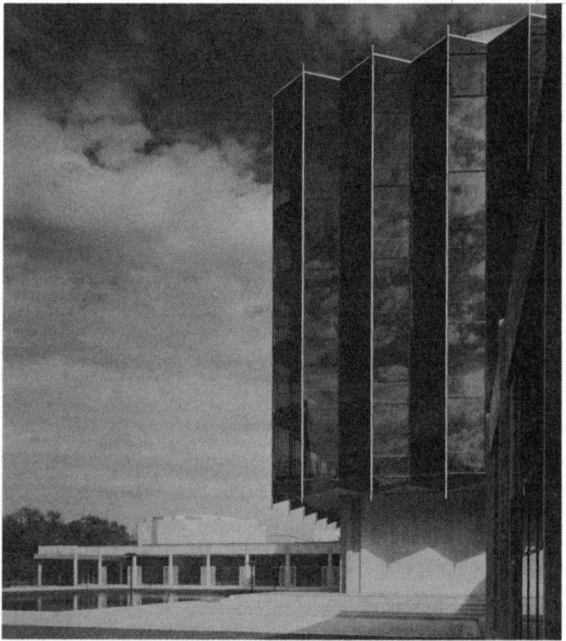

Fig. 58-2. Many modern structures use curtain wall construction. The glass in this building does not support the roof. Instead, it covers the framework which supports the entire structure.

case of a brick wall, plans and specifications must show (1) where the wall is to be placed, (2) its thickness, (3) the location and sizes of window and door openings, (4) the pattern for laying brick (sometimes called *bond*), (5) the type of joints, (6) the kind of mortar and brick, and (7) how the wall is to be tied into the frame.

Usually the exterior walls are enclosed by the general contractor with his own employees. Sometimes, however, this task is subcontracted to a specialty subcontractor: for example, one who does only masonry work.

A great many different craftsmen work on installing curtain walls. These include carpenters, bricklayers, stone masons, sheet metal workers, welders, glaziers (who install glass), and ironworkers.

Materials for Enclosing Exterior Walls

Exterior walls may be covered with many different types of materials:

1. Masonry,
2. Wood siding,
3. Panels of wood, plastic, glass, aluminum, enameled steel, or concrete, or
4. Other materials such as poured-in-place, reinforced concrete and stucco.

Door and window *frames* (often called *bucks*) are generally of steel, aluminum, or wood. Above each is a *lintel* (a beam) which supports the exterior wall above the opening. Below each frame is a *threshold* or sill to support the frame. See Fig. 58-3.

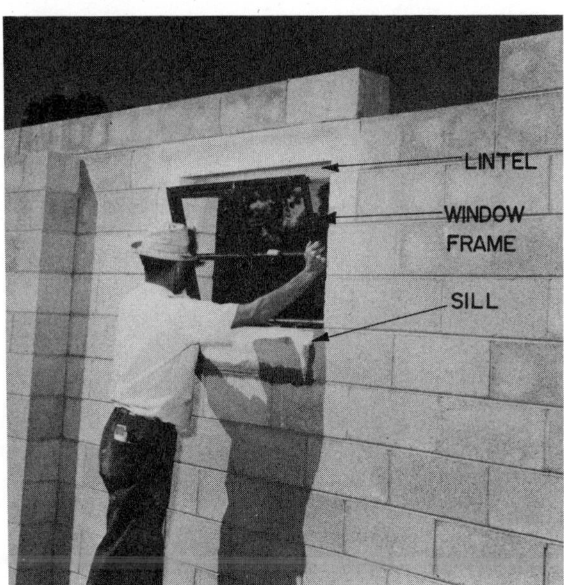

Fig. 58-3. The masonry work must be done accurately if other parts of the structure are to fit properly.

Masonry

Masonry materials have been used for exterior walls for thousands of years. The materials will not burn, are attractive, and are found nearly everywhere. Materials used in masonry walls are brick, concrete block, clay tile, stone (granite, limestone, marble, sandstone), and glass block. Mortar (a mixture of sand, water, and mortar cement) is placed between the masonry units to hold them securely in place.

A *brick* is a rectangular piece of clay, hardened in a very hot oven called a *kiln*. Most brick is solid. For some uses it is formed with cores or hollow channels. While brick comes in many sizes, the standard

Fig. 58-4. Brick is available in many textures and a number of sizes.

brick is $2\frac{1}{4}''$ high by $3\frac{3}{4}''$ wide by $8''$ long. Bricks are of many colors and textures, Fig. 58-4.

The many types of brick used for curtain walls may be divided into two general groups: common and face brick. While *common brick* sometimes is used as a facing, *face brick* is used where a special texture or color is desired.

Some brick walls are 8″ and more thick and are built entirely of brick. Some walls have only a 4″ brick veneer. (A *veneer* is an outside or surface layer.) For a thick wall, it is very common to use face brick on the exterior where it will show. Common brick is used on the inside where it will not show. In this case, we say that our wall is made of face brick "backed up" by common brick, Fig. 58-5. Other "backup" materials for brick (and also for stone) are concrete block and clay tile.

Fig. 58-5. Notice the masonry wall ties between the two walls. Together these two walls make up a bearing wall.

The appearance of a brick wall depends partly on the type of mortar joints used and the color of the mortar. The way the bricks are arranged also affects the appearance of a wall.

Concrete blocks are made from cement, sand, and some kind of aggregate, all mixed with water. Crushed stone and gravel are commonly used heavy aggregates. Lightweight aggregate materials include cinders and sawdust.

Concrete blocks generally are *cored.* A *cored* concrete block usually has two hollow spaces in it similar to the holes in the bricks in Fig. 58-4. Concrete blocks come in various sizes. The largest weighs about 50 pounds (about as much as can easily be lifted by hand), and measures $7\frac{5}{8}''$ by $7\frac{5}{8}''$ by $15\frac{5}{8}''$.

Concrete blocks are used in single or multiple thicknesses for commercial, industrial, or residential buildings. For use as the exterior layer of a wall, they may be given various colors and textures, Fig. 58-6. They are also used as "backup" for brick or stone facing.

Fig. 58-6. This man is working with concrete block. The mortar joints are neater and more durable when they are tooled or compressed. Vertical joints may be struck flush and horizontal joints tooled to give emphasis to the long lines of the building.

Clay tile used for masonry walls consists of cored blocks, hardened in a kiln. Various colors and textures are available, but most clay tile is light red in color and is fairly smooth on the outside. It comes in many sizes and shapes, the largest being about 12″ by 12″ by 12″. Many older buildings used clay tile as an exterior facing. Today its principal use is as a backup for a brick or stone facing.

Many older buildings were made of solid stone. Because of great weight and cost, stone is now used only as a facing or veneer, with a backup of common brick, concrete block, or clay tile. Various kinds of stone are suitable: granite, limestone, sandstone, marble, and slate. Stone facing is usually 3″ to 6″ thick. Heights vary from 2″ to 24″, and lengths run up to 48″ or more. Stone facing is so heavy that a derrick crane is required to handle all but the smallest pieces.

Other masonry materials include glass block, cobblestones (rarely used now), and various types of ribbon stone. Ribbon stone consists of thin layers of stone placed to achieve a decorative effect.

How Masonry Is Laid

Mortar is prepared in a mortar mixer, which is like a small concrete mixer. Mason tenders, or helpers (formerly called *hod carriers*), operate the mixer and keep the masons supplied with mortar and pieces of masonry, Fig. 58-7.

After the job is first *laid out,* then the first two courses are laid on top of the foundation. In *layout,* accurate measurement is very important to assure that walls are straight and that walls intersect at the desired angles. From then on, the brick, block, or stone laying begins. Care is taken to provide openings for windows and doors. Plans must be followed carefully. Joints must be kept at uniform thickness. Successful masonry work requires great skill and care on the part of the bricklayer or stonemason.

Among the tools used by a mason are:

1. Trowels to place mortar in joints,
2. A jointing tool to finish the various types of joints,
3. Masonry hammers and chisels to break and finish pieces into the odd sizes required, and
4. A level used with a 6′ folding rule and a line to keep the work straight and level.

Usually there is a power-driven masonry saw on the job to cut masonry pieces into the needed sizes.

Wood

Buildings with wooden frames are usually enclosed either with a brick veneer or with wood. Recently aluminum and vinyl siding have come into use also. When wood is used, there are usually three layers: sheathing, a vapor barrier, and siding.

Some sheathing is constructed of 1″ thick wood board placed diagonally across the studs. Plywood and sheets of wood chip or fibrous material also are used for sheathing.

The vapor barrier is usually roofing felt, but sometimes aluminum foil is part of the wood chip or fiber insulation. This barrier is

Fig. 58-7. Bricklayers often work from scaffolds. The man pushing the cart is called a "tender."

installed to prevent the passage of water vapor through the wall.

Wood siding can be built of *lapped boards* or shingles. Neither siding boards nor shingles are entirely waterproof, but because they overlap, the completed wall sheds water. The corners and ends of lap siding must be covered with wood or metal trim to prevent leaking. Both sheathing and siding are nailed to the wood studs of the frame.

Panels

Exterior walls may be built of panels, which are larger than individual pieces of masonry or siding, Fig. 58-8. Panels may be made of glass, plastic, aluminum, enameled steel, stainless steel, galvanized steel, reinforced concrete, or marble, Fig. 58-9. Various types of fasteners, such as special clips and bolts, hold the panels to the frame of the building. In some cases, panels can be nailed to wood or concrete frames with special nails. Sometimes, steel panels are welded to steel frames, Fig. 58-10.

Compared with masonry, labor costs for installing panels are fairly low. The panels

Fig. 58-9. Craftsmen who work for general contractors or specialty subcontractors install the exterior walls. These men are installing precut marble panels. Is this a load bearing wall?

Fig. 58-8. This exterior panel is a wood laminate.

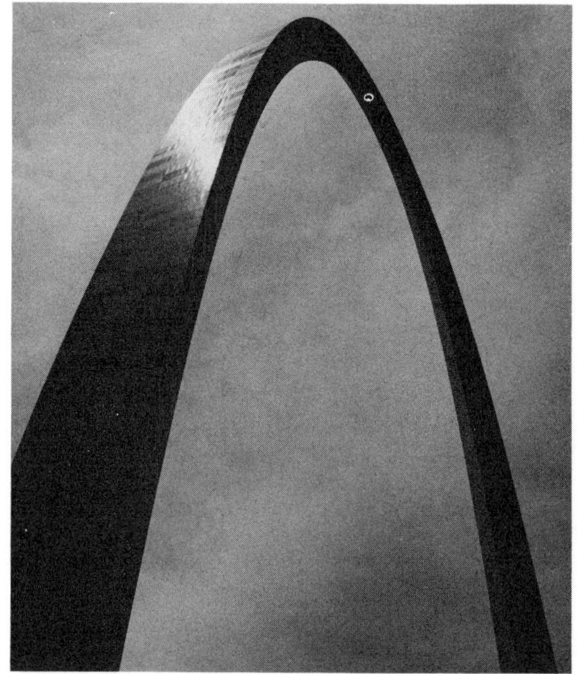

Fig. 58-10. Exterior panels are made of many materials. The Gateway Arch in St. Louis is covered with metal panels.

themselves, however, are often quite expensive. Joints between panels, and between each panel and the frame, are *caulked.*

There is a special type of panel construction known as *tilt-up.* Concrete slabs are poured in forms around the outside of a building, just as though they were pieces of pavement or sidewalk. After the concrete has hardened, a crane tilts each slab up into a vertical position where it becomes part of the wall. For multi-story buildings, the concrete panels are cast on the ground away from the building, hauled to a storage area near the building, and then lifted into place with a crane. The steel reinforcing rods in the panels are welded to similar rods in the frame, and the joints are filled with grout.

Stucco

Stucco, which is somewhat similar to concrete, is often applied on the outside of a building. It is made from masonry cement, sand, and water. Often plasticizing materials are added (such as hydrated lime and asbestos fibers). The end product has all the desirable properties of concrete. It is hard, strong, and fire-resistant. Stucco resists rot and fungus, and keeps its color, Fig. 58-11.

Stucco is generally applied over building felt and expanded metal reinforcement, which have been securely nailed to the framed stucture. Stucco should be applied in three coats. The first, called the *scratch coat,* must be firmly embedded into the metal reinforcement to form a mechanical bond. Next, the *brown coat* is applied. The final coat is called the *finish coat.* Stucco can be finished in many textures, patterns, and colors.

Fig. 58-11. Many walls are enclosed by the use of stucco. This work is done by plasterers and is part of the trowel trades.

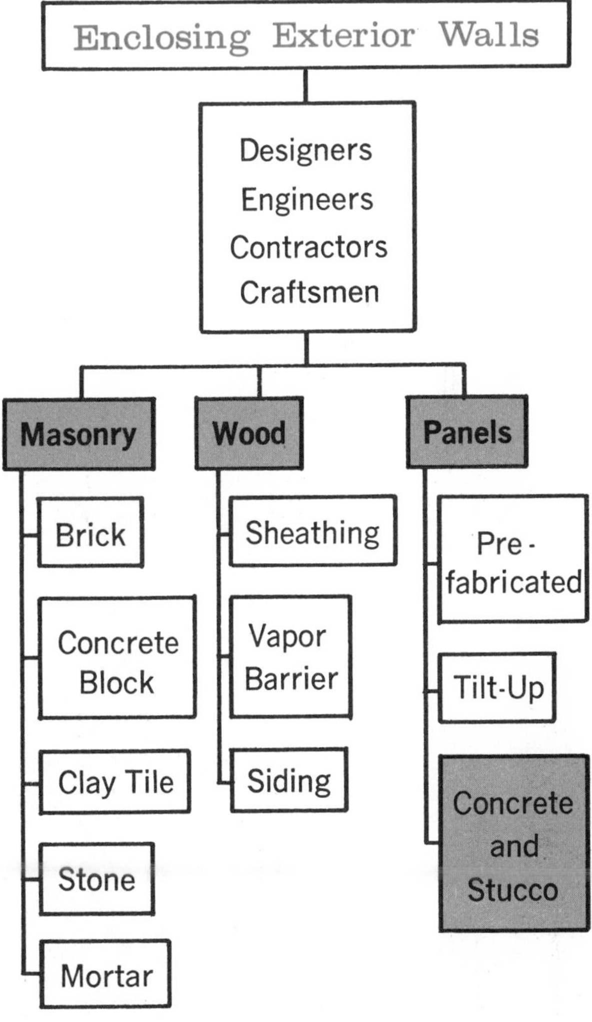

Summary

The framework of a building is covered by exterior walls of masonry, wood, panels of various materials, or stucco. The type of exterior wall is selected by the architect. The wall itself is installed by skilled craftsmen.

Terms to Know

exterior
curtain walls
civil engineer
lintel
threshold
door frame
window frame
masonry brick
tooled joints
ribbon stone
scaffolds
bricklayers
caulked
aligned
a tender
(hod carrier)
kiln
common brick
face brick
veneer
mortar
bonds
stretcher bond
cored block
tilt-up
aggregates
lapped boards
stucco
- a. scratch coat
- b. brown coat
- c. finish coat

Think About It!

1. Why is the exterior surface of a framed building sometimes called the "skin" of the building?
2. In your neighborhood, what is the most common type of "skin" or exterior surface on buildings?

READING 59

Striking

You have read how employers and workers reach agreements through *collective bargaining*. You also have read how they settle disputes by using the grievance procedure, arbitration, and mediation. In this lesson you will read about what sometimes happens when the dispute is not settled. A *work stoppage* (strike) may happen. A strike occurs when none of the members of a union goes to work until an agreement is reached.

Surprisingly, the strike, which seems to be a breakdown in relations between labor and management, usually leads to a prompt settlement. The reasons for this are that everyone loses money during a strike and that strikes are very unpopular with workers, with employers, and with the general public. Accordingly, the strike itself puts pressure on both sides to reach an agreement, Fig. 59-1.

Fig. 59-1. When a strike occurs, production is halted until the disagreement between labor and management is settled.

Even though strikes may make headlines when they do occur, they do not happen often. As you will see later, both labor and management avoid strikes if possible.

Causes of Strikes

The principal cause of strikes is the failure to reach a collective bargaining agreement, usually over an important issue such as pay or working conditions. When a collective bargaining agreement is written, its terms apply for a specified period of time, usually for one to five years. Shortly before the agreement expires (ends), labor and management begin talking to each other (negotiating) about a new agreement. After the old agreement expires, union workers may continue to work on a day-to-day basis, hoping to get a satisfactory new agreement. Only when these negotiations appear to break down do the workers go on strike.

Strikes do not often take place during the life of a collective bargaining agreement. Strikes happen more often when the terms of an agreement have not been reached. While an agreement is in effect, a strike can arise from many unsettled disputes such as: (1) the meaning (interpretation) of the agreement, (2) a claim by the union that the employer is not following the agreement or labor legislation, or (3) grievances.

In many cases collective bargaining agreements provide for voluntary arbitration of grievances. As explained in Reading 55, strikes sometimes come from jurisdictional disputes, but these generally are covered by a voluntary arbitration agreement.

A union does not usually call a general or prolonged strike except as a final effort after other means of negotiating have failed. Labor uses strikes as a force to balance the labor-management relationship and to bring about a return to collective bargaining in good faith.

How a Strike Is Conducted

Most strikes are organized by a union which is representing workers who are involved in a dispute with one employer, or with a number of employers in a certain area. When the union leaders who are negotiating with management believe that a strike is necessary, they call a meeting of the union members and discuss the situation. Then a vote is taken. If the membership votes to strike, a time and date are set, Fig. 59-2. On that date, all members of that craft union leave their jobs. By striking, they are saying that they will not return to the job until their demands have been met. They are not quitting their jobs but are only stopping work until such time as an agreement is reached.

When one craft stops work, other crafts may not be able to do their own jobs. Then all construction work stops. Also, the union may assign workers to *picket*. To picket means to walk back and forth in front of the site, carrying signs or banners stating that a certain local union is on strike, Fig. 59-3. Workers in other unions may not wish to cross this picket line. If they do not, they remain away from the job, causing construction to stop.

Fig. 59-2. Before taking a strike vote, members of the union discuss the issues.

Impact of a Strike

A strike causes both the contractor and his workers to lose a large amount of money. In construction, the employer receives money only for what he builds. When his employees do not work, nothing is being built, and no money is being received from the owner. Even though the contractor may not be paying his workers, some of his expenses continue. He must go on paying *overhead* (the cost of maintaining his home office and field offices). Also, the cost of equipment he is buying or leasing continues, whether any work is being done or not. Such losses may be especially great in the middle of a project. The contractor then cannot meet his completion date, Fig. 59-4. While most contracts provide for an extension of this finishing date in case of a strike, the contractor gets no additional money to

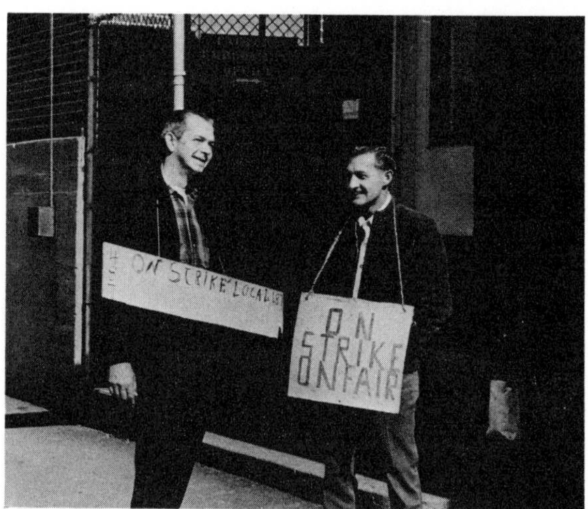

Fig. 59-3. Pickets walk back and forth in front of the site carrying banners stating that the local union is on strike.

cover his extra overhead and equipment costs.

Workers lose money when they strike, because they are not paid when they are not working. Some unions have a "strike fund" which provides for small weekly payments to workers while they are on strike. However, these payments tend to be quite small—only a small fraction of the usual weekly wage. Most workers have to dip into their reserves. Occasionally they seek temporary employment elsewhere, but jobs are usually very scare in the vicinity of a major strike.

Because strikes are a noncooperative means of settling a dispute and because both sides suffer heavy losses during the strike, bad feelings often develop. In many cases these bad feelings are not forgotten for a long time after the end of the strike. Then it is hard for workers and employers to work together as efficiently as they did before the strike.

Sometimes bad feelings develop between the parties in the dispute and the community. If an important industry is affected, then the whole community suffers. There is an immediate economic impact. Many bills go unpaid and the buying of consumer goods (even food) is reduced to bare necessities. In the case of construction, there may be a long delay in the completion of projects (such as housing and roads) that the community badly needs and really wants. Both management and labor may be blamed for such delays, Fig. 59-5.

Because of the effects of a strike on all concerned, neither party looks forward to a strike. When one takes place, pressure is placed on both sides to reach an agreement.

Fig. 59-4. This building will not be completed on time. The production schedule will be set back as a result of the work stoppage. Both labor and management will lose money.

Government Intervention

Because a strike may harm the general public as well as the employers and workers involved, the government sometimes takes action to prevent strikes and to control or end them. It should be stressed that such *government intervention* does not happen often in any industry, and it is extremely rare in the construction industry. Government officials do not like to intervene because they feel that, in our free enterprise system, management and labor should be free to work out their own problems without outside interference. Nevertheless, there are a few occasions when intervention is needed.

The government sets up rules which guide it in making a decision about when to act. The federal government will act under the

Fig. 59-5. If a strike continues for an extended period, it may take some time before the full work force gets back on the job.

following conditions: (1) when the strike causes great inconvenience to the public, (2) when the strike is harmful to the local or national economy, (3) when the strike is a threat to public health or safety, (4) when the strike is harmful to the defense program, and (5) when the strike has a harmful effect on countries outside the United States.

Settlement of Strikes

As a result of the tremendous pressure on both sides to settle the issues involved, most strikes are settled after a few days or weeks. Sometimes they run for months and in a very few instances, for years. Such long periods usually involve great financial losses to contractors and owners. Workers seek other jobs.

Summary

A strike is a work stoppage which takes place when other means of settling disputes between labor and management have failed. Strikes involve financial and other losses to employers, workers, and the general public. Such losses place great pressure on all parties to seek an early settlement of unresolved disputes.

Terms to Know

striking
labor
management
collective bargaining
expires
union
picket
overhead
strike fund
consumer goods
government intervention
intervene

Think About It!

1. Has there been a strike in the construction industry in your locality within the past few months? If so, what brought it about?
2. When a strike occurs, who loses? Why?

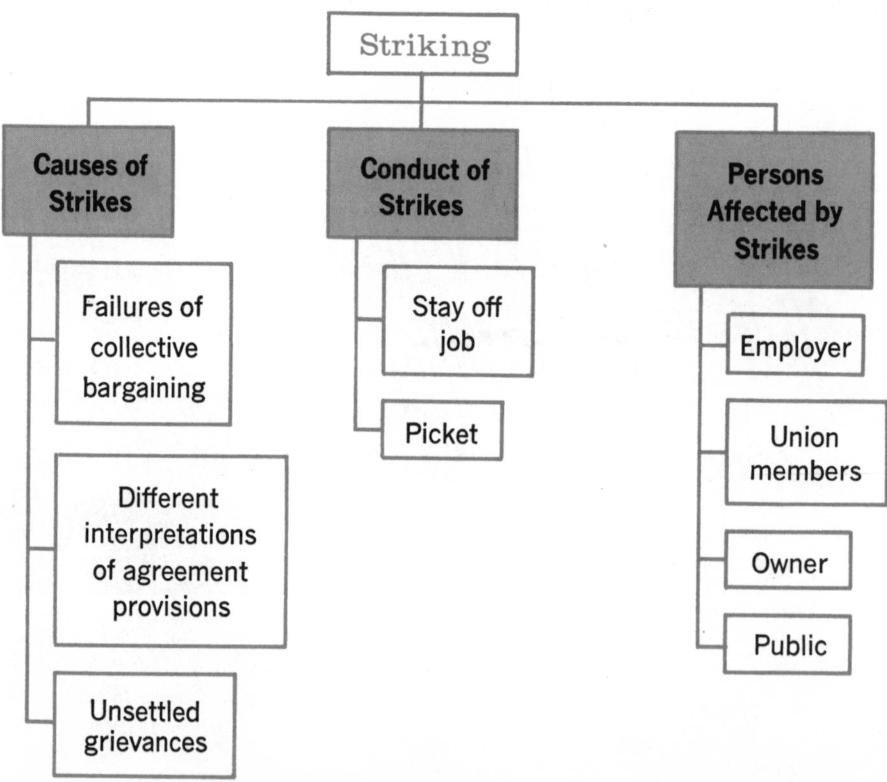

Insulating

This lesson explains insulating. It tells why insulation is needed, who installs it, how it works, what it is, and how it is put into a structure for its best use.

Reasons for Insulating

Insulation is used in a building for many reasons:

1. To restrict or cut down the flow of heat either into or out of a building (this adds to the comfort of the people inside and lowers heating and cooling costs),
2. To retard (slow down) the spread of fire (some insulation will not burn under any conditions, while others burn very slowly when exposed to intense heat),
3. To absorb noise, and
4. To serve as a vapor barrier by preventing the passage of humid air and reducing the *condensation* of water which might discolor wall surfaces or cause structural damage, Fig. 60-1.

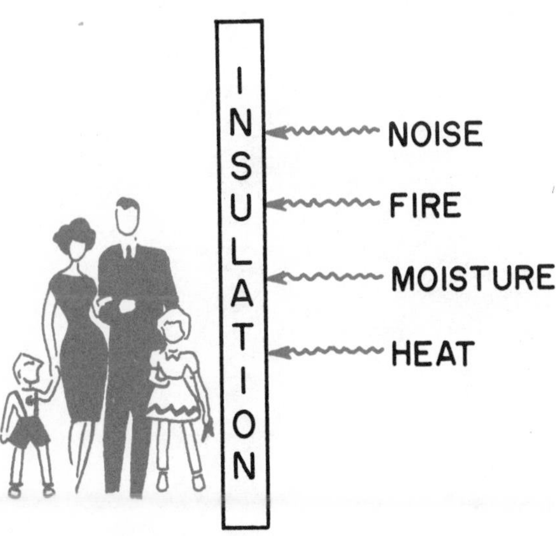

Fig. 60-1. Insulation helps to prevent the passage of heat, fire, moisture, and noise.

Three Kinds of Heat Transfer

Heat can move or be transferred in three ways:

1. By conduction,
2. By convection, and
3. By radiation.

Understanding heat transfer will help you to understand how insulation works to keep a steady temperature inside a structure.

Conduction of Heat

When heat energy travels through a solid, we say that the heat is being *conducted.* This happens when a silver spoon or an iron rod is heated at one end. The opposite end soon becomes warm. The metal did not move. Only the heat energy moved through the metal, Fig. 60-2.

The amount of time it takes heat to travel through a material depends on the insulating quality of the material. Iron, silver, and

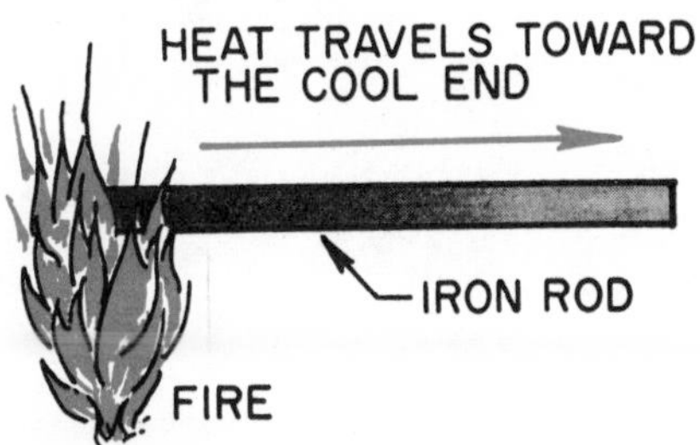

Fig. 60-2. Heat can be transferred by conduction.

some other metals conduct heat very fast. Glass, stone, and clay products conduct heat somewhat more slowly. Heat also moves slowly through many of the so-called "plastic" materials such as melamine and styrene. If you had a tumbler made of aluminum or stainless steel and another tumbler made of melamine plastic, which one would grow hot sooner on the outside if filled with hot water?

One way to slow down heat transfer by conduction is to process a material so that it becomes *porous* or fluffy. For example, glass is changed into an excellent insulator by spinning it into thin fibers and combining the fibers into a fluffy pad or *batt.* A great deal of air is trapped in fiber glass insulation, and heat energy cannot travel by conduction through air, Fig. 60-3.

Convection of Heat

When air is free to move, it carries with it for some distance any heat energy which has been put into it. An air mass pouring down from arctic regions brings very little heat with it. We call it a *cold wind.* Air which is heated in a tropic region and then moves northward we call a *warm breeze* or a *hot wind.* This is the principle which is used in warm air heating systems.

In the warm air heating system, the air is heated and then is moved slowly around the building. Since the heat is *conveyed* (carried) along with the air, the moving air is called a *convection current* and the process is called *heat transfer by convection,* Fig. 60-4.

In a poorly sealed building, the small openings create drafts (movements of air) in and out of the building. In winter, warm air escapes to the outside, and cold outdoor air replaces it. In summer, cooled air in the building escapes and is replaced by unpleasantly warm air. Escaping air makes the people inside uncomfortable and raises heating and cooling costs. Thus heat transfer by convection is part of the problem of maintaining desirable air temperature in a structure.

Radiant Heat Energy

Heat energy can be transferred in another, very different way. This is by radiation, Fig. 60-5. The sun's heat warms the earth after traveling millions of miles, mostly through empty space (vacuum).

Radiant heat energy (*heat rays*) passes through air without being absorbed. When the rays strike the surface of a solid object, several things can happen, depending on the kind of surface they strike. A mirror will reflect most of the heat rays. An object

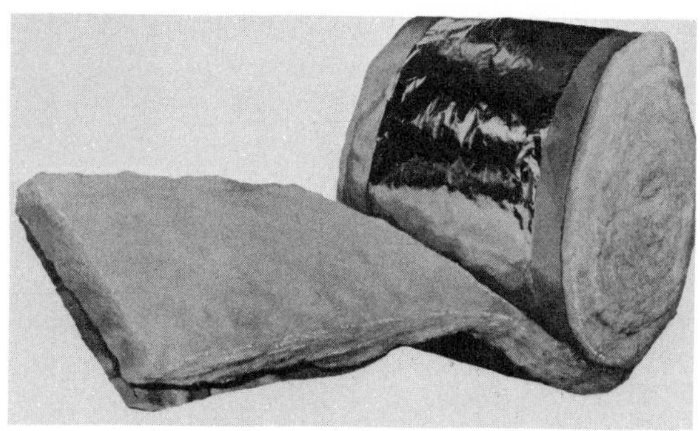

Fig. 60-3. This batt of insulation combines mineral (Glass fiber) material with metallic (aluminum foil) material.

Fig. 60-4. Heat can be transferred by convection.

painted white will reflect too, but not quite as well. Transparent glass will let most of the rays pass right through. (You can feel the sun's warmth through a closed window.) An object painted black will *absorb* a very large part of the radiant energy and will be heated. (A black car parked in the sun will get hot sooner than a white car.) A dull surface will absorb more heat rays than a shiny surface.

Insulating to Control Heat Transfer

In designing a building, the architect must provide for keeping unwanted heat out and for keeping wanted heat in. His knowledge of heat transfer by conduction, by convection, and by radiation helps him in selecting insulating materials.

Metal, once it has absorbed heat, will *conduct* the heat energy rapidly. But a metal surface which is light in color and very shiny will *reflect* heat that reaches it in the form of radiant energy. The rays are "bounced" off before they can be absorbed. Therefore a thin sheet of shiny, lightly colored metal will insulate against radiant heat energy, Fig. 60-6.

Concrete, plaster, and glass will conduct heat, although not as fast as metal. A great deal of heat would leak through the walls of a concrete structure, by conduction, if the walls were not lined with other materials. Heat loss through glass by conduction can be lowered by using two thicknesses of glass with still air trapped between the two thicknesses. Heat loss or gain through glass by radiation is not so easily prevented. This is one reason for using heavy draperies or blinds at large windows.

Excessive loss of heat by *convection* is partly controlled by sealing cracks in exterior walls and roof construction. This is true no matter what construction materials are used. But the materials must be applied by methods which allow for sealing against air drafts.

Who Installs Insulation

The architect decides upon the type of insulation to be used. Insulating characteristics of most materials are well known to him. On major structures, or where new materials or techniques are used, the architect may use the services of a mechanical

Fig. 60-5. Heat can be transferred by radiation.

Fig. 60-6. The shiny metal foil coating on this insulation material will reflect heat which reaches it.

engineer. The engineer can figure out what the heat loss per hour will be through any type of wall, ceiling, floor, or roof. The capacity of the heating or cooling unit must be larger than the heat which will be lost from (or gained by) the building. This means that a heating unit may be smaller if a building is well insulated. Insulation is selected which is in keeping with the design of the building and which, along with the heating and cooling system, is reasonable in cost.

Insulation is most often installed by the general contractor with his own employees, but sometimes it is subcontracted to roofers, masonry subcontractors, or even subcontractors who specialize in insulation.

Craftsmen who install insulation may be carpenters, insulators, masons, sheet metal workers, or roofers. Painters often do caulking work to seal joints.

Insulating Materials

Insulating materials are grouped into (1) mineral products, (2) vegetable products and (3) metallic products.

Mineral insulation is made from sand, glass, mica, asbestos, and certain plastics. It may be in the form of loose fill consisting of small particles. Loose fill is poured (Fig. 60-7), or it is forced into place with air pressure. Some mineral insulation is manufactured as batts (shaped strips wound up into rolls, as in Fig. 60-8). These batts are flexible, so they can be moved around to fit the space in which they are placed. Sometimes, mineral products are pressed into the form of stiff (called *rigid* or *inflexible*) sections or panels. Some common trade names for mineral insulation are Rockwool, Glasswool, and Zonalite.

The vegetable class of insulation includes materials such as cork, wood, and plant stalks. These are generally sold in pressed board or panel form, called *fiberboard* or *insulation board,* Fig. 60-9. The panels may be fastened to studs or rafters. Masonite, Celotex, and Roof Deck are common trade names for these products.

Metallic insulation, such as aluminum, is made to reflect heat by use of a bright shiny surface. Metallic insulation may be applied between the building members or glued to the back of gypsum board. This kind of application is referred to as *foil-*

Fig. 60-7. Loose-fill insulation is poured into the spaces in concrete block.

Fig. 60-8. Standard width batt insulation fits neatly between studs.

backed drywall. Metallic insulation is installed with the shiny surface toward the outside of the building. It reflects radiant heat energy back outdoors so that it will not pass through the insulation to the inside of the building.

Fig. 60-9. This "sound deadening board" is a form of vegetable insulation.

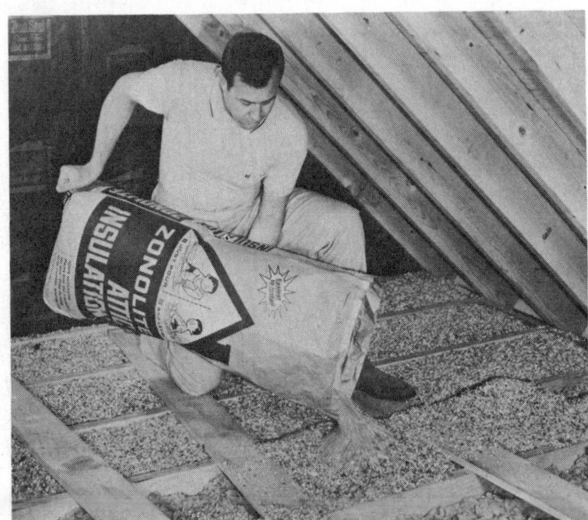

Fig. 60-10. The man installing loose-fill insulation works for the general contractor who is building the structure.

Installing Insulation

Loose-fill insulation can be poured into spaces, Fig. 60-10. Sometimes air pressure is used to blow loose insulation into place.

Batt or blanket insulation is manufactured in standard widths to fit between wall studs. Batt may be glued to a single sheet of multilayer kraft paper (the kind used in grocery bags), or it may be entirely wrapped. A paper flange on the edges of this kind of insulation is used for nailing or stapling it to the sides of the framing members.

Rigid insulation is often nailed in place, Fig. 60-11. This material is sometimes used as sheathing. Its use in roofing was covered in a previous lesson.

Sealing a Building

In addition to being well insulated, a building must be sealed against the passage of water and air through joints, Fig. 60-12. As explained in another reading, roof flashing serves this purpose on top of the building. Joints in the exterior walls, especially around window and door frames, must be completely caulked with a plastic putty. Weather-stripping will help prevent the passage of air around windows and doors. The dead air space between storm and

Fig. 60-11. This foamed plastic insulation has been installed between concrete block and brick veneer layers of this exterior wall.

Fig. 60-12. Here a mixture of concrete and insulation is being placed on a flat surface.

Insulating

Designers
Contractors
Craftsmen

Retarding
- Noise transfer
- Fire
- Passage of moisture
- Heat transfer
  - Conduction
  - Convection
  - Radiation

Materials
- Mineral
- Vegetable
- Metallic
- Loose
- Flexible
- Rigid

Installing
- Blowing
- Pouring
- Fastening

regular windows, or inside windows with two layers of glass, is effective in reducing the transfer of heat and in reducing the condensation of water.

Summary

Insulation is used for many reasons:

1. To restrict heat flow,
2. To slow down the spread of fire,
3. To serve as a deadening agent against noise,
4. To give comfort to the occupants,
5. To reduce heating and cooling costs, and
6. To stop water condensation.

Vegetable, mineral, and metallic insulation are used to control the gain and loss of heat. Insulating material comes as loose fill, flexible batts, and rigid panels. The proper sealing of cracks and openings helps to make insulation more effective.

Terms to Know

insulating
heat transfer
  a. conduction
  b. convection
  c. radiation
condensation
porous
batt
heat rays
reflect
transparent
absorb
capacity
insulating materials
  a. mineral
  b. vegetable
  c. metallic
flange
inflexible
sealed
weather stripping

Think About It!

1. If your home caught on fire, would it be better to have or not to have insulation in the walls and ceilings? Why?
2. Do you know if there is any insulating material in the outside walls and the ceilings of your home? If you do not know, how could you find out?

Applying Wall Materials

This reading concerns the interior wall surfaces of a building. Interior walls are the vertical surfaces enclosing all the rooms and hallways. These include the inside surfaces of the exterior walls and the surfaces of interior partitions which divide the space in the building.

In general, the interior walls are completed after the roof is on, after the exterior walls (including insulation) are completed, and after ceilings are installed.

Wall Materials

Many types of materials are used for interior walls, Fig. 61-1. Among these are wood and wood products, fabrics, metal, glass, plastic, gypsum board, plaster over lath, masonry, and tile. Masonry units may be brick, clay tile, concrete block, or a facing stone such as marble. Tile may be ceramic, rubber, enameled steel, aluminum, glass, or plastic.

Fig. 61-1. Many types of materials are used for walls. These walls are made of glass.

Who Installs Interior Walls

The architect decides how a building will be divided. He shows the layout on the floor plan. He also chooses the materials to be used and the design of interior walls. Sometimes an interior designer helps the architect to select wall materials.

The general contractor may install interior walls with his own employees. Or he may subcontract this work, especially when a very specialized trade such as tile setting is involved. Sometimes the manufacturer of movable partitions also installs them.

Many different craftsmen can apply interior wall materials. Among these are carpenters, plasterers, insulators, tile setters, masons, ironworkers, laborers, glaziers, and painters. Craftsmanship is extremely important, not only for the usual reasons (utility and durability) but also because the interior wall surfaces are those we see most inside a finished building.

Types of Partitions

Partitions may be classed as (1) fixed, (2) movable, or (3) room dividers. *Fixed partitions* are the most common type. These can usually be torn out easily (unless they form a load bearing wall), but they are not so easy to put back in elsewhere. See Fig. 61-2.

Some fixed partitions, principally in wood frame construction, carry part of the load of the floor or roof above. These are called *load bearing partitions.* In buildings with concrete and steel framework, load bearing partitions are seldom used at the present time, although sometimes the interior walls of barracks and dormitories carry loads above.

Some *movable partitions* are designed so that the people in a building can move them easily. They are often used in schools, churches, restaurants, and hotels to change room sizes rapidly. Some are sets of hinged, rigid panels. Others are flexible panels that hang from a ceiling track and fold like an accordion.

Other movable partitions must be adjusted by craftsmen, Fig. 61-3. These are panels constructed of metal or of wood or steel studs faced with gypsum board or wood. Often they are installed in runners or tracks which can be unscrewed from the floor and ceiling, making the panels easy to remove and put up in a new location.

Room dividers are partitions which go only part way up from the floor to the ceiling. They may be screens, grilles, planters, or counters. Room dividers may be either fixed or movable, Fig. 61-4.

Fig. 61-2. This is a fixed partition. It carries the load of the building upon it and cannot be moved.

Framing Partitions

A common form of partition is framed with wood studs, plates, and sills, and covered with lath and plaster, drywall, or paneling. In commercial buildings, steel studs are often substituted, Fig. 61-5. A

Fig. 61-3. Although this partition is movable, it must be moved by a craftsman.

Fig. 61-4. These shower stall partitions do not reach the ceiling and are thus classified as room dividers.

partition wall can also be solid, freestanding masonry, either with or without additional wall surfacing such as drywall.

In wood frame buildings, the framework for the partitions is usually erected along with that for the exterior walls. In concrete or steel frame buildings, interior partitions generally are not installed until completion of the roof and exterior walls. On high rise structures, they are sometimes installed before the roof is finished.

Applying Wall Materials

In drywall construction, large semirigid sheets of gypsum board are attached to the structural members. The gypsum board (also called *plasterboard*) has a hardened plaster core or center layer covered with strong paper, fiberboard, or felt. It comes in standard 4′ by 8′ and 4′ by 10′ sizes.

Drywall sheets are attached with self-drilling and self-tapping screws to metal frames, Fig. 61-6. They are nailed to wooden frames. Where the panels are installed on the face of masonry walls, 1″ by 2″ wooden furring strips first are nailed to the masonry. Then the gypsum board panels are nailed to these furring strips.

Nails for use with drywall materials have a large, flat head. Panels may be installed with the 4′ dimension running vertically or horizontally. Pieces of panels are cut to fit the surface they are used to cover. Openings are cut in the panels for doors and windows.

Joints are filled with a plasterlike compound. Then tape is pressed into the filler,

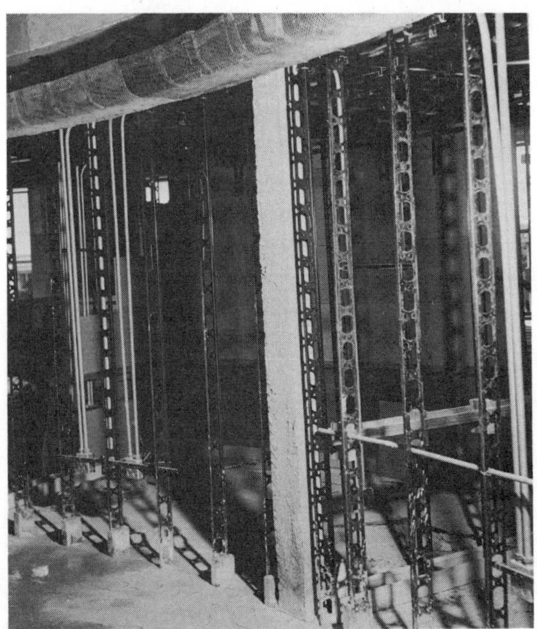

Fig. 61-5. Surfacing work has just started on these steel studs. Metal lath has been installed over part of the ceiling. Rock lath has been clipped to the studs in the background.

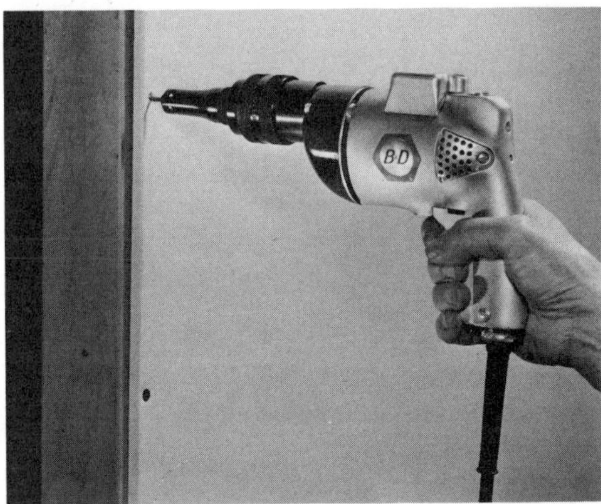

Fig. 61-6. This automatic, drywall screwdriver is used to fasten wallboard to either metal or wood studs.

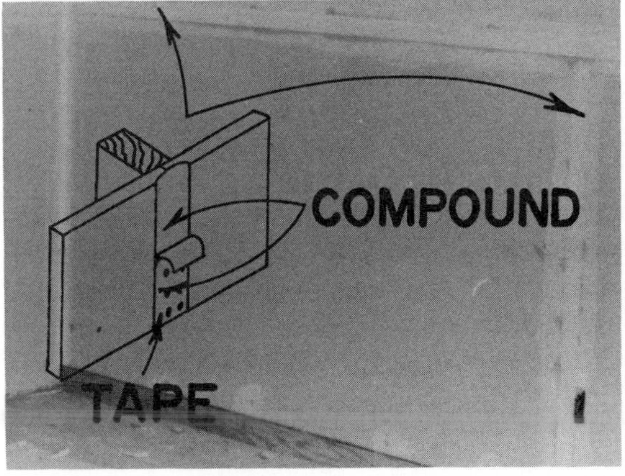

Fig. 61-7. Drywall joints are filled with compound and taped to provide a smooth finish.

Fig. 61-7. After this dries, one or two more coats of filler are added on top of the tape. The whole joint is then sandpapered to make it *flush* (even) with the surface of the gypsum board. When drywall is installed by a skilled craftsman, it is impossible to tell the location of the joints after painting.

In place of drywall, panels of natural or *simulated* wood are often used as wall coverings, Fig. 61-8. These come in many different patterns and colors. Sometimes the panels are given a vinyl (plastic) coating. They may be nailed to wooden framing or to furring strips. Sometimes the panels are attached by adhesives instead of nails.

When walls are to be plastered, metal or rock lath is applied first. The lath is installed by nailing it to wood or steel studs or furring strips. Then plaster is troweled or sprayed on the lath in several coats. The finish coat may be smooth or textured, Fig. 61-9.

Sometimes the interior surfaces of masonry walls are left without any finish. This is nearly always the case where glass block is used. Masonry walls in most warehouses and some factory buildings are left unfinished. Many masonry walls are simply painted on their interior surfaces.

Tile is often applied to walls of corridors, kitchens, and washrooms. Tile may be ceramic, plastic, rubber, glass or metal. Square tiles come in various sizes from one inch square up to six inches square. Other tiles are rectangular, round, or oval. Colors or shapes may be combined in many patterns, Fig. 61-10.

When a wall is to be tiled, a bed of tile mortar or adhesive is applied over a flat subsurface. Tiles are set (placed) in this

Fig. 61-9. This man is mixing plaster. He works for the subcontractor who has contracted to apply plaster to the wall surfaces.

Fig. 61-8. Panels of simulated wood are sometimes used for wall surfaces.

Fig. 61-10. The design formed by the different colored tiles is called a mosaic.

bed of mortar or adhesive. Large tiles are set one at a time. Small tiles are set in sheets, stuck onto a flexible backing material. For some kinds of tile, the joints between tiles are filled with *grout* (a mixture of white tile cement, fine sand, and water). Other tiles fit together so tightly that there is no joint space to fill.

Summary

Interior walls consist of the inside surfaces of exterior walls and of partitions. Movable or fixed partitions break up the inside of a building into smaller spaces. Many different materials are used for interior walls. The various materials require many different methods of application. Because interior wall surfaces are exposed to view, they should be designed for attractiveness and should be installed with special care.

Terms to Know

interior
vertical
plaster
plasterer
partition
  a. fixed
  b. movable
  c. room divider
plasterboard
flush
simulated wood
vinyl coating
adhesive
furring strip
tile

Think About It!

1. What kinds of wall materials have been used to cover the interior walls in your bedroom? Your living room? Your bathroom? Are they the same or different? Why?
2. Is there a difference between the interior walls of your school classrooms and those at home? If so, what is the major difference?

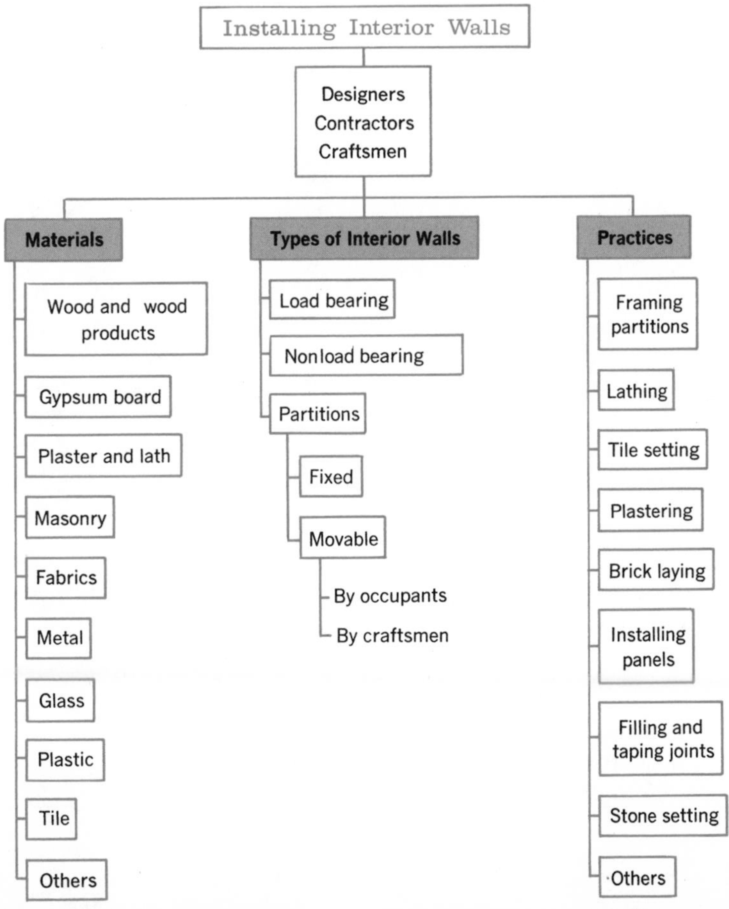

READING 62

Applying Ceiling Materials

This lesson is about ceilings, which are, the top surfaces of rooms. Ceilings limit the height of an enclosed space. They may also serve to:

1. Hide overhead structural framing and utilities,
2. Control temperature,
3. Control sound,
4. Provide fire protection, and
5. Add beauty.

The type of ceiling used depends on where it is to be installed and the wishes of the owner and/or the architect.

Selecting the Ceiling

Lath and plaster, drywall, and tile all have advantages and disadvantages as ceiling materials. A ceiling of lath and plaster has better fire resistance than drywall, absorbs sound better, and permits several different kinds of finish texture, Fig. 62-1. A lath and plaster ceiling is usually more expensive than drywall and must be completely dry before paint can be applied.

Lath and plaster ceiling is widely used in commercial construction, while drywall, being cheaper and not requiring a drying out period, is more common in residential work. Tiles are used in special cases if lowering the ceilings, sound deadening, or the appearance of tile is important.

Who Installs Ceilings

Ceiling materials are generally specified by the architect. He may consult with engineers on the structural framework design.

Usually the general contractor installs ceilings with his own employees, but sometimes the ceilings are subcontracted to a specialist, usually where *acoustical* (sound absorbing) ceilings are specified. Craftsmen who work on ceilings include carpenters, plasterers, iron-workers, insulators, painters, and ceiling tile workers.

Installing Ceilings on Wood Frame Construction

A common type of overhead construction is flooring supported by wooden joists. With

Fig. 62-1. Plastering on lath is the oldest and most common technique of installing ceilings.

this type of framing, ceilings may be of three types: lath and plaster, drywall, and tile.

To install a *lath and plaster ceiling*, metal lath is nailed to the underneath parts of the joists. (In older construction, wooden lath was used instead of metal.) Then plasterers, using trowels, apply several layers or coats of plaster over the lath. The final coat is put on to give a smooth or rough finish, as desired. Sometimes patterns are made in the finish.

In *drywall* construction, sheets of gypsum board are nailed to the structural members. Application is very much like the method for sidewall installation of a drywall system.

Standard *ceiling tiles* are 9″ by 9″ or 12″ by 12″ in size. They may be acoustical (sound absorbing) or nonacoustical. There are many types of ceiling tiles. Choice of tile is based partly on the finish desired. Tile materials are gypsum, vegetable and mineral fibers, and cork.

Ceiling tiles can be attached with *mastic* (an adhesive) to a smooth subsurface such as drywall. Usually narrow boards called *furring strips* are nailed across the bottoms of the overhead joists (running at right angles to the joists) and the tiles are stapled or clipped to the furring strips, Fig. 62-2.

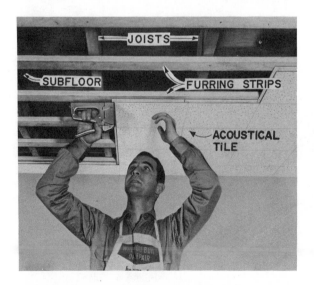

Fig. 62-2. This man is stapling acoustical tile to furring strips.

The bottom of a plank roof deck may form the interior ceiling of a structure. This is quite common in churches, auditoriums, and gymnasiums. It is sometimes used even in homes. The exposed beams or rafters often are designed to add to the beauty of the ceilings. Technically, because everything in these ceilings is part of the structural framework, these are not ceilings. The roofing system is dual-purpose, Fig. 62-3. It forms a roof and ceiling all at once.

Installing Ceilings Below Steel or Concrete Flooring

When the overhead flooring is steel or slab concrete, ceilings may be of three types:

1. The exposed underside of the floor above may serve as the ceiling.
2. Tile or other materials may be applied directly to the underside of the floor.
3. A suspended ceiling may be constructed.

In some warehouses and factory buildings, churches, and auditoriums, the underside of a steel or concrete floor is the ceiling for the room below, Fig. 62-4. In reality, there is no separate ceiling. Sometimes the underside of the floor is untreated. Sometimes it

Fig. 62-3. The roofing system is dual-purpose when it forms the roof and the ceiling with the same materials.

is painted or a layer of soundproofing material is sprayed on the surface.

Tile or plaster ceilings may be applied directly to the underside of the floor above. Tile (acoustical or nonacoustical) is cemented to the underside of the floor. This system is easy to use if the underside of the flooring is flat, as in flat slab concrete construction. Another method is to attach metal lath to the bottom of the floor above and cover it with plaster.

Fig. 62-4. The ceiling of this library is the underside of the concrete roof above.

Fig. 62-5. Suspended ceilings, either partial or complete, commonly are used in steel framed buildings.

If the floor above serves as a ceiling, or has ceiling materials attached directly to it, pipes, ductwork, and wiring may be exposed. These utility lines are ugly and many owners want them covered.

Also, it may be desirable to lower the ceiling height to reduce the space which must be heated and cooled. To meet these needs, *suspended or false* ceilings are installed, Figs. 62-5 and 62-6. Wire hangers are attached to the overhead construction, and a grid of inverted-T supports is fastened to the hangers. After the grid of supporting runners and cross ties is hung, the lengths of the hangers are adjusted by turn buckles or similar means until the grid is level. Then ceiling panels of acoustic material are placed into the grid openings.

Often *translucent* glass or plastic panels are spaced throughout a suspended ceiling in a suitable pattern. Light fixtures may be installed above these panels to provide an attractive system of concealed lighting, Fig. 62-7. In another type of suspended ceiling, the grid of runners and cross ties supports metal lath over which plaster is applied.

Fig. 62-6. This worker is installing a "false" or suspended ceiling which is several feet below the original ceiling.

Fig. 62-7. The entire ceiling in this office building is made up of translucent panels which are illuminated by concealed lights.

Summary

Ceilings limit the height of an enclosed space. They may also serve to: (1) conceal overhead framing and utility systems, (2) control temperature, (3) control sound, and (4) add beauty. Many kinds of craftsmen apply ceiling materials, and the materials range from marble slabs to acoustical tiles.

Terms to Know

advantages
disadvantages
lath
plaster
acoustical tile
consult
mastic
furring strips
suspended or false ceiling
drywall
translucent panels

Think About It!

1. Why are ceilings installed in buildings?
2. Can you name a room or a building where the ceiling is part of the roofing system?

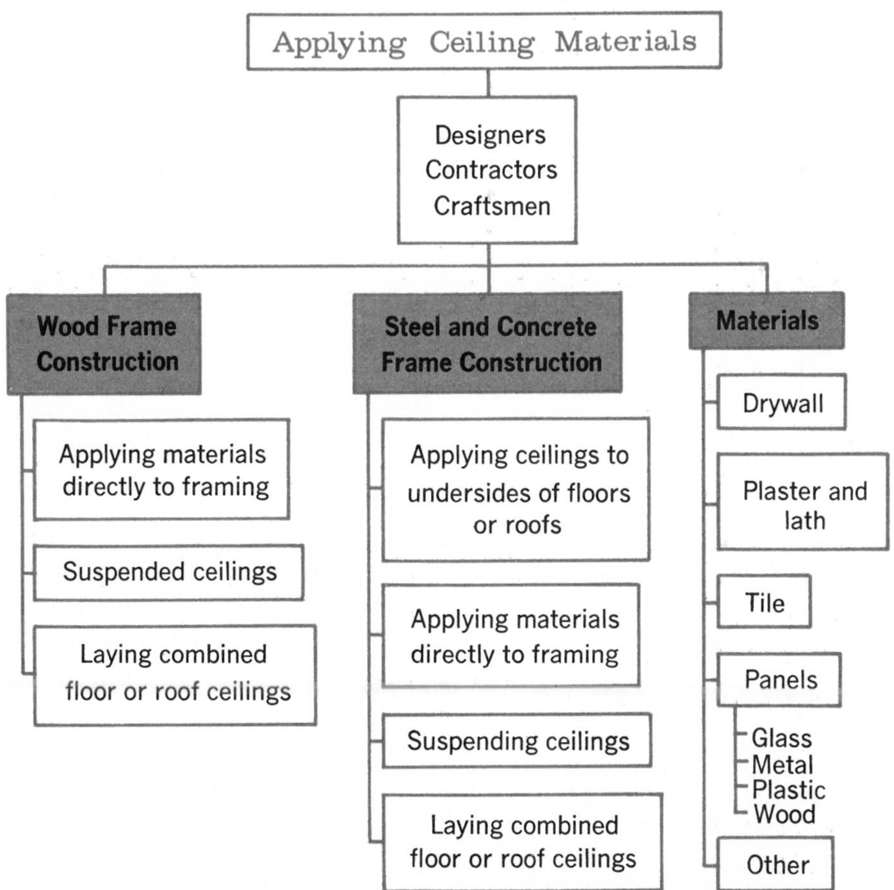

Laying Floors

This reading describes how the lower surface of a room is covered with flooring. Flooring materials can be divided into seven groups:

1. Concrete,
2. Terrazzo (a mixture of cement, sand, and stone chips),
3. Ceramic tile and stone,
4. Wood,
5. Metal,
6. Resilient (those which "give" a little when you walk on them), and
7. Carpeting.

In most floors, the "finish" layer or exposed material is installed on top of a subfloor, Fig. 63-1.

Who Installs Floors

The architect decides on the flooring material and design after considering how the floor will be used. He is concerned with both the *subfloor* and the *finished floor*. For instance, if heavy machines are to be stored or operated, he will consider the *loads* (the weight of the machinery). The architect may work with a structural engineer who is trained to provide for such loads. They work together in designing the floor system and the framework of a building.

The architect also considers foot traffic because some floor coverings wear out quickly in an area where many people walk. Another concern might be soiling and staining. For example, where machines require oiling, some oil may run or spill onto the floor. Ease and economy of cleaning, beauty, and the desires of the owner must all be considered. An interior designer may help the architect in selecting floor materials to meet all the requirements of a particular structure.

The general contractor may either install all of the flooring with his own employees, or he may subcontract all of it to a specialist. However, most often the general contractor installs the subfloor and subcontracts the finish floor to a flooring subcontractor. The subfloor is a part of the framework of the structure. Sometimes there is an *intermediate layer* between the subfloor and the finished floor surface. The intermediate layer (called *underlayment*) is usually laid by the flooring subcontractor's craftsmen.

A great many types of craftsmen are employed in laying finished floors: cement finishers, carpenters, terrazzo workers, tile setters, ironworkers, carpet layers, painters, and specialists who do one type of work (such as laying vinyl tile). Special tools and

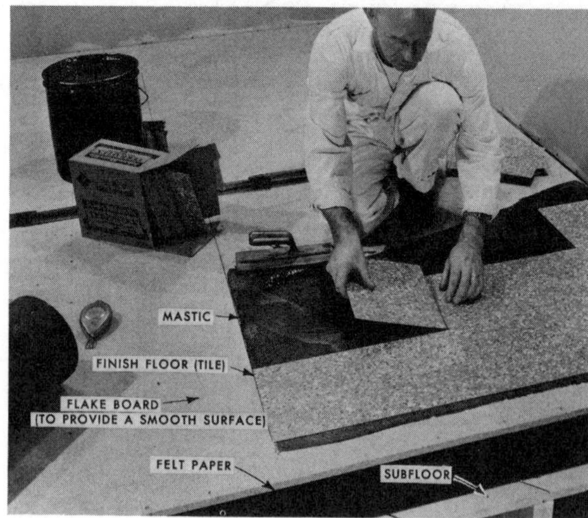

Fig. 63-1. Some floors are made up of several layers.

a high degree of skill are needed for installing floor coverings.

Concrete Floors

Concrete floors have either a separate topping or a *monolithic topping.* (Monolithic means *one piece of stone.*) A monolithic topping is constructed by spreading a mixture of sand and cement on top of a concrete slab *before* the slab hardens or "sets up." A separate topping is another layer of concrete poured on top of a concrete slab *after* it has hardened, Fig. 63-2.

Concrete floors are finished first with a straightedge (a board moved back and forth to make the concrete level). Then a *wood float* is used to bring water and cement to the surface. This gives a rather rough finish which is often used where a nonskid surface is needed.

To get a smoother finish, a *steel trowel* is used. On larger areas, the power float and the power trowel replace the wood float and the steel trowel which are hand tools, Fig. 63-3. Often a troweled finish is painted.

Sometimes the top surface of the concrete is brushed with a stiff broom to give a rough or nonskid finish. You may see this finish on a concrete road or sidewalk.

Fig. 63-2. One kind of flooring material is concrete. Here a concrete slab floor is being constructed.

Terrazzo Floors

A *terrazzo floor* is very much like a concrete floor with a separate topping, except that a large quantity of stone chips are embedded in the topping and the surface is ground to a high polish, Fig. 63-4. Terrazzo can be laid over existing concrete or over a wood subfloor. A bed of sand and ordinary cement mortar is applied about 1¼″ thick. The topping layer is prepared with white or colored cement and chips of marble, granite, or plastic ranging in size from a grain of sugar to a dime. The topping layer is ½″ to ¾″ thick. After the topping sets up, it is polished by grinding (*honing*) with a power hone.

Often brass or aluminum strips are placed in terrazzo to prevent cracking from temperature changes. Terrazzo will take heavy foot traffic with little wear and is quite popular in hallways of large buildings. Because it is easy to maintain, it is being used more and more, even in homes.

Fig. 63-3. Here a power trowel is used to smooth the concrete surface.

Ceramic Tile and Stone Floors

Ceramic tile comes in many standard sizes, ranging up to 12″ by 12″ in several standard shapes. Glazed tile is used in bathrooms for sanitary reasons. The surface glaze seals the tile against water, Fig. 63-5. Unglazed tile has many applications where a waterproof surface is not a requirement.

Stone for flooring is often of random (irregular) size and shape, although the thickness is usually ½″ to 1″. Some floors are laid with square or oblong stones in a definite pattern. Slate and marble are commonly used.

Both tile and stone are set in a bed of mortar, laid over the subfloor. The joints are filled with mortar. Ceramic tile and stone are often used for artistic reasons (to make a beautiful floor). However, ceramic tile is also used in commercial or industrial construction because of its superior wearing qualities, ease of cleaning, and resistance to oil spilled on the floor.

Fig. 63-4. A terrazzo floor is good looking and very durable. It is made up of several layers of material.

Fig. 63-5. Ceramic tile can be cemented and grouted to form a waterproof surface.

Wood Floors

There are three common types of wood floor:

1. Wood block,
2. Random length tongue-and-groove, and
3. Parquet flooring.

Wood blocks are about the size of bricks. They are often used in factories because they absorb water and oil, because they are poor conductors of electricity, and because they are easy to patch if damaged. The block is usually set in an asphalt mastic which also forms the joints, Fig. 63-6.

Random length tongue-and-groove flooring is generally of hardwood (oak or maple),

Fig. 63-6. Mastic is being spread with a toothed trowel on insulation board in preparation for laying hardwood block flooring.

but sometimes softwood such as pine is used. It is laid over a subfloor of plywood or softwood boards. Subflooring is used, whether the floor is laid over joists or over a concrete slab. Most of this kind of finish flooring comes $2\frac{1}{4}''$ wide and in random (assorted) lengths. The floor is sanded after it is laid. Some protective finish is applied after the sanding.

Hardwood tiles (*parquet flooring*) are manufactured from short lengths of wood. They are either nailed or cemented to the subfloor, often in elaborate patterns. These tiles commonly have tongue-and-groove edges.

Metal Flooring

The use of metal flooring is largely restricted to factories, industrial plants, fire escapes, and stair treads, Fig. 63-7. It is used because of its strength and fire-resistant qualities. Steel is the most commonly used material, although aluminum is sometimes used. Metal flooring may be solid with raised ridges to make it less slippery. Often it is in the form of an open grid or grating.

Resilient Flooring

Resilient flooring is elastic like a rubber ball. When your shoe strikes it, it "gives" a little bit, but when the shoe is removed, it resumes its original shape. This makes it more comfortable to walk on than a hard floor like concrete.

Resilient flooring for permanent installation is sold in two forms: rolls and tiles, Fig. 63-8. Several materials are suitable. *Vinyl plastic,* both alone and in combination with asbestos fibers, is widely used for kitchens and bathrooms. Asphalt, cork, silicones, melamine, and rubber also are among the ingredients of various resilient flooring products.

For many years flooring cut from rolls of *linoleum* was the only high quality resilient flooring sold that was entirely suitable for kitchens, bathrooms, or other areas where liquids spill onto the floor. Linoleum is a mixture of ground cork and linseed oil bonded to a canvas or burlap backing. It resists stains, is easy to clean, and lasts a long time. It has been manufactured in a great variety of colors and patterns. Similar flooring made from quite different materials is often called "linoleum", especially in the roll form.

Fig. 63-7. The use of metal flooring usually is restricted to industrial plants and fire escapes.

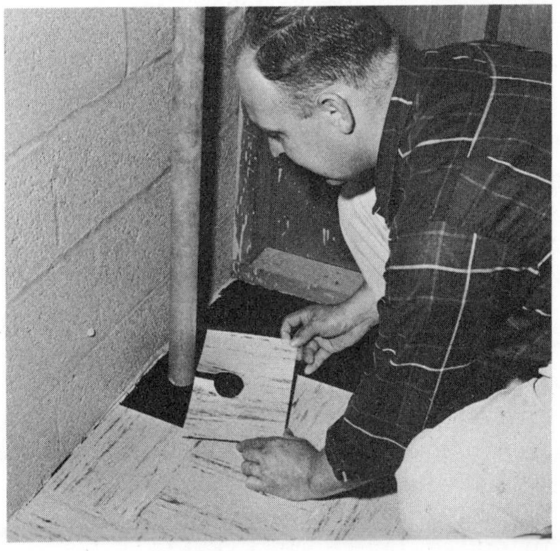

Fig. 63-8. Resilient flooring often comes in the form of tiles. This type of flooring also is available in rolls.

Roll flooring comes in a variety of widths up to 12′. It is typically 1/8″ to 1/4″ thick. When it is carefully installed, joints are almost invisible and any pattern appears to be continuous.

Tiles are usually square and come in 6″, 9″, and 12″ squares. Tiles of two or three blending colors are often selected for use together.

Flooring of vinyl, or vinyl combined with asbestos fibers, comes in roll and tile forms. It is flexible, strong, and very resistant to grease and other stains.

Asphalt flooring is a combination of asbestos fibers and certain petroleum products. Asphalt tile is somewhat cheaper than vinyl tile, but not so resistant to grease. Some roll flooring is made of asphalt-saturated felt, bonded to a thin surface layer of vinyl.

Rubber and cork flooring are somewhat more resilient (springier) than other types and also absorb noise more effectively. Rubber is used for tiles, stair treads, hall runners, and for heavy mats in areas where people stand at their work.

Most kinds of resilient flooring can be laid over either concrete or wood, but the subfloor surface must be smooth. Rough floorboards or concrete often are covered with plywood to provide a smooth surface. For some installations, a layer of felt paper is used under the resilient flooring. Tiles are usually laid with a mastic or adhesive. Mastic is used also for installing most roll flooring.

In laying a tile floor, the craftsman usually starts at the center of the room and works toward the walls, Fig. 63-9. Along each wall the tiles must be cut to fit such things as door openings, registers, and exposed pipes. Roll flooring also must be cut to fit around all the walls. Special skills are involved, and the craftsmen use specialized tools for cutting and fitting.

Some resilient flooring materials can be used above, on, or below grade. Some are not suitable for below grade (basement) installation. Cost, beauty, durability, ease of cleaning, and resistance to spilled liquids all must be considered in selecting resilient floors.

Carpeting

Carpeting is made from natural fibers (mostly cotton and wool) and from several man-made materials including acrylic, nylon, and rayon. It comes in rolls of many standard widths up to 18′. Carpeting is installed over a padding made of fiber, animal hair, or rubber. It comes in hundreds of styles, colors, weaves, and textures, Fig. 63-10.

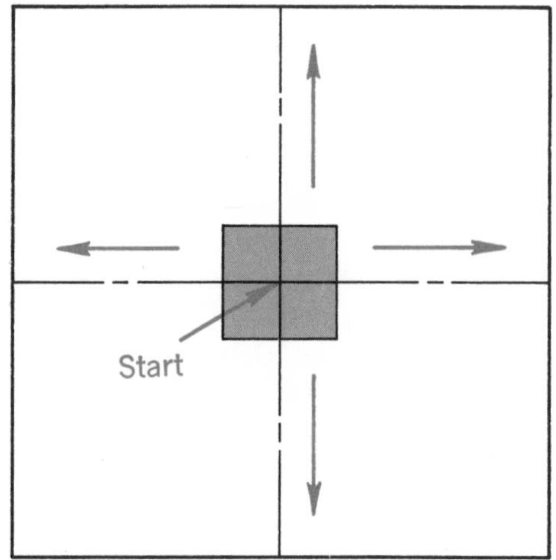

Fig. 63-9. Tiles are usually laid from the center toward the outside of the room.

Fig. 63-10. Carpeting provides a luxurious floor covering.

Carpeting was once restricted to those areas of homes where water and other liquids were not likely to be spilled. Now, however, stain-resistant carpeting is available for use in bathrooms and kitchens and even outdoors.

Carpet padding may be attached with an adhesive to the concrete or wood subfloor. It also may be tacked in place by staples or carpet tacks. Then the carpet is stretched on top of the padding and held in place by fasteners (called *tackless strips*) around the edges.

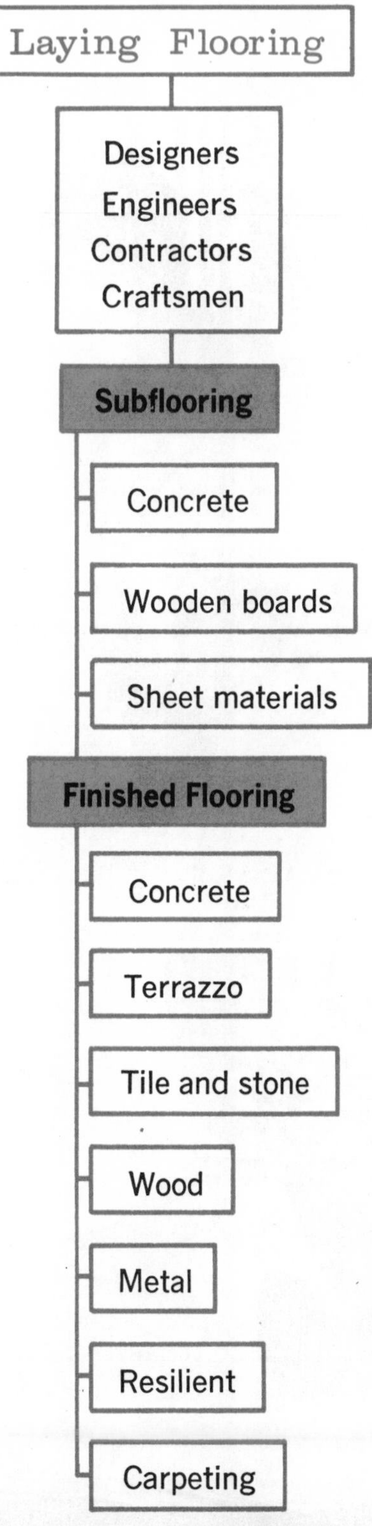

Summary

Floor coverings may be concrete, terrazzo, tile or stone, wood, metal, resilient flooring, or carpeting. Materials for floors are selected to fit the activities which will be carried out. Floor coverings usually are installed over a concrete or wood subfloor. A great deal of skill and care are required in installing floor coverings.

Terms to Know

subfloor
finished floor
terrazzo
ceramic tile
resilient flooring
monolithic
straightedge
wood float
steel trowel
honing
random
sanded
linoleum
durability
resistant
tackless strips

Think About It!

1. What material is used to cover the floor in your industrial arts laboratory? Is it the same or different than the flooring material in rooms in your home? If different, why?
2. In your local telephone directory, check to see how many companies specialize in applying flooring materials.

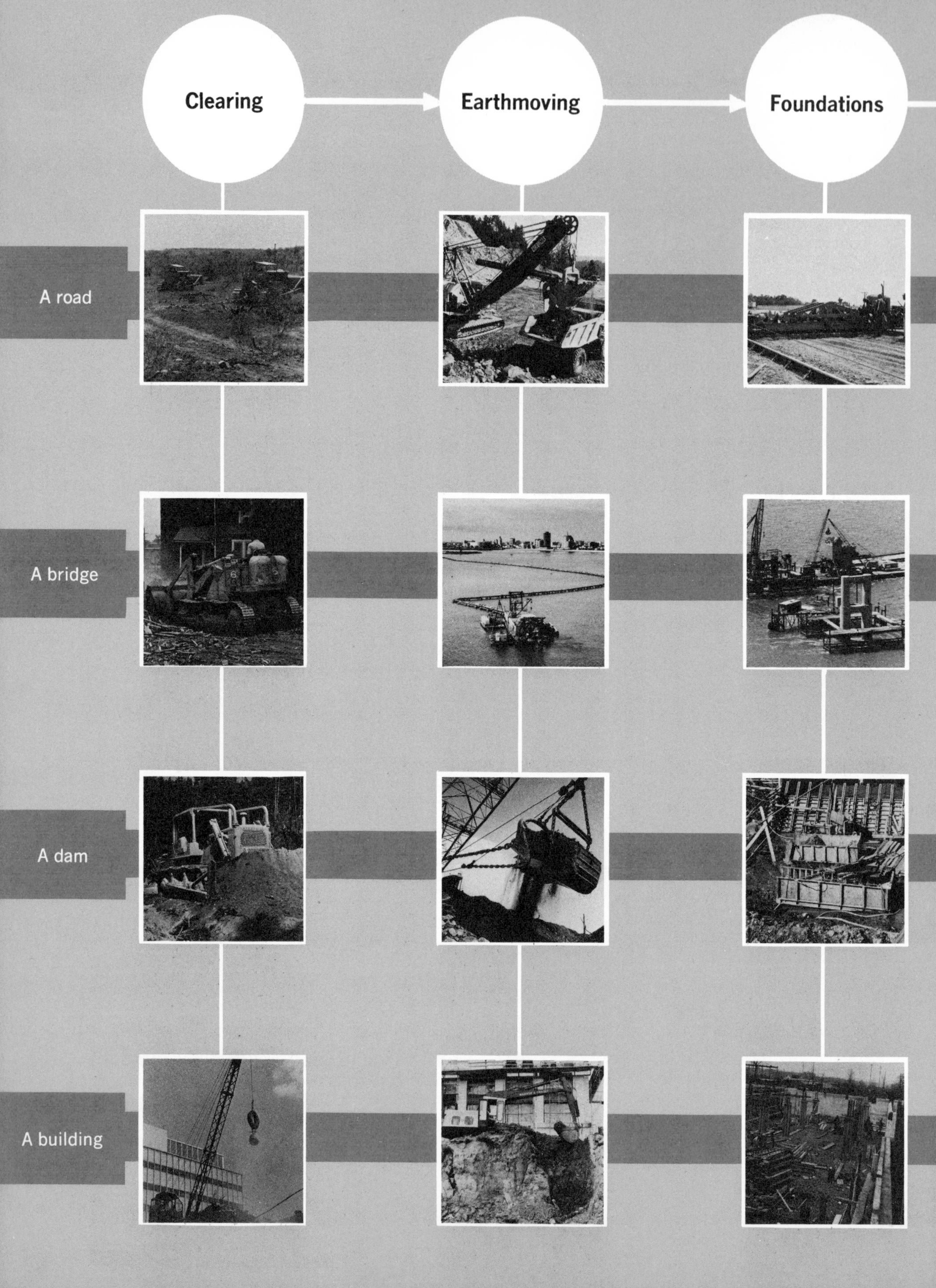
Clearing
Earthmoving
Foundations
A road
A bridge
A dam
A building

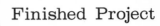

Superstructures → Utilities → Finished Project

READING 64

Finishing the Project

So far we have completed the basic construction work. In the case of a building, this might mean that the foundations and frameworks are complete, that the roof is on, that the exterior and interior walls are in place, and that ceilings and floors have been installed. This reading describes the steps taken to finish the project (those things which need to be done so that the owner may occupy or use the structure).

Finish work can be divided into four parts:

1. Trimming,
2. Painting and decorating,
3. Installing accessories, and
4. Cleaning up.

Trimming includes the coverings around window and door openings, cabinet work, and moldings. Where wood is used, the general term often applied is *millwork,* because most trim has been made at a factory or mill. Trimming or finish carpentry is covered in more detail later in this reading.

Painting and decorating are done to provide a protective covering and to present a pleasing appearance, Fig. 64-1. This work is presented in detail in the next reading.

Installing accessories includes hanging and connecting plumbing and electrical fixtures, hardware, and ornamental ironwork, Fig. 64-2. This also is covered in a later reading.

Cleanup relates to the final clearing away of the dirt and *debris* resulting from construction so that the structure may be occupied or used. There is no separate reading

Fig. 64-1. Finish work includes painting. Here a coating is being applied to a masonry floor.

Fig. 64-2. Electrical fixtures in this hydroelectric power plant control room are being installed by electricians.

on cleanup. It generally consists of gathering, burning, loading, washing, polishing, and other necessary but unskilled work.

Structures other than buildings also require finishing operations. For instance, on a stretch of highway, (1) a guard rail and signs must be installed, (2) bridges must be painted, (3) electric lighting fixtures must be installed and hooked up, and (4) the pavement must be painted with stripes, Fig. 64-3.

All of the above completion activities relate to the structure, Fig. 64-4. Completion of the site, which is usually the last operation in constructing a project, also is covered in detail in a later reading.

When the Finish Work is Done

The order in which the finish work is done depends upon (1) the type of building, (2) the finishes chosen, (3) the availability of subcontractors and craftsmen at a particular time, and (4) how the general contractor wishes to schedule his work. Thus the *sequence* (order) of operations is not a set pattern. Also, several operations may be going on at once. On a typical wood frame residence, the contractor's superintendent may decide to "trim out" (apply trimming and do cabinet work) first, then to paint the walls and ceilings, then to hang and connect the fixtures, then to sand and finish the floors, and finally to clean up the house so that it is ready for occupancy. On a high rise building, the finish work is usually done one floor at a time.

Who Does the Finish Work

The architect indicates on the plans and specifications the type of finish work desired. He may be helped by an interior designer. On matters of color and patterns, the owner usually will be consulted.

While a contractor may do finish work himself, nearly all of it (except the cleanup) is usually subcontracted. In this connection, let us see for a moment how a subcontractor operates by considering a washbasin. Before the wall materials are installed, the plumbing subcontractor "roughs

Fig. 64-3. Finishing this highway project includes painting lines on the pavement, erecting signs, and installing reflective markers.

Fig. 64-4. Some finish work is much more complex and involved than others. How many kinds of finish work can you find in this picture?

in" or installs the plumbing system right up to where the washbasin goes. This means that he brings in the hot and cold water lines and the drain pipe. He also installs the hangers which will support the fixture. Then the plumbing subcontractor leaves the job. He will work elsewhere while the exterior and interior walls, floors, and ceilings are being put in, the trim is installed, and painting is done. Then the plumber comes back to the job to hang and connect the washbasin.

Various tradesmen do the finish work. Some of them, like painters, may be coming for the first time. Others, such as carpenters, plumbers, electricians, and sheet metal workers, may be returning to the site to do the finish work several days or weeks after "roughing in." Other craftsmen who may be involved are ironworkers, welders, masons, tile and terrazzo workers, paperhangers, and plasterers. Finish work requires a high degree of care and skill. The craftsmanship of the finisher is what is seen most in the structure.

Trimming

Trimming is finish carpentry done to (1) enclose window and door frames, (2) cover joints between walls and floors or ceilings, and (3) build stairs and install cabinetwork (built-in shelves, cabinets, and counters).

This reading will concern wood trim, but trim is often made of many other materials, principally metals and masonry. These other materials involve different methods and different craftsmen.

Inside door frames include the parts shown in Fig. 64-5. These include the *door jamb* (the top and sides), the *door stop* which keeps the door from swinging through the opening, and the *casing*. (See Fig. 64-6.) If the casing is offset so that part of the jamb shows, the exposed part is called the *reveal*. Door hinges are called *butts*, while the cuts in the door which receive the butts are called *gains*.

After the door frame is installed, the carpenter hangs and fits the door. He installs both the hinges and the door "set" (the fixture which includes the door knobs, the latch, and lock). If there is to be one, he then installs the threshold (door sill) and the weather stripping.

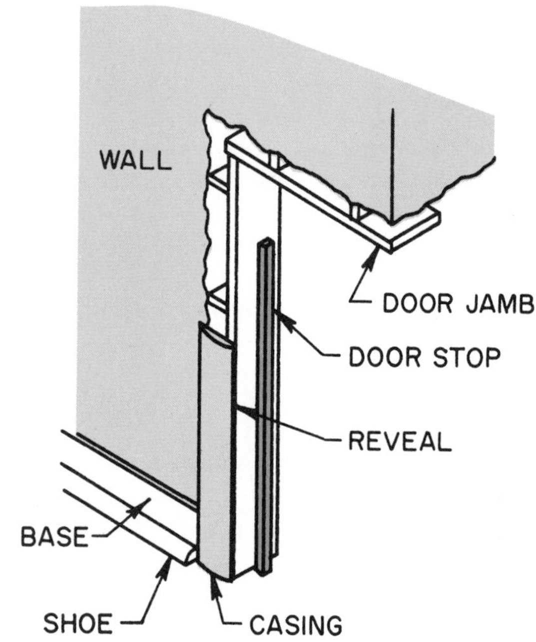

Fig. 64-5. This is an illustration of the trim on a door frame.

Fig. 64-6. Which part of the door frame is this man sanding?

Windows are framed somewhat as are doors. Instead of a threshold, a window has bottom parts called a *stool, apron,* and a *sill.* Window sashes are of many types and materials. Double hung, awning, jalousie, and casement windows are names of some of the common types. Glass is usually placed in sashes at the factory, though sometimes it is installed on the job.

Stair treads are supported by a cutout support or stringer. Often stairs are *prefabricated* (made up in a factory before reaching the job).

The joints between walls and ceiling may be covered by some kind of molding. Sometimes, if both the wall and ceiling are plasterboard, the joint is merely filled, taped, and sanded.

To prevent scuff marks around the bottom of interior walls, most rooms have a baseboard (base) and a quarter round (shoe), Fig. 64-7. In this and other trim, there are various cuts used to fit an adjoining surface:

1. Square joints which are cut off at right angles to the long axis of the piece of trim,
2. Mitered joints which are cut at an angle (usually 45 degrees) with the long axis, and
3. Coped joints.

Fig. 64-7. Is this carpenter installing the "base" or the "shoe"?

Cabinets may be prefabricated or built on the job. Wall cabinets are hung by fastening the cabinets to the studs. Cabinet doors are then carefully fitted. Counters in kitchens and bathrooms are covered with waterproof and stain-resistant materials such as ceramic tile or a hard plastic like Formica.

Clean Up

After craftsmen have completed their work, a crew (usually of laborers headed by a foreman) cleans up the debris from the various finish operations and prepares the structure for occupancy and use, Fig. 64-8. Sometimes the crew cleans one room at a time, while other operations are in progress elsewhere.

Summary

Finish work is necessary to prepare a structure for occupancy or use. This work

Fig. 64-8. After the craftsmen have completed their work, the site must be cleaned up. In large construction jobs this can be a sizable project.

may include trimming and cabinet work, painting, installing fixtures, and cleaning up. As finish work will be visible, it must be done skillfully and carefully.

Terms to Know

trimming
millwork
accessories
debris
"trim out"
door stop
casing
threshold (sill)
weather stripping
awning
interior designer
door frame
door jamb
jalousie
casement
prefabricated

Think About It!

1. Select a room in your home or your school. List several tasks that had to be done to *finish out* the construction.
2. Give two examples of finishing practices that must be used before a superhighway can be opened to traffic.

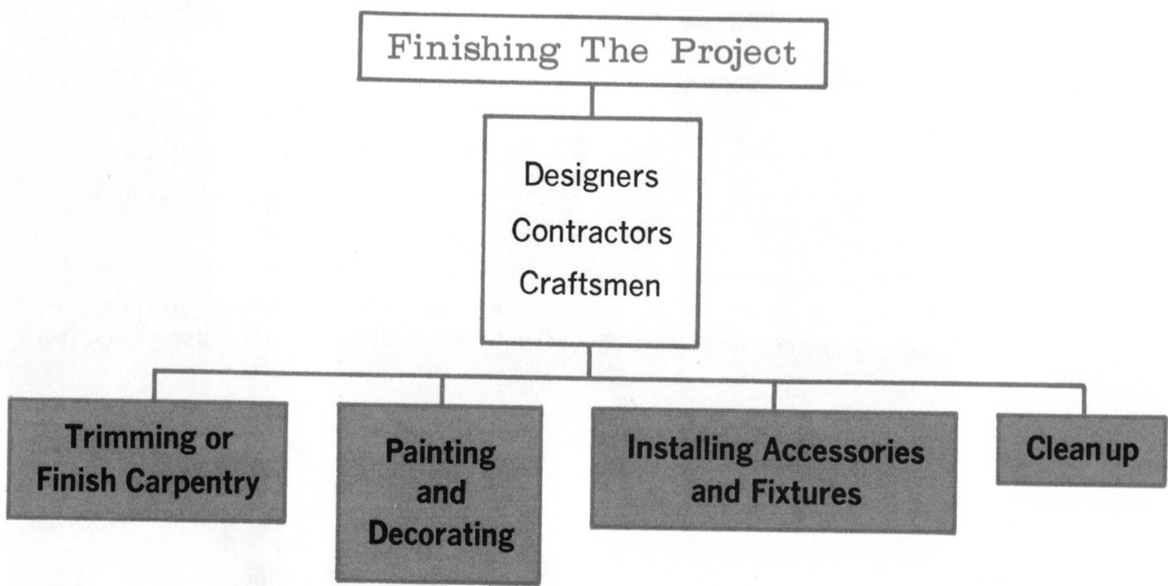

Painting and Decorating

READING 65

This reading concerns that part of finishing known as "painting and decorating." These two operations may serve one or more of the following purposes:

1. To protect part of the structure,
2. To make part of the structure easy to clean and maintain,
3. To present a pleasing appearance, or
4. To provide safety or informational markings. See Fig. 65-1.

While this reading will chiefly concern buildings, other structures also need painting and decorating. For example, the lane markings on highways (Fig. 65-2), steel bridges, and the gates of dams must be painted.

Fig. 65-1. How many of the four purposes for which painting and decorating are done does this exterior wall finish serve?

Both the exterior and the interior of a structure may be painted. Exterior painting may begin as soon as a structure is completely enclosed. Interior painting usually awaits completion of walls and trim. Floor finishing is generally one of the very last operations.

Who Does Painting and Decorating

The architect or engineer designing the structure decides on the type of paint and decoration. He is often helped by an interior designer or a representative of a paint manufacturer. Owners usually are consulted as to colors and patterns desired. There are so many kinds of paint, each with certain characteristics, that writing specifications for painting is extremely difficult. For instance, a vinyl (plastic) paint has been

Fig. 65-2. Painting is not limited to buildings. The lines painted on the highways provide safety or informational markings.

developed which will last for 50 years and will withstand (1) temperatures from minus 50 degrees to plus 150 degrees, (2) alternate wetting and drying, (3) the corrosive effect of chemicals in water, and (4) some abrasion (being rubbed against or scratched). This paint is extremely expensive and not attractive. It would not be used on a building but is excellent for coating the gate of a lock on a river or canal.

In selecting paint, some of the things which must be considered are:

1. Durability (how long it will last),
2. Cost of application,
3. Decorative effect,
4. Resistance to abrasion, particularly in the case of floor coatings,
5. Fire resistance,
6. Resistance to air pollutants,
7. Extent of prior preparation of surface, and
8. Waterproofing characteristics.

General contractors may do painting and decorating work with their own employees or they may subcontract the work to specialists, Fig. 65-3. Craftsmen include painters, paperhangers, cement finishers, floor finishers, waterproofing specialists, laborers, and sometimes artists.

Types of Paint

Choosing the right paint is important. On the average, when seven dollars is spent on painting, five dollars goes for *labor,* one dollar goes for ladders, brushes, putty, caulking material, and other supplies, and only one dollar goes for the paint itself. Thus a high quality paint is the best buy. It adds little to the total cost. To find out which paint to use and how to use it, ask an experienced painter or a paint dealer.

Paint itself is a mixture of a *vehicle* and a *pigment.* The vehicle is a liquid. It may be an oil such as linseed oil, or water, or a rubber or petroleum derivative. The pigment is a solid (for example, zinc white or titanium dioxide) which is ground into a very fine powder. Pigment gives body and color to the paint. The pigment is suspended (spread evenly) throughout the vehicle. After it is spread, the vehicle dries and forms a hard, tough film which holds the pigment in place.

Fig. 65-3. Painting is often subcontracted to specialists.

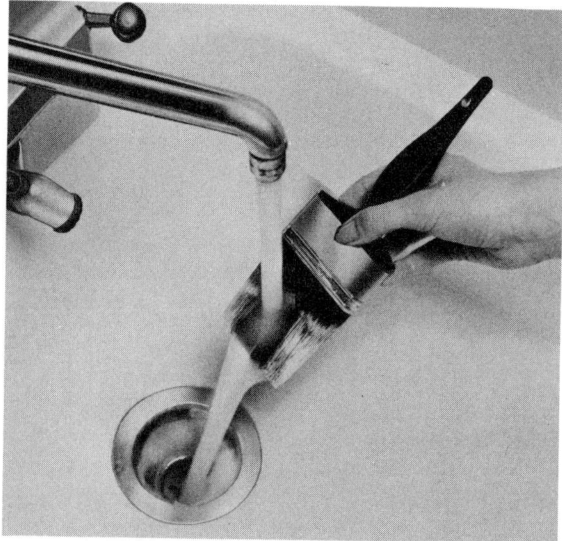

Fig. 65-4. Some paints are water soluble which makes it possible to clean a paintbrush in water.

Paints are often classified by the type of vehicle:

1. Oil base paints,
2. Water base paints, Fig. 65-4, including latex (sometimes called "rubber base"),
3. Polyvinyl acetates,
4. Alkyds, and
5. Asphaltic base paints.

Paints can be made mildew-resistant. They can also be made to *chalk*. (Part of the surface turns gradually to a chalky substance which rubs off to help keep the surface clean.) Some *enamel* paints have a high gloss. *Flat* paints are just the opposite. Their surface is dull or non-reflective.

Some paints are more or less all-purpose and can be applied over wood, metal, plasterboard, or masonry. There are special kinds of paints for floors, for masonry, for exposure to saltwater spray, and for metals. Some paints, like those with an asphaltic base, are good for waterproofing. Some paints are made especially for surfaces which have never been painted. Others are for areas that have already been painted.

Some paint must be thinned to make it easy to apply and to make it dry quickly. Thinners include turpentine, mineral spirits, and water, depending on the vehicle of the paint. There are special thinners for some paints. Some thinners cause the paint to stick to a surface better than the paint alone would adhere.

Besides thinners, many other substances may be added to paint to give it certain characteristics. Some of these will make the paint penetrate the surface much deeper or provide a better seal over the area. Other things, like fine sand, will give the paint a rougher, textured surface.

Other Coatings

Varnish is a solution of linseed oil and resins (soluble wood or plastic products). It provides a hard, clear surface, quite resistant to water. *Spar varnish* provides a waterproof surface. *Shellac* is a clear, quick drying mixture with alcohol as a vehicle and a resin as a pigment.

Stains are oil base or water base liquids which give a slightly tinted (colored) appearance to wood without hiding the grain.

Putty is a mixture of chalk and linseed oil. It has the consistency of taffy or caramel and hardens when exposed to air. Today, traditional putty is often replaced by a plastic material. Both can be used to fill holes or cracks. *Caulking*, formerly done with putty, is now done with a plastic caulking compound. A caulking gun, which is very similar to a grease gun, dispenses the compound.

How Paint Is Applied

The first step in applying paint is to prepare the surface. It is made clean and dry, and treatments (such as shellac on knots in wood) are applied.

Paint itself may be applied by brush, by roller, or by spray. A brush is used for irregular areas and where careful, fine work is needed. Paint is usually applied by brush to exterior trim. Rollers are used on large,

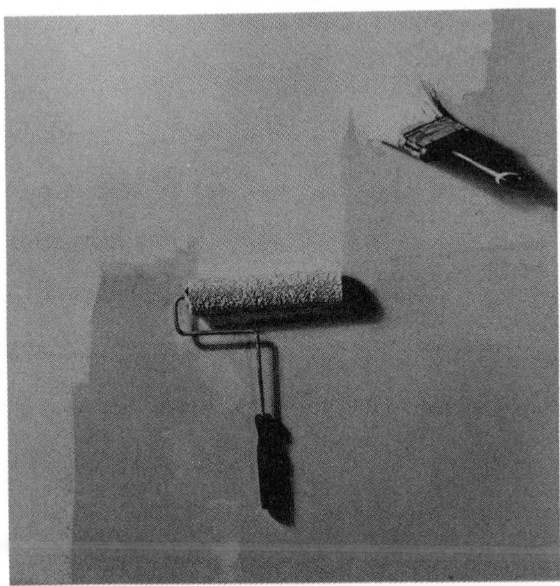

Fig. 65-5. Paint is often applied to large areas by roller and smaller areas by brush.

flat areas, as on interior walls and ceilings. Latex paints are especially easy to apply by roller, Fig. 65-5. Spray painting is economical because it can be done quickly, but it requires special equipment, Fig. 65-6. Spray painting is not good for fine, close work because the paint may get on another area which is not to be painted.

Paint may be applied in one coat or several. Each coat or layer must dry completely before the next is applied. A primary coat or undercoat often is applied first. Then one or two finish coats are applied.

Painters used to mix their own paint, but today most paints are mixed at the factory. The painter merely stirs the paint and thins it as needed. Even the stirring process is partly performed by the paint dealer who places the paint can in a shaking machine. Painters often "tint" paints, which means mixing in coloring to get exactly the color they want.

Structural steel members are usually scrubbed with a wire brush to remove rust. Then they are given a coat of paint at the shop. After the steel is erected, the shop coat, some of which has been damaged during erection, is covered with one or more field coats. The last field coat is often an oil base, aluminum-pigmented paint which gives the steel a silvery appearance.

Fig. 65-6. Paint is often sprayed on large surfaces.

Wooden floors are sanded, usually by machine. Then nail holes and joints are filled with a filler. Frequently a stain is applied next, followed by varnish. As many as four coats of varnish may be applied, after which the floors are waxed and polished by a power polisher.

Decorating

The most common form of decorating is with strip or sheet materials. Wallpaper is widely used, Fig. 65-7. Some wallpapers consist of printed paper sheets which come in rolls. Others are rolls of fabric with a paper or plastic surface.

Originally, wallpaper was applied to the wall with a flour and water paste. Today better adhesives are used. Some adhesives are even placed on the wallpaper at the factory. On the job, the sheets only need to be moistened.

Some buildings contain expensive and ornate decorations prepared by artists. Among these are *murals* (large pictures painted directly on a wall or ceiling with oil base paint) and *frescos* (a painting created on a wet plaster wall with water-color paint).

Fig. 65-7. Wallpaper is used as a wall covering in this house.

Finishing Masonry and Concrete

Masonry such as stone, unglazed clay tile, concrete block, or brick, is usually cleaned with a mixture of water and muriatic acid (a chemical). Also, any excess mortar is removed.

Concrete walls are patched with grout whenever there are holes remaining from form ties or where there is any *honeycomb* (the minor exposure of aggregate). Any excess concrete which has oozed out of a joint in the forms is chipped off. Other treatment given concrete may consist of:

1. Rubbing the surface with a stone,
2. Applying muriatic acid, or
3. Applying a very thin layer of grout to hide holes or to give a smooth appearance, Fig. 65-8.

Fig. 65-8. Concrete is often cleaned with acid and sealed with grout to cover any holes.

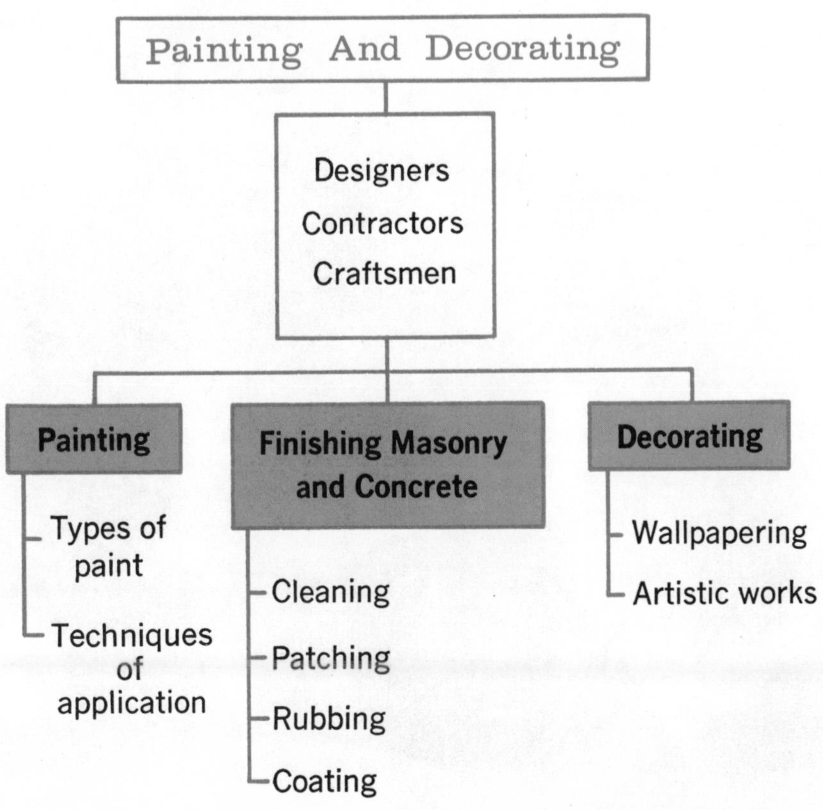

Summary

Painting and decorating provide a protective coating, easy maintenance, a pleasant appearance, and may provide safety or information. The selection of the type of paint and its method of application should be referred to an expert. Painting and decorating should be carefully planned. They should also be done by skilled craftsmen, for they cover most of the interior and at least part of the exterior of many structures.

Terms to Know

durability
decorative
abrasion
air pollutants
putty
caulking
water soluble
shop coat
vehicle
pigment
enamel paint
flat paint
thinner
resins
varnish
spar varnish
shellac
stains
field coat
primary coat
sanded
wallpaper
murals
frescos
expert
appearance
honeycomb

Think About It!

1. Do the specifications for paint used to line highways differ from the specifications for paint used on your walls or woodwork at home? If so, in what ways?
2. What *decorating* materials can you identify in your home?

Installing Accessories

This reading describes the installation of accessories. Accessories include:

1. Plumbing and piping fixtures such as washbasins and grilles over street drains;
2. Electrical fixtures such as lights and signs;
3. Heating, cooling, and ventilating fixtures such as furnaces;
4. Communications fixtures such as telephones;
5. Ironwork such as handrails and ladders; and
6. Hardware such as mailboxes.

Accessories, more commonly called *fixtures,* are things which are permanently attached to structures. A *furnishing* is something that is merely moved in and set in place. Some accessories may be considered as either fixtures or furnishings. For instance, large, immovable road signs are definitely fixtures. A movable or temporary road sign could be considered a furnishing. See Fig. 66-1. In the case of a building, when one is sold, the buyer and seller usually decide what they will consider *fixtures* (to be left in the structure) and what will be *furnishings* which the seller may remove, Fig. 66-2.

Fig. 66-1. Roads and bridges have accessories. Here lights, fencing, and guard rails provide safety for motorists and pedestrians.

When Accessories Are Installed

Generally no accessories are installed in a structure (or even brought to the site) until the structure can be locked or guarded. This is to prevent theft or vandalism. Many fixtures are quite expensive, and it may take a long time to replace them.

Installing most fixtures consists of two operations: (1) attaching them to the struc-

Fig. 66-2. Fixtures are left in a home when it is sold, but furnishings are not.

ture or setting them in place on their own bases, and (2) hooking them up to utility lines.

As you will recall, the main utility lines are roughed in and inspected early in the production work. After most of the production work is completed, fixtures may be installed. The various craftsmen who install fixtures return to the site for this work, Fig. 66-3.

Sometimes fixtures must be hung or set before some of the main structural work can be completed. For example, street drains and manholes are set in place so the roadway surface will be level with and tight against them.

Who Installs Accessories

Accessories are selected by the designer, builder, or owner of a structure. Nearly always the desires of the owner are determined. The design of the structure is often adjusted to support accessories of heavy weight or to provide for heavy utility loads (for instance, electric power). An interior designer is often consulted in selecting accessories for buildings.

Most general contractors subcontract the installation of accessories to a specialist (Fig. 66-4), but often the general contractor uses his own employees to place ornamental iron and hardware.

Craftsmen who install fixtures include carpenters, plumbers, steam fitters, electricians, sheet metal workers, ironworkers, welders, and painters. As with all finish work, a great deal of skill and care is required. Many special tools are used.

Installing Plumbing Accessories

In light (home) construction, plumbing accessories either are hung on some part of

Fig. 66-3. The main utility lines for these lights were roughed in early in the production work. The light fixtures are installed near the time when the project is completed.

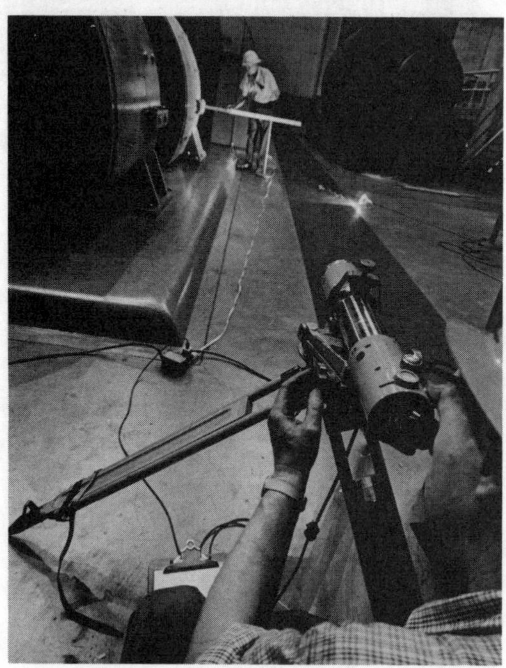

Fig. 66-4. The installation and adjustment of some accessories, such as this motor generator, require the services of a field engineer. Others do not.

the structural framework or are set on the floor, on counters, or on foundations of their own. Plumbers and electricians make most of the connections. Many gas companies, however, require that gas connections be made by their own employees, and all gas companies inspect gas connections within a structure. Each accessory is tried and tested for proper operation and the absence of leaks, Fig. 66-5.

In highway and heavy construction, plumbers and pipe fitters also install accessories. These may include grates and cover plates over drains on bridges and highways, accesses to pipeline valves and controls, and similar accessories which are added after the main structural work is completed.

Installing Heating, Ventilating, and Air Conditioning Systems

Heating and air conditioning units are hooked up to ducts by sheet metal workers, to electrical cables by electricians, and to water and drain pipes (when needed) by plumbers.

Registers are connected to the ducts in the wall, floor, or ceiling through roughly finished holes, Fig. 66-6. The metal facing of the register overlaps the wall surface so that the rough edges of the hole cannot be seen. Registers are attached by screws and may be removed easily.

Vents are provided beneath the gables in attics, under *soffits,* in crawl spaces under buildings, and in partitions. Filters are put in the duct system to remove dust from the air.

After the heating, ventilating and air-conditioning system is completed, it is completely adjusted and checked. The dampers and thermostats are set. Sometimes this cannot be done until a change of season. For example, heating systems cannot be tested in the summer.

Exhaust fans are connected to vent pipes, through walls, to draw out or "exhaust" steam, smoke, and odors. Exhaust fans also may be installed to draw out heat and bring in fresh air. Timing devices are often put in to turn fans on or off at certain times.

Installing Electrical Accessories

In buildings, lighting fixtures often are installed over outlet boxes which were put in

Fig. 66-5. These stainless steel steam kettles are connected to plumbing lines which were roughed in earlier.

Fig. 66-6. Registers not only control the rate and direction of conditioned air into a room, but they provide a neat, finished job.

place during the roughing in of the electrical lines. Usually the outlet box includes machine screws for attaching a fixture, but sometimes extra framework is built to support the fixture. At this same time, other outlet boxes which are not covered by light fixtures are covered with plain or ornamental covers after all connections have been made and switches and outlets have been installed.

Outdoor lighting often involves heavy fixtures which need a crane for handling. Installing these accessories may mean earthmoving, concrete work, and ironwork as well as electrical work. Outdoor accessories and their controls and connections also need to be weatherproof.

Other electrical accessories which are installed include built-in appliances, heating elements, and electrical machinery, Fig. 66-8. Some buildings, such as hospitals, even require the installation of extra electric power plants which can operate in case the regular electric power system fails.

Installing Communications Accessories

Although complete communications systems can be installed after a structure is completed, it is far better to have the lines and equipment designed and roughed in along with the rest of the work. The final installation of the accessories consists of hanging or placing the communications devices and hooking them up, Fig. 66-9. Again, cover plates are installed to protect all connections and controls.

Fig. 66-8. An electrical accessory, a large transformer, is being installed in a steam electric plant.

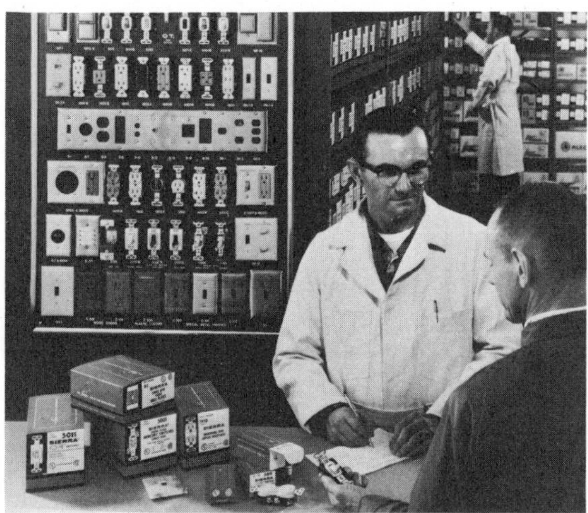

Fig. 66-7. The electrical contractor has many types of accessories to choose from.

Fig. 66-9. A telephone is a familiar type of communication accessory.

Installing Ironwork

Ironwork accessories consist of all interior and exterior ironwork which is not part of the structural frame. Part of this work may be called *ornamental ironwork* (often called *miscellaneous iron*) if it is fancy or ornamental. It includes stair and balcony railings, partitions, grillwork, signs, signals, and walkways. It is used not only on buildings, but also on other structures such as bridges (handrails and ladders), towers (stairways), and roads (guard rails). Ornamental ironwork is usually installed by ironworkers and welders. See Fig. 66-10.

Fig. 66-10. This man is installing ironwork.

Installing Hardware

Door and window hardware is usually installed with the trim, Fig. 66-11. Also, there are other items of hardware and miscellaneous equipment to be installed: mirrors, shower and toilet partitions, push plates, kick plates, door stops, mailboxes or slots, built-in cabinetwork (bookcases and medicine cabinets), and street numbers.

Fig. 66-11. Hardware, such as the shower doors, door handles, and towel racks, usually is installed last.

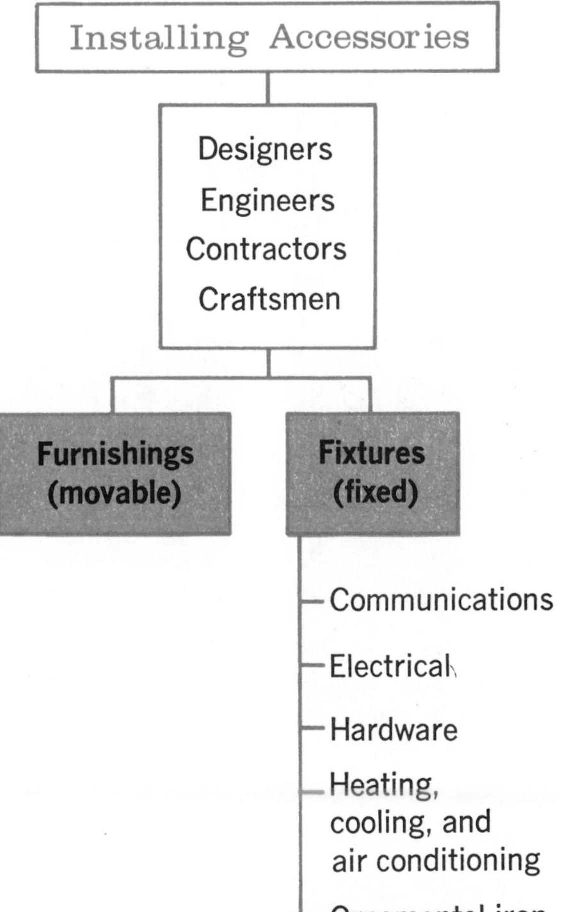

Summary

Among the last operations in finishing a building are the installation of accessories, including those for (1) plumbing; (2) heating, cooling, and ventilating; (3) electrical heat, light, and power; and (4) communications. Along with these, miscellaneous iron and hardware are installed. Installation consists of attaching the accessories to the structure, or setting them in place, connecting the necessary utility lines, and checking the operation.

Terms to Know

accessories
fixtures
registers
vents
furnishings
appliances
installation
residential
ventilating
dampers
exhaust fans
soffit
outlet
ornamental ironwork

Think About It!

1. What is the difference between a fixture and a furnishing? Can you locate three of each in the room in which you are now?
2. What fixtures or accessories would need to be installed on a new school playground? A new football field with track and field facilities?

Completing the Site

This reading covers the work necessary to complete the site. This might be called the *finish work* outside of the structure itself. Finish work includes:

1. Providing access routes such as driveways, roads, and sidewalks;
2. Building exterior features such as patios and fences;
3. Sloping and finishing the earth;
4. Planting vegetation such as trees, shrubs, and lawns; and
5. Final cleaning up.

These operations are often called *landscaping*. See Fig. 67-1.

Fig. 67-1. How many kinds of finish work can you find on this site?

The purposes of site completion are to increase the usefulness of the project and to improve its appearance. Site completion is especially important in the construction of highways and dams. In these projects, it is often said that "grass is a major construction material."

Who Completes the Site

The site work outside the structure is designed by the architect-engineer. Where this work is extensive, or specialized, the designer may consult a landscape architect, an agricultural engineer, or an *agronomist* (a specialist in the production of crops, to include grasses).

Contractors may do the site completion work with their own employees, or they may subcontract the work to specialists. In the case of planting trees, shrubs, and grass, a separate subcontract may be issued to a landscaping company, Fig. 67-2. However, if the contractor had awarded an excavation subcontract for the original grading of the site, the finish grading would also be included.

Fig. 67-2. A subcontractor, usually a landscaping company, may do the finish grading and landscape work.

Craftsmen who may work on site completion include nearly all trades. Most commonly employed are carpenters, cement finishers, operating engineers, electricians, masons, painters, and plumbers.

Constructing Access

If an *access road* or a *railroad spur* is to be built, it usually is constructed at the beginning of the project so that materials and people can get to the site. For instance, an access road will be graded, and temporary bridges and culverts will be installed. A minimum surface (usually loose gravel, sometimes with a thin coat of asphalt) will be applied.

After the structure is almost completed, the final base courses, surfaces, pavements, and drainage structures (such as culverts) will be put in place as a part of site completion. Sidewalks, walkways, parking lots, and driveways are also installed, Fig. 67-3. The processes used in providing access are similar to those in other grading and paving operations.

Building and Installing Features

Features include patios, fences, walls, benches, pools, statues, plant boxes, and exterior lights, Fig. 67-4. As with access roads, sometimes part of the work is done before the structure is complete. For instance, the cable for an electric outdoor post lantern would be installed along with roughing in the electrical work in the structure. This cable would be brought to the spot where the lantern is to go and *stubbed out* (left sticking out of the ground with the end taped).

Fig. 67-3. Sidewalks, culverts, and driveways are a part of finish work.

This early placement of cable eliminates the need to drill through exterior walls and tear up sidewalks and lawns. During the site completion, the lantern post is set in concrete, the lantern attached, and the wiring hookup completed. In other cases, a feature like a bench is completely installed as one of the last outside operations.

Shaping the Surface

In most projects, the *rough grading* is completed as part of preparing the site. Whenever possible, the site should be graded so as to provide temporary drainage during the construction of the structure. This reduces the damage which may be caused by rainfall during the progress of the job. Good drainage also makes it easy for workers to get back to work quickly after work has been stopped for bad weather.

The final or *finish grading* is accomplished during the site completion phase, Fig. 67-5. The slopes are carefully selected and surveyed. Too steep a slope will let rainwater rush down too fast so that the soil will wash away (erode). If there is no slope, rainwater may stand in puddles until the soil soaks it up, and some soil quickly becomes waterlogged. The slope selected for a site de-

Fig. 67-4. This outdoor garden combines a number of features including a pond, outdoor benches, and brick patio. Can you find others?

pends on the kind of soil, the amount and frequency of rainfall, and the type of soil cover in the form of plants or pavement.

Finish grading is done in about the same way as the other earthmoving you have studied, but graders, rollers, and light duty or small hauling equipment (such as a front end loader) are used in place of heavy, high production equipment. Stones and debris are removed, and then the surface is graded and rolled to give the earth the exact shape and the firmness desired.

Drainage structures such as bridges, culverts, and manholes are sometimes installed during the first preparation of the site. On other projects drainage structures are put in during the completion of the outside work.

Providing Vegetation

Providing vegetation for a site will be divided into three operations: (1) soil preparation, (2) planting trees and shrubs, and (3) seeding or sodding lawns or planting ground cover. After the fine grading is completed, the top surface of the earth may or may not be a type of soil in which trees, shrubs, and grass will grow. If the soil is good enough to grow the vegetation required, fertilizer is spread. Usually light plows, harrows, or similar soil "tillers" are used to loosen the soil and mix it with the fertilizer.

Often a graded surface will not support plant life. Then topsoil is needed. *Topsoil is rich in organic matter and readily grows most kinds of plants.* Sometimes topsoil is hauled to the site, but it is quite expensive and sometimes hard to find for large projects.

If possible, the topsoil which covered the site in its original state is carefully removed at the start of the excavation and rough grading. It is placed aside in "stockpiles" for later use in completing the site. The topsoil is then spread and mixed with fertilizer.

Trees and shrubs are planted first. Usually, when they are delivered to the site, there is a ball of earth covered with a heavy, coarse fabric called *burlap* around the roots of each tree or shrub. The exact spots where the trees and shrubs are to go are marked with stakes. The hole that is dug for each plant is a little larger than the plant's ball of earth. It is deep enough so that when the plant goes into the hole, the top of the ball of earth is level with the ground surface. See Fig. 67-6.

The soil removed from the hole may be fertile topsoil, or it may be silt or heavy clay. If it is silt or clay, it should be taken away and replaced with topsoil. If it is good topsoil, it may be mixed with peat moss and sometimes fertilizer. Then the topsoil is put around the plant's ball of earth in the hole. Adding water helps the topsoil to settle around the ball. Water also is needed by the living plant when it is moved.

Trees must be *staked* to prevent the wind from blowing them over. Stakes may be put at three equally spaced points around the

Fig. 67-5. Here the workman is fine grading the earth to make a lawn.

Fig. 67-6. Here a helicopter is used to plant trees on this highway beautification project.

tree. Then wires are run tightly from these stakes up to the trunk of the tree. A short piece of rubber hose is used to protect the trunk of the tree from damage by the wire. Tree trunks should be wrapped so that the hot sun and dry winds will not harm the layer of cells just under the bark.

Earth which is not covered with living plants or other surfacing washes away (erodes). Ground cover may be a formal lawn around buildings or coarse vegetation along dams and highways. The type of ground cover is chosen to fit the needs for the control of surface water.

There are three methods of obtaining a ground cover of grass: sodding, sprigging, and seeding. *Sod* is grass specially raised for the purpose. It includes the whole root system and some topsoil. Sod is cut in strips and laid on top of bare ground, giving a complete, ready-made ground cover, Fig. 66-7. Sodding is quite expensive. Its use is limited to lawns and areas where erosion might be critical, such as around the abutments (ends) of a bridge.

Sprigging is done with sod. The sod is broken up into small plugs or sprigs of grass which are planted one at a time. The sprigs are planted 6″ to 12″ apart and do not cover the entire ground surface. As the grass grows, it spreads so that it eventually covers the entire surface. Sprigging is usually somewhat less expensive than sodding.

Seeding means planting seed (by hand or machine), Figs. 66-8 and 66-9. With proper care the grass seeds sprout, grow, and eventually form a ground cover. Seed and young grass must be protected from the direct sun and from the wind. The seed may be worked into the ground by raking, and a *mulch* (a very thin layer of straw or peat moss) may be applied for protection.

Fig. 67-7. One technique of covering the ground with grass is to apply sod.

In all these methods, the proper application of fertilizer and frequent watering are necessary to give the grass a good start.

In shady locations other plants, such as ivy, sometimes make a better ground cover than grass. Lawn areas that are hard to reach with a mower may also be covered with ivy or other low growing plants. This kind of ground cover is begun from a process like sprigging, except individual plants are set out in a spaced pattern. These plants spread to cover the total area.

Cleaning Up

The last phase of completing the site is cleanup. This includes removal of temporary structures and equipment, collecting and dis-

Fig. 67-8. This man is discing the compacted soil so seeds can be planted.

Fig. 67-9. Lawn seed is being sown by machine at this school.

posing of trash and debris, and removal of all equipment and surplus materials from the site.

Summary

Completing the site consists of (1) adding or completing access routes; (2) building features; (3) finishing the grading of the ground; (4) planting trees, shrubs, and grass; and (5) cleaning up.

Terms to Know

landscaping
finish work
agronomist
landscape architect
culverts
vegetation
sodding
sprigging
agricultural engineer
access road
railroad spur
features
stubbed out
graded
drainage
rough grading
finish grading
erode
seeding
fertilizer
soil tillers
topsoil
stockpiles
burlap
silt
peat moss
mulch

Think About It!

1. On a piece of notebook paper, make a drawing (plan view) of your home or school site. Locate and label accesses, exterior features such as patios and fences, plantings such as trees or bushes, and other objects or features that were placed there when the site was completed.

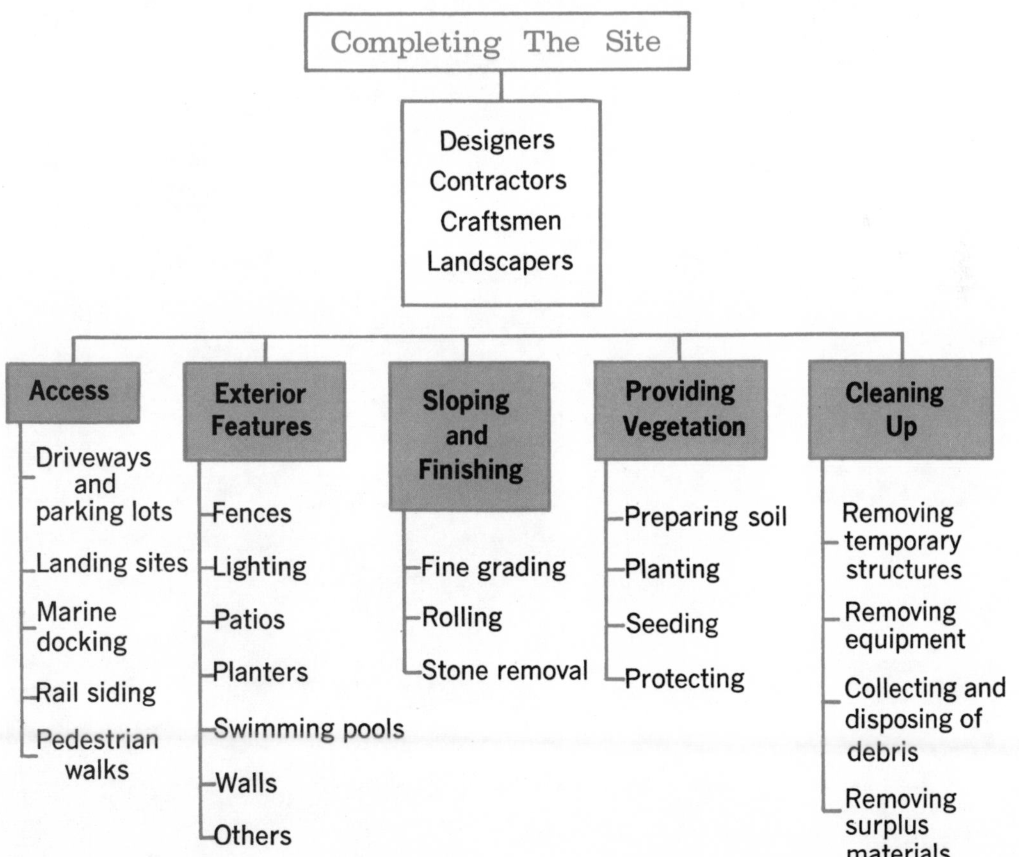

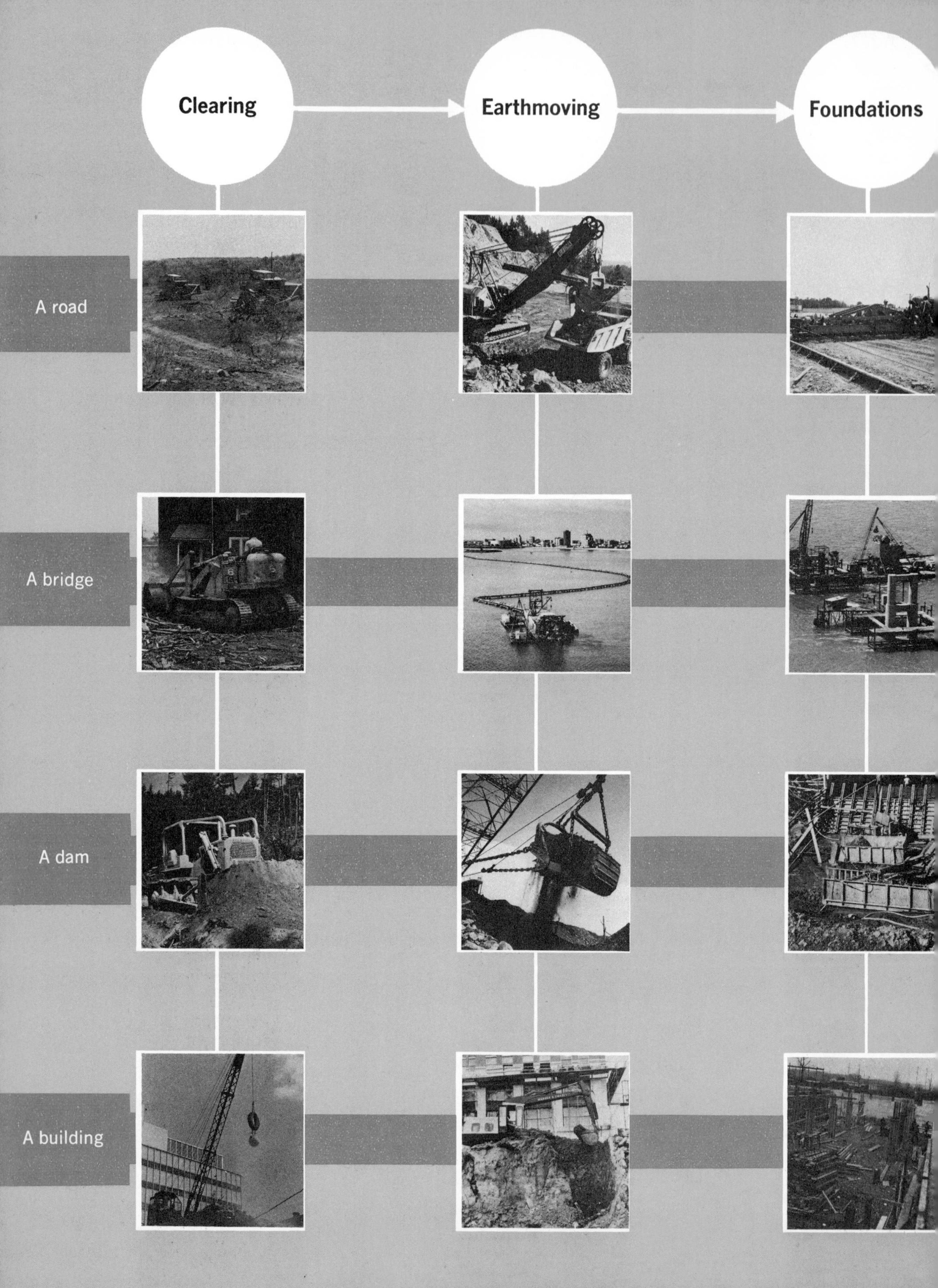
Clearing
Earthmoving
Foundations
A road
A bridge
A dam
A building

Superstructures
Utilities
Finished Project

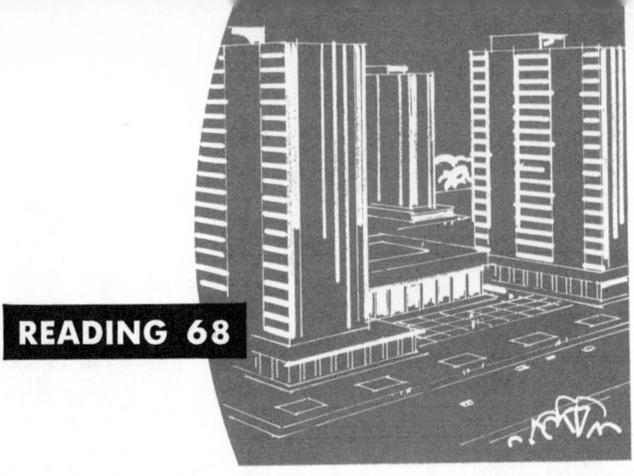

READING 68

Transferring the Project

After all the work is done at the job site, the project is transferred from the contractor to the owner. This reading describes how the owner takes over (accepts) the project from the contractor, and how the owner's contracts with the architect-engineer and with the general contractor are completed.

You will recall that there are many different ways of designing and building a project and many different types of construction contracts. In today's reading, we shall consider that the owner has a fixed price contract with an architect-engineer to design the project. A general contractor will build it.

The transfer of the project will be discussed under four headings: (1) inspection, (2) releases, (3) warranties, and (4) final payment.

Inspection

At the time construction is completed, the project is inspected very closely, Fig. 68-1. The inspectors include representatives of the contractor, of the architect-engineer, and sometimes of the owner. The inspectors look at every part of the job in detail to see that the work has been done according to the construction contract (including the plans and specifications). All mechanical and electrical equipment is tested to see that it operates properly.

The inspectors make up a list of defects called a *punch list*. Most defects are very small (a smudge on a wall). Some defects may be major (unevenness in a highway). There may be only a few items on a punch list, or none. On a large project, there may be several hundred.

As soon as the punch list is put together, the contractor begins correcting the defects. He may use his own employees, or he may call a subcontractor back to the job if the defect is the fault of the subcontractor.

After the contractor corrects the defects on the punch list to the satisfaction of the architect-engineer and the owner, no more work remains to be done on the job itself, Figs. 68-2 and 68-3. However, there is still a certain amount of paper work (papers to be exchanged between the contractor and the owner) before the owner accepts the job and makes final payment. The sections which follow tell about this paper work.

Releases

As you know, the word *release* means *let go of*. (If you hold a pencil above your desk

Fig. 68-1. When the project is completed, an inspection is made. For example, this device is used by inspectors to test the smoothness of completed highways.

and release it, you let go of it.) A contractor sometimes has a claim on a construction contract. He releases or lets go of it after it is settled.

First, let's see what a claim on a construction contract is. A contractor might find that the soil beneath the structure contains more rock than was shown on the plans. As rock is more expensive to excavate than ordinary earth, the contractor believes he is entitled to more money for cutting out the rock than was agreed upon in the original contract. The contractor then presents a *claim* (a request for the extra money) to the owner through the architect-engineer. If this claim has not yet been settled when all the work on the project is done, the claim is said to be *outstanding* at the end of the job.

If there are outstanding claims at the end of the job, the contractor and the architect-engineer attempt to *settle* (reach an agreement on) these claims as soon as possible. If no agreement can be reached, the contractor, architect-engineer, and owner then decide how the claim is to be settled (arbitration, legal action), Fig. 68-4.

Fig. 68-2. Any defects in the construction, such as the holes in the face of this concrete, are placed on a punch list and are corrected by the contractor.

After the claims are settled, the contractor signs what is known as a *release of claims* in which he lets go of all claims he may have against the owner. This means that the contractor may not present any new claims and that he is satisfied with all settlements of old claims.

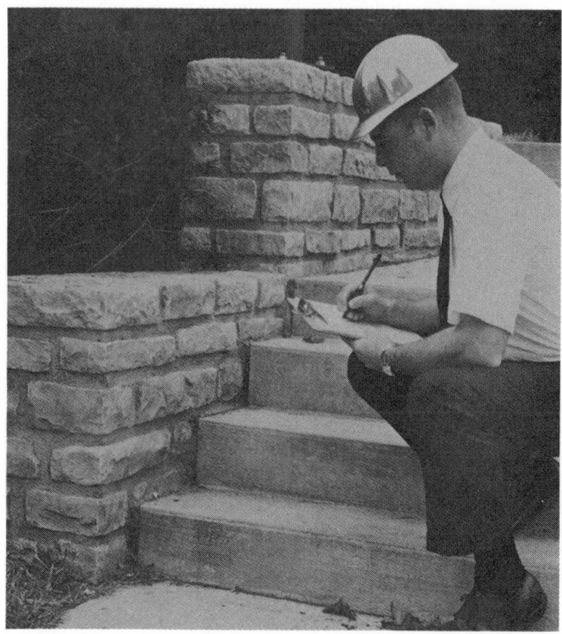

Fig. 68-3. This inspector is checking corrective work that was done by the contractor.

Fig. 68-4. Settlement of a claim may require legal and court action.

2. Labor or Machinery, material or fuel (or both).
3. Constructing, altering, erecting, improving, repairing, removing, digging or drilling as the case may be.
4. House, mill or other building, structure, furnace, water craft, well, gas pipe line, coal mine, street, road, sidewalk, way, drain, ditch or sewer. If a street etc., "abutting on", may be inserted instead of "situated on".
5. Owner, part owner, lessee, contractor, subcontractor or other person, as the case may be.
6. Performed or furnished.
7. Land, buildings, leasehold, etc., as at 4.
8. Is or was the owner, part owner or lessee, as the case may be.

☞ This affidavit must be filed in the office of the Recorder of the County or Counties in which the labor was performed, or the material, etc., furnished within 60 days from the date the last of the same was performed or furnished. Rev. Code 1311.06.

A copy of the affidavit must be served on the owner, part owner or lessee, or his agent, within 30 days after the filing. If neither can be found in the County, then the copy must be posted in some conspicuous place on the premises, within ten days after the expiration of the 30 days. Rev. Code 1311.07.

CERTIFICATE OF SATISFACTION OF MECHANICS' LIEN

Rev. Code 1311.20

IT IS HEREBY CERTIFIED that the amount claimed in the within affidavit for a lien upon the premises of Lot numbered 83 of Blackacre Estates No. 1 *therein described, has been fully paid and satisfied and the Recorder is authorized to discharge such lien of record.*

Dated this 23rd *day of* January 1902

Douglas Fitch

A B C Builder's Supply Corporation

AFFIDAVIT FOR MECHANICS' LIEN

A B C Builder's Supply Corporation

TO

Flath Homebuilders

Received for Record January 26, 1902

at 10 *o'clock* A.M.

Recorded January 27, 1902

in Franklin *County*

Record of Liens, Vol. 307

Page 43

[signature] *Recorder*

Recorder's Fee, $ 2.00

COLUMBUS BLANK BOOK CO., COL., O.

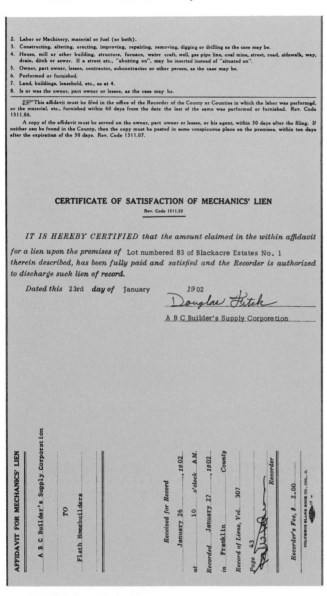

COLUMBUS BLANK BOOK CO., COL.
Rev. Form L20

AFFIDAVIT FOR MECHANICS' LIEN

Rev. Code 1311.04, .06

The State of Ohio, Franklin **County, ss.**

Robert G. Jack, Attorney at Law, for A B C Builders Supply Corporation

of Columbus, Ohio 43215 *, whose address is* 85 East Gay Street

being first duly sworn, says that he furnished certain [2] materials

in and for [3] constructing *a certain* [4] house

situated on the land hereinafter described, in pursuance of a certain contract, with Robert Flath dba Flath Homebuilders, 42 East Gay Street, Columbus, Ohio,

the [5] contractor

whose address is 42 East Gay Street, Columbus, Ohio 43215.

The last of such [2] materials *was* [6] furnished

on the 10th *day of* October 1900 *and there is justly and truly*

deponent therefor from the said Robert Flath dba Flath Homebuilders

over and above all legal setoffs the sum

Twelve Hundred Eighty Dollars ($1280.00) *Dollars, for which amount depon*

claims a lien on said [7] land and buildings *of which* Sleepy Hollow Land Company, 100 E. Broad Street, Columbus, Ohio 43215 and John P. Doe, 208 Sleepy Hollo Lane, Columbus, Ohio 44442 are [8] *the* owners

which premises are described as follows:

Situated in the State of Ohio, County of Franklin, and Township of Athens, and further described as follows:

Being Lot Numbered 83 of Blackacre Estates No. 1 as the same is numbered and delineated upon the recorded plat thereof, of record in Plat Book 37, pages 2 through 18, inclusive, Recorder's Office, Franklin County, Ohio.

Grantor obtained title in Deed Book 285 Page 179.

Premises also known as 208 Sleepy Hollow Lane, Columbus, Ohio 44442.

Robert G. Jack

Robert G. Jack

Sworn to before me and signed in my presence, this 31st *day of* November 19

This instrument prepared by
Robert G. Jack
Attorney at Law
85 East Gay Street
Columbus, Ohio 43215

/S/ Charlene Hall
Charlene Hall, Notary Public
Franklin County, State of Ohio
My Commission Expires:
November 18, 1918

The other type of release is a *release of lien.* Let us first see what a lien is. If a craftsman, supplier of materials, contractor, or subcontractor has not been paid for materials provided or services rendered, he may obtain from a court a lien against the property of the owner. This means that the owner's property becomes the security for the amount of money due.

As an example of a lien, a paving subcontractor surfaced a large parking lot for a motel. The owner of the motel did not pay the general contractor for the parking lot. Likewise the general contractor did not pay the paving subcontractor. The subcontractor then got, from a local court of law, a lien against the whole motel property. If the subcontractor is not paid, he can have the motel property sold and can collect the amount due him out of the money from the sale.

In actual practice, such a forced sale of the property rarely happens. The owner and the general contractor usually agree to pay the subcontractor.

At the end of the job, the owner normally requires the general contractor to provide a complete release of lien on behalf of the contractor himself, his subcontractors, suppliers, and craftsmen. This release of lien assures the owner that his property is not the security for any debt and that the general contractor has paid all the people who have worked on the job or supplied materials for it.

Warranties

A *warranty* is a promise that a certain item will be free from defects in materials or workmanship for a specified period. In construction, there are two types of warranties: those provided by the contractor and those provided by suppliers.

Most construction contracts provide that the contractor shall, for one year, fix any defects due to faulty workmanship. If the paint on the house starts to peel after nine months, it is the contractor's obligation to come back and make the necessary repairs. Many contractors prize their reputations so highly that they will voluntarily correct trouble which may develop long after the one-year period has ended at no expense to the owner.

Suppliers often warrant their products for periods of one year or longer. For example, manufacturers of air conditioning equipment may warrant the compressor unit for 5 years.

At the time the construction work is completed, the contractor hands over to the owner the warranty certificates of the suppliers. The contractor also gives the owner all the necessary manuals and operating instructions for installed equipment such as water heaters, stoves, dishwashers, and air conditioners, Fig. 68-5.

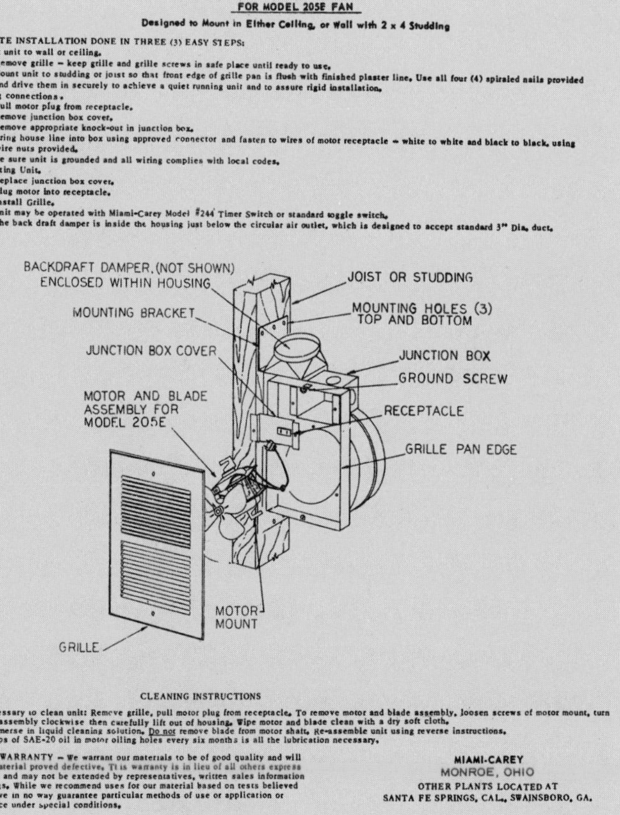

PHILIP CAREY

PHILIP CAREY CORPORATION

INSTALLING & CLEANIHG INSTRUCTIONS

FOR MODEL 205E FAN

Designed to Mount in Either Ceiling, or Wall with 2 x 4 Studding

-ETE INSTALLATION DONE IN THREE (3) EASY STEPS:
unt unit to wall or ceiling.
Remove grille – keep grille and grille screws in safe place until ready to use.
Mount unit to studding or joist so that front edge of grille pan is flush with finished plaster line. Use all four (4) spiraled nails provided and drive them in securely to achieve a quiet running unit and to assure rigid installation.
ing connections.
Pull motor plug from receptacle.
Remove junction box cover.
Remove appropriate knock-out in junction box.
Bring house line into box using approved connector and fasten to wires of motor receptacle – white to white and black to black, using wire nuts provided.
Be sure unit is grounded and all wiring complies with local codes.
rating Unit.
Replace junction box cover.
Plug motor into receptacle.
Install Grille.
Unit may be operated with Miami-Carey Model #244 Timer Switch or standard toggle switch.
The back draft damper is inside the housing just below the circular air outlet, which is designed to accept standard 3" Dia. duct.

CLEANING INSTRUCTIONS

ecessary to clean unit: Remove grille, pull motor plug from receptacle. To remove motor and blade assembly, loosen screws of motor mount, turn e assembly clockwise then carefully lift out of housing. Wipe motor and blade clean with a dry soft cloth. immerse in liquid cleaning solution. Do not remove blade from motor shaft. Re-assemble unit using reverse instructions. rops of SAE-20 oil in motor oiling holes every six months is all the lubrication necessary.

WARRANTY – We warrant our materials to be of good quality and will material proved defective. This warranty is in lieu of all others express ed and may not be extended by representatives, written sales information ings. While we recommend uses for our material based on tests believed , we in no way guarantee particular methods of use or application or ance under special conditions.

MIAMI-CAREY
MONROE, OHIO
OTHER PLANTS LOCATED AT
SANTA FE SPRINGS, CAL., SWAINSBORO, GA.

7V-6571 REV. D

NO. 7301 Rev. 7/68

Fig. 68-5. These are the warranty and operating instructions for a circulating fan.

Fig. 68-6. The contract is considered closed when the final payment is made.

Final Payment

After all defects on the job have been corrected, and after the contractor presents the owner with releases of claims and liens and with warranties and operating manuals, the owner formally accepts the project. He then pays the contractor all amounts due under the contract, Fig. 68-6. At this time, the contract is considered as *closed* (ended). The owner takes over all responsibility for the project, and the contractor is released of all responsibility, except as may be provided for in the warranty. The contract between the owner and the architect-engineer is closed in a similar manner.

Summary

At the completion of construction, the project is transferred from the contractor to the owner. This involves inspecting and correcting defects, release of claims and liens, providing warranties, and final payment.

Terms to Know

transferring
inspection
release of claims
claim
outstanding
settle
lien
warranty
closed contract

Think About It!

1. When is a project *closed?* What does this mean to the contractor? To the owner?
2. What would be some examples of *punch list* items for a new highway? A new house?

Servicing Property

READING 69

You have read about the processing of materials to construct a project. After the project is completed, processing does not stop. Certain activities must be carried on so that the project can serve the use for which it was built. We call these activities *servicing* or *postprocessing*. (*Post-* means *after*.) This reading concerns servicing, which consists of five activities:

1. Operating,
2. Maintaining,
3. Repairing,
4. Altering, and
5. Installing.

As examples, suppose that a new school has just been completed. *Operating* personnel might include a man to operate the heating plant and a watchman to guard the property. *Maintenance* people would include a custodian to sweep the floor and dispose of refuse and a painter to repaint the rooms when they need it, Fig. 69-1. A *repairman* might be a glazier who replaces broken windows or an electrician who fixes lights that do not work. A *carpenter* might perform an alteration job of adding an extra partition in one of the rooms. An *electrician* is installing when he puts a new public address system in a school building.

Servicing is not a minor item. The money spent in America for operating, maintaining, repairing, altering, and installing amounts to about one-half the cost of all new construction. See Fig. 69-2.

Fig. 69-1. In a school, maintenance people are needed to do many things which keep the facility operational. This includes such things as changing light tubes.

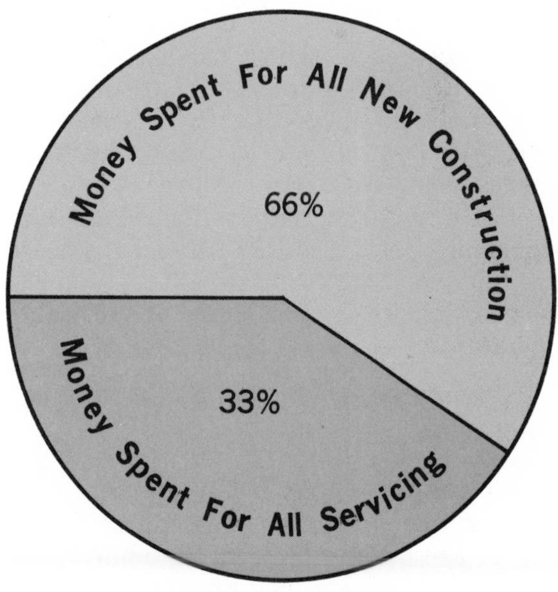

Fig. 69-2. Half as much money is spent for servicing construction as is spent for all new construction.

Who Does the Servicing

The owner has the responsibility for all servicing. Sometimes the owner does all his housekeeping, maintenance, repair, alteration, and installation himself. Sometimes the owner hires one or more employees to do the work. For example, the owner of a house might hire a painter for two days to redecorate a room.

Often, these employees are hired on a permanent rather than a temporary basis, as when a city hires operators for a sewage disposal plant. See Fig. 69-3. Often the owner hires (contracts with) a company. For instance, the owner of a house may hire a plumbing contractor to open a clogged drain or repair a leaky faucet. Many industrial firms contract with a protective agency to police their plants or with a maintenance service to provide *char* (housekeeping) *services* such as sweeping and polishing floors and cleaning windows.

Changes are sometimes so major that they are designed by architects and engineers and are constructed by general contractors who may use several subcontractors. Some changes and installations cost more than the original structure.

The knowledge, skills, and materials involved in most postprocessing are the same as those required for the original construction. Workers from every trade or craft are employed in servicing. There are also other service workers in construction whose construction knowledge is limited. Among these are guards, highway patrolmen, janitors, lockmen on navigation locks, and elevator operators.

Operating

Operating a project involves two things: keeping the equipment running properly and protecting the project. Mechanical and electrical equipment may represent as much as half the cost of a structure. Most of this equipment may have automatic controls so that the operator need not be present at all times. However, an operator or technician must make certain checks of the equipment at stated periods: daily, weekly, or monthly. Some facilities require 24-hour operators. An example is a central heating plant for a large hospital or skyscraper. Another might be a lock on a river where there is continuous boat traffic.

Large and expensive properties need security protection, not only to prevent theft

Fig. 69-3. Operators are required to keep this power and water system operating smoothly.

Fig. 69-4. Painting must be done regularly to maintain surfaces.

and vandalism but also to sound the alarm in case of fire or take action in case of a breakdown of equipment. Modern protective devices, such as automatic fire and burglar-alarm systems and closed-circuit television, have lowered the number of watchmen and guards needed, but there is still a need for someone to be present in many cases. Some projects, such as highways and harbors, require constant police patrols.

Maintaining

Maintaining is taking care of property. Maintenance may be divided into those things which must be done regularly (housekeeping) and those which may be done at stated periods (changing filters on a ducted heating or cooling system). In a house, we usually call vacuuming and mopping floors, dusting, and trash removal housekeeping. In commercial and industrial buildings, they are known as char services.

Often there is a regular schedule of periodic maintenance, such as changing filters every two months, painting interiors every four years, mowing the grass every two weeks, or sandblasting the exterior masonry walls every 25 years. Some maintenance, such as changing light bulbs in an industrial building, is done on a "spot" basis, whenever the need arises. See Figs. 69-4 and 69-5.

Repairing

Repairing is fixing. As time passes, most structures are damaged or begin to show wear and tear. There are many reasons for this. Conditions outside the structure, such as weather extremes or air pollution, may cause damage. Bad choice and treatment of materials or poor workmanship during construction may put faults in the structure which must be corrected years later. Overloading, improper use, or neglect of a structure may also damage it. Finally, the natural deterioration of some materials with aging may be severe enough so that work must be done on the structure. Repairs done when needed prolong the life of a structure and increase its value and efficiency.

Repairs make use of some of the practices you read about in constructing buildings. Of course repairs are done on a smaller scale. The whole structure is not built again. For example, a hole in a wall may be repaired or a section of a road may be torn out and replaced. See Fig. 69-6.

Fig. 69-5. Highway maintenance, such as mowing grass, keeps highways safer and more attractive.

Fig. 69-6. Roads need to be repaired by resurfacing when they wear out.

Repairs may be quite minor, such as replacing a broken window, Fig. 69-7. Sometimes they are major and cost a great deal of money. As examples, the lead roof of a large, 75-year-old church had to be repaired and given a coat of plastic treatment. This cost $200,000. Also, masonry units on the limestone facing of a 44-story office building were falling into the street. The entire exterior masonry had to be inspected and repointed (the mortar joints repaired and some of them replaced).

Another type of repair is the replacement of equipment. For instance, the water heater in a home might begin to leak after 10 years. The old heater must be taken out and a new one installed. Sometimes only one part of a piece of equipment needs to be replaced, such as a switch on a built-in oven.

Altering

Altering (remodeling) means changing the structural form of a project. Alterations usually involve adding or removing some basic part of the structure. The usual reason for making alterations is to change the project for new needs. A two-lane highway, for example, may be widened into four lanes to carry more traffic.

Fig. 69-7. Unlike resurfacing a highway, some repairs are minor. Just the same, if they are not made promptly, much additional repair may be needed.

When a structure is altered, it may be made larger or smaller in size. If an owner wished to make his warehouse larger, he could do several things. He might move a wall to widen or lengthen a space. He could also add another story or make the basement larger.

The practices for altering a structure are similar to those used in building it. However, where the load bearing framework is to be changed, it often is necessary to carry the load on different temporary and permanent supports. For instance, where a load bearing wall is removed, it must be replaced either by a column or by a heavier beam above. For this reason remodeling tends to be quite expensive, both to design and to construct. In one case a 100′ section of the wall of an old church was moved outward about 15′ at a cost of over a million dollars.

Unit costs for alterations tend to be quite high. A house was built for $12 per square foot. A room added two years later cost $33 per square foot, Fig. 69-8.

Installing

Installing usually involves *placing new equipment in a structure.* This means that a manufactured product of some sort is added to the structure. A simple case might be the installation of a television antenna.

Fig. 69-8. This house is being altered to provide an extra room.

A more complicated example might be the alteration of an office building into a laboratory. This might mean installing a heavy compressor to provide compressed air service. The air compressor might be so heavy as to require extensive structural changes or alterations.

Installing is sometimes done by manufacturing employees. Sometimes it is done by construction crews. When specialized equipment is involved, installing may even be done by manufacturer's representatives working along with construction workers. Individual contracts for large installations usually state who will do the actual installing at the site. This work is often done to modernize old construction by installing new equipment within an old structure.

Summary

Servicing or postprocessing of property takes place after the completion of construction. Postprocessing consists of operating, maintaining, repairing, altering, and installing.

Terms to Know

servicing	repairing
processing	altering
postprocessing	installing
operating	char services
maintaining	deterioration

Think About It!

1. How does *postprocessing* differ from *processing?* Is postprocessing important in construction?
2. Using a street, highway, or bridge in your community as an example, list several servicing activities that should be carried out now to improve its condition.

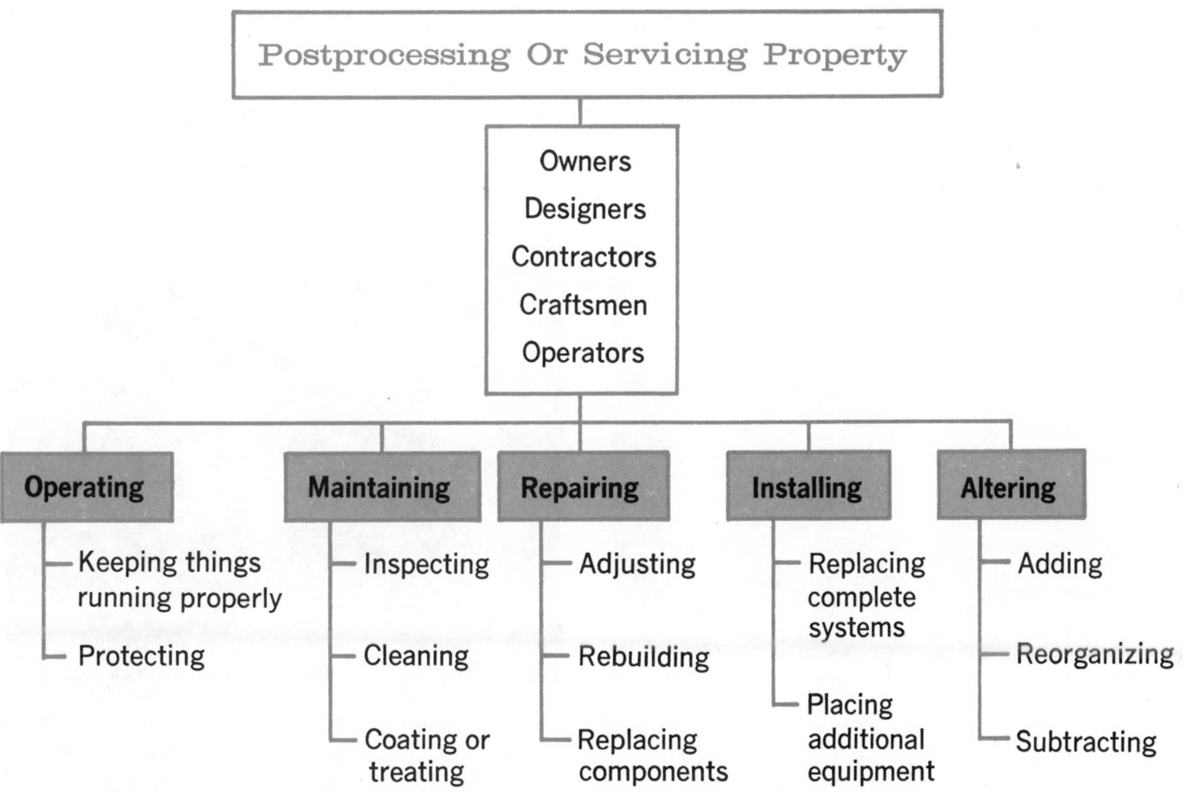

READING 70

Building Dams

This reading tells how dams are built. A dam consists of material (earth, concrete, masonry, steel, or wood) which is placed across a stream to block the flow of water. We shall consider the following topics:

1. Purposes of dams,
2. Materials used,
3. Who builds dams,
4. Planning and design,
5. Features,
6. Land acquisition, and
7. Construction.

Purposes of Dams

When a stream is dammed, the water level rises on the upstream side of the dam. The slopes of the stream valley form a *reservoir* to hold or store water, Fig. 70-1.

Water in a storage reservoir has many uses. It may be piped to a city. It may be used for watering livestock or for growing crops. Dispensing water over cropland is called *irrigation,* Fig. 70-2.

Another function of a dam is to control the flow of water downstream. The outlet works of a dam can be designed to regulate flow so that there will never be too much water in the stream below the dam. This control prevents the stream from rising above its banks to flood farm land or urban areas. We call this function *flood control,* Fig. 70-3.

Dams also function to allow enough water to flow downstream. Some streams tend to dry up partly or wholly in seasons when there is little rainfall. The outlet works of a dam can regulate water flow so that a river always will be deep enough for boats and so that it will carry away the effluent from sewage disposal plants of cities along the river (pollution abatement). A special kind

Fig. 70-1. When water in a stream is dammed, the water level rises and forms a reservoir.

Fig. 70-2. One function of a dam may be to provide water for irrigation.

of dam for navigation is used on rivers and canals in connection with locks which permit boats to pass through.

A purpose of dams closely connected with flood protection is to control the erosion (washing away) of river banks. When it rains very hard for a long time, a great deal of water falls on the land. If this water runs off too rapidly, it picks up and carries with it bits of soil. (You may have seen how muddy a river is after a hard rain.) When a river rises due to heavy rains, it moves faster. The swift current may erode the soil along the stream banks. It may undercut road beds or the substructure of bridges. Dams can be used to hold back some of the extra water temporarily, thereby reducing this erosion.

Fig. 70-3. Another function of a dam is to prevent flooding which results when uncontrolled water overflows the banks of streams or rivers.

A further purpose of some dams is to capture the energy of falling water. As it drops from the high elevation of a reservoir, water can be made to run generators which produce electricity. A power plant which harnesses energy this way is called a *hydroelectric plant,* Fig. 70-4.

Still another purpose of a dam is to form a lake for recreation (swimming, boating, water skiing, and fishing) and for the preservation of fish and wildlife, Fig. 70-5.

Many dams serve more than one purpose and are called *multipurpose projects.* For instance, the Keystone Dam near Tulsa, Oklahoma, regulates the flow of the Arkansas River (1) to prevent floods, (2) to permit navigation, and (3) to carry away sewage effluent. The dam also provides water which will eventually be used by the City of Tulsa for home and industrial pur-

Fig. 70-4. The energy of falling water can be converted into electrical energy in a hydroelectric plant such as this one.

Fig. 70-5. The reservoirs created by dams may create recreation facilities.

poses. Also, the dam produces hydroelectric power and provides a large lake for recreation, fish, and wildlife.

A secondary purpose of a dam is to provide a roadway which may be used, instead of a bridge, across a stream.

Materials

While it is possible to make a dam of a single material such as earth, concrete, masonry, steel, or wood, most of the larger dams use a combination of materials. For instance, the Keystone Dam is built of earth, steel, and concrete, with a small amount of wood and masonry.

Who Builds Dams

A great many different people may own or *initiate* a dam and reservoir project. A farmer may place a small earth dam across the upper part of a little stream to prevent soil erosion and provide water for livestock. A real estate developer may build a dam to create a lake for recreation. A city may build a dam to store water for residential and industrial use. A special district (made up of several cities and counties) may construct a dam to store water for flood control, electric power, recreation, or water supply.

Within the Federal Government, there are three agencies which build dams:

1. The Soil Conservation Service of the Department of Agriculture, which builds small dams to prevent soil erosion and floods;
2. The Bureau of Reclamation of the Department of the Interior, which builds larger dams for irrigation, flood control, and electric power; and
3. The Corps of Engineers, U.S. Army, which builds large projects for flood control, navigation, and electric power.

The dams built by these three agencies may also serve other purposes, such as water supply, recreation, and fish and wildlife conservation. See Fig. 70-6.

Small upstream dams are important in preventing soil erosion, controlling floods, and supplying water. However, most of this reading will be devoted to larger projects.

Dams are designed by civil engineers, assisted by mechanical and electrical engineers, lawyers, real estate appraisers, and sometimes agronomists (specialists in crops and soils), Fig. 70-7. Engineers also serve as managers to operate the project after completion of construction. In addition, they supervise the work of the contractors.

Dams are constructed by one or more general contractors. Usually there is more than one contract. Sometimes two or more contractors work together on a single large contract, forming what is called a *joint venture*. Most of the work is usually done by the general contractor with his own employees. Special parts, such as seeding and mulching or structural steel, may be subcontracted.

A large dam project can include many structures other than the dam itself, such as buildings and highways. The project may employ nearly every type of craftsman including operating engineers (equipment

Fig. 70-6. The water tunnel area seen under construction here is just one part of a government initiated dam project.

operators), carpenters (mostly for concrete forms), ironworkers, and laborers.

Planning and Design

The first planning step, a feasibility study, was mentioned in Reading 5. A feasibility study may take a long time; 5 to 10 years is not unusual. Public hearings are held so that those in favor of the project and those who oppose it may voice their opinions. A preliminary choice of site is made, and a very general design is prepared, including cost estimates. This permits figuring the approximate cost. Among the features to be considered are (1) the soil conditions, (2) the amount of water that can be stored, (3) the cost of the dam itself, (4) the cost of buying the real estate, and (5) the problem of moving existing roads, railroads, and utility lines outside the reservoir.

A complete economic analysis is made to determine both the yearly benefits (damage prevented and value of water supplied, for example) and the yearly costs (interest on the cost of the project and operating expenses). A benefit-cost ratio is also figured. For instance, if a dam is to be only for water supply, if the value of the water will be $120,000 per year, and if the yearly cost will be $100,000 per year, the annual benefit-cost ratio is $120,000/$100,000 or 12 to 10. The feasibility study is referred to a legislative body for approval (Congress, in case of a Federal project).

Fig. 70-7. This hydraulic engineer conducts research and uses his findings in the design of dams.

In selecting a site for the dam itself, it is desirable to find a spot where the river valley narrows, Fig. 70-8. The narrow dam site should be downstream from an area where the valley is much wider. Soil conditions along the banks must be carefully checked for their ability to withstand the weight of the dam and the pressure of the water. The availability of construction materials is checked. Also the soil beneath should not be so porous as to permit water to leak under the dam.

The area being considered for a reservoir is usually crisscrossed with roads, railroads, electric power lines, telephone lines and cables, and gas and oil pipelines. Sometimes there are even cities or towns in the reservoir areas. All of these things must be moved (or relocated) so they will not be flooded out by the waters of the reservoir.

Many times the cost and time required to accomplish relocations is greater than the cost of the dam itself. For instance, imagine the cost of moving a major railroad or interstate highway eight miles from its present position. Usually more effort is spent on designing relocations and reaching agreements with their owners than on the design of the dam, Fig. 70-9.

Features of a Dam

The principal features of major earth dams are (1) an earth embankment, (2) a concrete and steel outlet works, and (3) a concrete spillway, Fig. 70-10. The outlet works may include a power plant.

The purpose of the earth *embankment* is simply to hold back the water. It usually has an "impervious" clay core which does not transmit water. The upstream face of

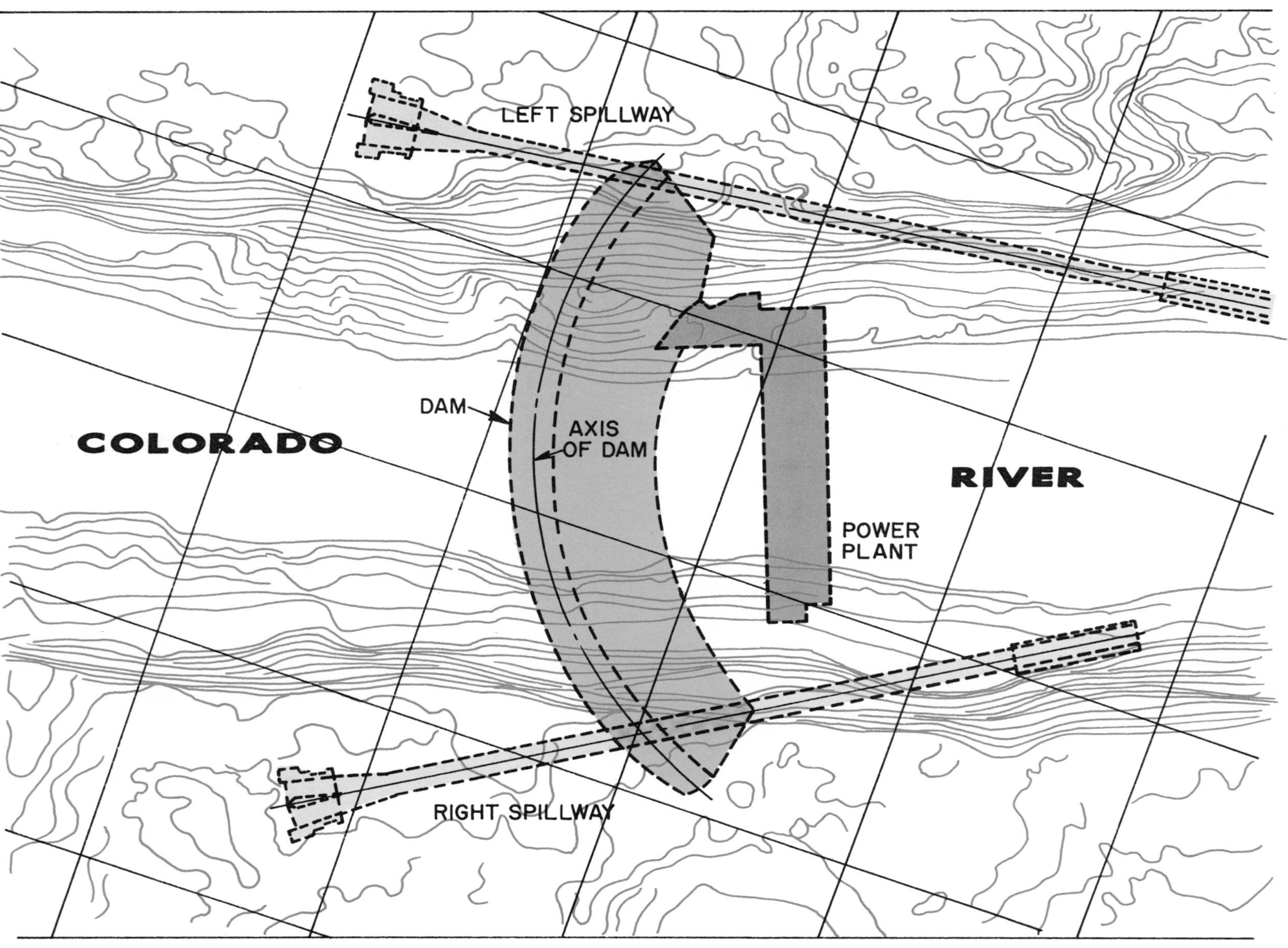

Fig. 70-8. The Glen Canyon Dam was placed at a narrow place in the Colorado River. What kind of map is this?

the embankment is covered with stone (called *rip-rap*) to prevent erosion from waves.

The *outlet works* are gates used to regulate the flow of water from the reservoir through the dam. Sometimes the gates are in tunnels.

The *spillway* is an emergency way to discharge water automatically in case very heavy rainfall above the dam should cause the reservoir to overflow.

Fig. 70-9. The construction of a dam is often a vast and complex project which requires the construction and relocation of many systems and facilities.

Fig. 70-10. This dam has an earth embankment and a concrete spillway. What is the purpose of a spillway?

Land Acquisition

The land for the dam site and the access roads is the first to be bought. Other land is acquired in stages, moving upstream from the dam site. The land for relocations is purchased as needed. On a major project, land acquisitions may take from two to seven years.

Construction

There are many ways of constructing a dam. The typical one described below gives a time schedule of contracts. Keep in mind that while work is going on at the dam, other work is being done on relocations.

The first contracts are for an access road to the dam site and for a construction field office. Sometimes the site is so far away from a town that a small city must be built there to house the workers. Because of the expense, this is avoided whenever possible.

The next contract is for excavation of the abutments (ends) of the dam.

Then a contract may be signed for the cofferdam which encloses part of the em-

Fig. 70-11. Water is often tunneled around a dam while it is being built. In this case the tunnel is being cut through solid rock.

bankment and the outlet works. This cofferdam is placed so that the first stage of the embankment and the outlet works can be built on dry land, Fig. 70-11. The river continues to flow in its original channel.

After the outlet works are complete and the first stage of the embankment is well under way, another contract is let for removing the cofferdam, moving the river channel so that it passes through the outlet works, and constructing the second stage of the embankment. For this, another cofferdam is often needed.

The spillway may be part of the first or the second stage of embankment. Sometimes it is at a location away from the dam. The spillway may be a tunnel through the earth which discharges water below the dam, out of the face of the canyon wall. See Fig. 70-12.

Usually, the final major contract is for construction of a power plant, if one is provided.

All in all, it takes a long time to build a large dam. It may take ten or more years in some cases. See Fig. 70-13.

Summary

Dams are built for water supply, flood control, navigation, recreation, and other purposes. Usually dams are built of several different materials. The planning, design, and construction of a large, multipurpose dam are a major undertaking, often requiring years for final completion.

Fig. 70-12. The back of a dam, as viewed in this picture, usually is seen only during construction. Why?

Terms to Know

reservoir	outlet works
irrigation	spillway
flood control	embankment
pollution abatement	impervious
erode	relocations
hydroelectric plant	abutments
joint venture	cofferdam

Think About It!

1. Is there a large dam in your region? If so, how does it affect your life?
2. What are some of the services provided by a multipurpose dam?

Fig. 70-13. Preparing for construction can be a major task. In this project, the Glen Canyon Dam, the equipment had to be lowered into the construction area. The speck in the sky is a large truck being carried to a site.

READING 71

Bridge Building

This reading describes how bridges are built. A bridge is a structure which carries railroad, highway, foot, or pipeline traffic over an obstacle such as a river, another highway, or a railroad.

Bridges, like other structures, consist of two parts: the superstructure and the substructure. The superstructure supports the traffic load. The substructure supports the superstructure. The substructure consists of abutments (ends) and intermediate piers (if any) as shown in Fig. 71-1.

Bridges may be fixed or movable. Fixed bridges are permanently anchored in place. Movable bridges on rivers either lift, open, or swing out of the way to permit the passage of boats that are too tall to pass under the bridge. See Fig. 71-7.

A bridge is said to be either a *through bridge* or a *deck bridge*. In a through bridge, the roadway is between the main beams or trusses. In a deck bridge, the roadway rests on top of the main beams or trusses.

Who Builds Bridges

The owner of a bridge may be a division of government (federal, state, city or county). The owner may also be a railroad, a pipeline company, or other businesses. An individual may own a small bridge.

Bridges are designed by civil engineers, sometimes assisted by architects and by the manufacturers of steel and concrete products.

There are several methods of contracting for a bridge. A general contractor may receive an award for the whole job. He may build the abutments, piers, and roadways with his own employees, but he may subcontract the superstructure to a steel com-

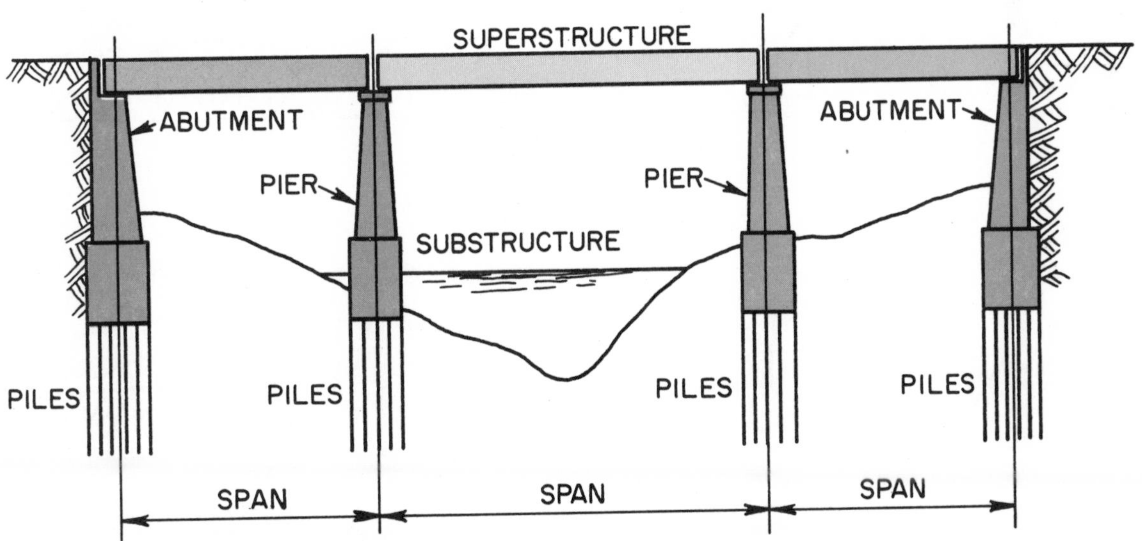

Fig. 71-1. A typical bridge structure consisting of three simple spans.

pany which manufactures, fabricates (puts together), and erects the superstructure.

Sometimes two or more contractors, one a specialist in heavy concrete work and the other in bridge superstructures, will work together as a team to do the job. At other times, the owner may award separate contracts for the substructure and the superstructure.

Principal craftsmen employed in building bridges are ironworkers, operating engineers (equipment operators), carpenters, cement finishers, and laborers.

Materials

The substructures of bridges are generally made of concrete. Masonry was used, in place of concrete, on older bridges. Wooden or steel piles are used to support the concrete where the earth alone does not give enough support. Superstructures may be made of steel, concrete, masonry, or wood. Often materials are combined. A superstructure consisting of a concrete roadway, placed on steel girders, may rest on a substructure of concrete abutments.

Precast concrete beams are often used. These are made in a concrete products yard from which they are hauled to the job. Often precast concrete beams are prestressed (contain steel wires that are stretched and tightened). Prestressed beams are stronger than ordinary reinforced concrete.

Types of Fixed Bridge Superstructures

One of the simplest types of bridges is the *reinforced concrete slab,* as shown in Fig. 71-1. It can be used for relatively short spans and fairly light loads.

Often trusses are used in place of beams to support a roadway. A *truss* is a rigid framework made by connecting long, straight pieces of wood, steel, or aluminum so as to form triangles (three-sided figures). Examples of trusses are shown in Fig. 71-2.

Arch bridges are very attractive. They are used for spanning deep ravines. The oldest arches were made of stone and masonry. Modern arch bridges are made of steel and reinforced concrete. Fig. 71-3

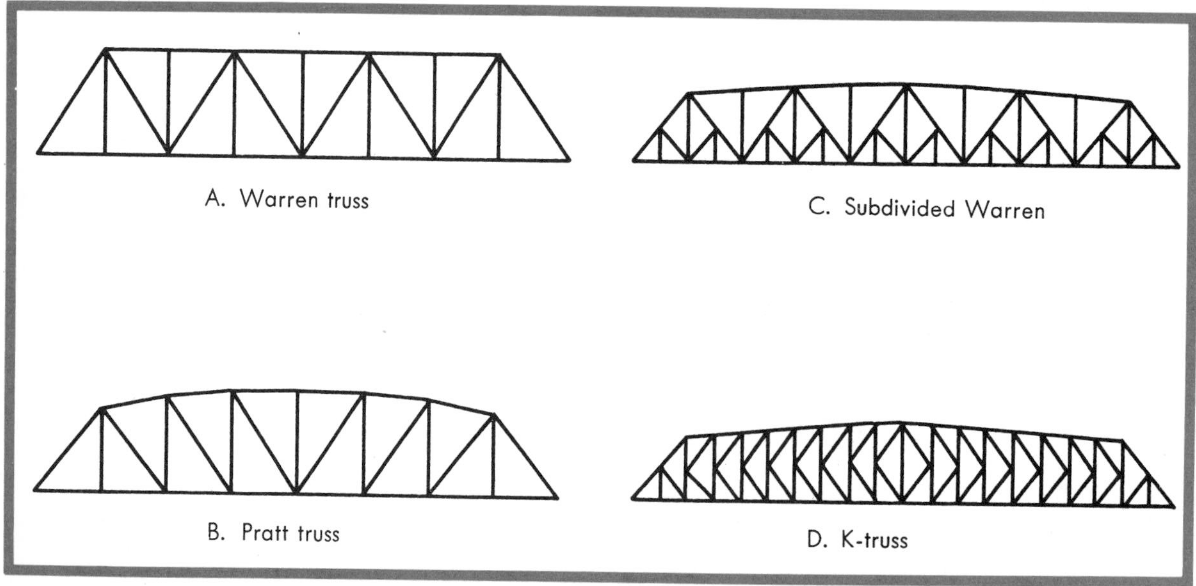

Fig. 71-2. Modern simple trusses.

shows a *spandrel braced* steel arch. The roadway and the arch ring are connected by diagonal bars, known as spandrels.

Arches of reinforced concrete are very common. There are different ways to apply the load from the roadway to the arch. Figure 71-4 shows an open spandrel reinforced concrete arch.

The *cantilever bridge* is used for fairly long spans (up to 2,000′). While cantilever bridges may be built of reinforced concrete or steel girders, the most usual form of support on a fairly long bridge is steel trusses, as shown in Fig. 71-5, A and B views.

Suspension bridges (Fig. 71-6) are used for the longest crossings. The principal load carrying elements in suspension bridges are the cables. The cables are made of thousands of parallel, galvanized-steel wires. They pass over towers and are anchored at the ends of the side spans. To reduce the sag at the center, stiffening trusses are put

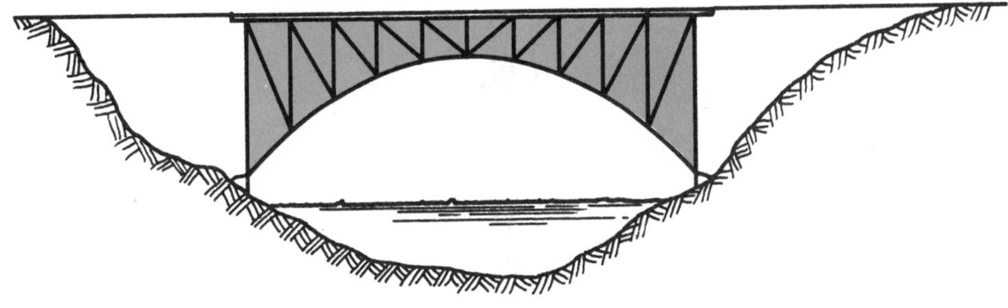

Fig. 71-3. Spandrel braced steel arch.

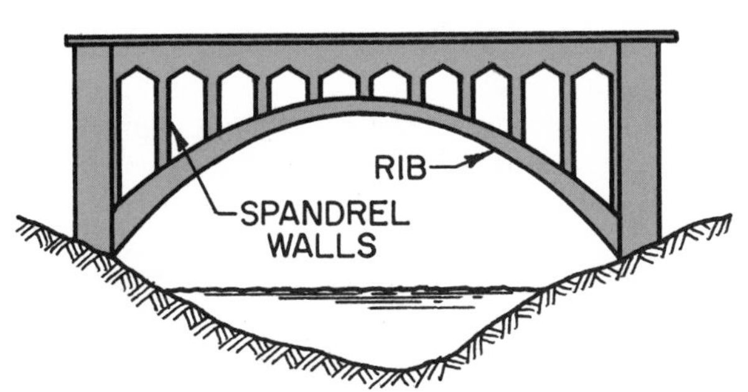

Fig. 71-4. Open spandrel reinforced concrete arch.

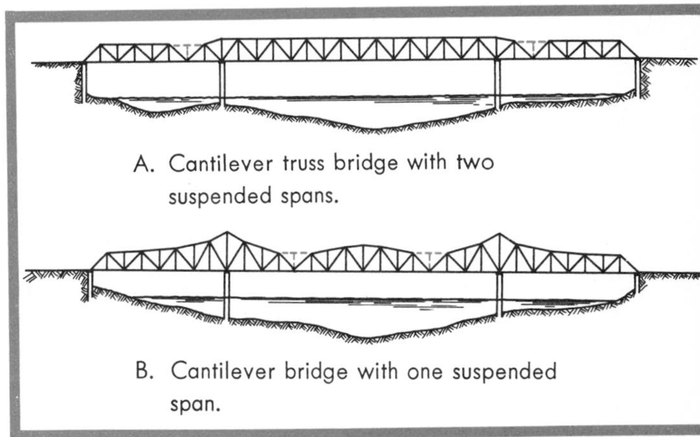

A. Cantilever truss bridge with two suspended spans.

B. Cantilever bridge with one suspended span.

Fig. 71-5. Cantilever bridges.

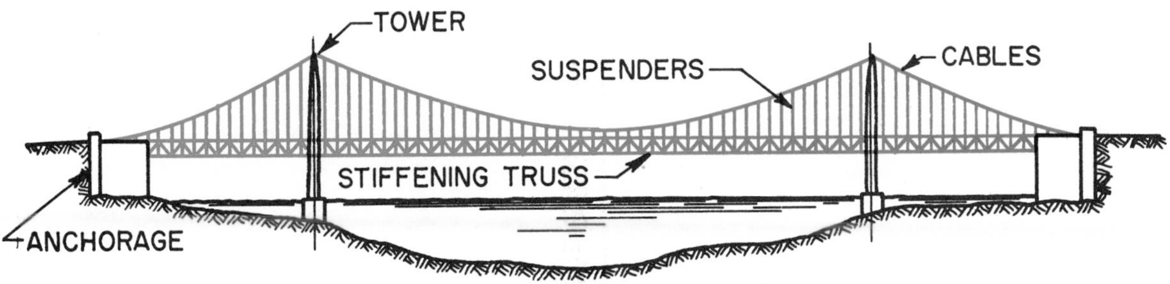

Fig. 71-6. Modern suspension bridge.

in, along the roadway, throughout the whole length of the bridge. The longest bridge in the world is the Verrazano-Narrows suspension bridge in New York. It has a span of 4,260′. The Golden Gate Bridge in San Francisco has a span of 4,200′.

Movable Bridges

Where boats in a waterway are too tall to pass under a bridge, a movable bridge is used. However, with the heavy vehicular traffic and heavy boat traffic of today, the trend is to high level, fixed bridges. Movable bridges are of three types:

1. The bascule (Fig. 71-7A),
2. The lift (Fig. 71-7B), and
3. The swing (Fig. 71-7C).

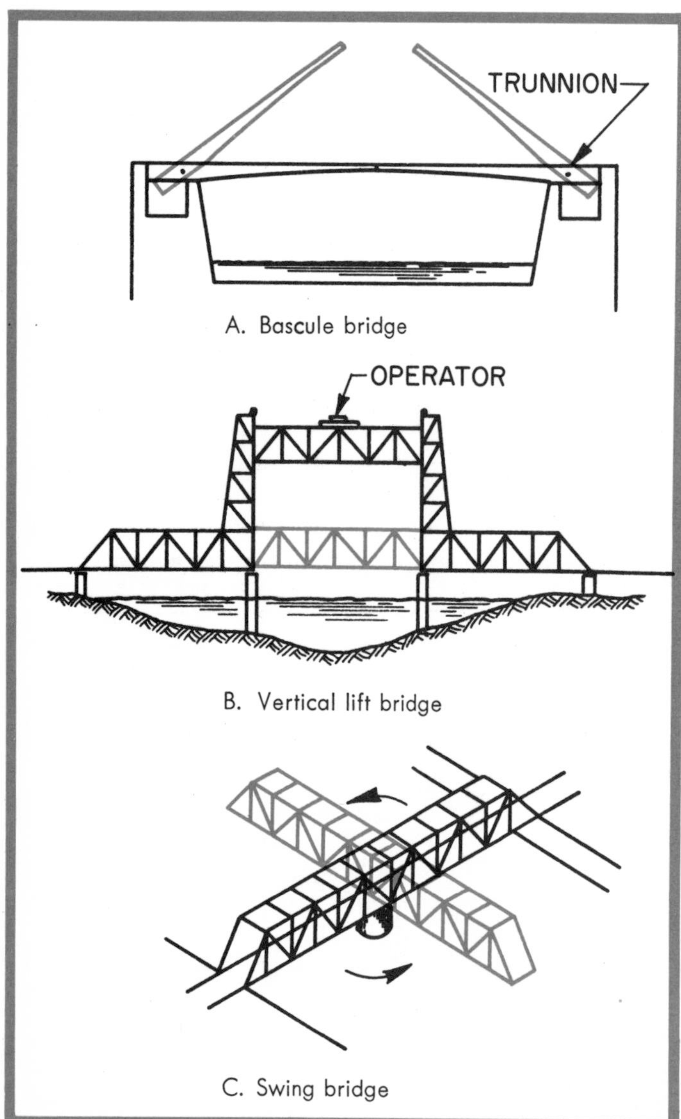

Fig. 71-7. Movable bridges.

Temporary Bridges

Temporary bridges are often made of wood, with wooden abutments and wooden pile bents or trestles, Fig. 71-8. Floating bridges are also used in military operations and under emergency conditions. Boats called *pontoons* are tied together and partially covered with a roadway of timbers or steel.

Planning and Design

The planning and design phases (feasibility study, preliminary design, cost estimates, and final design) for a bridge are the same as for any other construction project. The important decisions with respect to a

Fig. 71-8. Temporary bridges, such as this one in South Vietnam, are built by the military. Floating bridges are also used.

bridge are the type of bridge to be used, the material for the superstructure, and the exact location. No set rules for these decisions can be given.

Some of the questions which might arise are:

1. Should the bridge be fixed or movable?
2. How many intermediate piers should be placed, if any?
3. At what elevation should the bridge be located?
4. Should the bridge be a deck or a through bridge?
5. Should plate girders or reinforced concrete beams be used?
6. Should an arch, a cantilever, or a suspension design be used?

Consideration is given to the length of the obstacle to be spanned, the loads to be carried, the contours of the land, foundation conditions, the requirements for clearance below the bridge, and the appearance.

Substructure

Abutments support the ends of a bridge. They also serve as retaining walls to support the earth lying under the approach roadway. Piers are intermediate supports used when there is more than one span. Abutments and piers are usually made of reinforced concrete. They must rest on an earth formation which can support them and also the load of the superstructure and the traffic. If the earth formation is very far underground, the piers are placed on piles. Together, these piers and piles provide a substitute for a natural rock formation.

Piles can be made of timber, steel, or concrete. *Abutments* and *piers* should be constructed so they will not settle much.

The construction of abutments follows the usual techniques for earthmoving, placement of concrete, and pile driving which you have already studied. Placing piers deep underwater requires special methods involving floating cranes, barges, divers, and sometimes temporary cofferdams similar to those used in building dams.

Erecting the Superstructure

Methods for erecting the superstructure of a bridge vary with the type of bridge. For bridges using steel and precast concrete supports, as much assembly work as possible is done in a fabricating shop away from the site. For instance, many truss pieces can be welded or bolted together at the shop. The assembled unit can be quite large, as long as it can be transported and lifted into place. The unit is carried to the site by truck, rail, or barge, and it is hoisted into place with a crane. It becomes part of the structure by fastening with welds or bolts, Fig. 71-9.

When the concrete is put in place on the bridge itself, it is usually necessary to provide a large number of supports (called *falsework*) to hold the weight of the forms and the wet concrete. After the supports are placed, the concrete roadway is formed and placed. Sometimes a steel grille replaces the concrete roadway on parts of some bridges where the weight must be reduced.

Fig. 71-9. An ironworker must be an acrobat. These workers are bolting two beam frames together.

The final step consists of placing features such as ladders, guard rails, lights, and signs. Steel bridges are also given at least one coat of paint after they are erected.

Summary

Bridges are built to carry traffic over an obstacle. They have two major parts: the substructure and the superstructure. Bridges are either fixed or movable. Examples of fixed bridges include reinforced concrete slab or slab and beam, steel beam or plate girder, truss, arch, cantilever, and suspension bridges. Types of movable bridges are the bascule, lift, and swing. Bridges must be carefully designed and erected to insure the safety of the traffic crossing the obstacle.

Terms to Know

permanently anchored
through bridge
deck bridge
operating engineers
prestressed
precast
span
girders
truss
spandrels
cantilever bridge
suspension bridge
pontoons
obstacle
intermediate supports
falsework

Think About It!

1. Could you move around your community with ease without crossing a bridge? How many times do you cross a bridge each day?
2. List some human activities that could not go on in your community or state without the use of bridges.

Road Building

This reading tells the story of a road, from the time it is planned until it is finished. The road is a section of U.S. Highway 54 in central Kansas, Fig. 72-1. It is about 1½ miles long and includes a bridge. While this is a special story of one road, most roads are built in much the same way. The usual steps—planning, designing, contracting, acquiring land, constructing the road, and inspecting—were followed.

Feasibility Study

The feasibility study for a reservoir, made by the staff of the Army Engineers, indicated that part of U.S. 54 would be flooded by the waters of the reservoir. The road either had to be relocated or raised so that it would not be under water. Therefore, the feasibility study for the road concerned how and where the road should be rebuilt.

The Army Engineers used rainfall information and considered clearances for small boat traffic on the reservoir to decide (1) how wide the opening for the bridge had to be and (2) how much clearance there should be under the bridge to permit boats to pass under.

Fig. 72-1. This is the story of Highway 54 and the relocation of this bridge.

Several different ways were considered for rebuilding the road without stopping traffic on U.S. Highway 54 during construction.

Plan 1—The engineers thought of moving the road about a mile to the north, but the route would have been too long.

Plan 2—The engineers thought of moving the bridge about 500′ to the south, but soil and foundation conditions were poor.

Plan 3—The engineers thought of raising the height of the road by building an embankment above the present road and building a new bridge, but this would have been too costly.

Plan 4—The engineers considered raising the bridge and embankment 10′, using the five old piers and adding a sixth pier and seventh span for the wider opening needed.

The fourth plan was adopted as the least costly, as having the shortest construction time, and as interfering least with traffic, Fig. 72-2.

Funding

Money was provided on the following schedule:

1st year—Planning and designing; buying the land.

2nd year—Starting work on road and bridge.

3rd year—Completing road and bridge.

Designing and Engineering

It was agreed by the Army Engineers that the Kansas Highway Commission would design the road and bridge and would award the contracts. The Army Engineers and the Kansas Highway Commission made a *cost reimbursable contract*. In this contract the Army Engineers agreed to pay the Commission for all costs involved in designing and building the project.

The road and bridge were designed by the Kansas Highway Commission staff, Fig. 72-3. The steps taken are the ones used for designing nearly all roads.

A detailed survey was made of the site. Holes were bored to test the soil and to determine foundation conditions for the new highway, Fig. 72-4.

The Commission staff made a study to find the best materials for the high embankment needed on the bridge approaches. They considered how much the bank should slope and the kind of earth which was available in the area for fill. The way of placing and rolling the fill was selected.

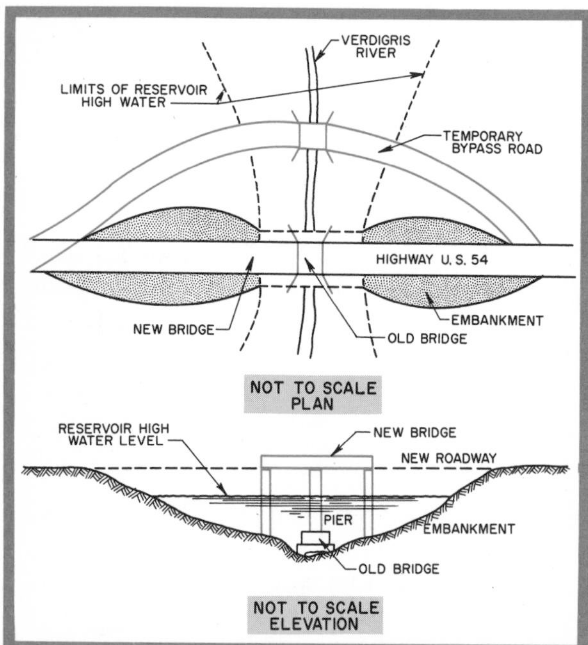

Fig. 72-2. This plan was decided upon. The bridge will be raised 10′.

For the extra span of the bridge, it was decided to use the same type of superstructure (steel girders) and pavement (concrete) as in the rest of the bridge. A study of the road revealed that the best type of surface material for the road would be a flexible pavement: asphalt or blacktop.

The problem of how to avoid blocking traffic during construction was studied. It was decided to build a *bypass* detour just

Fig. 72-3. The Highway Department designed the relocation project.

Fig. 72-4. The Highway Department had to make test borings and study soil conditions before and during construction.

north of the site. The detour was to be far enough away so that it would not interfere with construction.

The bypass road was then designed. A double-surfaced asphalt road and a wooden bridge were found to be the least expensive for the detour.

After all these questions had been decided, the Commission went ahead with detailed working drawings, specifications, and schedules. As a guide, it used the standard specifications of the Kansas Highway Department and the rules of the U.S. Bureau of Public Roads.

Bidding and the Construction Contract

After final approval of detailed plans and specifications, the bidding papers were made up, adding standard rules for Kansas Highway contracts. An *Invitation to Bid* was given to all contractors who had shown an interest in jobs of this kind. The job also was announced in newspapers in the area and in statewide and regional trade or contractors' publications, Fig. 72-5. A thirty-day period was given for the contractors to prepare their bids. During this time an owner's estimate was made to use later in checking the bids. On the appointed day, bids were received and opened.

After careful checking of the bids, a contract was *let* (issued). The successful bidder then gave a performance bond (deposit). Shortly after that, he was given a notice to start the work.

CONSTRUCTION NEWS

60

TAKING BIDS:

2/23, 11 A.M., SUBWAY STRUCTURE (CONTR K-5) HSK — CHICAGO ILL (CITY)

2/23, 11 A.M., SUBWAY STRUCTURE (CONTR K-4) (SPECS 8.68-68-4 RSXX — CHICAGO ILL (CITY)

2/23, 12 NOON, SITE WORK (FOR INSTAL OF NEW OUTDOOR 34 KV STRUCTURE) RS — WILMETTE ILL (COMMONWEALTH EDISON CO)

2/23, 2 P.M., BRIDGE AND HIGHWAY RELOCATION, KANSAS HIGHWAY COMMISSION, TOPEKA

2/23, 8 P.M., WATER DISTRIBUTION SYSTEM (SPEC ASSMT #67 CO 737) $1,065,000 — PALOS HILLS ILL (CITY)

LOW BIDDERS:

SEWER CONTROL REHABILITATION (67-40) (DRS-CLS-S) RIVER GROVE ILL FOR METRO SANI DIST — #464 217 D

LOW & ONLY BIDDER:

STAGG CONST CO — 4451 N RAVENSWOOD CHGO ILL $105,798

Fig. 72-5. An invitation to bid was placed in newspapers and trade journals.

Construction

The area around the site was mostly pasture land, so very little clearing was necessary, Fig. 72-6. The first operation was the layout of the site by a surveyor.

There had to be another route for traffic before construction on the permanent road and bridge could begin. Therefore, the temporary bridge and bypass road were built, Fig. 72-7. Piling for the temporary wooden bridge were driven, and the beams and roadway were added. At the same time, the grading and paving for the bypass road

Fig. 72-6. The site was cleared, excavated, and filled.

were done. About three months after starting, traffic was detoured from the main highway to the bypass. The contractor could now begin constructing the permanent bridge.

While the bypass was being built, the contractor's field and office personnel were very busy. They made schedules, bought materials, rented or bought needed equipment, hired workers, made detailed shop drawings, and made subcontracts. As soon as the traffic was detoured, the contractor began the two main parts of his job: the bridge and the embankment.

The whole superstructure was lifted about three feet at a time by hydraulic and screw jacks. I-beams were then put in place of the jacks. Then a 2½′ *lift* of concrete was placed around the I-beams. Four lifts of this kind raised the bridge 10′.

As soon as the embankment near the ends of the bridge was made high enough, new abutments (end piers) were constructed of concrete. While this was going on, the steel work for the extra span was being made in the shop. Also the new sixth pier was built.

Finally, the new seventh span was lifted into place (Fig. 72-8), and the concrete roadway over the new span and new sections of guard rail were put in.

Meanwhile, construction of the embankment was proceeding. After tearing out the old road with a bulldozer and rooter and excavating to the right level, the contractor began the fill. Tractor scrapers carried earth from nearby pits. As each 6″ layer of fill or earth was placed, it was rolled by sheepsfoot rollers that were pulled by tractors, Fig. 72-9. This packed down the soil in the embankment according to specifications.

Stone riprap was placed on the sides of the embankment to keep it from being washed away by rain or by the waters of the reservoir. Then the embankment top was seeded and coated with straw to hold the seed in place. Finally, the asphalt surface of the road was placed, Fig. 72-10.

Fig. 72-8. Steelwork for the seventh span was placed.

Fig. 72-7. A bypass was constructed so traffic could continue while work was being done on the bridge.

Fig. 72-9. The new embankment was rolled, one layer at a time, by a sheepsfoot roller.

When the road and bridge were finished, they were opened to traffic, Fig. 72-11. The bypass was closed, the bypass bridge was taken down, and the bypass road was torn up.

Inspection

During all steps of the construction, inspectors of the Kansas Highway Commission were busy. They checked on the firmness of the fill, on the quality and strength of the concrete, on the placement of reinforcing steel, and on the correct alignment of all parts of the job. They insisted that plans and specifications be followed exactly.

Upon final completion of the highway, a detailed inspection was made by the Army Engineers and the Kansas Highway Commission. The contractor was given a list of things to correct. When these defects had been corrected, the Commission accepted the work from the contractor and gave him the final payment.

Summary

You have followed the story of a road through the steps of the feasibility study, the design, the contracting, the acquiring of land, the construction, and the inspection. These are the steps usually followed in road building.

Fig. 72-10. The new roadway and bridge were paved with asphalt.

Terms to Know

clearance	Invitation to Bid
funding	to *let* contracts
cost reimbursable contract	detoured
permanent	hydraulic
specifications	screw jacks
asphalt	a *lift* of concrete
blacktop	sheepsfoot roller
bypass	acquiring of land
	feasibility

Think About It!

1. How would your life be changed if there were few or no roads in your community?
2. Has the Interstate Highway System affected your life? Ask your parents how these roads have affected them.

Fig. 72-11. Finally, after being modified and inspected, the road and bridge were reopened. How the bridge was raised can be seen by comparing this picture with the bridge shown in Fig. 72-1.

READING 73

Building Skyscrapers

Skyscrapers became possible about 100 years ago when technology developed elevators and metal framework for buildings, Fig. 73-1. Before that, the weight of most buildings was carried by the walls themselves so that the lower part of a tall structure had to have very thick walls. The lack of elevators limited most business and apartment buildings to about six stories.

Skyscrapers have many uses: office buildings, apartments, hotels, and universities. Most recently skyscraper construction has been used for assembling rockets to launch spaceships.

Fig. 73-1. Steel has played a vital role in making skyscrapers possible.

One of the world's tallest buildings is the Empire State Building in New York. Its height is 102 stories or 1,239′. One of the world's most spacious buildings is the Apollo/Saturn V vehicle assembly building at Cape Kennedy, Florida, Fig. 73-2.

Who Builds Skyscrapers

The initiator (and owner) of a skyscraper may be:

1. A commercial or industrial company which needs a large amount of office space,
2. A real estate developer (an individual or a corporation) who rents office or apartment space for a profit, or

Fig. 73-2. The Apollo/Saturn V assembly building contains more space than any other government building in the world.

3. A governmental unit needing office space for its employees.

A skyscraper is such a major undertaking that it is usually designed by several architectural and engineering firms. These firms will include specialists in foundations, structural framework, and utility systems within the building.

A general contractor is usually selected to construct the skyscraper. He will employ many subcontractors to do mechanical work, electrical work, and other special jobs. In addition, he will nearly always subcontract the erection of the steel in a steel frame building. Complicated foundations are also subcontracted.

Nearly all types of building tradesmen are employed in the building of a skyscraper, Fig. 73-3.

Planning and Design

The first step of planning is a *feasibility study* for the initiator, Fig. 73-4. The study will consider whether there is a need for the skyscraper, whether offices or apartments can be rented profitably, and even whether the skyscraper will be good advertising for a company. Also considered is the availability of a good site.

Having made the decision to erect a skyscraper at a certain location, the owner then buys the land for the site. This is usually done by a middleman such as a realtor.

It may take several years to buy all the land needed. Often the site consists of several plots of ground, each owned by a different person or group of persons. Some plot owners may not want to sell, or they may ask very high prices for their land.

While land is being bought, the design begins. Skyscrapers place heavy loads on their foundations. The heavy load is caused by the weight of the structure and by wind. Sometimes the design of a foundation must include a means of resisting earthquakes. The superstructure must be carefully designed so that the framework has enough strength

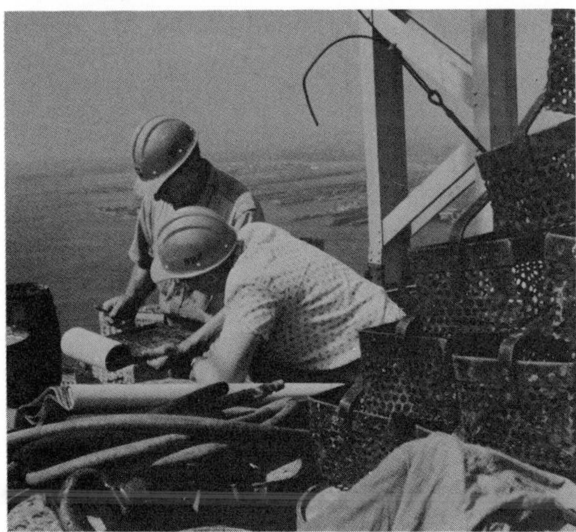

Fig. 73-3. Many men, including engineers and tradesmen, help in the building of a skyscraper.

Fig. 73-4. This structure will be a large office building. In the planning stage it was determined that enough office space could be rented to make the structure feasible.

and so that the building has a pleasing appearance. Heating, ventilating, piping systems, and electrical and communications networks inside the building must be planned. Also, consideration must be given to architectural details such as exterior and interior walls and finishes. All in all, the drawings and specifications for a skyscraper might well weigh over 1,000 pounds and might cover several acres if laid out flat.

Demolition

Very few skyscrapers are built on open fields or vacant lots. Usually the first operation on the site is tearing down or *demolishing* existing buildings, Fig. 73-5. This is usually accomplished with crowbars, cutting torches, bulldozers, and a heavy ball suspended from the boom of a crane. Safety of both the wrecking crew and the general public is most important in demolition work.

Foundations

Because of the heavy loads on skyscraper foundations, an attempt is made to carry them down to bedrock wherever possible. Where bedrock is several hundred feet below the surface, pilings are often used.

Steel sheet piling, tightly braced, usually is driven around the outside edge (perimeter) of the site to provide support for streets near the site, underground utilities, subways, and existing buildings, Fig. 73-6. Sometimes very elaborate supports, called *underpinnings,* must be provided for nearby (adjacent) structures. Steps must be taken to pump out underground water.

Other foundation operations include excavating the soil, placing the footings or piling, and placing the underground portions of the exterior walls.

Framework of Superstructure

The framework of a skyscraper is made of steel. However, recent techniques using reinforced concrete permit erecting a high rise building with *load bearing walls,* thus eliminating the framework, Fig. 73-7.

A steel framework consists of *beams* (horizontal members) and *columns* (vertical members). The beams *carry the weight of the walls and the floors* and prevent the columns from moving sideways. The columns *carry the loads from the beams and from wind* down to the foundation.

Fig. 73-5. Often an existing structure is cleared away to make room for the new one.

Fig. 73-6. Steel sheet piling is being placed on this site.

The members of a steel frame building are joined by high strength bolts, welds, or rivets. Rivets are not used very often. As much as possible of the framework is *prefabricated* in the shop and joined together on the site.

Members may be lifted into place with a traveling, long boom crane on the ground. (This equipment can hoist materials as much as 20 stories.) Lifting may be done from the ground with a *tower crane.* Also, a *guy derrick* on top of the building may be used to lift materials. It can be moved up two stories at a time.

Usually the framework for two stories is erected at once. Members are hoisted into place and fastened by temporary bolts. Then the beams are made level and the columns *plumb.* After this, the permanent connections are made with high strength bolts or welds, Fig. 73-8. Then the process is repeated two stories at a time until the framework is "topped out."

Fig. 73-7. Recent findings have allowed reinforced concrete to be used in high rise structures.

Floors and Walls

Floor systems may be of concrete, steel, or a combination of these. Exterior walls are usually of masonry or of metal, glass, or plastic panels. See Fig. 73-9.

When the frame is up a few stories, the contractor will begin to enclose the interior by installing the floor systems (all except the top covering) and the exterior walls. Normally, this work is done one story at a time, beginning at the bottom. However, it is not necessary to wait for one story to be 100% complete before starting the next one.

Fig. 73-8. Steel members may be riveted together with high strength steel rivets.

Fig. 73-9. Exterior walls are enclosed. Various kinds of materials are used: glass, masonry, metal.

Utilities

Installation of the utilities involves plumbing, ductwork, electrical and communications lines, and elevators. Usually the installation of utilities begins right behind the structural framework.

Interior Finishes

Each story is finished out after it is closed in by the floors and exterior walls. This involves insulating, installing interior partitions, finishing floors, trimming, applying interior wall finishes, and installing accessories and fixtures.

Coordination

Building a skyscraper requires that everyone involved work together closely. Working space is quite limited, and there is very little room to store construction materials and equipment. The capacity of the temporary hoists and elevators used during construction is likewise very small. These elevators are carefully scheduled by a computer months in advance, Fig. 73-10. As an example, if the schedule calls for lifting electrical conduit to the 26th floor at 9:45 a.m., on August 20, the electrical contractor must have the conduit on the site at that time as well as the men to load and unload it.

Fig. 73-10. The elevators at the site are in such demand that their use if often scheduled months in advance.

Summary

The skyscraper is a structure that is quite different from almost any other. It gives the greatest amount of useful space on the least amount of land. Although skyscrapers have been built in other countries, their development and widespread use are mostly American.

Terms to Know

skyscraper	wrecking crew
elevator	underpinning
initiator	excavating
feasibility study	plumb
erect	tower crane
site	guy derrick
demolition	"topped out"
crowbar	coordination
cutting torch	capacity

Think About It!

1. Why do you think the development and widespread use of skyscrapers is uniquely American?
2. What is the tallest building in your community? How many floors does it have? Can you give some reasons why it was made so high?

Constructing in the Future

Construction technology (the use of tools, equipment, and techniques to build things on a site) must change often to meet the changes in the world's needs. Changes in construction technology will take the form of new designs, advanced techniques of construction, better materials, more productive equipment, and more highly skilled workmen.

The Challenge

In the years ahead, the construction industry faces major challenges. It must provide for the needs of a steadily increasing population and for a better life for the people of the future, Fig. 74-1.

The size of the building job which faces us is great. By the year 2000, or in about 30 years, we must construct as much in the United States as is now standing, Fig. 74-2. The needs of many other nations, especially those in Latin America, Africa, and Asia, are also great.

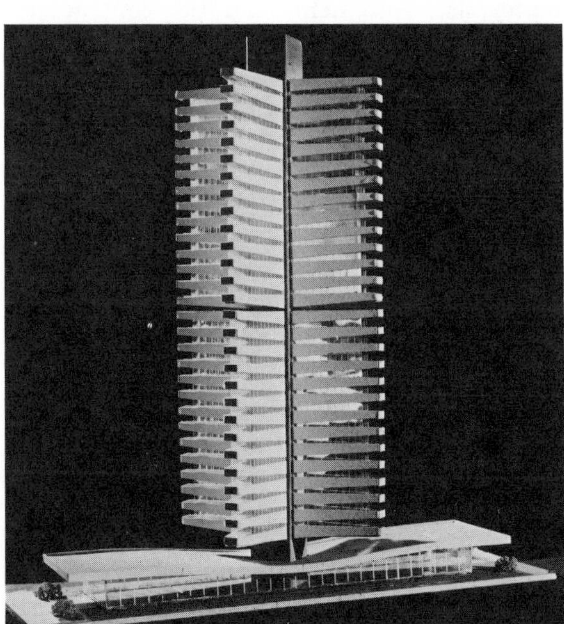

Fig. 74-1. Construction in the cities will be challenging. This futuristic model suggests a reinforced concrete frame using glass so that every floor is bathed with natural light.

Fig. 74-2. Construction technology will change as much as or more than it has already changed. Early settlers obtained lumber or timbers by what is now an outdated method—sawing logs on an elevated framework. Today we are capable of cutting the same materials with a beam of light (laser). You will help determine the technology of the future.

Rebuilding of large parts of our cities is very important. Poor housing is a major cause of unrest among those of our people who spend their lives in poor surroundings, both in cities and in rural areas. Somehow, we must have better houses at a lower cost.

Although our country generally has enough total rainfall, some areas of the country are too dry. Major construction projects must be started to provide high quality fresh water for all the people, for the agricultural production of food and fiber, and for industry. One water project which is now underway in California will cost several billion dollars. Some parts of the world urgently need a cheap method of taking the salt out of seawater so it may be used as fresh water.

Our airports, highways, railroads, and waterways are not now able to meet our needs. The transportation facilities we have must be made larger, and many new ones must be built for the increased traffic of the future, Fig. 74-3. Our manufacturing plants must be expanded. More facilities are needed for education, government, recreation, flood control, and reduction of air and water pollution. All these needs must be met at a cost our people can afford.

Fig. 74-3. One of the major areas of concern of future construction technology is that of improving transportation systems.

Construction technology faces the challenge of a huge job to be done. It also faces a great many *obstacles*.

First, the development of the new technology has been slow. Compared with the science of electronics (radio, television, radar), construction technology has almost stood still. Many improvements in building have already been started. However, they have not been developed to the point of everyday use.

Second, there has always been a *resistance* to change. Many buildings today are only a little different from those of 100 years ago. The methods of building them also remain much the same. Laws, ordinances, building codes, labor practices, and testing laboratory requirements are based mostly on products we have now. It takes years to introduce a new item or material and to have it accepted. Many aluminum and plastic products are not yet accepted in certain locations.

Third, a great percentage of the cost of a facility is in addition to the cost of labor, materials, equipment, and the contractor's overhead and profit. This percentage is made up of legal, financing, insurance, and other administrative charges. Ways need to be found to lower these costs.

Meeting the Challenge

To help meet the construction needs of tomorrow's world, new developments are underway in design, methods, materials, and use of manpower.

Advanced and imaginative designs hold special promise. Among these is *the modular system.* In this system all dimensions of buildings are designed in standard stock sizes of building products. The modular system is already in use in some areas. It results in easier design and construction, takes less labor, and greatly lowers waste, Fig. 74-4.

Second, there are prefabricated units such as Habitat '67. This was designed by Mr. Mosche Safdie and was built at Expo '67 in

Montreal, Canada. The building has 354 precast concrete box housing units. These units were prefabricated in a factory where they were fitted with trim, doors, plumbing, wiring, insulation, one-piece molded bathrooms (eliminating over 500 handmade connections), and laminated-plastic kitchen packages.

More recently, the 21-story Palacio del Rio Hotel in San Antonio was designed and constructed by the H. B. Zachry Co. in less than 10 months. Each room unit was built in a factory or yard. The room units were complete with furniture. Even the beds were made! Then the units were transported by truck to the job site and hoisted into place with a crane. See Fig. 74-5.

Fig. 74-4. New and promising techniques of construction call for precasting modular units such as these.

Fig. 74-5. The precast units, finished and furnished, are set in place by a crane.

Fig. 74-6. Other promising techniques of construction call for remodeling of existing structures.

Third, there is the development of designs for remodeling older structures that are substandard, but structurally sound. A great many 100- to 200-year-old houses in Philadelphia have been converted into modern buildings which keep their original outward appearance, Fig. 74-6. Prefabricated units have been tried for remodeling older housing in New York and Boston.

Other new methods show promise. For excavation, nuclear explosives will be used. It has been estimated that almost a billion dollars can be saved in the excavation of the new Panama Canal by using atomic blasting.

New techniques of management and planning also will lower the cost and increase the efficiency of construction. The Critical Path Method (CPM) and Program Evaluation and Review Technique (PERT) ways of scheduling construction are already in use. Computers, data processing, systems analysis, and *input-output* and *simulation models* also can be used for the design and management of construction, Fig. 74-7.

Fig. 74-7. The computer will greatly aid the engineer and designer in the future. An engineer, using a light pen and a keyboard, can vary the size and strength of the beam and instantly see the results on the computer's TV-like screen.

The future will see more development and use of building products which are now undergoing change. Wood will be molded into many new shapes. There will be more use of laminates such as plywood and built-up, glued, thin panels. Better preservatives and finishes will greatly lower the maintenance needed.

Plastics will be used much more for features such as wall panels, prefabricated kitchens and bathrooms, and flooring, Fig. 74-8. Plastic forms for concrete will replace other materials. Fiber glass will be used more in construction. Fiber glass structural shapes, such as I-beams, are already on the market.

The durability and strength of metals such as steel and aluminum will be improved. Development of a material with the strength of steel, but with less weight, will be eagerly sought. Other materials such as plasterboard (gypsum board) and clay products will be greatly improved in strength, fire resistance, and reduction of maintenance.

The use of prestressed and precast concrete will increase. Better roofing materials

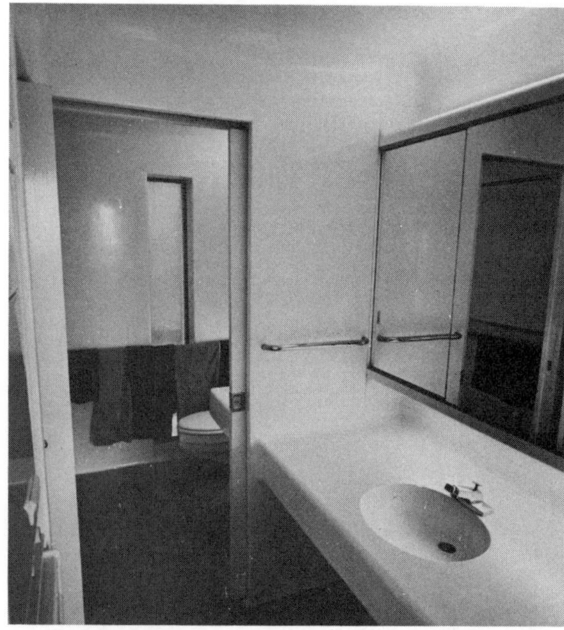

Fig. 74-8. Plastics will be molded and prefabricated into complete units as in this futuristic bathroom.

will be used. *Adhesives* will replace fasteners such as welds, nails, bolts, and mortar which are used now. *Epoxy resins* are already being used because of their great strength. A compact package may be developed for a single house that contains heating, ventilating, air conditioning, water supply, and waste disposal units.

In general, construction equipment will be more powerful, be able to do more, become more specialized, and operate at far greater speeds than today's models. One example of a new development will be a more flexible crane. Much of the scaffolding and falsework now needed will then become unnecessary.

A major trend will be the need for more skilled labor and less common labor. Many changes in labor practices will be needed. For example, new materials with prefinished, low maintenance surfaces will greatly lower the need for painters. New materials and methods of construction will require new skills. To learn these skills, construction workers will be constantly retrained.

The Distant Future

Further down the road into the twenty-first century, the city of the future may be a completely enclosed unit which could exist anywhere, even on another planet, Fig. 74-9. The trend toward such construction is seen today in covered shopping malls and sports arenas such as the Houston Astrodome. A city of the future may be completely roofed over, and the air may be heated, cooled, and

Fig. 74-9. In the future we may be living, working, and traveling in controlled environments.

Fig. 74-10. The future may see man exploring and constructing in space and under the sea.

purified. Such an enclosed city is said to be *encapsulated,* meaning that it is placed within a covering or capsule. It would be heated and air-conditioned with purified air, free from all pollution. It would have its own nuclear power plant, and all wastes would be reclaimed.

Transportation would be powered by engines which would release no pollutants into the air. A high standard of housing would be provided for all the people in the city. Most of these features can be provided by present day technology.

Summary

Unfulfilled needs of the present, plus those arising in the future, for housing, transportation, water, power, industrial development and pollution-abatement present a major challenge to construction technology.

To meet this challenge, there must be developed new designs, methods, and materials, as well as additional manpower skills.

Terms to Know

obstacles
modular system
dimensions
prefabricated units
laminated plastic
remodeling
encapsulated
flexible
epoxy resins
adhesives
molded
substandard
computers
data processing
system analysis
preservatives
durability
reclaimed waste

Think About It!

1. Why has the development of construction technology been slow in the United States?
2. Within the next 30 years, or by the year 2000, what changes will have to be made if we are to meet the demands for structures of all kinds?

Constructing Housing

Practices of site clearing, setting foundations, building superstructures, installing utilities, and finishing projects are used in building houses, just as they are used in building other constructed works. However, house building equipment usually is small as compared with that used in commercial and heavy construction. Even so, each year housing construction makes up more than half of the total production of the construction industry.

House construction has been important to man from his very beginning. In this lesson you will read about house construction of the past, the present, and the future. Then, for the next several weeks, you will study house building techniques as you design and construct a model of your dream home.

Fig. 75-1. Man's earliest houses were caves.

The Past

House construction is as old as man. From the beginning, man had to have shelter to protect him from animals and from the weather. The first houses were natural shelters such as caves and rock ledge overhangs, Fig. 75-1. As man left his caves to move to new hunting grounds about 20,000 B.C., he developed movable homes much like the teepees used by the Plains Indians of the United States. These movable homes were made of animal hides stretched over a wooden frame. They were put up wherever man found a good food supply. This kind of

Fig. 75-2. Early houses in America were made like this. Men wove a lattice of saplings to form the wall. The wall was then plastered with mud.

Ranch

Colonial

Cape Cod

Oriental

Spanish

Georgian

House Styles

structure is still used today by the nomads of Northern Africa and the Near East.

Through the ages man changed from a being who moved from place to place looking for food to a being who settled in one place. In this place he tamed his animals and planted his crops. It was at this time that the field of house construction began. Man had to use whatever natural materials he could find to build his houses. At first there were brush houses, stone houses, mud wall houses, log houses, and houses using combinations of these materials, Fig. 75-2. A little later, as man learned to make bricks from straw and mud, there were brick houses. These materials were used through the ages and are still used even today to construct homes.

The Present

Man of today is a settled being. He lives with his family in a house close to his place of employment. This house may be a conventional type house, a precut house, or a prefabricated house.

The *conventional house* is one which has all the construction processes done at the site. The material is brought in and cut to size and erected on the site.

Tudor

The *precut house* is one in which most of the material is precut to size at the manufacturing plant. Then it is brought to the site and erected.

The *prefabricated house* is one in which the house is constructed in sections at the factory and then is brought to the building site and erected. Some houses are constructed using combinations of these three kinds of construction.

The area of house construction is listed by the United States Department of Labor as part of the Contract Construction Industry. In 1965, approximately 20% of the entire labor force of the United States worked directly or indirectly in occupations which support house construction. In 1965, the gross national product was 676.3 billion dollars. Included in this figure was the total outlay of 26.7 billion dollars for nonfarm residential buildings.

The Future

The trend in the field of house construction will be to the *suburban* kind of *residential areas*. These will be located near cities where most of the future centers of population will be located to meet the housing needs of city workers.

The suburban type residential areas will be made up of town houses, apartments, and individually owned houses. There are many proposed plans of construction, and most of these involve the use of prefabricated or precut elements. See Fig. 75-3.

Many new methods of house construction will be developed in the future because of new materials being developed and the engineering talent being used to create new building systems. The adoption of these new methods, however, will not be easy. The new methods must be cheaper and easier to use than the present methods. The problem of meeting the standards of local building codes and labor practice will demand that the building codes and regulations be redesigned.

Fig. 75-3. Many feel that the planned community, such as the one at Reston, Virginia, will typify suburban housing in the future. The town houses and apartments are owned by the residents.

Summary

The field of house construction began with early man's need to protect himself. Now the value of the housing produced each year is more than half the total value of the annual production of the construction industry.

The housing needs of the future will require the building of two million units a year beginning in 1970. In the construction industry, there is a continuing search for better methods and materials to make possible more efficient and comfortable homes.

Terms to Know

conventional house	occupations
precut house	residential
prefabricated house	planned community

Think About It!

1. Why is there a greater demand for housing units now than ever before in history?
2. Do most of your classmates live in apartments or single family homes? In your community, which type of housing is growing more rapidly? Why?

Your Dream House

You have studied the importance of the housing industry and read that new methods of house construction will be developed in the future. You should also realize that, due to changes in our way of life, families will be wanting different types of space and facilities. In thinking toward the future, preparing to plan your dream house, you should give careful thought to what your dream house should be like. Before a site is selected, and before any detailed design work begins, a written statement should be drawn up telling what the family who will live in the house wants, Fig. 76-1.

Personal Needs

Even within one area there are wide differences of family size and way of life. A designer must understand the needs and wants of a family before he can plan. He must know how many people are in the family, how they live, and how they want to live, Fig. 76-2.

Fig. 76-1. Before plans for your dream house are drawn, your family's needs and wants should be determined.

The space needed, especially the number of bedrooms, depends on the size of the family. Also, size of the house depends on what the family wants for comfort and convenience. Therefore the family's way of life should be known and written down. The family members may not have thought too much about what they want until they are asked about it.

The designer must know if the living room is to have dining space in it. The kitchen must be carefully thought out, and needed equipment must be listed. For example, if a woman bakes a lot, she might want two ovens. Number and sizes of bedrooms, closets, baths, storage spaces and special spaces for family work and play should be listed. Swimming pools and recreation rooms might also be important to the family.

Immediate personal needs are what the family wants now. However, future needs also should be thought of. It is much cheaper to plan ahead for future needs than to have to move in a few years.

Income Requirements

There are wide differences of income within an area. Each family must sit down and carefully figure how much it is worth, Fig. 76-3. The statement of space they need and money they have or can get very often conflict. However, figures should be very clearly stated. Too often, people have *mortgage payments* that are very hard to meet. To think big is fine in the planning stage. However, a family must be practical, too.

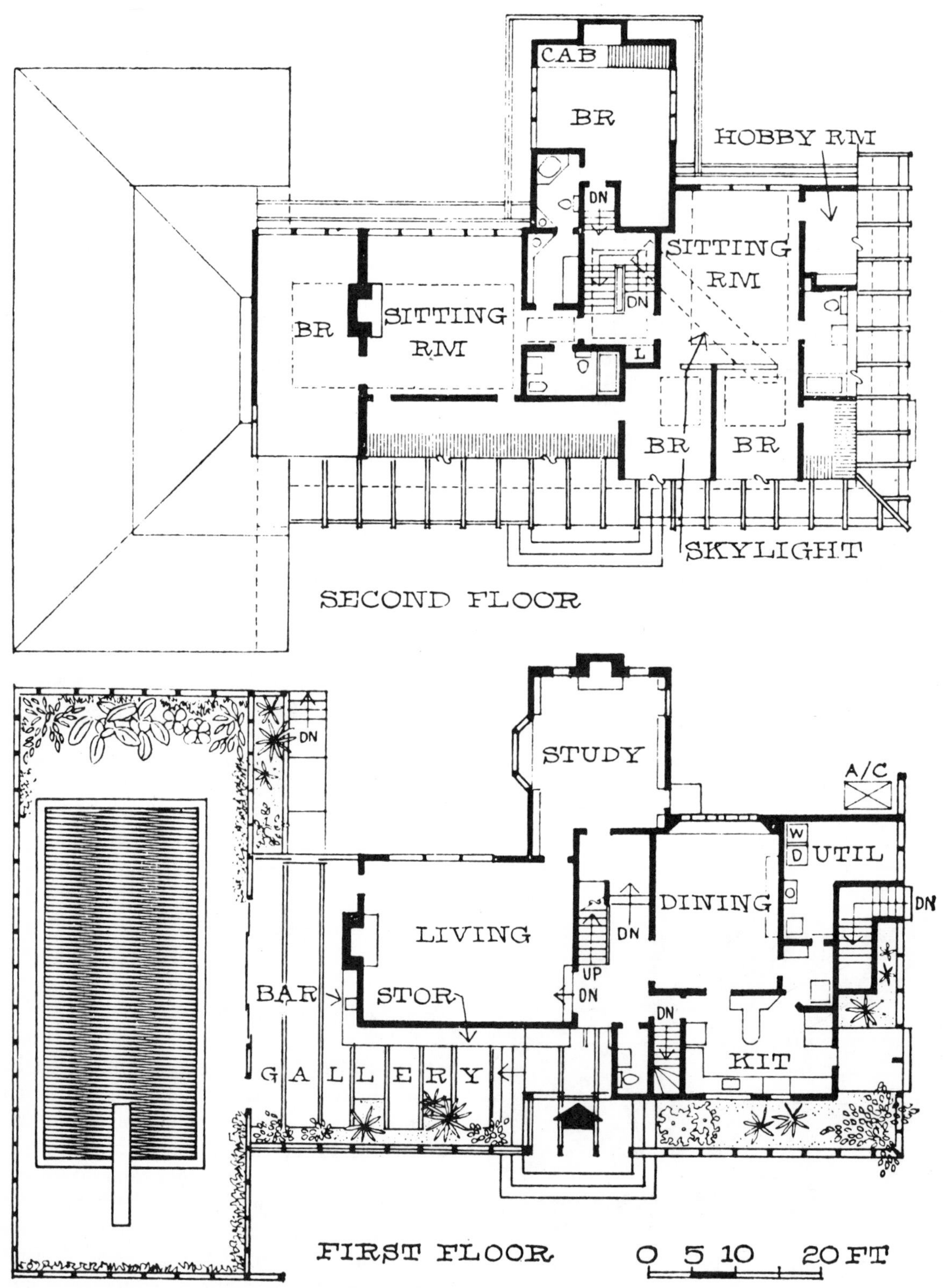

Fig. 76-2. The designer must plan the house around the needs and desires of the family.

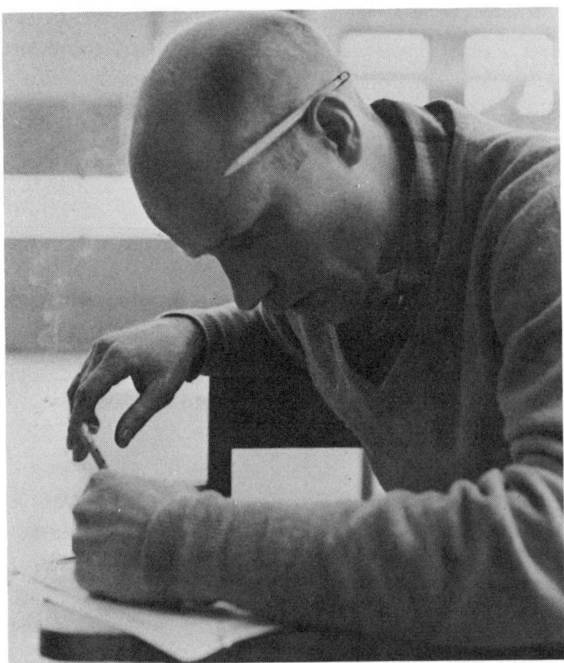

Fig. 76-3. Careful thought and consideration must be given to initial planning.

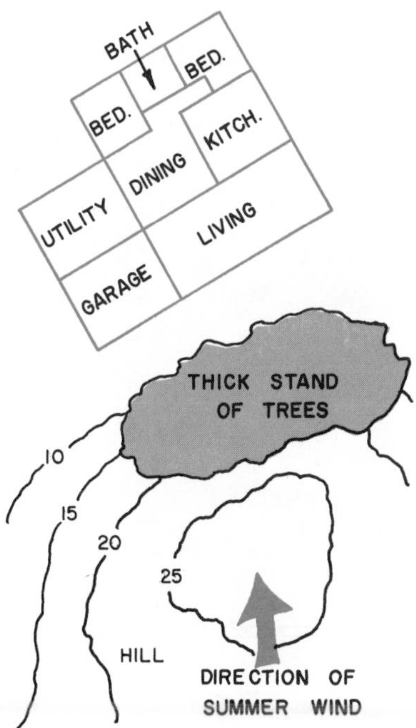

Fig. 76-4. The direction of the wind and geographic conditions are very important in selecting a site for your home.

Before a lending institution gives out a mortgage, it considers many things. First, does the person have enough assets? *Assets* are anything of any value that can be easily turned into cash. A car, furniture, real estate, bonds, stocks, and cash are all assets. Second, how much money does the person make? This has a great bearing on the amount of mortgage given. Usually a loan agency figures that no more than one week's pay should be a monthly payment. It also figures that the total cost of a home should not be more than two and one-half times a person's income a year. Third, how reliable is the person? In other words, how long has he held recent jobs? Does he go from one job to another often? Are his bills paid on time? Does he have a good reputation? Is he a good provider for his family? Many times these last things are the ones important to whether a person gets a mortgage or not.

Geographic Conditions

There are some factors in the design program which do not have to be listed because they are common to all well-designed houses in a certain area. These factors include such geographic conditions as climate, tradition, cost, materials, and workmanship. See Fig. 76-4.

Local climate has much influence on design. A house built in Maine is much different from one in Florida. Can you name some of these differences? Would these differences affect the cost of building?

The area in which the house is to be built often influences the style of house being planned. There are areas where tradition is important. A great change from this is not wanted. If you, for example, are going to build in a highly contemporary or modern area where there are many flat-roofed, masonry-stucco, one-story homes, you would not be very popular with the neighbors if you built a three-story Colonial home with huge pillars in front. Whether or not a home is sold easily depends on how it fits the *tradition of the area.*

Having materials and craftsmen nearby also affects design. In most areas, materials from that area are widely used because they usually are much cheaper and easier to get. The same is true for craftsmen. If you have to have a craftsman brought in, it is much more expensive. He must be paid for travel and, in many cases, for food and a place to stay. He usually must be paid more because he generally is much in demand.

Architectural Design

Most people thinking about a house have a definite picture in mind. The purpose of the design process is to design a house that the person wanting it likes.

Size, material, and color are important factors in appearance. The overall measurements of the house are related to room size and ceiling heights. Dimensions for rooms wanted should be compared with rooms whose measurements are known and can be seen.

Most home designs fall under two main styles. First, there are *traditional homes.* These are built in styles and customs from the past. These include Colonial, Georgian, Tudor, Spanish, Cape Cod, Oriental, and many others. Second, there are *contemporary homes,* Fig. 76-5. Contemporary means being of the present time or age. These include ranch, split level, multilevel, and other modern designs.

Summary

A dream house can become a reality if certain basic steps are followed, Fig. 76-6. The size, tastes, and functional desires of the family should be studied. The family's income and their geographic and design choices also are important. In addition, you need to look into the future to try to decide what will be needed then. A family and its needs change, but once a house is built, it remains much the same.

The design of a house should depend upon the needs and wants of the family. What

Fig. 76-5. This contemporary plywood house meets the needs of a family's size, taste, and functions.

Fig. 76-6. A dream house becomes a reality if careful planning and thought are given to the project.

they desire should be written out to form a program which can be used by the designer. This information is important in the design of a dream house.

Terms to Know

designer
income requirements
mortgage payments
geographic conditions
architectural design
tradition of the area
assets
reliable
traditional homes
contemporary homes

Think About It!

1. How many friends do you know that live in what they would call their *dream house*? What are some reasons that some may not live in a dream house?
2. What can you do now and within the next 15 to 20 years to help you obtain your dream house?

READING 77

Selecting and Purchasing a Lot

When you build a house, it must be constructed on a piece of land. Your choice about which piece of land to use may be more important than the design of the house itself, Fig. 77-1.

Topography

In judging a site or lot, the *topography* is important. The *relief* and the locations of natural features and any man-made structures are noted. The kind of soil, soil conditions, and drainage must be known. Test pots or holes can be dug cheaply to determine what is below ground, Fig. 77-2.

Zoning

Residential construction must follow whatever *zoning* and planning regulations apply in the neighborhood. The size or money value of the house sometimes is controlled. Zoning regulations may limit how much of the lot may be covered with structures. They also may give easements and minimum *setbacks* from property lines.

A site not governed by zoning regulations may cause serious problems. For example, if you build or buy a home in an area without zoning, you may find later that a noisy factory or some other large structure is being built right next door to you.

Fig. 77-1. The lot that is chosen will influence the kind of living and enjoyment that the family has.

Fig. 77-2. If you do not know the condition of the subsurface on your site, a test boring of the soil should be made.

Utilities and Services

Water, electricity, and facilities for sewage disposal should be available at the house site or nearby. Fuel gas and telephone service are usually necessary. If any of these is not available at the site, the distance to the connections should be considered. Long connections may be very expensive to put in and to service.

Many sites lack some of these public utilities and services. Then private facilities can be considered. For example, the lot owner may have a well drilled and pumps installed to furnish water.

Other Checks for Lot Selection

The availability of public services affects the value of property. The distance from a fire house or water hydrant may have a direct bearing on your fire insurance rate. The location with regard to schools and the quality of the schools are important concerns in picking a home site. Home owners also should check how far they must travel to satisfy their shopping needs. The nearness of public transportation, medical services, and recreation areas also should be considered in selecting a lot, Fig. 77-3.

Fig. 77-3. Are there schools and shopping centers nearby?

Cost

Tax rates are different in different areas. You should find out about the local tax rate and what taxes must be paid on the site that you are considering. A person could purchase a site, only to find that he could not afford to pay the taxes if he built on it. On the other hand, high tax rates may reflect very good schools and other services, which improve property value, Fig. 77-5.

It is also wise to find out what assessments or debts there are, if any, on the property. Sometimes payments for public utilities and

Fig. 77-4. Are you going to live in a city or in the country, on flat or sloped land? If you travel frequently, you may want to live near the airport. If you do not, the noise from the airport may be disturbing.

streets are charged to the properties which they serve. These payments affect the price of the lot. See Fig. 77-6.

How much should be paid for a lot? This varies according to the price of the home you wish to build. It will cost you the same amount to build the same house on a low cost lot as it will on an expensive lot. In most cases you will have better *resale value* if you pick a better lot. It is not wise to place a $50,000 home on a lot worth $1,000 or a $10,000 home on a $15,000 lot. Each person must use his own good judgment as to whether the lot he is considering fits the value of his planned house. There is no set ratio or formula that can be used.

The Purchase Offer

After a buyer chooses a lot, he must enter into a contract for buying it. Usually the first step is for the buyer to make a *purchase offer*. This offer is a written or spoken agreement to buy a lot from its owner for a certain amount of money.

Terms and Conditions

Your purchase offer should describe the lot, state the price you are willing to pay, name a closing date, and state the amount of the deposit or binder money. By requiring these terms and conditions, a buyer protects himself against some kinds of future problems.

Professional Counsel

Many professional people can help you in a real estate transaction. The first is the *realtor* who lists and sells the property. Later your *lawyer* will prepare the purchase offer or contract, check to make sure the lot is clear of liens and claims, and figure out the closing costs. Each of these men or women receives a fee or commission for their professional services.

Usually a surveyor is involved in a real estate deal. His job is to provide a survey showing (1) all boundaries; (2) the exact size, shape, and level of your lot; and (3) the position of topographic features such as

Fig. 77-5. The municipal or county tax office can tell you what taxes would have to be paid on the lot you are considering.

Fig. 77-6. Electricity is provided on this lot for the convenience of potential homeowners.

wells, streams, roads or streets, and utility lines. He is paid by either the buyer or seller, as agreed in the contract.

A banker or lending institution may be involved either by furnishing advice or by lending money for the financing of a lot.

Titles and Deeds

After your lawyer has prepared or examined the deed and after the closing has taken place, the deed, abstract, and survey are taken to the county court house or county seat. There a *Registrar of Deeds* sees that they are officially recorded or *registered.* This makes the transaction legal, Fig. 77-7. Recording the deed and abstract insures the buyer that if he loses his copy he can obtain another copy. As the owner "of record" he is protected by many laws and also has some legal responsibilities. The deed and abstract become part of the public record and can be examined by anyone wishing to do so. Many times a copy of the survey is also recorded along with the deed.

Summary

As the head of a family, ready to buy a lot and build a house, you should judge both the present and the future character of the neighborhood you are considering. You will want to check to see if zoning regulations, public services, schools, churches, shopping centers, and recreational facilities are satisfactory.

Soil conditions and terrain will need to be carefully checked before the site is purchased. Other factors such as easy access, natural features, and cost must be considered.

In making a purchase offer, you are agreeing to buy a lot for a set price under certain stated terms and conditions. When both you (as the buyer) and the seller have signed a purchase offer, it becomes a legal contract.

Many fees are involved in purchasing property. There are closing costs and commissions (fees) for the realtor, lawyer, and the surveyor.

After the abstract and deed have been drawn up and signed by both parties, they are recorded with the Registrar of Deeds. The deed shows the transfer of the property and lists you as the new owner. The abstract shows the history of your property. After all papers are recorded, you become the legal owner, and the papers become a part of public record.

Fig. 77-7. Deeds are filed in the office of the county Registrar of Deeds. Your lawyer and county officials can help you get information from these records.

Terms to Know

topography
relief of the land
zoning regulations
setbacks
easements
resale value
purchase offer
closing date
closing cost
deposit (binder money)
transaction
realtor
abstract
deed
Registrar of Deeds
terrain
contract
commission

Think About It!

1. What things should you consider when you are deciding what community you would like to live in?
2. Why are lawyers, realtors, and banks important in the process of selecting and purchasing a piece of land?

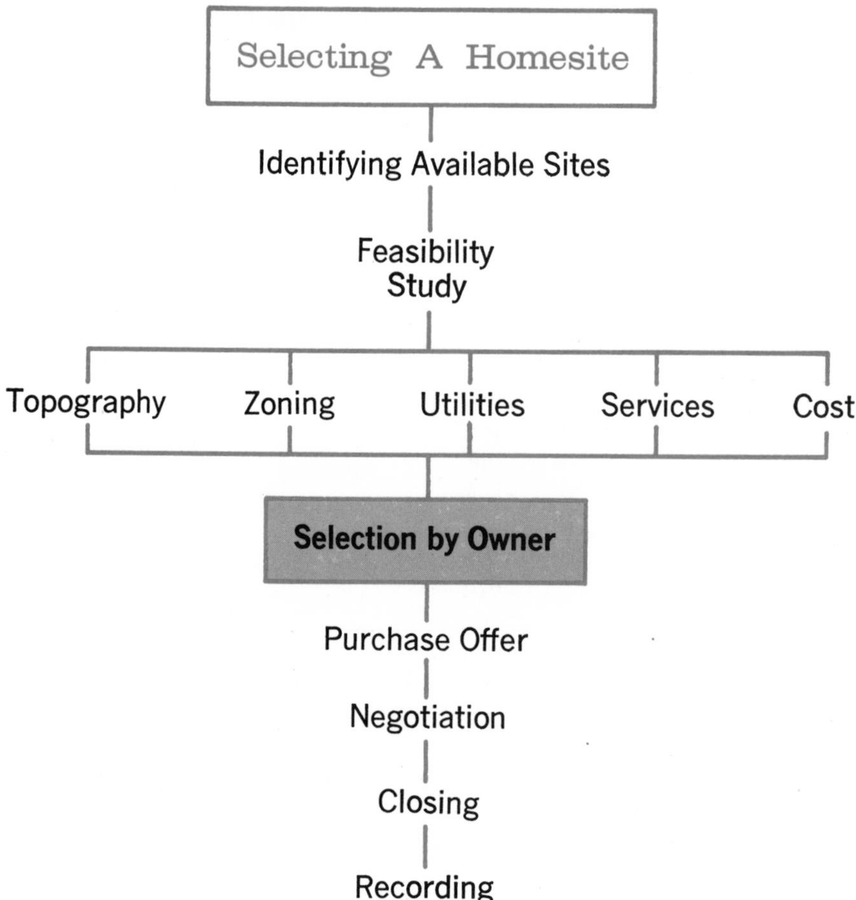
Selecting A Homesite
Identifying Available Sites
Feasibility Study
Topography
Zoning
Utilities
Services
Cost
Selection by Owner
Purchase Offer
Negotiation
Closing
Recording

Planning the Living Space

READING 78

Many activities go on in a home, and the house must be designed for them. Household activities may be broken down into two groups: *basic* and *nonbasic*. Both groups are considered when designing a house or making up a design program, Fig. 78-1. *Basic activities are those which occur in all homes. Nonbasic activities are those which are not necessarily carried on in all homes.* (Nonbasic activities like sewing or refinishing furniture might be quite important in homes where they do occur.)

When the activities to be housed have been identified, room-relationship diagrams are drawn. Based on these diagrams, the drawings used in construction are prepared.

Fig. 78-1 A designer should plan a house for basic and nonbasic activities.

Basic Activities

The *basic activities* which go on in a house require:

1. Sleeping spaces,
2. Eating spaces,
3. Relaxing spaces, and
4. Washing spaces.

One further need is storage space. Some storage space will be required near almost all of the spaces listed above. Space is needed for food, clothes, medicine, books, household appliances, and many other items.

Spaces for basic activities are usually divided into separate areas. For example, bedrooms and bathrooms generally are separated. In the same way, the living room, used for relaxation, and the kitchen, used for cooking, are separated.

Fig. 78-2. A do-it-yourself home workshop is considered a nonbasic area.

Nonbasic Activities

Nonbasic activities are those that are not always needed. What is included as nonbasic depends on family likes and needs. For example, a man who enjoys "doing-it-himself" may consider a large work space as basic, Fig. 78-2. In most homes, however, a workshop is not necessary for comfortable living. Dens, studies, dressing rooms, children's playrooms, and sewing rooms are examples of nonbasic parts of houses. Nonbasic rooms are planned and added according to the likes and needs of the family or individual building a house.

Quiet and Noisy Areas

When a house is planned and designed, it is a good idea to keep quiet and noisy rooms apart from each other. The sleeping and study spaces should be placed close together, but separated from the noisier spaces where people will eat and work, Fig. 78-3.

Planning Rooms

After listing the spaces wanted in a house and separating the quiet areas from the noisy areas, we begin to plan sizes for all the areas and to think of them as rooms. There are several things to consider when planning a room. Most important, perhaps, is the way in which the room will be used. The purposes of the room will largely determine the planning of doors, windows, lighting, size, and what will be built into the room, Fig. 78-4. For example, a bathroom is used for washing. Its purpose tells us that it need not be as large as a living room used for relaxing. Nor would a bathroom have large picture windows, as do many living rooms.

When a room is very long and narrow, it is usually hard to arrange the furniture in it. A room that is very large with a high ceiling may be hard to heat evenly. Also, furniture may seem lost in such a room. If a room is too small, you may have a boxed-up or stuffy feeling, and the area may not be big enough for the activities planned.

These mistakes can be overcome by following basic rules. Generally, it is good

Fig. 78-3. Quiet and noisy areas should be separated.

Fig. 78-4. In planning living space, one must consider the view, traffic patterns, and placement of furniture.

practice to plan a room so that its width is two-thirds of its length. For example, a room 10′ wide should be 15′ long since the ratio 10 to 15 is the same as the ratio 2 to 3. This is only a general rule, however.

An important feature to consider while planning a room is what kind of furniture will go into it. If furniture is not considered at the planning stage, you may find yourself standing in the middle of a finished room wondering where to put your special easy chair or the piano.

Traffic Flow in the House

Traffic flow refers to the paths people take in getting from one area to another in a house. This must be planned at the very beginning so that people may go from one area to another easily. In deciding what traffic areas are needed, you must consider the kinds of activities which each family member will have and the various reasons for moving from one room to another. Decide which areas will have people walking through them most often. Traffic flow is a factor in deciding whether the house should be one story or two and whether a separate hall or corridor is needed. The area used for the flow of traffic in a house generally takes up about 10 percent of the total area, Fig. 78-5.

DINING
KITCHEN
BATH
BED
LIVING
STUDY
BED
ENTRY
TRAFFIC FLOW

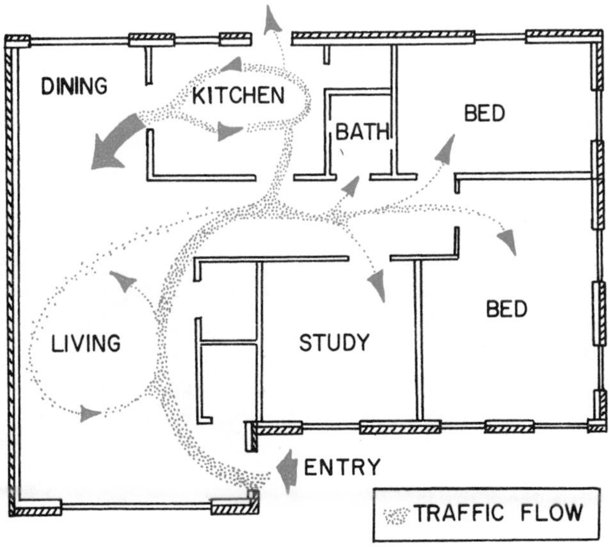

Fig. 78-5. This floor plan of a house shows the traffic flow for twenty-four hours.

Models

A house is often a person's first exposure to building and design. Plans and elevations may not be enough to help him understand the design. To help his clients understand plans, the designer uses *perspective drawings, models,* or both. These make the plans more meaningful to the client and show him clearly what the designer has in mind. A designer may make models for his own use, too. They often help him get a better picture of site layout, details, and appearance. See Fig. 78-6.

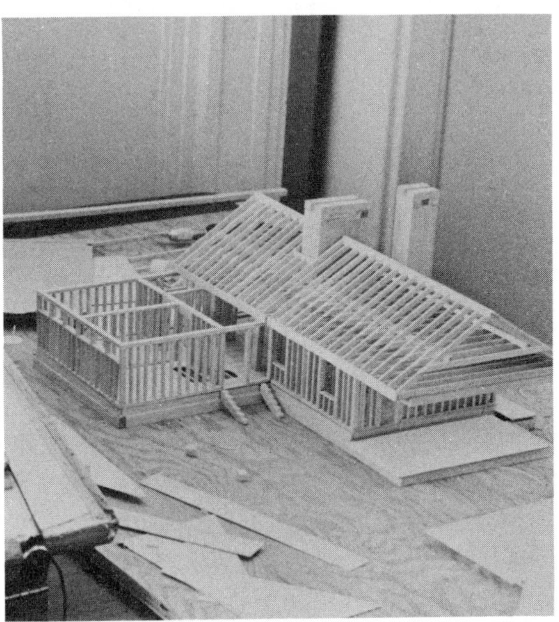

Fig. 78-6. Building a scale model of a house helps the designer and homeowner to see what the house will look like. Models also help to solve structural problems.

Preliminary Budget (Cost)

In planning and designing a house, *cost* is very important. For this reason, it is important to plan carefully how your money will be spent. There are three major costs in building a house. These are:

1. Buying the site or land on which to build,
2. Paying people such as architects, engineers, and lawyers to design and give advice about the house, and
3. Paying for materials and construction.

You must decide how your money will be divided among these three major costs.

As an example, suppose you have $15,000 to spend for a house. You might spend $3,000 for buying the site, $1,000 for design and advice, and $11,000 for construction. It is a good idea to save a small amount of money for emergencies which may come up later. Also, you will need additional money for furnishings. Their cost is usually not considered to be part of the cost of the house.

At the planning stage, your estimates will be very rough, and you may wish to change your plans later. You might find that for an extra $200 you could buy a much better site. If you decide to do this, you will have $200 less to spend on advice and construction.

Perhaps you find that you do not have enough money to build all the rooms you want, Fig. 78-7. Then you have several choices. You may give up some of the rooms. You may ask the designer for a house plan that will let you add rooms at a later date. You may decide to spend less for the site. It is not wise to cut costs by using poor materials in the house. You may pay later, in repairs and replacements, much more than you saved.

Hidden Costs (Service Needs)

A house, just like a car, will need servicing, Fig. 78-8. Services are paid for over a long period of time. Because of this, many people don't realize how high these costs are. Sometimes the total of all these costs have been higher than construction costs.

The choice of materials used for building and the way the house is constructed help determine the amount of servicing that will be needed later. Cheap materials, bad design, and poor workmanship almost always lead to high repair and maintenance costs. While designing, planning, and building, question the "cheap deals." It will save money later.

Fig. 78-7. Price may force one to make a room, or the entire house, smaller or less luxurious.

Fig. 78-8. The cost of servicing both interior and exterior features must be considered.

Summary

Certain activities in a house are called *basic*. These are eating, sleeping, relaxing, and washing. Other activities are *nonbasic*. They depend on personal likes. Examples of nonbasic features or rooms are dens, workshops, and dressing rooms. A house is planned around a family's needs for basic and nonbasic activities.

In the planning stages of a house, it is best to keep rooms for noisy activities apart from rooms intended for quiet activities. Sizes are chosen for each room according to the purposes of the rooms and how you will want to furnish them. Space for traffic

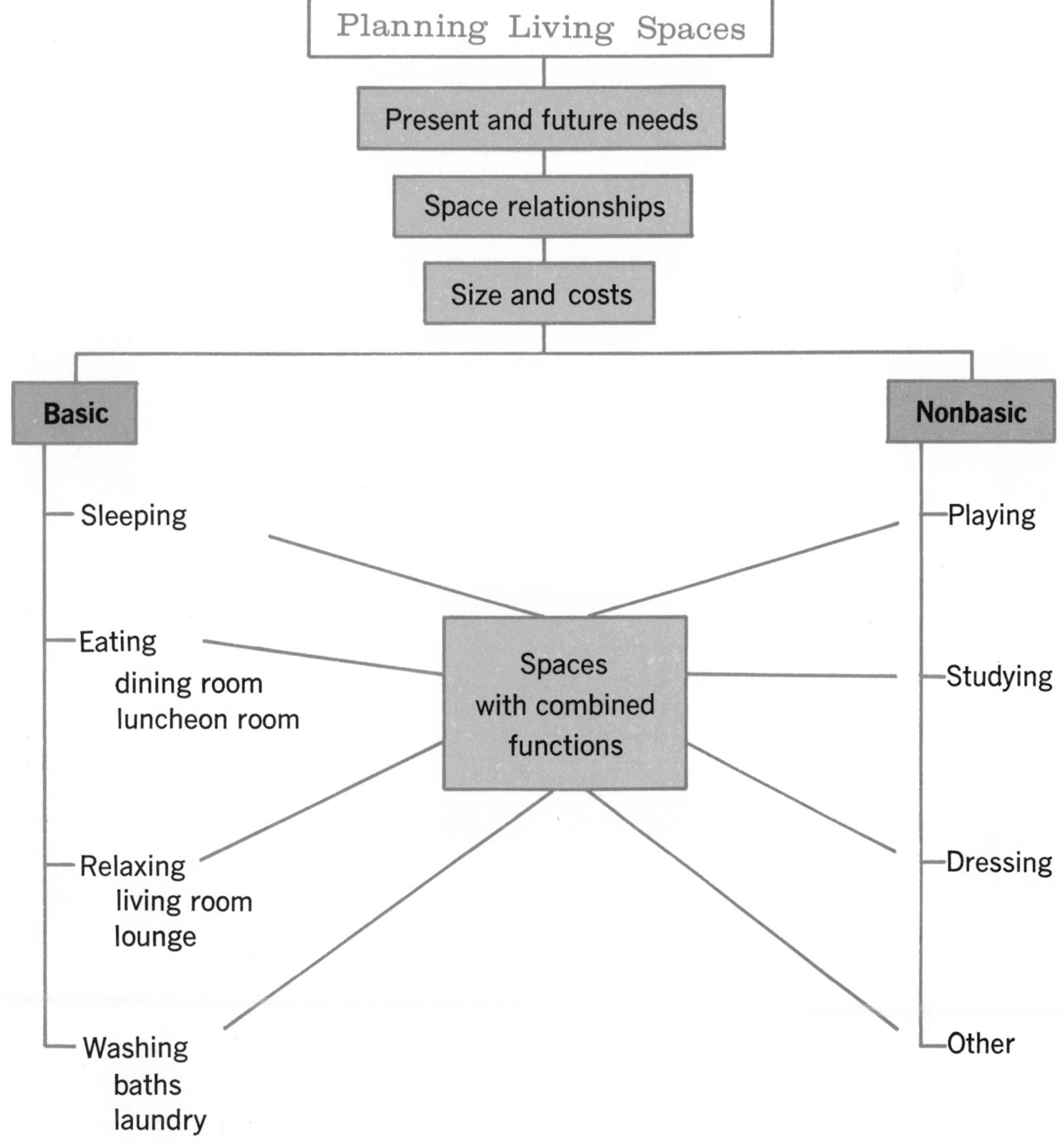

throughout the house should be planned. Next, room-relationship diagrams are made.

Designers may use models and perspective drawings in explaining a design. Some people find it hard to read and understand plans, elevations, and sections. A model can be of great help to such people.

Planning includes drawing up a rough budget. You must decide how much to spend for the site, for professional advice, and for construction. You must also keep in mind the costs of servicing your house over a long period of time. Your budget may require redesigning some of the spaces or features before the final design and detailed drawings are made.

Terms to Know

basic activities
non basic activities
traffic flow (inside)
perspective drawings
scale model
estimate
budget
space relationship
service costs

Think About It!

1. Does your present home have enough space to carry on all *basic* activities? If not, which activities require more space?
2. On a piece of notebook paper, make a sketch of the floor plan of your home. Identify the traffic pattern for a typical day.

Preparing Working Drawings

The basic design of a house must be finished before working drawings can be made. All the information needed for building a house is given by a set of working drawings and specifications. This reading will describe working drawings, what they are, and why they are needed.

The Plot Plan

A plot plan is a drawing of the top view of a lot, Fig. 79-1. Its major purpose is to show where the house goes on the lot. The lot size is given in feet and tenths of a foot. The house is located from the street (the front) and from the sides of the lot. The locations of wells, septic tanks, sewer lines, gas lines, and water lines also are shown. Often other information is given, such as the locations of sidewalks, driveways, streams of water, trees, and many other features.

The plot plan should also give the elevation of the ground levels of the house above the local *datum level.* Elevations of the first floor, the garage floor, the finished curb, the crown of the street, and the finish grade level of each main corner of the house should be shown. *The datum level is an assumed basic level which is used as a reference for determining heights.* In many areas this datum level is a part of the building code, and it controls all building standards for that area.

When sanitary sewers are not available, *septic tanks* are required for the sanitary disposal of waste. The size of the tank and the length of *leaching* (slow draining) *lines* are controlled by local and state codes. The septic tank and *leaching field* are not usually drawn on the plumbing plan, but they are placed on the plot plan.

Landscaping can be shown on the plot plan. However, this is usually put on a separate drawing in order to avoid confusion.

Floor Plans

The most important single working drawing is the *floor plan.* All other drawings depend on it. *The floor plan is a horizontal section through the building,* Fig. 79-2. It is usually taken just below the tops of the windows and doors. The main purpose of the floor plan is to show the locations of the walls, partitions, and all openings. A very simple floor plan will show only this. However, most floor plans show much more detail. In a complete set of plans for a large project, data about plumbing, electrical, heating, and air conditioning systems are placed on separate sheets. On small jobs, this information may be placed on the floor plan.

For a two-story building, the first floor must be drawn first. The exterior (outside) walls of the second floor can be traced from the first-floor plan if they are directly over it. If the walls of the second floor are different or set back, structural support must be put underneath. This is shown by dashed lines on the plan for the floor below. Interior (inside) walls do not necessarily have to line up unless they are bearing walls or unless they contain vents or piping from the wall below. Stairways must be carefully lined up, and space must be allowed for head room.

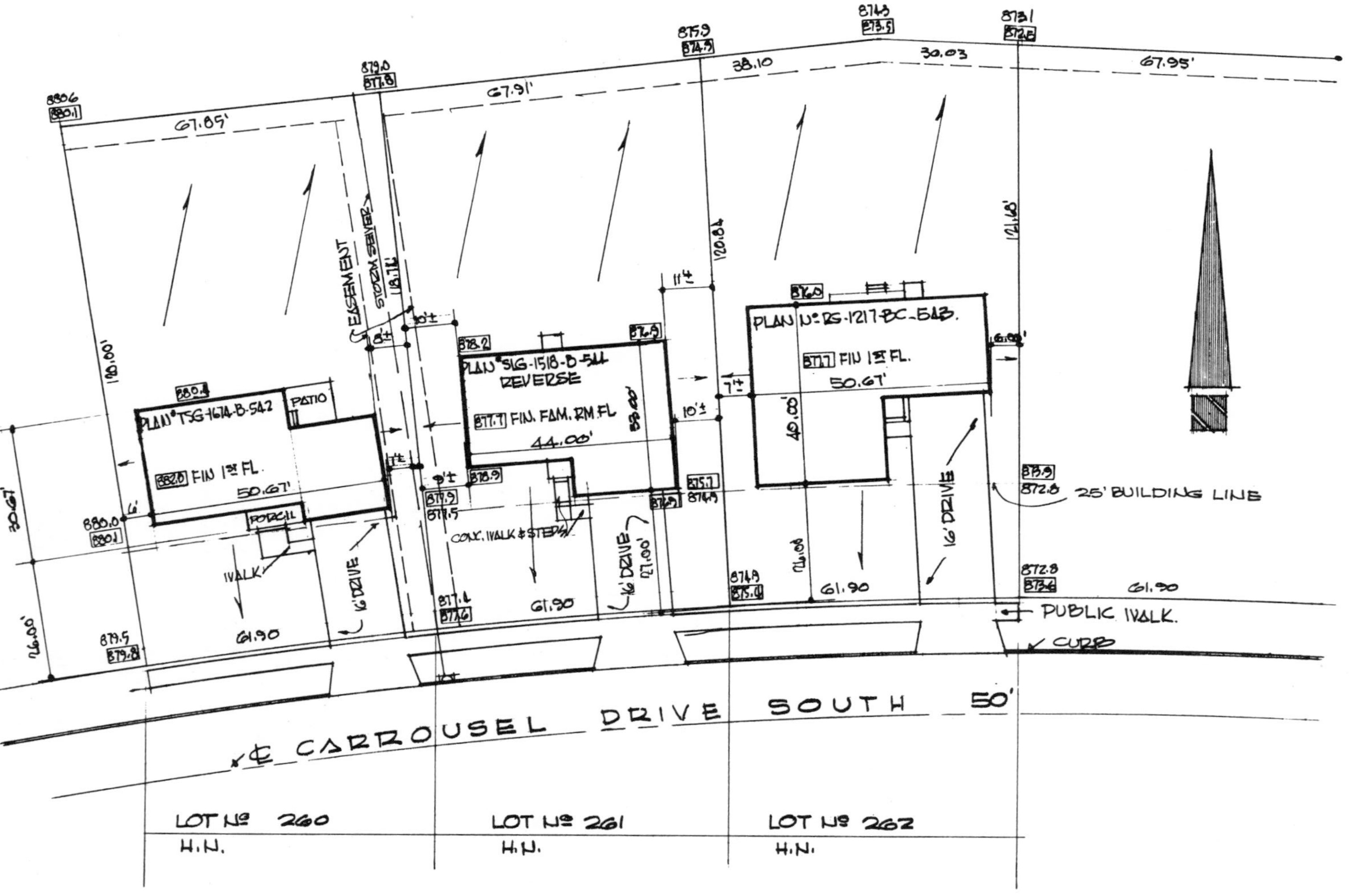

Fig. 79-1. Plot and grading plans. Scale 1" = 20'

Exterior Elevations

An exterior elevation is a working drawing that shows the finished appearance of one side of the outside of a building, Fig. 79-3. Each elevation shows one view of the building based on the floor plan and the structural sections. All surface materials are shown. The locations of important structural features such as the floor line, plate line, and window and door heights are given. Enough exterior elevations are drawn to give a complete description of the building.

Structural Sections

Structural sections are views taken through a building at points which will best show the details of important structural and architectural features. Whenever there is a change in shape or construction methods, a

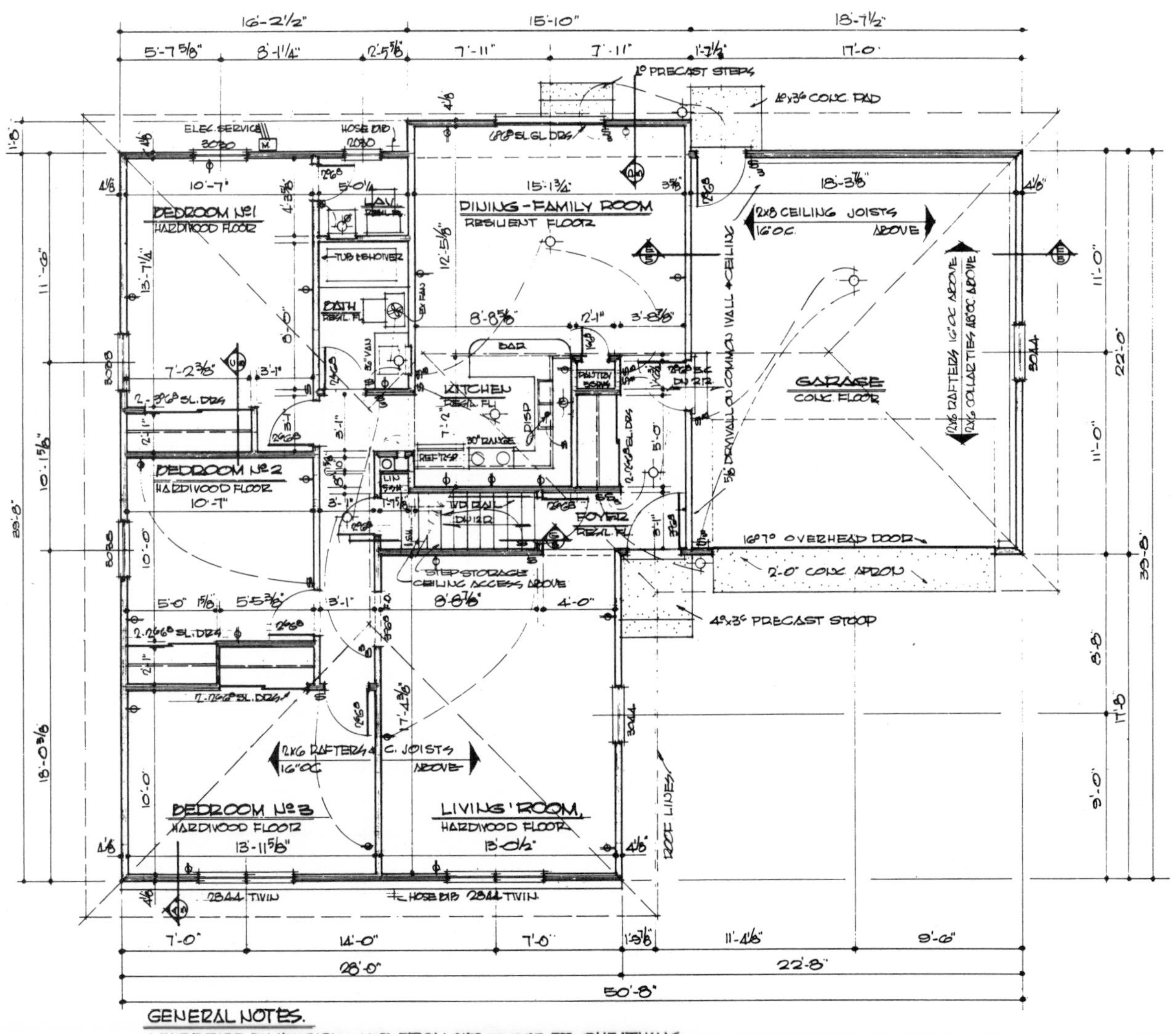

Fig. 79-2. First floor plan. Scale ¼ ″ = 1′

new section must be drawn. Generally the structural sections are drawn on separate sheets and to a larger scale than the general drawings. Section drawings show how measurements compare among foundation, floor, wall, ceiling, and roof systems. See Fig. 79-4.

Details

Because working drawings are drawn to a small scale, certain parts of a building need separate, more complete drawings. These are the *detail drawings.* As the main drawings are made, the architect notes parts that should be detailed. Then, when he is ready to detail, he has a list at hand and will not need to search through the plans to find out where the problems are.

Details may be divided into two broad groups: (1) standard details and (2) custom or "one of a kind" details.

Standard details usually are repeated many times throughout a building. Most of

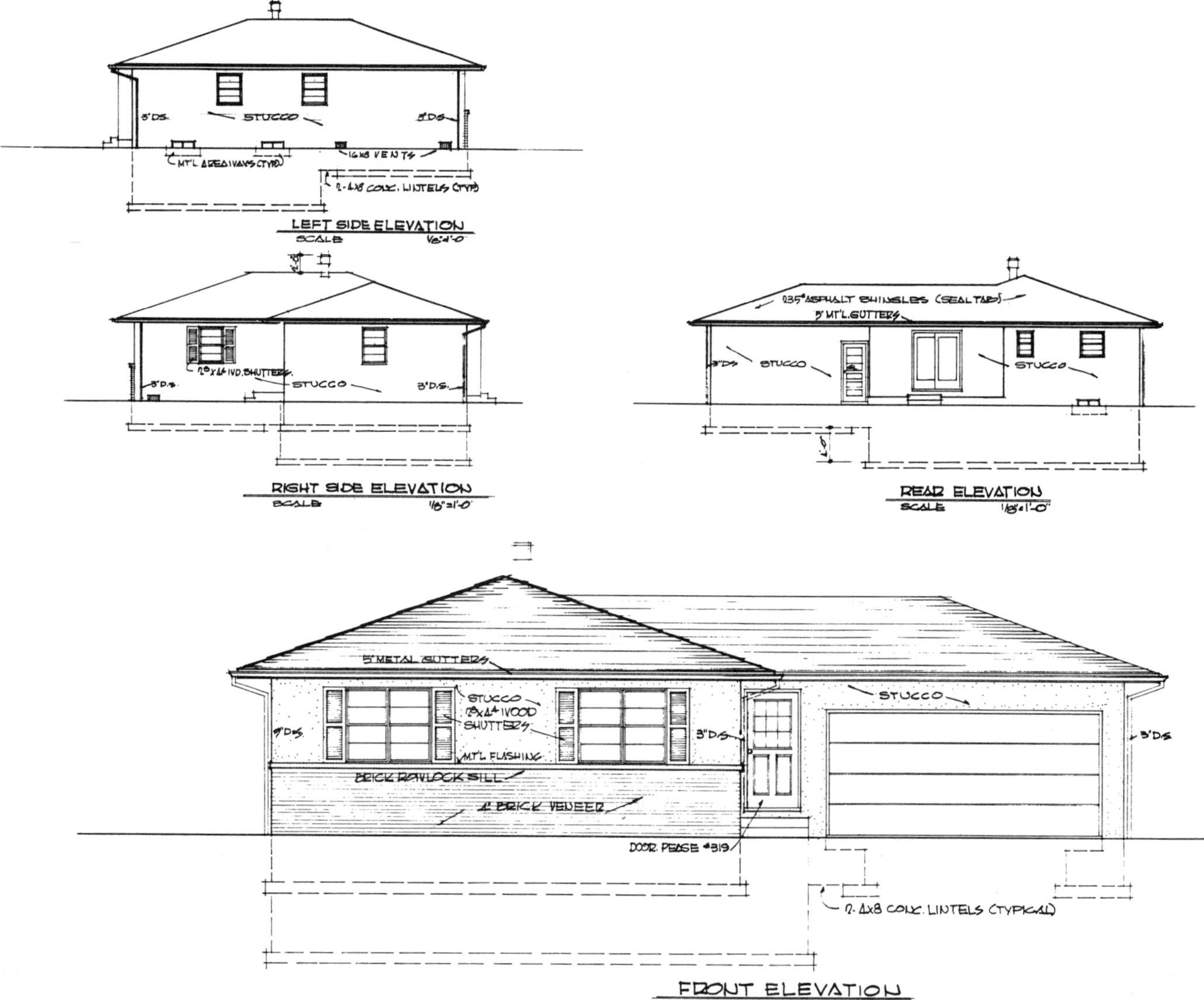

Fig. 79-3. Exterior elevations. Scale ¼ ″ = 1′

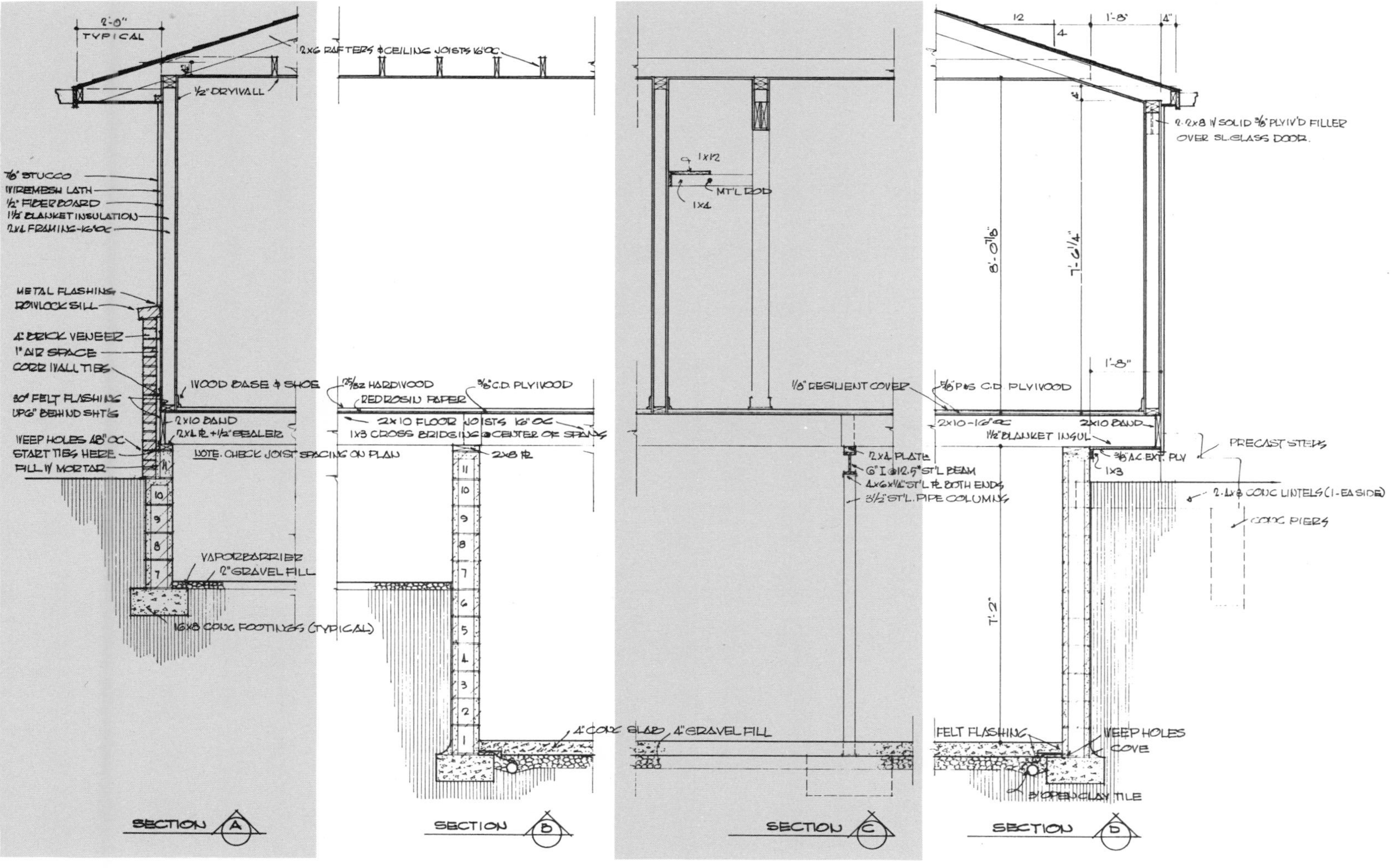

Fig. 79-4. Wall sections. Scale $3/4'' = 1'$

them are used so often in construction that they are well known both to the designer and to the contractor. For example, a standard detail might show a window of a standard size and type. Manufacturer's details are usually excellent and widely known to both designers and contractors. Drawings need not be cluttered with standard details such as these. Details of standard window sections, door knobs, light fixtures, and so forth are generally not needed. They can be identified on the plans by a reference number.

Custom details usually show the solution of a problem peculiar to a particular house. Thus, examples of custom details might be a specially-designed staircase or the method by which special kitchen cabinets are to be built and fitted into the kitchen. They differ

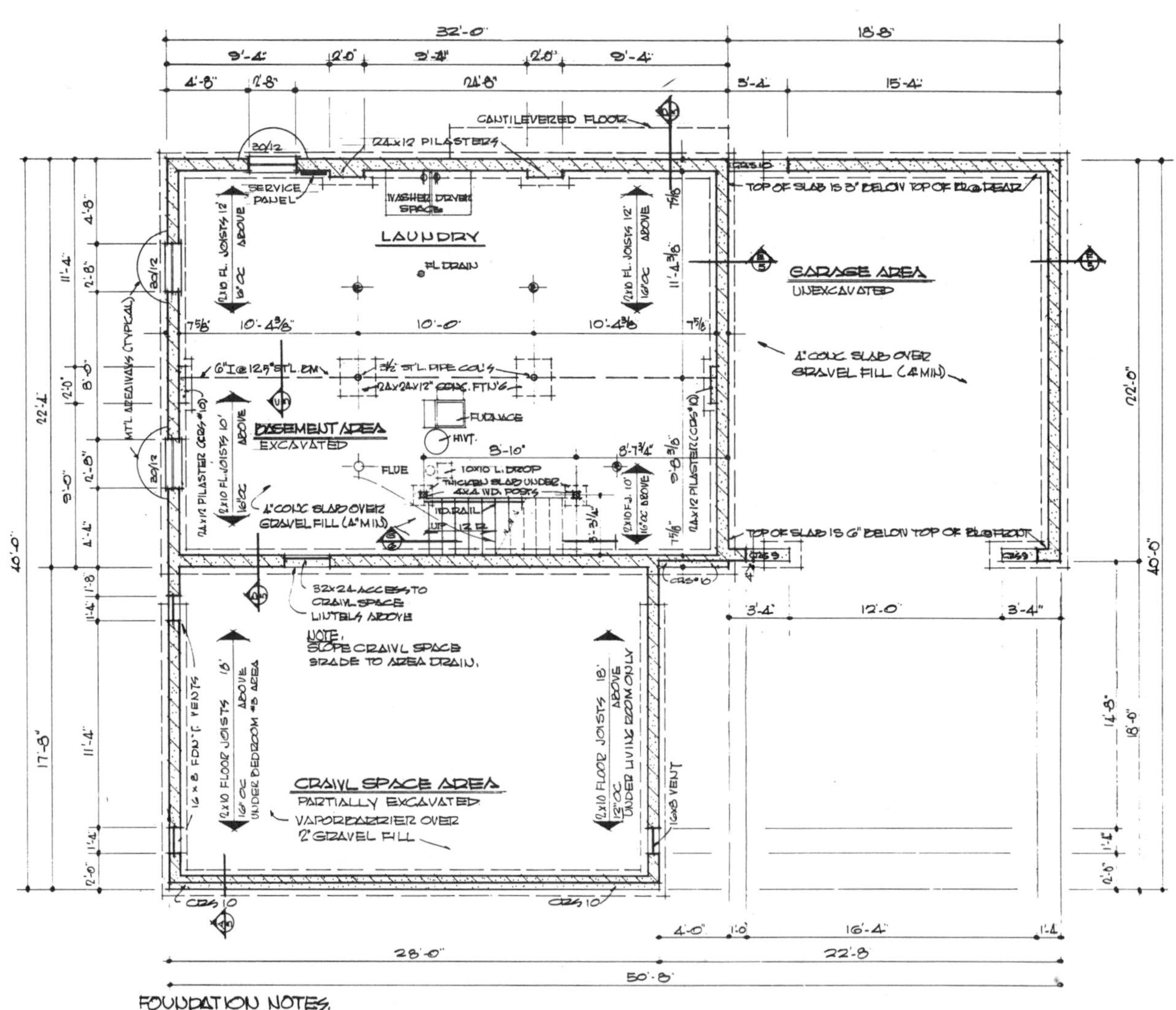

Fig. 79-5. Foundation and basement plan. Scale ¼" = 1'

from standard details in that they are specially designed for one house, and they usually occur only once in the building.

Both standard and custom details may be further divided, as follows:

1. Structural details (those related to the structure),
2. Plumbing and wiring details (those related to utility systems), and
3. Finish details (those related to finished surfaces such as wall paneling, stairs, and cabinet work).

Generally the architect works out the structural details before completing the utility and finish details.

The items most often needing detailing are stairs, fireplaces, cabinets, and other built-in and special construction designs. Details of *cornice construction* are a good example of special construction design.

Foundations or Basement Plans

The *basement plan* shows the basement layout and the footings. When no basement is to be built, there must be a foundation plan which shows the footings and foundation wall, Fig. 79-5.

Many kinds of foundations and floor systems are in use today. Two types are used most often in house construction. One type, *wood floor construction,* uses exterior foundation walls and interior supports to carry the construction load above grade. The other type, *concrete floor or slab construction,* uses footings to carry the wall load. The floor load is carried by the soil under the slab.

Each type of foundation has advantages. Wood has better texture and appearance than concrete. It is easier to install plumbing, heating, and electrical lines in wood floor construction. Concrete floors are usually cheaper and quicker to build than wood floors. They also are quieter, because noise is not easily transmitted through concrete.

The floor plan can be followed as a guide in drawing a foundation plan. Much time can be saved by taping a piece of tracing paper over a floor plan and tracing the exterior walls and the locations of such features as fireplaces, chimneys, and stairways.

A basement plan includes (1) windows, (2) doors, (3) columns and girders needed to support load bearing walls, (4) the heating plant, (5) the water heater, (6) footings, (7) laundry facilities, (8) underground plumbing, and (9) partitions.

Roof Plan and Joist Layout

On small residential construction, *joist details* are given to show the placement, size, and spacing of the flooring system. Normally, information on the roof plan is limited to the type of roof, its pitch, and a typical section to show placement of principal roof members. All structural members are shown

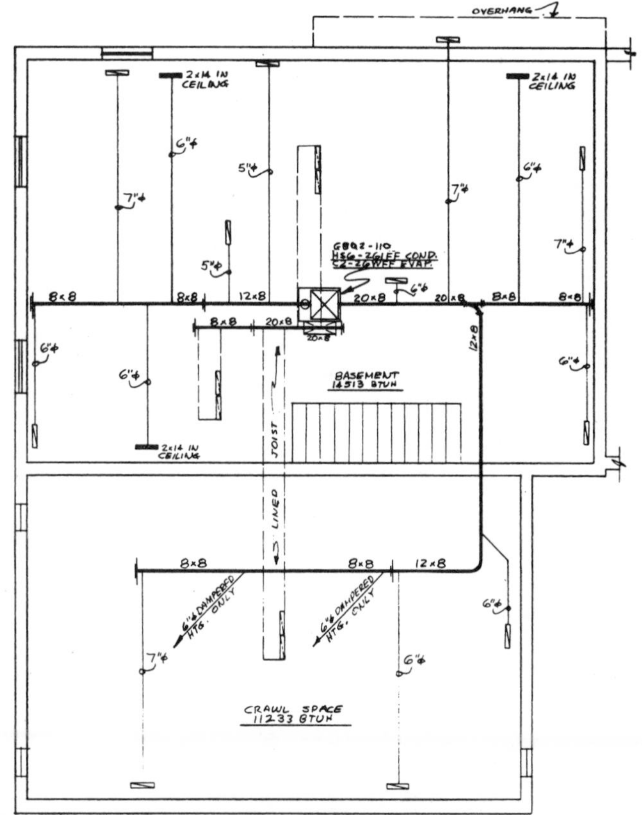

Fig. 79-6. Basement heating plan.

in their proper relationship based on the other portions of the plan.

Electrical Plan

The *electrical drawing* is a plan view of the building, which is begun with a tracing from the floor plan. When finished, it shows the service entrance and meter, all the electrical outlets and controls in the house, and a description of all the symbols used on the drawing. Before starting the actual electrical drawings, it is necessary to plan the kind, number, and the location of outlets. These decisions are based upon lighting needs, the locations of electrical appliances, and requirements of the electrical code or Bureau of Fire Underwriters.

Heating, Ventilating, and Air Conditioning Plan

Figures 79-6 and 79-7 show the *plan view* of the building. The drawings are based upon a tracing from the floor plan. They show all heating, ventilating, and air conditioning equipment above and below ground. Sizes and kinds of all lines, ducts, and equipment are shown. This plan must fit in with the structural sections, the floor plan, and plumb-

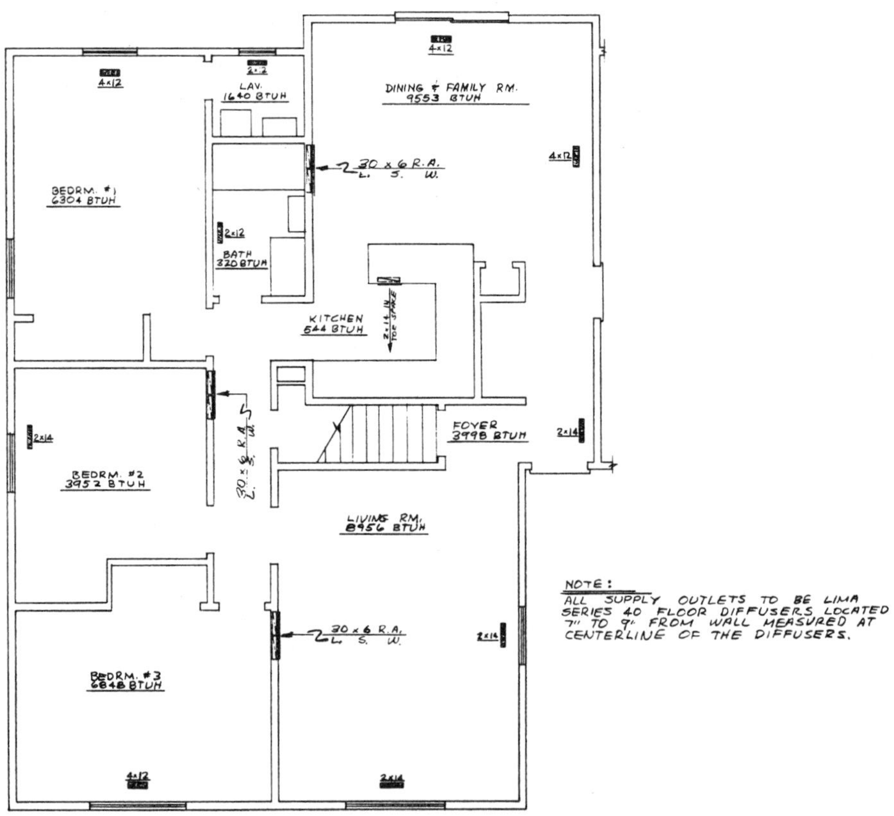

Fig. 79-7. First floor heating plan.

ing and electrical plans. Much thought must be given to coordinating these plans. Supply and return lines must not get in the way of the structural members such as floor joists, beams, plates, and studs. Headers and trimmers may be necessary where structural members have to be cut.

Plumbing Plan

The *plumbing plan* is a plan view of the building. As with other plan views, it may be based upon a tracing from the floor plan. It shows all plumbing lines and fixtures above and below the ground. Soil and waste lines, gas lines, hot and cold water lines, steam lines, air pipes, and all fixtures and appliances such as dishwashers and garbage disposal units are described. This plan is also closely related to the rest of the plans in the set. Most soil and waste lines are designed to work by gravity flow or natural run off. Therefore, they must slope downward, and this also is shown on the plan.

Summary

Working drawings play an important part in construction. They show or give most of the information needed for building a house. The basic kinds of working drawings are: (1) the plot plan, (2) floor plans, (3) exterior elevations, (4) structural sections, (5) details, (6) foundation or basement plan, (7) roof plan and joist layout, (8) electrical plan, (9) heating, ventilating, and air conditioning plan, and (10) the plumbing plan.

Terms to Know

working drawings
plot plan
datum level
septic tank
leaching lines
leaching field
floor plan
exterior elevation
structural sections
detail drawings
standard details
custom details
cornice construction
basement plan
foundation plan
wood floor construction
concrete floor construction
joist detail
pitch (of a roof)
electrical drawing
coordinating
plumbing plan

Think About It!

1. What would happen if a builder or contractor tried to build a house without the necessary drawings?
2. Why is the floor plan considered to be the most important working drawing?

READING 80

Writing Specifications

All the information needed to build a structure cannot be put on the working drawings. Therefore, much information is given in specifications. *Specifications are written instructions, conditions, and descriptions which tell the builder how to do the job properly.* Specifications also protect the interests of everyone involved: the architect, the builder, and the owner.

Categories

Specifications are arranged in three general categories:

1. Legal documents,
2. Conditions, and
3. Technical descriptions.

In the *legal documents section* are the advertisement for bids, invitation and instruction to bidders, owner-contractor agreements, and bond forms.

Fig. 80-1. In the technical descriptions section of the specifications, the right kind of brick for the job is specified.

The *conditions section* states the rights and responsibilities of the designer, the owner, the contractor, and any subcontractors.

The *technical descriptions section* lists the materials and methods to be used for building the structure, Fig. 80-1. This is generally divided into architectural, civil, and structural, plumbing, heating, mechanical, and electrical sections. Each section is organized to include: (1) the scope of the work to be done, (2) the complete description of materials to be used, (3) general requirements or the usual work standards and practices, and (4) special requirements or unusual work standards or practices.

Fig. 80-2. The specifications writer must have access to many kinds of product catalogs. Many hours are spent in retrieving and selecting costs, sizes, standards, and requirements of each item that goes into a house.

FHA Form 2005
VA Form VB4-1852
Rev. Jan. 66

For accurate register of carbon copies, form may be separated along above fold. Staple completed sheets together in original order.

Form approved.
Budget Bureau No. 63-R055.11.

☒ Proposed Construction

DESCRIPTION OF MATERIALS

No. ______ (To be inserted by FHA or VA)

☐ Under Construction

Property address ______ City ______ State ______

Mortgagor or Sponsor ______ (Name) ______ (Address)

Contractor or Builder Candlelite Homes, Inc. (Name) 1442 Pershing Dr. Col. Ohio (Address)

INSTRUCTIONS

1. For additional information on how this form is to be submitted, number of copies, etc., see the instructions applicable to the FHA Application for Mortgage Insurance or VA Request for Determination of Reasonable Value, as the case may be.
2. Describe all materials and equipment to be used, whether or not shown on the drawings, by marking an X in each appropriate check-box and entering the information called for in each space. If space is inadequate, enter "See misc." and describe under item 27 or on an attached sheet.
3. Work not specifically described or shown will not be considered unless required, then the minimum acceptable will be assumed. Work exceeding minimum requirements cannot be considered unless specifically described.
4. Include no alternates, "or equal" phrases, or contradictory items. (Consideration of a request for acceptance of substitute materials or equipment is not thereby precluded.)
5. Include signatures required at the end of this form.
6. The construction shall be completed in compliance with the related drawings and specifications, as amended during processing. The specifications include this Description of Materials and the applicable Minimum Construction Requirements.

1. EXCAVATION:
Bearing soil, type Clay 2000 #

2. FOUNDATIONS:
Footings: concrete mix 5 Bag 2000 # mix; strength psi ______ Reinforcing As required
Foundation wall: material 8x8x16 Conc. Blk Reinforcing As required over sewers
Interior foundation wall: material ---------- Party foundation wall ----------
Columns: material and sizes 3 1/2" dia. steel Piers: material and reinforcing 24"x24"x12" conc.
Girders: material and sizes 3- 2x10 df beam Sills: material ----------
Basement entrance areaway ---------- Window areaways none
Waterproofing 1/2" Cement Parge-1 coat asph. Footing drains 3" drain tile to curb
Termite protection Top course solid termite block
Basementless space: ground cover 2" Gravel; insulation Vaporbarrier; foundation vents 6x16 (2)
Special foundations 8" dia. piers under 4'-0" x 8'-0" patio 5 bag mix w/reinforcing
Additional information: ______

3. CHIMNEYS:
Material Galv. Iron Prefabricated *(make and size)* Duro-vent 5" or equil
Flue lining: material ______ Heater flue size G.I. 4" Fireplace flue size ______
Vents *(material and size)*: gas or oil heater ______; water heater G.I. 3"
Additional information: ______

4. FIREPLACES: Gas Log Lighter See Detail Sheet
Type: ☒ solid fuel; ☐ gas-burning; ☐ circulator *(make and size)* ______ Ash dump and clean-out 10x10 (outside)
Fireplace: facing 4" brick; lining Firebrick; hearth Cut Stone; mantel Cut Stone
Additional information: ______

5. EXTERIOR WALLS: Doug. Fir, hemlock
Wood frame: wood grade, and species 2x4 20% std. con. gr. ☐ Corner bracing. Building paper or felt 30# felt
Sheathing Fibreboard; thickness 1/2"; width 48"; ☒ solid; ☐ spaced ______" o. c.; ☐ diagonal;
Siding ______; grade ______; type ______; size ______; exposure ______"; fastening ______
Shingles ______; grade ______; type ______; size ______; exposure ______"; fastening ______
Stucco 3 coat Rietter; thickness 7/8"; Lath 1x1x18 ga. Keymesh; weight 1.8 lb.
Masonry veneer 4" brick $50.00 Sills Roloc Lintels 3 1/2x3 1/2x5/16 Stl.
Masonry: ☐ solid ☐ faced ☐ stuccoed; total wall thickness ______"; facing thickness ______"; facing material ______
Backup material ______; thickness ______"; bonding ______
Door sills ______ Window sills ______ Lintels ______
Interior surfaces: dampproofing, ______ coats of ______; furring ______
Additional information: ______
Exterior painting: material Exterior oil base; number of coats 2
Gable wall construction: ☒ same as main walls; ☐ other construction ______

6. FLOOR FRAMING: 2x10 df const. gr.
Joists: wood, grade, and species 20% std.; other Hemlock; bridging 1x3 yp.; anchors ______
Concrete slab: ☒ basement floor; ☐ first floor; ☒ ground supported; ☐ self-supporting; mix 5 1/2 Bag; thickness 4";
reinforcing ______; insulation ______; membrane ______
Fill under slab: material 3/4" gravel; thickness 4". Additional information:
1/2" flex-cell under sill plate

7. SUBFLOORING: *(Describe underflooring for special floors under item 21.)*
Material: grade and species Fir plywood; size 3/8x48; type interior
Laid: ☒ first floor; ☐ second floor; ☐ attic ______ sq. ft.; ☐ diagonal; ☒ right angles. Additional information: ______

8. FINISH FLOORING: *(Wood only. Describe other finish flooring under item 21.)*

Location	Rooms	Grade	Species	Thickness	Width	Bldg. Paper	Finish
First floor	3 bdrm. hall	#1	Oak	25/32	2 1/4	red rosin	sand, fill, varnish
Second floor	living, famil						and shellac.
Attic floor	sq. ft.						

Additional information: ______

9. PARTITION FRAMING:
Studs: wood, grade, and species Doug Fir 20% Std. Const. Gr. size and spacing 2x4 @ 16" oc. Other
Additional information:

10. CEILING FRAMING:
Joists: wood, grade, and species Doug. Fir or Hemlock 20% std. Const. Other B.C. of Truss Bridging 1x4 Catwalk
Additional information:

11. ROOF FRAMING:
Rafters: wood, grade, and species 20% Const. Gr. Doug. Fir @ 16 oc. Roof trusses (see detail): grade and species
Additional information: See truss Drawing

12. ROOFING:
Sheathing: wood, grade, and species C.D. Fir ; ☒ solid; ☐ spaced ___" o.c.
Roofing Asphalt shingles ; grade A ; size 3/8x48 ; type interior
Underlay 15# Felt Seal Tab ; weight or thickness 235 ; size 1x3 ; fastening 7/8" Galv
Built-up roofing ; number of plies ; surfacing material
Flashing: material ; gage or weight ; ☐ gravel stops; ☐ snow guards
Additional information:

13. GUTTERS AND DOWNSPOUTS:
Gutters: material G.I. ; gage or weight 26 ga. ; size 5" ; shape O.G.
Downspouts: material G.I. ; gage or weight 26 ga. ; size 3" ; shape Square ; number 4
Downspouts connected to: ☒ Storm sewer; ☐ sanitary sewer; ☐ dry-well. ☐ Splash blocks: material and size
Additional information: Tile to curb

14. LATH AND PLASTER
Lath ☐ walls, ☐ ceilings: material ; weight or thickness ; Plaster: coats ; finish
Dry-wall ☒ walls, ☒ ceilings: material Gypsum ; thickness 1/2" ; finish paint
Joint treatment Perfi-tape system per Mfgs. specifications

15. DECORATING: *(Paint, wallpaper, etc.)*

Rooms	Wall Finish Material and Application	Ceiling Finish Material and Application
Kitchen	Two coats Latex Base Rolled on	Same as Walls
Bath	Two coats Latex Base Rolled on	Same as Walls
Other	Two coats Latex Base Rolled on	Same as Walls

Additional information:

16. INTERIOR DOORS AND TRIM:
Doors: type Flush H.C. ; material Mahogany Lauan ; thickness 1 3/8
Door trim: type Ranch ; material W. Pine Base: type Tear Drop ; material W. Pine ; size 3 1/4
Finish: doors Natural 2 coats shellac ; trim Paint same as walls
Other trim *(item, type and location)*
Additional information:

17. WINDOWS:
Windows: type Horiz. slider Sing. hung ; make Stanley ; material Alum. ; sash thickness inter
Glass: grade SSB ; ☐ sash weights; ☐ balances, type ; head flashing Integral
Trim: type DW Return ; material Gypsum Paint Same as walls ; number coats 2
Weatherstripping: type Compression ; material Vinyl and pile Storm sash, number
Screens: ☐ full; ☒ half; type Alum. frame ; number all ; screen cloth material Fiberglass
Basement windows: type Hopper ; material Alum. ; ☒ screens, number All ; ☐ Storm sash, number
Special windows Marble Stools
Additional information:

18. ENTRANCES AND EXTERIOR DETAIL:
Main entrance door: material Mahogany H.G. ; width 3' ; thickness 1 3/4" Frame: material wp ; thickness 5/4 "
Other entrance doors: material Fir H.C. ; width 2'-8" ; thickness 1 3/4" Frame: material wp ; thickness 5/4 "
Head flashing Weatherstripping: type Friction brass ; saddles alum. vinyl
Screen doors: thickness ___"; number ; screen cloth material Storm doors: thickness ___"; number
Combination storm and screen doors: thickness 1 "; number 1 ; screen cloth material Alum.
Shutters: ☐ hinged; ☐ fixed. Railings Louvers 2 - 24x30 louvers
Exterior millwork: grade and species Clear Fir 1 x 6 Paint Oil Base ; number coats 2
Additional information: 3/8" ac. exterior plywood soffit

19. CABINETS AND INTERIOR DETAIL:
Kitchen cabinets, wall units: material Scheirick bronzeglow or Springfield Cabinet Birch veneer on wood frame ; lineal feet of shelves MPS ; shelf width 12
Base units: material same ; counter top formica ; edging formica
Back and end splash 4" ceramic Finish of cabinets Factory applied ; number coats 3
Medicine cabinets: make Grote or equil ; model
Other cabinets and built-in furniture Built in vanity in main bath fabricated linen front in half bath room dividers in family room and living room
Additional information:

20. STAIRS:

Stair	Treads Material	Treads Thickness	Risers Material	Risers Thickness	Strings Material	Strings Size	Handrail Material	Handrail Size	Balusters Material	Balusters Size
Basement	Fir	1 5/8	OPEN		Fir	2 x 10	WF.	2x3 rd.	NONE	
Main										
Attic										

Disappearing: make and model number
Additional information:

21. SPECIAL FLOORS AND WAINSCOT:

	Location	Material, Color, Border, Sizes, Gage, Etc.	Threshold Material	Wall Base Material	Underfloor Material
Floors	Kitchen	Armstrong inlaid linoleum-Tricino Pattern	ss	rubber	5/8" T&G
	Bath	Armstrong inlaid linoleum- " "	ss	rubber	5/8" T&G
	Dining	Armstrong inlaid linoleum- " "	ss	rubber	5/8" T&G

	Location	Material, Color, Border, Cap. Sizes, Gage, Etc.	Height	Height Over Tub	Height in Showers (From Floor)
Wainscot	Bath	Ceramic tile 4 1/2 x 4 1/2		6'-0"	
		Ceramic tile 4 1/2 x 4 1/2 Wet wall to vanity	3'-9"		

Bathroom accessories: ☒ Recessed; material Ceramic; number 7; ☒ Attached; material Ceramic; number 5

Additional information:

22. PLUMBING:

Fixture	Number	Location	Make	Mfr's Fixture Identification No.	Size	Color
Sink	1	kitchen	Crane	# 5131 Dbl. Bowl	32 x 21	White
Lavatory	2	bath	Crane	# 3-175	18 x 24	White
Water closet	2	bath	Crane		Standard	White
Bathtub	1	bath	Crane-Farfax	# 2-200	60"x30"	White
Shower over tub△	1	bath			Standard	Chrome
Stall shower△						
Laundry trays						
Disposer	1	kitchen	Insinkarator	# 333		
		Hot and cold water taps in	laundry area			

△☒ Curtain rod △☐ Door ☐ Shower pan: material

Water supply: ☒ public; ☐ community system; ☐ individual (private) system.★

Sewage disposal: ☐ public; ☐ community system; ☐ individual (private) system.★

★*Show and describe individual system in complete detail in separate drawings and specifications according to requirements.*

House drain (inside): ☐ cast iron; ☐ tile; ☒ other Copper House sewer (outside): ☐ cast iron; ☒ tile; ☐ other

Water piping: ☐ galvanized steel; ☒ copper tubing; ☐ other Sill cocks, number 2

Domestic water heater: type Automatic; make and model Rund E.T. 3036; heating capacity 25.7 gph. 100° rise. Storage tank: material Glass lined; capacity 30 gallons.

Gas service: ☒ utility company; ☐ liq. pet. gas; ☐ other Gas piping: ☐ cooking; ☒ house heating.

Footing drains connected to: ☒ storm sewer; ☐ sanitary sewer; ☐ dry well. Sump pump; make and model Tile to curb ; capacity ; discharges into

23. HEATING:

☐ Hot water. ☐ Steam. ☐ Vapor. ☐ One-pipe system. ☐ Two-pipe system.

☐ Radiators. ☐ Convectors. ☐ Baseboard radiation. Make and model

Radiant panel: ☐ floor; ☐ wall; ☐ ceiling. Panel coil: material

☐ Circulator. ☐ Return pump. Make and model ; capacity gpm.

Boiler: make and model Output Btuh.; net rating Btuh.

Additional information:

Warm air: ☐ Gravity. ☒ Forced. Type of system Extended plemium perimeter system

Duct material: supply G.I.; return G.I. Insulation , thickness ☐ Outside air intake.

Furnace: make and model Lennox G 9D-110 Input 110,000 Btuh.; output 88,000 Btuh.

Additional information:

☐ Space heater; ☐ floor furnace; ☐ wall heater. Input Btuh.; output Btuh.; number units

Make, model Additional information:

Controls: make and types Minn.-honeywell

Additional information:

Fuel: ☐ Coal; ☐ oil; ☐ gas; ☐ liq. pet. gas; ☐ electric; ☐ other ; storage capacity

Additional information:

Firing equipment furnished separately: ☐ Gas burner, conversion type. ☐ Stoker: hopper feed ☐; bin feed ☐

Oil burner: ☐ pressure atomizing; ☐ vaporizing

Make and model Control

Additional information:

Electric heating system: type Input watts; @ volts; output Btuh.

Additional information:

Ventilating equipment: attic fan, make and model ; capacity cfm.

kitchen exhaust fan, make and model Miami - carey

Other heating, ventilating, or cooling equipment

24. ELECTRIC WIRING:

Service: ☒ overhead; ☐ underground. Panel: ☐ fuse box; ☒ circuit-breaker; make 100 amp. Number circuits 8

Wiring: ☐ conduit; ☐ armored cable; ☒ nonmetallic cable; ☐ knob and tube; ☐ other

Special outlets: ☐ range; ☐ water heater; ☒ other Furnace, Disposer, Washer, Dryer

☒ Doorbell. ☐ Chimes. Push-button locations Front and rear doors Additional information:

25. LIGHTING FIXTURES:

Total number of fixtures 18 Total allowance for fixtures, typical installation, $ 90.00

Nontypical installation

Additional information:

26. INSULATION:

Location	Thickness	Material, Type, and Method of Installation	Vapor Barrier
Roof			
Ceiling	3"	Blown in Johnsmanville Spintex	
Wall	1/2"	Fibreboard	Integral
Floor			

HARDWARE: *(make, material, and finish.)* # 800 series interior and exterior locks by westlock of California, Tulip design with brass finish US#3. Butt hinges W4. National cabinet hinges, brass pulls and magnetic catches.

SPECIAL EQUIPMENT: *(state material or make and model.)*

Venetian blinds ______ Number ______

Kitchen range Tappan EUV-5-C-B 30" drop-in

Refrigerator ______

Dishwasher ______

Garbage disposal unit Insinkarator #333

Automatic washer ______

Clothes drier ______

Other ______

27. MISCELLANEOUS: *(Describe any main dwelling materials, equipment, or construction items not shown elsewhere; or use to provide additional information where the space provided was inadequate. Always reference by item number to correspond to numbering used on this form.)*

Built in vanity in main bath
Walltex on kitchen soffit
Walkin closet in main bedroom
Room dividers in family room and living room

PORCHES: 4'-0" x 8'-0" Concrete patio rear
4'-0" x 3'-0" Concrete stoop rear Three Risers
4'-0" x 4'-0" Concrete stoop with three risers front

TERRACES:

GARAGES:

Two car constructed same as house with 5/8" drywall on ceiling and wall adjacent to house.
Door from the house to the garage is a 2'-6" solid core

WALKS AND DRIVEWAYS:

Driveway: width 10'-0"; base material gravel; thickness 6"; surfacing material Asphalt; thickness 2"
Front walk: width 3'-0"; material Concrete; thickness 4". Service walk: width 3'; material con.; thickness 4"
Steps: material Concrete; treads 10"; risers 7 1/2". Cheek walls ______

OTHER ONSITE IMPROVEMENTS:

(Specify all exterior onsite improvements not described elsewhere, including items such as unusual grading, drainage structures, retaining walls, fence, railings, and accessory structures.)

LANDSCAPING, PLANTING, AND FINISH GRADING:

Topsoil ______" thick: ☐ front yard; ☐ side yards; ☐ rear yard to ______ feet behind main building.

Lawns (~~seeded~~, sodded, or ~~sprigged~~): ☒ front yard Comp; ☒ side yards Comp; ☒ rearyard Comp

Planting: ☐ as specified and shown on drawings; ☐ as follows:

1 Shade trees, deciduous, 2" caliper.
______ Low flowering trees, deciduous, ______' to ______'
______ High-growing shrubs, deciduous, ______' to ______'
______ Medium-growing shrubs, deciduous, ______' to ______'
2 Low-growing shrubs, deciduous, 2' to 3'

2 Evergreen trees. 3' to 4', B & B.
2 Evergreen shrubs, 1 1/2' to 2', B & B.
______ Vines, 2-year ______

IDENTIFICATION.—This exhibit shall be identified by the signature of the builder, or sponsor, and/or the proposed mortgagor if the latter is known at the time of application.

Date ______ Signature ______

Signature ______

Selection of Materials and Equipment

To prepare a set of specifications correctly, a designer must know what materials and equipment are available and have access to complete descriptions of each, Fig. 80-2. He must make a list of the materials and equipment which are needed and then completely describe them in correct trade terms. In selecting materials and equipment, a designer tries to meet the needs of the owner. There are nine major factors to consider (Fig. 80-3):

1. **Economy.** The cost and appropriateness of the item.
2. **Quality.** What grade of excellence of the material, fixture, or appliance is wanted?
3. **Is it functional?** Will it serve the purpose for which it is intended?
4. **Ease of installation.** Is the item easy or hard to install? Will its installation require special tools or equipment?
5. **Appearance.** Is it pleasing to the eye? Will it fit in with the general scheme the designer has in mind?
6. **Codes.** Building codes must be followed. All utility items, fixtures, and appliances must pass area safety and building codes.
7. **Service requirements.** Can the equipment be repaired easily, quickly, and by qualified workmen in the community?
8. **Warranty.** Does the equipment carry a guarantee? Is the entire unit guaranteed or will the owner be required to pay labor or shipping charges?
9. **Size.** Items such as furnaces, water heaters, and dishwashers often must fit a preplanned space in a structure. The model ordered must be one that fits.

A designer considers many other things while preparing specifications. Questions that must be asked are:

1. Are the products easy to get?
2. What are the delivery dates?
3. What are the weights?

Sometimes compromises have to be made. That is, one desired feature must be given up for another that is more important.

Fig. 80-3. All nine factors are considered when selecting a suitable material.

Summary

If the drawings and the specifications for a house are accurate and complete, the finished product should be exactly as the owner and the architect expected it to be. Also, the rights of all the parties involved will be protected. The specifications include legal documents, statements of conditions, and technical descriptions of required materials and work practices.

Terms to Know

specifications	installation
compromise	appearance
functional	codes
economy	service requirements
services	warranty
quality	

Think About It!

1. How do specifications protect the interests of the architect, the builder, and the owner?
2. What problems might come up if the specifications are not complete?

READING 81

Financing and Contracting

After the plans and specifications for a house have been developed, it may be necessary to have them approved by a lending agency. Professional people on the agency's staff can examine the plans and estimate the value of the house. Based on this estimate, they also can decide how much money the agency can lend for building this house. This does *not* mean that the bank has granted a loan. It only indicates whether the owner should go ahead as planned, or whether he must change his plans to reduce the cost, Fig. 81-1.

If a loan is approved, most lending agencies issue a *letter of commitment*. This commitment is the legal "go ahead" signal. The written commitment generally states the loan amount, term and interest rate, time limit for accepting it, and other conditions that the lending agency wants included, Fig. 81-2. After the financing is approved, the owner must arrange for the work to be done.

Owner-Architect Agreement or Contract

One kind of arrangement is an *owner-architect agreement*. The architect, for a fee, will take care of the whole project for the owner. This saves the homeowner a lot of work and cuts down on his problems. Under this agreement, all the owner has to do is make the payments as the architect approves them. He then moves in when the house is finished.

Owner-Contractor Agreement or Contract

In an *owner-contractor agreement*, the owner and contractor sign an agreement which describes what the contractor will do for the price of his bid. The contractor is responsible for the whole job. He furnishes all the materials and sees that all work is done right. He supervises all subcontractors and orders and pays for building materials and labor. He schedules delivery of materials to the job and acts as the general supervisor. As with the owner-architect agreement, here, the owner also has no direct responsibility for construction. He is asked to select colors and finishes, light fixtures, and appliances before they are applied or installed. His major responsibility is to see that the general contractor is paid according to contract.

Owner-Subcontractor Agreement or Contract

Unless a person has had experience in contracting and construction, he probably should not make an *owner-subcontractor agreement*. Under this plan the owner acts as the general contractor. He supervises the job and keeps it moving. This is very hard for someone with no experience. He asks subcontractors for bids. If he knows nothing about the reliability of the contractors, he may contact some that are unreliable. After he receives the bids, he must decide which ones to accept. If a person contracting his own job understands only the prices, he likely will choose the lowest bids. In many cases, these are not the best bids. The owner must then take the responsibility for all materials,

Credit Report

Ordered: ____

Application for a Conventional Loan from
BLOOMINGTON FEDERAL SAVINGS AND LOAN ASSOCIATION

To Appraiser ____

Date ____

Name ____ Date ____

Mailing Address ____ Phone: Bus. ____ Res. ____

City and State ____ Term of Loan: ____ Rate ____

TYPE OF LOAN

- ☐ Existing Building
  - ☐ New Construction
  - ☐ Previously Occupied
- ☐ Construction
  - ☐ Contractor or Builder
    - ☐ Sold ☐ Speculative
  - ☐ Owner Occupant
    - ☐ Contract
    - ☐ Labor Equity
    - ☐ Payout after Completion
- ☐ Refinance

Property Address ____

City and State ____

Legal Description ____

DIRECTIONS ____

ESTIMATED PAYMENT

Principal & Interest $ ____

Taxes ____

Insurance ____

Other ____

Total ____

Ratio: Loan to: Appraisal ____

Purchase Price or Construction Cost: ____

Broker: ____

Abstract at: ____

I (We) hereby apply for a first mortgage loan of $____ to be repaid in monthly installments to be applied first to interest and the balance to principal, and offer as security a mortgage on the following described property:

Dwelling: Single ____ Two Family ____ Apartments ____ Other ____

Construction: Frame ____ Brick ____ Stucco ____ Other ____ Roof ____ No. Stories ____

Exterior: Weatherboard ____ Brick ____ Insulbric ____ Asbestos ____ Other ____

Rooms: 1st Floor ____ Baths ____ Floors ____ Utility ____ 2nd: ____ Baths ____ Floors ____

Basement: ____ Floor ____ Heating System ____ Water Htr. ____ Bath ____

Remarks ____

Connected Utilities: Water ____ Electricity ____ Gas ____ Sewer ____ Septic Tank ____

Garage: No. Cars ____ Attached ____ Frame ____ Brick ____ Block ____ Pavement ____

Age of Building ____ Size of Lot ____ Last Tax Paid ____

When Purchased ____ Purchase Price $ ____ Construction Cost $ ____

Cost of Improvements or Repairs: To Date ____ Planned Now ____ When Remodeled ____

Amount of Original Mortgage, When Made, Balance Due ____

Name of Present Owner ____

Mortgage Held By ____

Places of Residence for Last 7 Years ____

Loan No. ____ DATE ____	PURPOSE OF LOAN ____
Appraisal ____ Rate ____ %	
Orign. Amt. ____	
Bal. Due ____	
No. Advances ____ Amount: ____	
Payment Record:	

PERSONAL

Mtg ____ H&A ____

(Husband) NAME ____ Address ____

Age ____ Married ____ Children ____ Ages ____

Employed By ____ Address ____

Type of Business ____ Term of Employment ____

Position ____ How Long ____ Previous Position ____

Previous Employers ____ Reason For Change ____

____ Reason For Change ____

(Wife) NAME ____ Age ____

Employed ____ Position ____ How Long ____

INCOME: Salary ____ Paid By ____

Wife ____ Paid By ____

Rent or Contract ____

Other Sources ____

LIFE INSURANCE

Company	Amount	Company	Amount	Borrowed

Obligations Due to Banks ____ Personal Loans ____ Credit Union ____ Other ____

Installment Payments ____ Nature ____ Amount ____ (____)

____ Nature ____ Amount ____ (____)

____ Nature ____ Amount ____ (____)

Bank Account at ____ Checking Savings SAVINGS ACCT. HERE ____

Bank Account at ____ Checking Savings

MERCHANT REFERENCES

____ Address ____

____ Address ____

____ Address ____

Own Other Real Estate? ____ Location ____

Value ____ Encumbrances ____

INSURANCE: ☐ Assume ☐ Furnish Own ____ ☐ Association Furnish ____

The undersigned agree to furnish a complete and merchantable abstract of title or guarantee policy, continued so as to show said mortgage to be a first record lien, which shall remain in the hands of said Association together with all insurance policies and other recorded and necessary required securities for use of the lender until the said loan is paid.

Applicant further agrees to pay on demand all costs incidental to the processing of the loan application—including fees for preliminary abstracting, appraisal, recordings, title examination, final abstracting, etc.

____ (SEAL)

____ (SEAL)

Fig. 81-1. If you were to seek a mortgage loan, you would have to answer questions such as the ones on this sample application form.

workmanship, time schedules, payrolls, and liabilities on the job.

If a person has had enough experience in contracting and building, this method is the least costly. He can do many of the small jobs himself. He also saves himself a supervising fee which can amount to as much as 10% of the total cost of the job. Under this plan, the owner must make sure that the lending institution will accept this method. Many lending firms require that a good, reliable, authorized contractor build the house.

No Owner Contract with Others

It is possible for a person to build an entire house himself. Some people have done this. However, very few people who need financing can get it if they build this way. This is because few people are skilled enough to do all the work and to do a professional job. A lending institution wants to be sure the house will be sound. Also, it takes a long time for someone to build an entire house by himself. Most loan commitments set a date when the work is to be finished. It is difficult for one person, building his own house, to meet this time limit.

If the owner receives his letter of commitment, he can go ahead along one of several paths. Each individual must pick the contracting method that best suits his needs, Fig. 81-3.

Summary

After the plans and specifications have been completed, a person wanting to build a home usually goes to a lending agency to get approval on a loan. (See Fig. 81-4.) After a loan application has been submitted and approved, the lending agency generally prepares a written commitment stating the terms and conditions that the agency requires. This commitment gives the applicant the "go ahead" signal to begin work on his house.

Next, the owner may contract with an architect to take care of the whole project. He may hire a general contractor, or he may act as his own contractor and hire various subcontractors. In a very few cases, he does all the work himself.

Fig. 81-2. Commercial banks and savings institutions are just two sources for borrowing money for house construction.

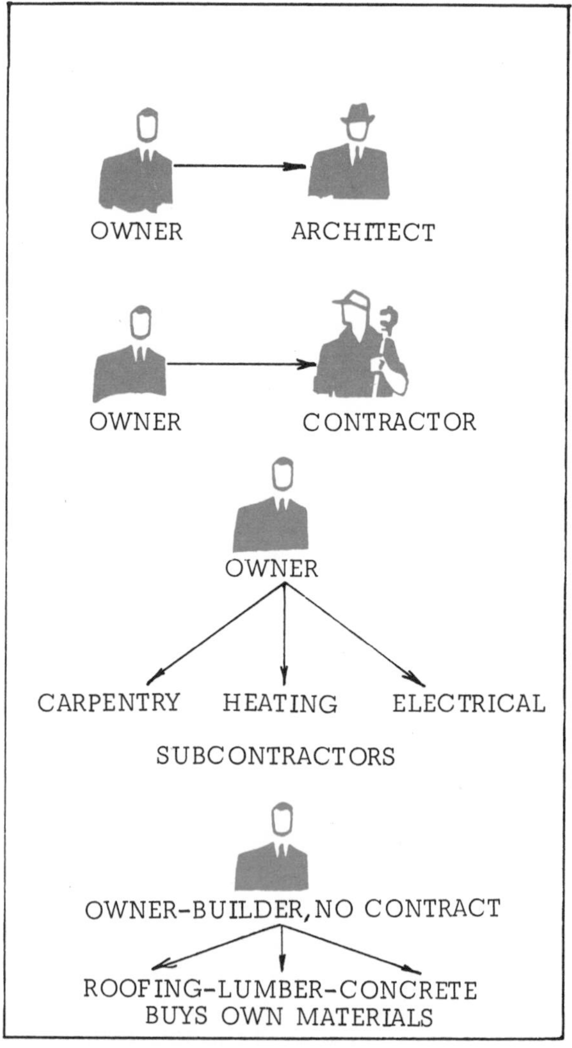

Fig. 81-3. Different ways of contracting.

Terms to Know

letter of commitment
lending agency
owner-architect contract
owner-contractor contract
owner-subcontractor contract
loan

Think About It!

1. How do mortgage interest rates affect the size home you can buy?
2. What experience and training would you need to act as an owner-builder without any contract? Do you think you would ever try this?

SAMPLE SCHEDULE OF DIRECT REDUCTION LOAN

RATE %	PAYMENT	LOAN	TERM: YEARS	MONTHS	PERIODS
8.00	$167.29	$20,000.00	20	0	240

PAYMENT NUMBER	PAYMENT ON INTEREST	PAYMENT ON PRINCIPAL	BALANCE OF LOAN	PAYMENT NUMBER	PAYMENT ON INTEREST	PAYMENT ON PRINCIPAL	BALANCE OF LOAN
1	133.33	33.96	19,966.04	72	112.86	54.43	16,875.13
2	133.11	34.18	19,931.86	84	108.35	58.94	16,193.02
3	132.88	34.41	19,897.45	96	103.45	63.84	15,454.29
4	132.65	34.64	19,862.81	108	98.16	69.13	14,654.24
5	132.42	34.87	19,827.94	120	92.42	74.87	13,787.77
6	132.19	35.10	19,792.84	132	86.20	81.09	12,849.39
7	131.95	35.34	19,757.50	144	79.47	87.82	11,833.13
8	131.72	35.57	19,721.93	156	72.18	95.11	10,732.52
9	131.48	35.81	19,686.12	168	64.29	103.00	9,540.56
10	131.24	36.05	19,650.07	180	55.74	111.55	8,249.67
11	131.00	36.29	19,613.78	192	46.48	120.81	6,851.64
12	130.76	36.53	19,577.25	204	36.46	130.83	5,337.58
24	127.73	39.56	19,119.39	216	25.60	141.69	3,697.85
36	124.44	42.85	18,623.55	228	13.84	153.45	1,922.00
48	120.89	46.40	18,086.55	240	1.10	164.95	.00*
60	117.03	50.26	17,504.99				

*The final payment is usually somewhat different from the regular payment and is shown on the last line.

Fig. 81-4. Notice how the amount of your payments that reduce the principal changes over the life of the loan.

READING 82

Building the Substructure

After the contract for building a house is made, the first step in construction is preparing the site. In the construction of a house, this means clearing obstacles, stripping topsoil, filling and grading, and draining. With the site cleared, the substructure is constructed. The major operations in this work are excavating, setting foundations, providing drainage, and backfilling.

Clearing Obstacles

The *obstacles* usually found on a site are brush, trees, rocks, or buildings. These must be removed before construction may begin. Trees may be allowed to stand if they will not be in the way of the construction, Fig. 82-1. Trees left on the site must be protected from injury by construction equipment.

Buildings on the site may need to be torn down and hauled away. If the building is small, such as a garage or shed, and will not be in the way, the contractor might use it for storing materials and equipment before removing it.

Stripping Topsoil

To insure a supply of topsoil for later landscaping, the contractor has it *stripped* off the site. By using a bulldozer, he strips the topsoil and places it into stockpiles. When landscaping operations begin, the topsoil is used for the finish grading, Fig. 82-2.

Fig. 82-1. Although brush is removed, often some trees are allowed to stand.

Fig. 82-2. Usable topsoil is stripped off the site and stockpiled for later use.

Filling and Grading

Some building sites need topographic changes before construction can begin. These changes may be leveling hills, filling ditches, or filling the basement of a building which has been torn down.

The *fill* used on construction sites may be found on the site itself, or it may be hauled in. Fill found on the site is moved by a bulldozer to the spot where it is needed. Fill brought to the site is hauled in by dump trucks, dumped where needed, and leveled by a bulldozer. Grading and leveling operations, when necessary, usually are done with a bulldozer or a front end loader. In most cases, the soil is distributed on the site, Fig. 82-3.

Drainage

An important consideration in site preparation is what to do about water. The contractor must be prepared to remove water which is there and to remove water that might collect at the site during construction. If existing water is the problem, the contractor can have his men dig ditches to drain the site, pump out the water, or divert the source of the water and then fill the site, if necessary, Fig. 82-4.

Fig. 82-3. Grading and filling provide the proper land contour for building.

Surveying

Once the site has been prepared and the surveyor has determined the location of the individual building lots (Fig. 82-5), the principal building lines of the house are set up. In most cases the house is laid out parallel to the main road or the front property line, Fig. 82-6. The distance is called the *building setback*. This distance is often covered by local building codes.

Fig. 82-4. The contractor has provided these drainage ditches to drain the site.

Fig. 82-5. A surveyor determines the location of the building lots.

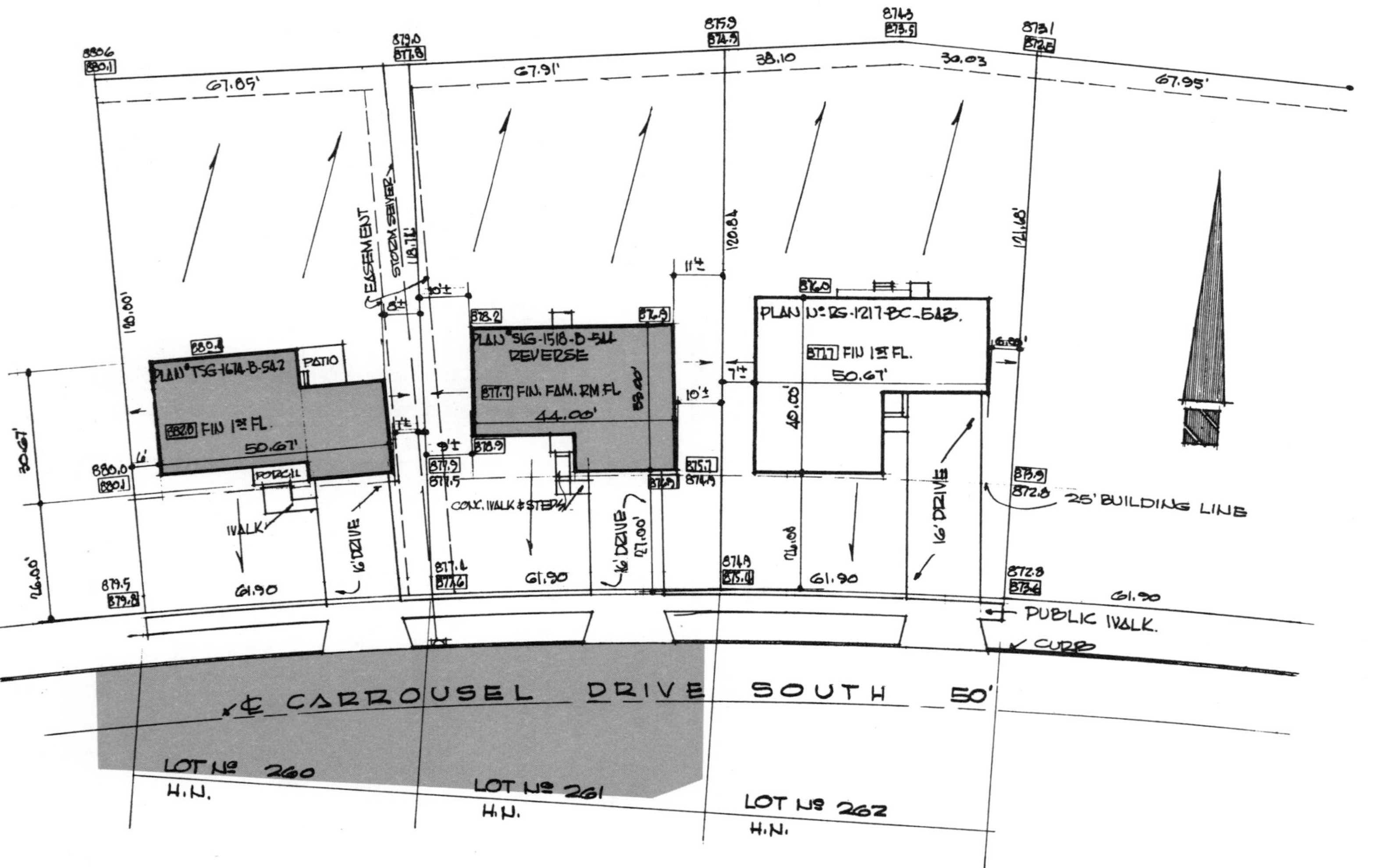

Fig. 82-6. The building is often placed on the lot so that it is parallel to the front of the lot.

The workman measures in from the property boundary line by setting his *transit* at the required angles and measuring the required distances to locate *control points.* These are the points from which he measures both vertical and horizontal distance. Control points are put any place where they will be safe from construction equipment. The actual layout of the building usually is done by using the *batter board method,* Fig. 82-7.

The job of setting property boundaries is usually the work of a registered surveyor. The placing of a building on a property may be done by either a surveyor or by a person employed by the building contractor. As an example, the placing of a large commercial building might be set up by a registered surveyor, whereas the placing of a residential property might be done by the job superintendent.

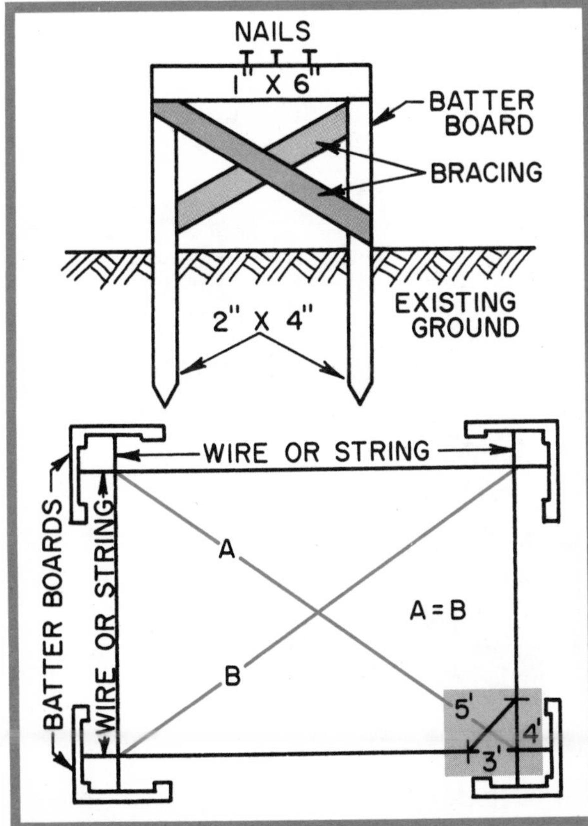

Fig. 82-7. Building layout.

Excavation

There are several common kinds of substructure excavations. Some houses require the use of a combination of two or more kinds. There is a *full excavation* which gives a basement under the whole house. A *crawl space* design calls for partial excavation. This gives only enough room under the structure for installing and servicing circulatory systems. A *slab-on-grade* has no space under the house. The only excavation needed for this is for the footings and the foundation walls.

The major pieces of equipment used for foundation excavation are the crawler tractor, the front-end loader, and the backhoe. Each of these can be used for the removal of large amounts of earth. The backhoe, however, has the advantage of being able to dig foundation trenches neatly and simply, Fig. 82-8.

It must be kept in mind that, no matter what kind of foundation you have, the digging is done to satisfy the dimensions called for on the plans and the contract drawings. Some trenches are hand dug, but this takes

Fig. 82-8. This is a backhoe. It can be used to excavate for foundations as well as service trenches.

much time and is usually done only to give the earth a final, clean shape. It also is done when it is impossible to get equipment in to do the job.

The trenches for services to the house can be excavated at the same time as the excavations are made for the structure. To put these in at the beginning will save the extra expense of having them dug later and cutting up the site again. Also, it will be useful to have temporary water lines and electricity on the site at an early date so the workers can use them in their work.

Setting Foundations

Foundations include the load bearing surface, the footings, and the basement wall, if any. These are the lowest part of the structure and are mostly below grade. Foundations must be strong enough to support the structure that will be resting on them.

Careful study of the soil should be made before starting the footings. The footing is usually wider than the foundation which will rest on it. How much wider it is depends on the ground conditions. The softer the earth, the wider the footing needed. The weight of the structure also is important. A multistory house needs wider footings than a single-story house, on the same soil. A rule used often is that the width of the footing is to be twice the width of the block to be used, and the depth of the footing is to be the same as the width of the block.

Where the earth is firm and the sides of the trench will hold their shape without crumbling, no forms to hold the concrete are necessary. The trench will serve as its own form, and the concrete mixture is placed directly into it.

The foundation walls, when they are used, are built on the footings. It is important to anchor the foundation walls to the footings with common reinforcing rods. Also, the sills and the framing of the house superstructure need to be anchored to the foundation walls. This is done by putting in anchor bolts 6′ on center and embedded in the top of the foundation walls.

Drainage

Drain tile should now be laid around the outside of the foundation walls so that the

Fig. 82-9. The crawler tractor cannot be used to excavate service trenches.

Fig. 82-10. Study the relationships among the footing, drain tile, foundation wall, and bearing surface.

basement will stay dry. These tile are put in along the entire footing. The drainage tile system empties into a dry well, storm sewer, or another outlet away from the foundation and lower than the floor. When necessary, an underground pump in a well is used to catch and get rid of extra ground water. See Fig. 82-10.

Backfilling

Backfilling is putting earth back against the foundation after the foundation has been put in. Before backfilling to the foundation walls, it is best to crossbrace and shore up the inside of the foundation wall. Many basement walls have collapsed due to the pressure of soil settlement on the outside wall. First of all, the wall should be completely cured. The fill must then be scooped in a little at a time. Any large rock or sudden jolt on the foundation may cause a crack which will allow water to seep in, Fig. 82-11.

With the footing and foundation walls in place, the substructure is complete. Work on the superstructure may begin.

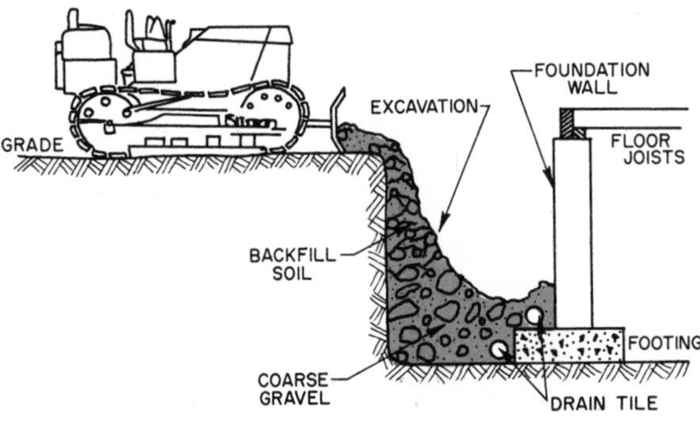

Fig. 82-11. Backfilling must be done carefully to prevent damage to the foundation.

Summary

Many operations are used in preparing the site. Obstacles such as water, trees, rocks, and buildings must be removed. Once this is done, the topsoil should be removed and saved for landscaping the lot. The site should then be filled and rough graded.

When the site is fully prepared, the contractor lays out the location of the house. Workmen then mark the location by using batter boards. The site is now ready for excavation. The size and kind of excavation to be done depend on the foundation plans.

The foundation is put in next. After the foundation is in, drainage tile is laid around the outside of the foundation walls so that the basement will stay dry. Then the excavated earth is put back or backfilled against the foundation walls. This completes the substructure.

Terms to Know

obstacles
stripping topsoil
drainage
parallel
building setback
control points
excavation
  a. full
  b. crawl space
  c. slab-on-grade
backfilling
crossbrace

Think About It!

1. Are basements common in homes in your community? What excavation problems would limit their use?
2. Why is it important to strip off and save topsoil during the clearing operation? Is the topsoil of higher quality than subsoil in your region of the country?

READING 83

Building Walls

Wall systems are one of the basic elements of the superstructure. The designer of a wall system considers: (1) functional performance, (2) costs, and (3) finished appearance.

Functional performance includes the following:

1. Structural strength to support loads,
2. Weather tightness,
3. Privacy,
4. Fire resistance,
5. Ability to have utility systems put in,
6. Ability to have finished materials attached to it, and
7. Places for doors, windows and other openings.

Fig. 83-1. These 2″ x 4″ studs are spaced at 16″ on center. The frame is braced with diagonal bracing to keep the building plumb and to prevent collapse.

The *total cost* of a wall system depends on these factors:

1. The cost of the materials and labor,
2. The maintenance cost, and
3. The effect on the cost of operating the structure (for example, how the heat loss through the walls will influence the cost of heating a house).

The *finished appearance* depends on the choice of finish materials. These, in turn, may affect:

1. The spacing and span of structural members,
2. The type and physical properties of subsurface materials, if any, and
3. The method of construction.

Common wall systems include stud wall construction, panelized construction, masonry construction, and post and beam construction.

Stud Wall

The usual stud wall is made of 8′ lengths of 2″ x 4″ lumber which are spaced 16″ or 24″ on center. These spacings permit the use of standard widths and lengths of panel sheathing and siding. The stud system carries the loads of all vertical members, such as the roof. The space between the studs may be used for insulation, heating, plumbing, and electrical materials, Fig. 83-1.

A stud system should be put up quickly so that the roof can be attached to it to give cover for people working on the inside. Then they don't have to worry about the weather. A stud system has the advantages of giving excellent structural strength and using low cost basic materials. The stud system also provides a base for many finishes and can be made on or off the site.

Panelized Walls

Wall panels and *component systems* may consist of preframed panels made of precut wood studs to which sheathing has been fastened. Fabrication may include putting in insulation, vapor barriers, wiring, inside and outside finishes, windows, and doors. Panels may be fabricated off the site in any size that can be handled, Fig. 83-3.

Prefabricated wall panels have many advantages and have proved to be excellent in structural performance. However, they require careful design to be able to accommodate mechanical equipment. They may need special handling and building procedures (Fig. 83-4), and they may not be acceptable to local building codes.

Fig. 83-2. Interior and exterior frames are made on the floor. They are tilted up and nailed in place.

Masonry Walls

Masonry walls made from concrete block are the easiest to construct. They may simply continue from the foundation. Openings are left for doors and windows. Brick walls with a *cavity* are more commonly used. This method uses two separate walls which can be brick and brick, brick and tile, or brick and block. A space (cavity) is left in between them. The two walls are held together by using metal ties, Fig. 83-5. Many kinds

Fig. 83-3. A crane places the wall panel of a prefabricated house. The wall is lined with a single panel 3/8″ thick, 8′ high, and 20′ long.

Fig. 83-4. A precast wall panel is erected for this house.

of stone walls also are used for outside walls. One big problem of masonry walls is that of insulation. Masonry construction transmits cold or heat. To stop this, insulation can be poured directly into the cavity, or the walls can be furred on the inside with insulation put in between the furring strips.

Brick or stone veneer is a nonload bearing masonry facing put on over other structural materials. The veneer makes the exterior surface weatherproof.

Usually masonry walls are left exposed. However, they may be finished on the outside with stucco or other coatings. Masonry walls are used because they are strong and have low maintenance costs.

Post and Beam Walls

Post and beam wall systems are made of posts which carry the loads of floors, roofs, and ceilings. Nonbearing wall sections are put between the posts. Posts are generally 4″ x 4″ lumber spaced 4′ to 8′ on center. Wall areas between posts are framed, sheathed, and finished much like other wood panel systems. They are used mostly as weather barriers and give support to the posts. This kind of construction is used widely on ranch style homes where the natural look of beams and posts is wanted.

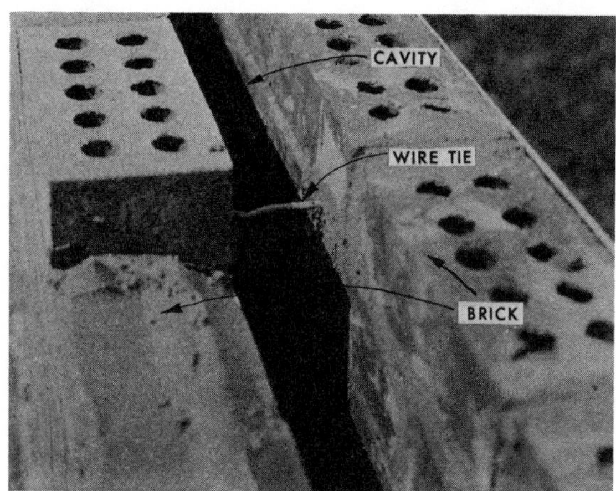

Fig. 83-5. Two brick walls are held together by metal ties.

Summary

The selection of the basic kind of wall to be used greatly affects the selection of material for the rest of the building. The basic kinds of walls are (1) stud walls, (2) panel walls, (3) masonry walls, and (4) post and beam walls.

Stud walls are used in conventional and in precut kinds of construction. Lumber is used throughout, and each piece is handled and installed separately. Panelized walls are made and installed as units. Masonry walls are the most fire-resistant kind of wall, and they are very strong. They also need the least amount of maintenance. Post and beam walls are used where special effects of exposed posts and beams are wanted for appearance.

Terms to Know

functional performance
structural strength
overhead
maintenance
stud wall
fabricate
prefabrication
component system
cavity
insulation
transmits
veneer
stucco
on center
appearance

Think About It!

1. Why do you think 2″ x 4″ studs commonly are placed 16″ on center in walls?
2. What style of wall construction has been used in your school building? Is this style often used in homes?

Building Floors and Ceilings

READING 84

In house construction there are two major kinds of flooring material used as subfloor. These are *concrete* and *wood.* A large variety of materials are used as finished floor surfaces and for ceilings.

Concrete Subfloors

For houses without basements or for unexcavated portions under houses, a concrete slab-on-earth is an excellent kind of subfloor, Fig. 84-1. The earth under the slab should be well packed down by *tamping and rolling* to prevent any settlement of the floor slab.

Fig. 84-1. This concrete slab-on-earth is an excellent subfloor. The heating ducts and water pipes are already under the floor.

A coarse, gravel-type fill should be placed over this finished subgrade and compacted. This fill can be coarse cinders, slag, gravel, or crushed stone. The fill acts as an insulator and as a protection against moisture from the ground.

Where drainage can be a problem, drain tile should be put in around the outside edge of the outside wall footing and connected to proper drains. If you are locating the house on high ground or in a dry climate, the tile may not be necessary.

Where needed, steps can be taken for putting in ducts for heating systems, plumbing lines, and electrical conduits under the granular fill. Much care should be taken to make certain that these lines rest on firm, packed soil and that the fill dirt also is packed down. *If these lines settle, expecially the plumbing lines, they can cause much trouble and costly repairs.*

A 1″ thick, continuous, waterproofed, rigid *insulation strip* should be put in between the foundation wall and the edge of the floor slab. This will keep frost and cold from coming through the outside foundation wall to the inside floor. It also acts as an expansion strip to absorb expansion and contraction of the slab as the temperature changes.

To keep moisture from rising from the earth under the slab, a *vapor barrier* must be installed. The two most popular vapor barrier materials are asphalt-impregnated (filled) fiber sheets and polyethylene film. They are put over the granular fill. Caution must be used not to puncture or put holes in this vapor barrier. Before the concrete is placed, metal reinforcement in the form of wire mesh is cut and laid over the vapor barrier. See Fig. 84-2.

Concrete for the floor slab should be made with durable, well-graded aggregate. It may be delivered to the site by ready-mix trucks or it may be mixed on the job. To smooth the wet concrete, it is screeded, floated, and then troweled, Fig. 84-3.

Wood Subfloors

If floors are built on joists, the joists are covered with a subfloor on which the finished flooring is installed. If boards are used for the subflooring, they should be placed diagonally across the floor joists. These boards are generally 1″ thick and 6″ to 8″ wide. Plywood and other manufactured sheet products also are used for subflooring. They are placed at right angles to the joists.

Joist floor systems provide space for heating, air-conditioning, electrical, and plumbing equipment. These floors also are easily insulated to keep heat loss low and to reduce sound transmission. See Fig. 84-4.

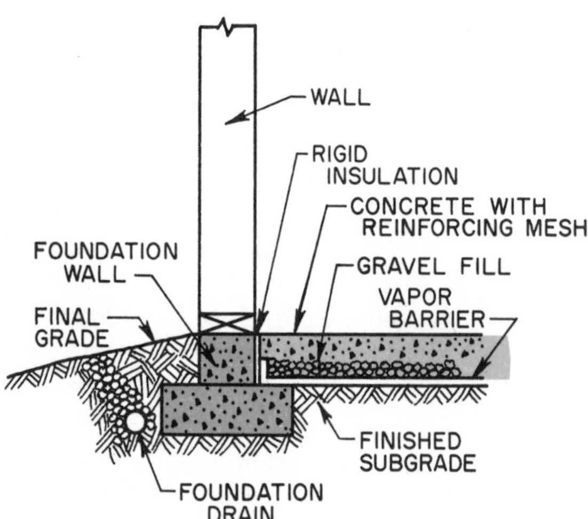

Fig. 84-2. Concrete slab floor construction.

Other Floor Systems

Plank and beam systems are made by the use of 2″ x 6″ or 2″ x 8″ tongue-and-groove or splined planks. They are installed over beams which generally are spaced 4′ or 8′ on

Fig. 84-3. These men are striking off a concrete floor slab.

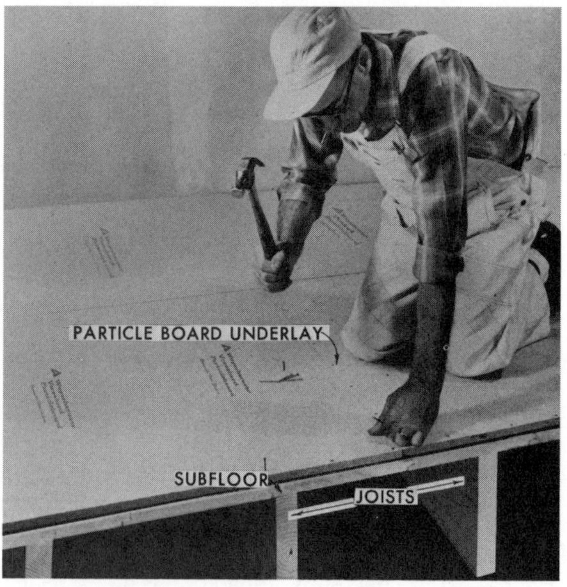

Fig. 84-4. Tile will be installed on top of this subfloor system.

center depending on the beam sizes. The planks serve as the subfloor and may be the finished floor. They transmit the floor loads to fewer and larger members than do conventional wood-joist floor systems. Finished flooring such as hardwood flooring may be put on directly over the planks. Sheet and tile flooring must have an *underlay,* Fig. 84-4.

Paneled floor systems have many forms. One common system uses plywood panels 1⅛″ thick spanning between beams spaced 4′ on center. Panels serve as a combination subfloor and underlay. Other systems are made of simple preframed panels. There are other kinds of paneled floors such as *stressed skin* and *sandwich panels.* Paneled construction does give many of the advantages of component fabrication, but the incorporation of heating, air conditioning, electrical, and plumbing equipment requires careful design.

Finished Floors

There are many different kinds of finished floors. These include wood, linoleum, asphalt, ceramic tile, flagstone, cork, vinyl, and carpeting. Before most of these can be applied on wood subfloors, an underlay of hardboard, plywood, or particle board must be put in at right angles to the subfloor. If the subfloor is diagonal the underlay can be installed in any direction. Most of them can be applied directly to concrete, Fig. 84-5.

Each finished floor material requires special techniques for installation on concrete and on wood. Special fasteners and adhesive are needed in each case.

Ceilings

One-story homes can have different kinds of ceilings. There can be the plank and beam ceilings which leave all the members exposed, Fig. 84-6. The most common ceiling is one installed over ceiling joists. Ceiling joists are installed the same as floor joists. However, they rest on the rafter plate of the outside wall and on a load bearing inside wall. Bridging is not generally installed between these joists.

Multistory homes have floor-ceiling type systems. This means a joist installation in which the the joists serve two purposes. They support the flooring for the second floor, and

Fig. 84-5. This man is laying out lines to install tile on top of the concrete.

Fig. 84-6. In a plank and beam ceiling, the roofing material is also the ceiling material. Notice that the beams have been wrapped in protective paper.

they serve as the members to which the finished ceiling below is attached, Fig. 84-7.

If prebuilt roof trusses are used, the bottom chords of the trusses serve as the ceiling joists. The finish ceiling material is applied to these as it would be to conventional ceiling joists.

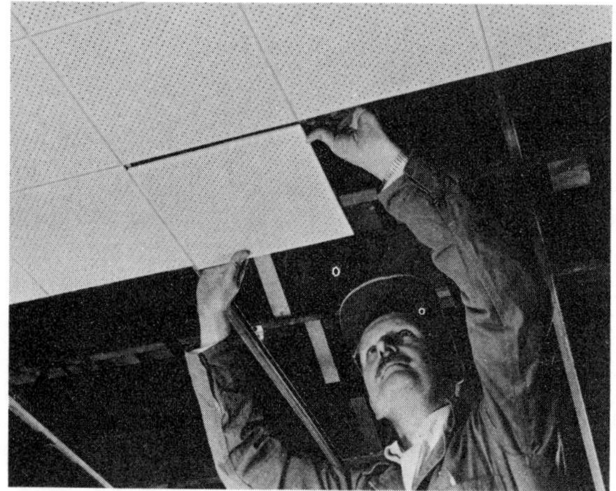

Fig. 84-7. This man is installing acoustical tile to special strips which have been attached to the floor joists of the second floor.

Summary

The two main kinds of subfloors in house construction are concrete and wood. Houses without basements usually have concrete slabs as their floors. Houses with full or partial basements generally have wooden subfloors with some kind of finished flooring over them.

When a concrete floor is used, the finished floor is put directly on it. Therefore, it must be troweled to accommodate the finished floor wanted. When wood finished floors are installed, they generally are nailed to the subfloor. Other finished flooring usually requires an underlayment over the subfloor. This underlay can be hardboard, plywood, or particle board. Regardless what kind of floor is used, provisions must be made for installing heating, plumbing, and wiring.

Ceilings are built much the same as floors. When prebuilt roof trusses are used, the bottom chords of the trusses become the ceiling joists.

Terms to Know

tamping and rolling	aggregate
compacted	underlayment
component	plank and beam
insulator	joists
vapor barrier	trusses

Think About It!

1. Are the floors in your home constructed of wood frame or concrete? Are most floors in homes in your neighborhood built this way?
2. Why do you think metal is not a common material used in floor or ceiling construction?

READING 85

Building Roofs

You have already learned much about the flat roofs often found on commercial and industrial structures. This reading will describe the sloped or pitched roofs which cover most homes.

Functions of Roofs

The roof protects the interior from wind, rain, snow, loss of heat in the winter, and excessive heat in the summer. The roof structure also may add a pleasing appearance or character to a building. Each of these factors must be considered in designing and building a roof.

Styles of Roofs

Certain well-known architectural styles are best identified by looking at the roof of the building. Several basic designs will be discussed in this reading. Variations and combinations of these basic designs make a great many roof designs from which to choose.

Fig. 85-1. This flat roof combines economy of materials with enough strength. The overhanging cornice also offers protection from the sun.

The *flat roof* is the least expensive and easiest to construct. In the North, this kind of roof has to be made very strong to support the weight of snow. Even with the extra material used to add strength, less total material is needed for a flat roof than for a sloped roof. See Fig. 85-1.

The *shed roof* is like a flat roof that has been raised on one side. It slopes in only one direction. The shed roof is not often used alone. It is often used along with other roof designs. A carport, a patio, or an extra room may be covered by a shed roof, Fig. 85-2.

The *gable roof* has two sloping surfaces, one on each side of the center line of the building. The end walls of the building go up to the peak of the roof, forming what is known as a *gable end*. This roof style is most commonly combined with other styles of roofs. The pitch or slope of a gable roof can vary from almost flat to very steep, Fig. 85-3.

Fig. 85-2. This is a shed roof. It is flat but not level. It covers a carport.

The *hip roof* has four surfaces which all slope upward toward the center of the building. If the building is square, the four surfaces meet at a point in the center. However, since few homes are exactly square, a hip roof generally has a short ridge section. The hip roof is one of the most common types of roof found on homes today, Fig. 85-4.

The *gambrel roof* is used on houses of Dutch Colonial design. It is like the simple gable, except that each half is split into a shallow upper section and a steep lower section. This allows for better use of the attic space. The gambrel roof was developed in the United States in colonial times so that the homeowner could avoid paying a tax imposed on two-story houses. See Fig. 85-5.

The *mansard roof* is an American Colonial design. Each side of a mansard roof is split into two surfaces like the gambrel. It is also like the hip roof because all four sides

Fig. 85-3. A gable roof is a combination of two shed roofs. Gables are commonly used when attic space is desired.

Fig. 85-4. In a hip roof all surfaces slope toward the center.

Fig. 85-5. The roof on the left side of this house is a gambrel type. What type roof is on the right?

Fig. 85-6. The mansard roof allows the attic space to be used. The near vertical roof becomes an interior wall. Notice the dormers on the third floor.

slope toward the center. In the mansard roof, the lower slope is nearly vertical while the upper slope may be nearly flat, Fig. 85-6.

The *dormer* is an addition to one of the other roof types. The dictionary defines it as a "houselike structure added onto a roof, providing space for windows or ventilation for the inside of the house," Fig. 85-6. Dormers are used with *pitched roofs.* At the point where they join, a valley is formed. Dormers are roofed at the same time as the rest of the roof.

There is also the *contemporary roof* which has many different and unusual curves and slopes. Among these are the *vaulted, serpentine, parabolic* (Fig. 85-7), and *domed roofs.*

Many interesting and pleasing roof designs can be made of various combinations of the basic roof designs. Each of these variations, however, makes the roof harder to construct and more expensive.

Roof Framing Terms

Roof construction has its own vocabulary. Several terms are identified here in Fig. 85-8 showing a gable roof intersecting with a hip roof.

In describing the slope of a roof, we use the same terms that are applied to hills and to stairways. We say that a steep roof *rises sharply,* and that a roof with a very slight slope *rises gently.* The rise is a vertical mea-

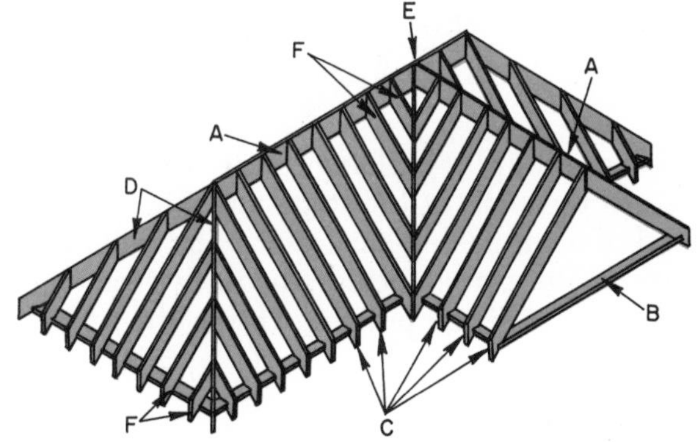

Fig. 85-8. Typical roof construction.
A. Ridge
B. Plate
C. Common rafters
D. Hip rafters
E. Valley rafter
F. Jack rafters

Fig. 85-7. The seldom seen hyperparabolic roof is anchored in the ground at two points. The roof members are under tension.

Fig. 85-9. In a simple gable end, the run is one half the span.

surement. It can be combined with the *run* (a horizontal measurement) to describe a slope in exact numbers. If you climbed the hill in the picture, you would move upward (vertically) 2,000′ while moving horizontally 1,000′. This slope can be written as a common fraction and reduced to lower terms:

$$\frac{\text{RISE}}{\text{RUN}} = \frac{2{,}000}{1{,}000} = \frac{2}{1}$$

The span of a building is the distance between the walls of the structure. For a gable end, the run is one-half of the span and the rise is the perpendicular distance from the center line of the building to the top of the ridge. See Fig. 85-9.

Roofing the Building

After the roof has been framed and covered with sheathing of shiplap, tongue-and-groove, square cut boards, or plywood sheets, the roof structure is completed and is ready to receive the roofing.

Fig. 85-10. This roofer is installing red cedar shakes on a Colonial home.

Some of the most popular materials for covering a sloped roof are asphalt shingles, wooden shingles, metal, slate, tile, and sheets of fiber glass or other plastic materials. The careful selection of roofing will greatly add to the beauty of a home, Fig. 85-10.

Gutters and Downspouts

Gutters (eaves troughs) and downspouts prevent rainwater from dripping down the walls of a building. They carry the water away from the house. This helps preserve the outside of the house and foundation, Fig. 85-11.

There are many kinds of gutters. Among those in general use are the type-K or square gutter, the half-round gutter, and the built-in gutter. Downspouts or conductor pipes may be either rectangular or round in shape. Wooden gutters are made of Douglas fir or red cedar and are fitted and nailed onto the fascia with galvanized nails. Metal gutters and downspouts are made of galvanized iron, aluminum, or copper.

Gutters and downspouts are installed on the fascia with various hangers or spikes and sleeves. The joints are soldered or filled with a special mastic (filler) to keep them

Fig. 85-11. Gutters and downspouts carry water from the roof away from a building.

from leaking. All gutters should be sloped toward the downspouts 1″ for every 12′ to 16′ of gutter length. The downspouts are fastened to the side of the house with special hangers.

Summary

A roof sheds water, gives protection from the weather, and adds beauty to a home. There are several styles of roofs. The most popular are the flat, shed, gable, hip, gambrel, and mansard roofs. There are many others that are combinations of these.

Some of the most popular materials for roof coverings are asphalt shingles, wooden shingles, metal, slate, tile, and sheet plastic. Each of these is put on in different ways by skilled workmen. The roof must be installed with great care because it is one of the most important parts of the building.

Gutters are installed after the roof covering is finished. They catch the water that runs off the roof and carry it away through downspouts or conductor pipes.

Terms to Know

basic roof styles
- a. flat
- b. shed
- c. gable
- d. hip
- e. gambrel
- f. mansard
- g. dormer
- h. contemporary

intersection

roofing terms
- a. ridge
- b. plate
- c. common rafter
- d. hip rafter
- e. valley rafter
- f. jack rafter

rise

run

span

Think About It!

1. What style of roof does your home have? Are the buildings on each side of your home the same? If not, what style of roof does each have?
2. How do the seasons and weather affect roof design where you live?

READING 86

Enclosing Exteriors

The material used and the operations needed for enclosing exteriors depend mainly on how the walls are constructed. Walls may be classed as (1) stud walls, (2) panelized walls, (3) masonry walls, and (4) post and beam walls. Most homes now have stud or masonry walls, although panelized walls are becoming more popular, Fig. 86-1.

Sheathing

Outside sheathing is used on all kinds of outside walls except masonry walls. It is nailed directly onto the framework and forms a base for finish siding, shingles, or other coverings, Fig. 86-2. Sheathing can be individual boards or panels of plywood, gypsum, or insulating board. Each one of these has separate and distinct characteristics. The panels are more popular because they go on faster than board sheathing. In precut and prefabricated construction, the sheathing is needed to make the frame rigid for easy transportation.

Board sheathing can run at a diagonal to the studs, or it can be applied at right angles to the studs. The latter is called *horizontal sheathing,* Fig. 86-3. *Diagonal sheathing* gives greater strength because it ties together sills, joists, plates, and studs, Fig. 86-4. However, this method is more costly because it takes more time to install and more material is wasted.

Fig. 86-1. Panelized walls, although uncommon, are increasing in popularity. These panelized units are made of sheet metal.

Fig. 86-2. Sheathing forms a base for finish siding.

Plywood sheathing comes in 4′ x 8′ sheets which are generally nailed at right angles to the studs. Vertical joints between plywood sheets should be on different studs in succeeding rows of sheathing. This is called *breaking joints.*

Insulation board comes in several sizes and is nailed in much the same way as plywood. In precut and prefabricated panels, plywood and insulation board are generally attached vertically to the studs. Gypsum sheathing generally comes in 16″ x 48″ sheets and is nailed perpendicular to the studs. Gypsum is easy to install but extra care must be used because it is easily damaged.

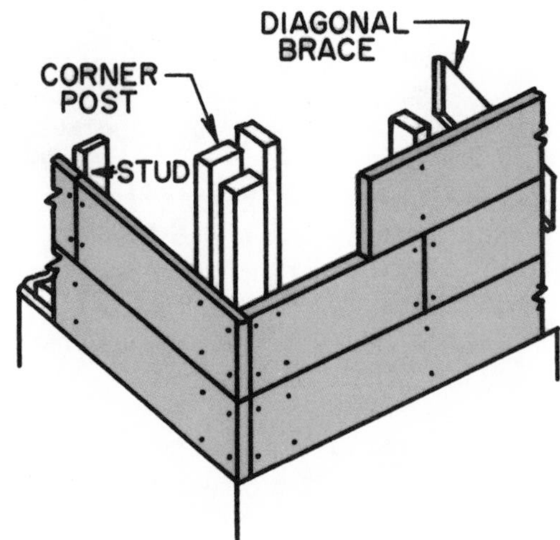

Fig. 86-3. Horizontal sheathing.

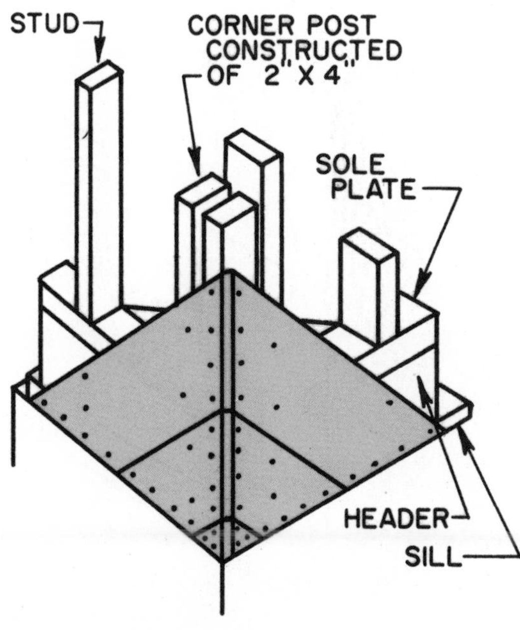

Fig. 86-4. Diagonal sheathing.

Installing Windows

After all the sheathing has been completely installed, the windows can be put in, Fig. 86-5. Most modern window units come completely assembled. The sash and frame are made of metal, plastic, or wood. They are braced, primed, and ready to be installed. The manufacturer's specifications are followed in installing them.

Installing Doors

Outside door frames are installed in much the same way as window frames. The carpenter must work very carefully, making sure the frame is installed plumb and level, or he will have trouble hanging the door itself. Door frames must fit the type of building construction. They also must be in harmony with the window frames. Doors can be made of metal or wood. Doors and frames now come in ready-to-hang units which are prefabricated at a factory.

Fig. 86-5. Once the sheathing is on, the windows and doors are installed.

An outside door unit must be weather stripped because it has a very high heat loss factor. Weather stripping comes in many materials including metal, rubber, plastic, and felt. Weather stripping may be built into the frame or threshold, or it may be installed after the door is hung.

Louvers

There must be ventilation of the attic space or the space between a ceiling and a flat roof. Therefore, *louvers* are installed in the gable, in the soffit, or in the roof, Fig. 86-6.

Finished Siding

Before installing siding, building paper or 15-pound felt is put on the outside of a frame building for two reasons. One is to provide a moistureproof barrier on the outside. The other reason is that it insulates against heat loss, Fig. 86-7.

Finished siding is put on a house (1) to shed water, (2) to resist vapor penetration, (3) to provide insulation, and (4) to add beauty.

A great many exterior materials are used for finished siding. These include masonry, wood, fiberboard, plywood, asbestos mixtures, aluminum, enameled steel, plastic, glass, poured-in-place concrete, and stucco. Reading 58, "Enclosing Exterior Walls," describes the various forms in which each type of material is available.

To make the walls more weatherproof, caulking compound is used wherever there are any cracks or joints. Corners are fitted with a corner board, mitered, or covered with a metal cap.

Cornices

The cornice is the part of a house where the roof and sidewall meet. In most houses the roof overhangs or sticks out from the wall. The main purposes of a cornice are to shed water away from the sidewalls and to provide an edge from which water may drip.

Fig. 86-6. This carpenter is installing ventilating soffit panels.

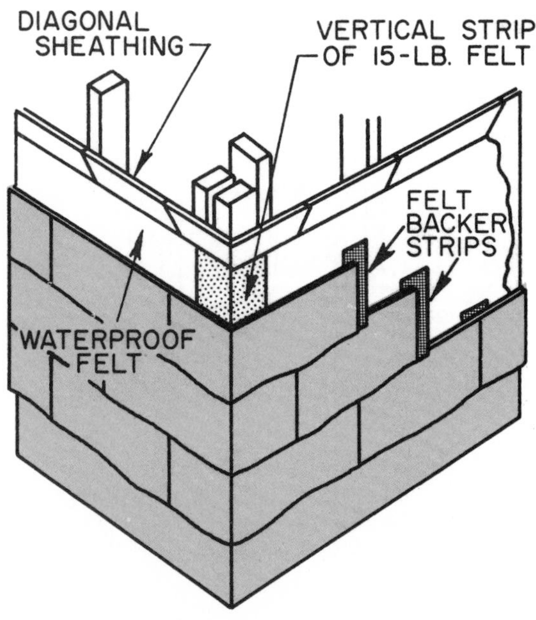

Fig. 86-7. Installing finished siding.

Cornices are either open or closed. With open cornices the rafters are exposed under the overhang. With closed cornices the rafters are boxed in and covered, Fig. 86-8.

The main elements in a cornice assembly are the fascia, the soffit, and the frieze (the uppermost part of the sidewall where it joins the soffit). Many times the soffit is vented by the use of louvers or by screening a portion of the space to help ventilate the attic. This allows air to circulate in the attic.

Usually metal gutters are attached to the fascia by spikes or by metal hangers. These also help protect the side of the house by carrying water away to a conductor pipe. The conductor pipe then carries the water away from the house.

Summary

Sheathing is installed on the outside of most wood framed homes. The kind installed will, in many cases, depend on the cost of the building and on the kind of finished siding that is to be used.

Windows and doors are put in place after the sheathing is completed. Care must be taken to see that the units are level and plumb. Louvers for ventilating attic spaces are also installed at this time.

After building paper is put on the sidewalls, the chosen finished siding is put on. There are many kinds of sidings. All kinds must be installed according to the manufacturer's instructions.

The cornice is that part of the building where the roof and the sidewall meet. The cornice finishes the closing in of the house. Elements such as gutters and louvers are installed on it.

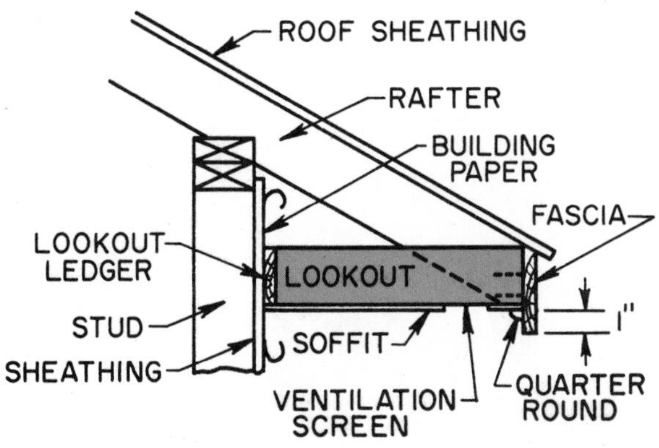

Fig. 86-8. Boxed cornice.

Terms to Know

sheathing	soffit
horizontal	louvers
diagonal	mitered
perpendicular	cornice
insulation board	fascia
weather stripping	frieze

Think About It!

1. What building material for exterior walls is most common in your neighborhood? Have materials changed from those used in older homes or buildings?
2. How do you think home exterior walls will be covered 30 years from now? Why?

READING 87

Roughing in Utilities

Roughing in utilities means placing all the parts which must be inside spaces before the spaces *can be enclosed.* There is an order of importance in doing this. Generally utilities are roughed in in this order:

1. Heating,
2. Plumbing, and
3. Electrical work.

Sheet metal ducts are less flexible than electrical wires or plumbing, Fig. 87-1. Also, it is much easier for the electrician to run wires than it is for a plumber to install pipes.

Heating

Before installing a heating plant you must decide how large a heating unit is needed and how much heat is needed in each room or area. This is done by figuring the heat loss of the house. The factors that are needed in figuring heat loss are:

1. Size of rooms,
2. Size and kind of windows,
3. Size and kind of doors, and
4. Size and kind of exposed walls, ceilings and floors exposed to an unheated area.

Prevailing winds and the normal temperature of the area also are factors to be considered. These are all compiled and a Btu (British Thermal Unit) heat loss is figured. All heating units are sized according to Btu inputs and outputs. From the heat loss, you

Fig. 87-1. Generally, the ductwork system for heating and cooling is the first utility to be roughed in. Since plumbing and wiring systems are more flexible in nature, they are easier to rough in around the ductwork.

Fig. 87-2. Heating and cooling specialists are installing a heating plant. The size of the heating unit was found by figuring all heat loss factors.

can figure the amount of heat that is needed and the amount of radiation or registers that are needed in each room, Fig. 87-2.

Heating can be classified under two headings, *wet heat* and *dry heat*. *Wet heat* refers to the agent that heats the room. In this case it can be hot water or steam with water as the agent. *Dry heat* is hot air heat, with air as the agent, or radiant heat from electricity. There are advantages and disadvantages to both. Wet heat may give you more uniform heat. However, there is no way that you can install humidity control and air conditioning in the same unit.

Many fuels such as gas, oil, coal, and electricity are used to provide heat. The one that is usually chosen is the one that is the easiest to get at the lowest rate.

Besides the heat source, the kind of heating system also must be chosen. The system selected will depend on the owner's preference, cost, and whether the system is to include provisions for both heating and cooling, as well as air treatment. A person living in a coal mining region may find it economical to use coal. A person living in an oil refining area may find it cheaper to use oil.

Fig. 87-3. Ductwork carries heated or cooled air.

Wet heat radiators may be tubes installed in the walls or ceilings. They are generally installed as units in each room, and they are placed so they are on an outside (exposed) wall. The theory behind this is that if you can heat the cold air before it gets to the inside of the room, then the room will be warm and draft free.

Hot air systems have registers located on the outside or inside walls depending on the system chosen. The perimeter loop system places the hot air registers on the outside walls and the cold air intakes on an inside wall. This system was devised to copy the wet heat theory and has been very successful. The conventional system has the hot air registers on the inside wall and cold air intakes on exposed walls.

The three main methods of sending heat to a room are (1) ductwork (sheet metal pipes), Fig. 87-3; (2) trunk lines (either water lines or electric lines); and (3) individual unit heaters. The methods used to distribute the heat in the room are *convection* or *radiation*.

When the heating system depends on forced air circulation to distribute the heat, you have the chance to install humidifiers, electronic air filters, and air conditioning in the same unit. These would have to be provided separately when the heat is distributed by radiation. However, radiant heat is usually more uniform throughout the space being heated.

Either centrally located or individual unit heaters can be installed wherever it is most convenient and best for heating purposes. If they are *combustion units,* they should be near a chimney. Electric heaters can be put anywhere it is convenient to place them.

Electric heat is gaining rapidly in popularity. It provides very clean heat and generally has individual controls for each room. Houses with electric heat need more insulation and tighter construction because electric heat is more expensive, and heat loss must be cut to a minimum.

Depending upon the kind of heating system selected for a home, one or more craftsmen may be involved in the installation. A system requiring ductwork is installed primarily by sheet metal workers. Electricians put in electrical heating systems along with other electrical work. Plumbers put in hot water systems along with other piping.

Plumbing

Before a plumber starts to put in pipes he must carefully study the plans and specications to see where the fixtures are to be installed, what the size and style of these fixtures are, what size pipes are needed for these fixtures, and where the pipes are to be run. He then lays out and marks where these pipes are to go. After they are all laid out, he drills and cuts out the openings. These give him a target to shoot for when he is running the lines under the openings.

A plumber generally runs the soil pipe, which is the large drain pipe, and smaller drains first, Fig. 87-4. To run soil pipe you have to start at the sanitary sewer connection which is just inside the foundation wall. All drain lines have to slope toward the sanitary sewer. About 1/4″ to 1′ is the standard slope for drain lines. These lines run to the fixtures and continue up through the roof where they act as vents.

Vents allow the fixtures to drain properly and prevent the siphoning of water from the traps under each fixture. If you did not install a vent, it would be the same as turning a bottle full of liquid upside down. The liquid just gurgles out because air can't get into the bottle easily. The same principle applies to a drainage line. A trap is installed under each fixture to keep sewer gas and odors from entering the room from the sewer.

Water lines generally start from the water meter, which also is just inside the foundation wall, and run to all the fixtures. To prevent accidents, the cold water is always on the right side as you face the fixture. The hot water line starts from the water heater and runs to all the fixtures where hot water is needed. The hot water line is always on the left side as you face the fixtures. The outlets of water lines are generally shut off with test plugs or nipples and caps until the inside walls and floors are completed. They are removed when the fixtures are installed.

Fig. 87-4. This plumber is making a soil pipe connection by applying an adhesive to the plastic T-joint.

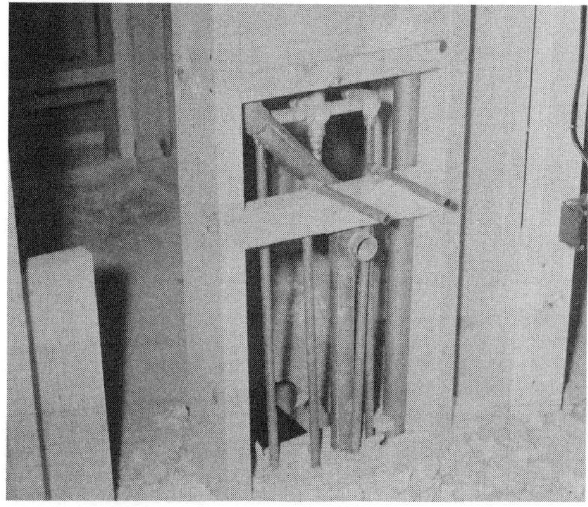

Fig. 87-5. Here water supply lines have been roughed in for the bathroom.

Permanent fixtures such as bathtubs and shower bases are installed at the same time as the roughing in takes place because they must be built into the walls, Fig. 87-5.

Electricity

The electrician generally hooks up the service to the house very early in construction so other craftsmen working on the house can have electric power.

After the heating and plumbing have been roughed in, the electrician will locate the number of outlets as set by codes and specifications and attach the boxes to the walls. He will then drill all the holes needed to run the wire to these boxes, Figs. 87-6 and 87-7. The wire is attached to the box and left coiled up in the boxes. The feed end is attached to the panel box, but it is not hooked up to the terminals. This leaves the circuit dead, and no electricity flows through it until the time comes to finish the installation.

There are many other appliances and fixtures that may have to be roughed in. Examples of these are communications lines (Fig. 87-8), the ductwork for kitchen fans, and the ductwork for laundry chutes.

Summary

The term *roughing in utilities* means to install all the parts which must be put in before the framework can be enclosed. Heat-

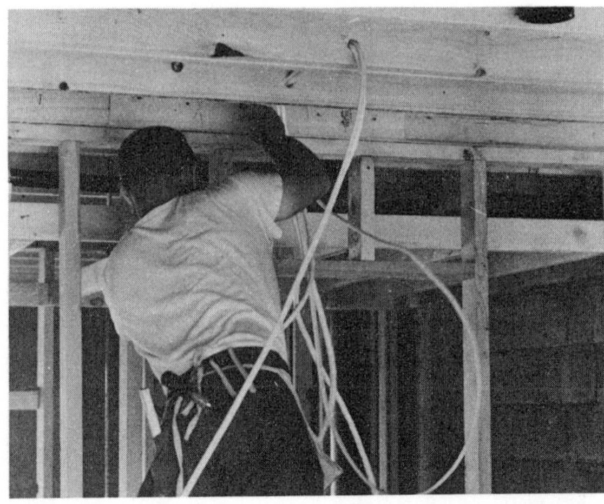

Fig. 87-7. The electrician runs the wiring through the holes that have been marked and drilled.

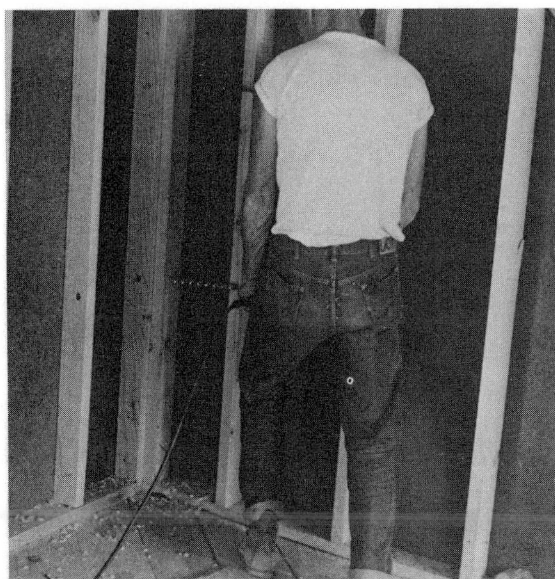

Fig. 87-6. This electrician is drilling holes in the studs so that wires may be run through.

Fig. 87-8. Wires are being tied into the telephone outlets which were roughed in earlier.

ing, plumbing, and electrical work are usually installed in that order. There is a variety of heating, plumbing, and electrical fixtures and installations which differ according to the type of house, the desires of the owner, the codes of the area, and the plans and specifications to be followed. The roughing in of utilities must be accurately and completely done to avoid costly repair work after the framework has been enclosed.

Terms to Know

roughing in utilities
wet heat
convection
radiation
dry heat
radiator
registers
perimeter loop system
conventional system
combustion units
siphoning
plumber
electrician
Btu

Think About It!

1. Why are the heating utilities roughed in before plumbing or electrical utilities?
2. If someday many homes will be built in factories, will the utilities be installed on the site or in the factory? Where will they be connected?

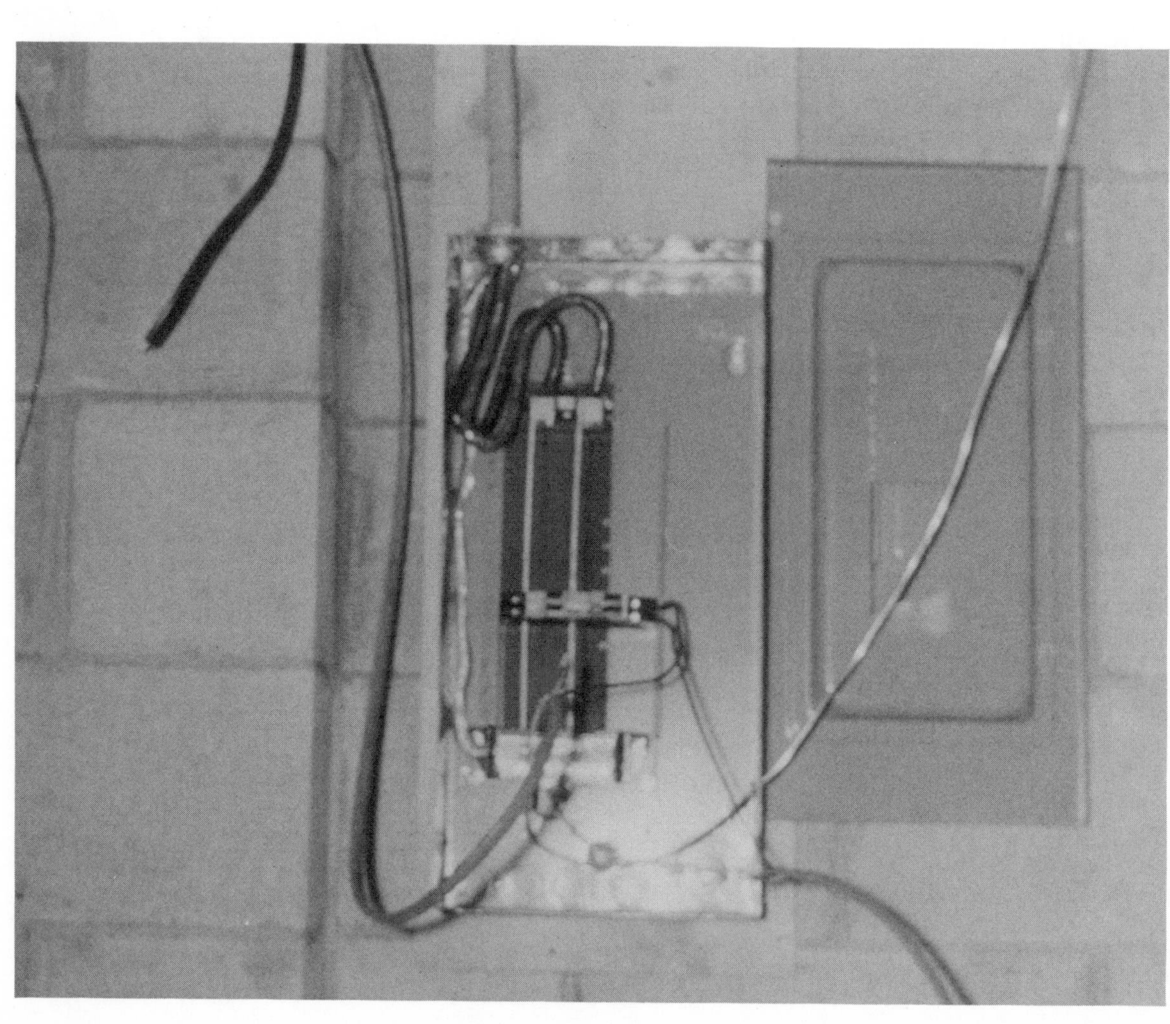

Working on the Interior

After the plumbing, heating, wiring, air conditioning, and any other utilities have been roughed in, enclosing operations can continue.

Insulation

Insulation must be installed in the outside walls, ceilings, and sometimes in the floors. Modern insulation comes in *batts, blankets, rigid slabs, loose fill,* and *aluminum and copper foil.* Batts are commonly used for insulating framed walls. Batts are made with one surface as a vapor barrier. They usually have flaps along the sides for easy attachment to studs. *The vapor barrier must always face the inside of the house,* Fig. 88-1. Batts also may be used between the ceiling joists. However, loose fill is easier to use where the ceiling is already installed.

Fig. 88-1. Batt insulation has been installed in the outside walls of this house. The shiny covering on the inside of the batts forms a vapor barrier.

Enclosing Walls and Ceilings

In the past, *plaster over lath* was the most widely used inside wall and ceiling finish. Today, plasterboard, plywood, hardboard, insulating fiberboard, plastic laminate, tile, and masonry finishes also are common.

In lath and plaster walls, rock lath or metal lath is used as a base for the plaster.

Fig. 88-2. The plasterer is adding a little sand to the mixture. This plaster will be applied over the scratch coat.

The plasterer first puts on a brown or *scratch coat* of plaster. After this coat has dried, a white finish coat is troweled on the wall, Fig. 88-2. The technique of plastering requires a person to be highly skilled in this trade.

In *drywall* construction, plasterboard is applied to the wall or ceiling either by nailing or by fastening with adhesives, Fig. 88-3. The next step is to fill and tape the joints and fill the depressions made by setting the nailheads below the surface, Fig. 88-4. One or more extra applications of filler are made after the first coat dries. After the final coat of filler has been put on, it must be lightly sanded until it is even with the surface of the plasterboard.

Plywood walls or other manufactured panels can be used for interior finishing. They come in plain, decorated, or scored sheets. These may be put directly on the studs by using finishing nails or adhesives. A stronger and more desirable installation is one in which plasterboard is put on the wall, as a base, with the panels put on over it.

Hardboards are made with many face patterns for interior finishing. They come in several widths and lengths. Some have to be finished, and some come already finished. They are *tongued and grooved* on the edges and, many times, on the ends.

Insulating boards for interior finishing come in regular 4′ x 8′ sheets and in smaller sizes for use in ceilings. They can be applied with nails, staples, or adhesive. Some are perforated with many holes to improve their soundproof qualities.

Plastic laminates come in various sizes and are put on walls and ceilings by using adhesives or metal channels. They should not be nailed.

Tile in plastic, steel, ceramic, or glass is in common use for interior finish. It often is used in bathrooms and kitchens. Either plywood or plasterboard is a good base for tile. Tile is installed with adhesive. The joints are filled (grouted) after the tile is in place.

Masonry products have an important place in interior finishes. In addition to brick, tile, concrete block, and natural and cast stone or various kinds, thin veneers of brick and tile can be used. Sections of these may be fixed by adhesives to a solid backing. The joints are filled after the units are in place.

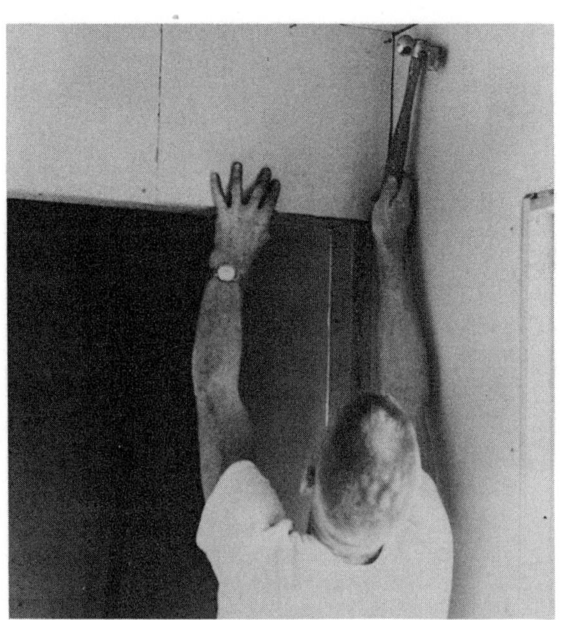

Fig. 88-3. This man is nailing up gypsum drywall. Notice his special hammer.

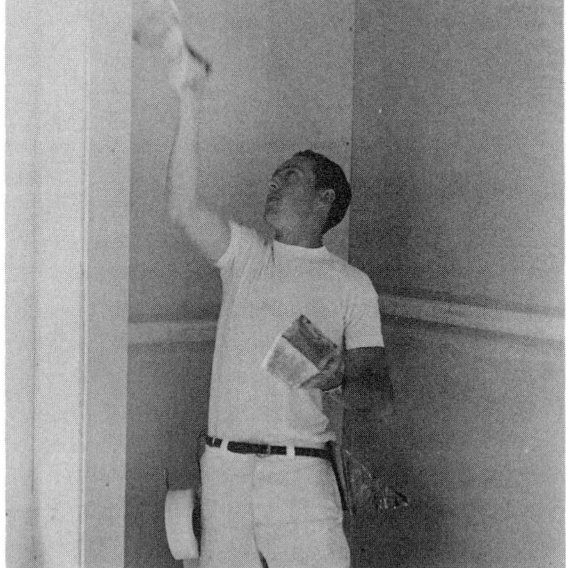

Fig. 88-4. Here the gypsum wallboard joints get filled and taped to make a smooth joint.

Stairways

Most stairs in homes are straight. However, there are some *spiral* and *angular* stairways. Today the parts of staircases used in most homes are stock items and can be gotten easily, Fig. 88-5. The three main parts of a staircase are the stringers, the treads, and the risers. *Stair risers* are usually 6¾″ to 8″ high. *Treads* are 10″ to 11″ wide. Risers and treads should be such that one can walk up and down with a normal, easy stride. A general rule for building a comfortable stair is: *one rise plus one run should equal 17″*. For ease in moving furniture, stairs should be no less than 3′ wide. There are many different styles of stairways. The style and decor of the house help decide what stairway style is used.

Doors

An inside door unit consists of jambs, casings, stops, door, and hardware.

To install a door unit, the *jambs* are installed first. Great care must be taken to make certain that these jambs are plumb and square. *Casings* are installed next. They are nailed onto the edge of the jamb and into the wall.

The *door* is hung next. It is sawed and planed to fit the inside of the jambs with about 1/16″ top and side clearance and about ½″ clearance off the floor.

The *butts* or *hinges* are now ready to install. *Gains,* which are slots for hinge leaves, are cut in, and the leaves are screwed onto the door and onto the jambs. These leaves should match perfectly so that the pins can be inserted when the door is hung. If the door does not close freely, more planing is done wherever the door rubs.

The *lockset* is installed and then the door stops. *Door stops* are strips of wood which are placed against the closed door and nailed to the jamb. See Fig. 88-6.

Doors and frames also are available in units that are ready to hang. This is another step in prefabrication. All that needs to be done is to plumb and square the unit into the rough opening and to nail it in place.

Inside Trim

There are many different uses for inside trim. The trim around windows and doors is

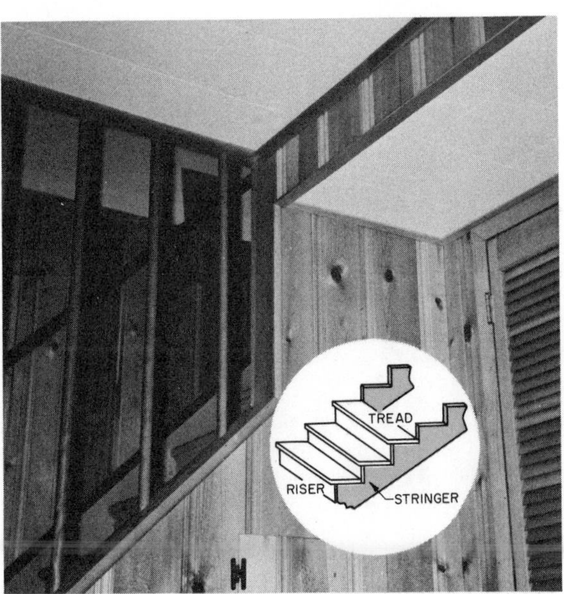

Fig. 88-5. Stairways, although often made from stock parts, can require much fitting.

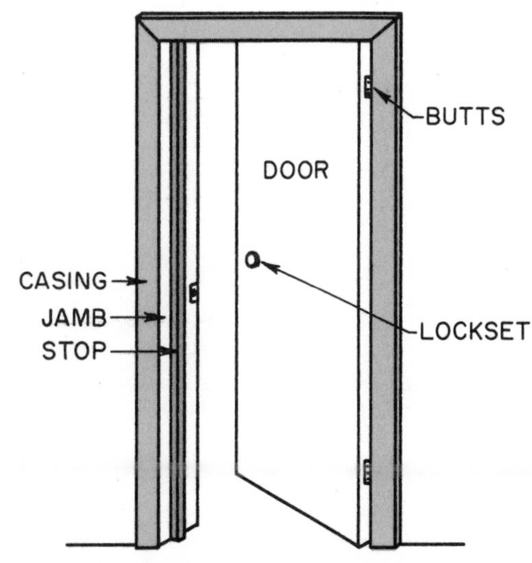

Fig. 88-6. Inside door unit.

called a *casing.* The trim where the walls meet the floor is called the *baseboard.* The lower part of the window trim is called the *stool.* Directly under this is the *apron.*

There are many moldings. They are used to cover cracks or joints, or to add beauty.

The lumber for trim must be dried in a kiln and well seasoned before installing. All inside trim is nailed with finishing nails which are set below the surface. The nail holes are filled. The two most popular joints for trim work are *mitered* and *coped joints,* Fig. 88-7.

Flooring

Flooring materials include hardwoods, resilient flooring, ceramic tile, and carpeting. Each has advantages, and many need special floor preparation.

Floors of hardwood are still the choice for many modern buildings. Red or white oak, birch, beech, and maple all are used in making flooring, Fig. 88-8.

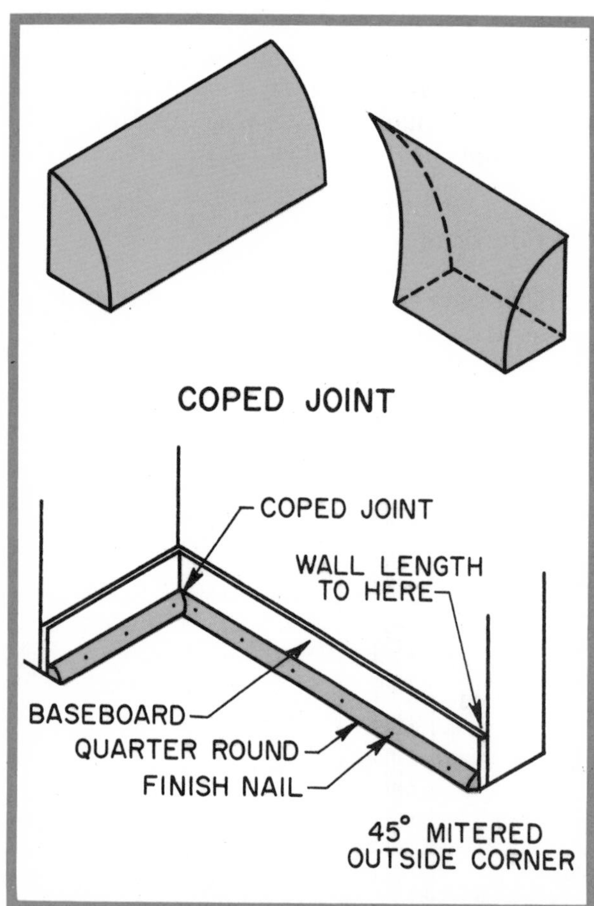

Fig. 88-7. Floor molding.

Fig. 88-8. Here the man is laying the last row of hardwood flooring blocks.

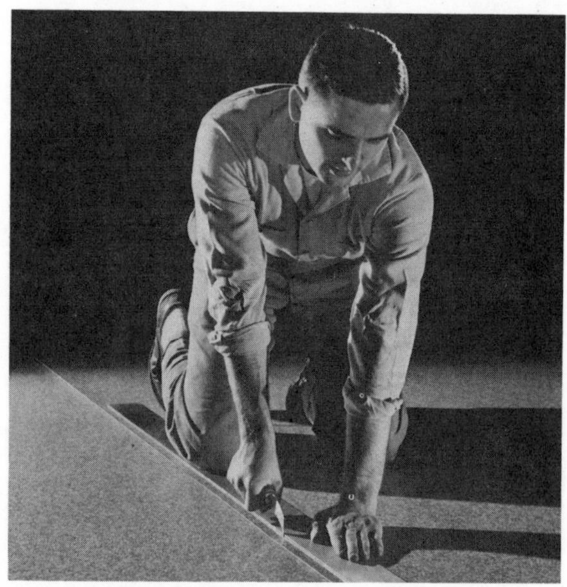

Fig. 88-9. This man is installing resilient flooring.

Resilient flooring has grown in usefulness with advances in design and quality. It comes in large rolls and is cut to fit the room with the fewest joints possible. It also comes as individual tiles, Fig. 88-9.

Resilient flooring materials include linoleum, asphalt, rubber, asbestos, vinyl, and cork. Resilient floorings are laid over the subfloor with a suitable adhesive. Sometimes *underlayment* is laid over the subfloor before the flooring material is laid.

Ceramic tile is becoming more and more popular as a floor covering because newer, low-cost methods have been found for its installation. Other finish materials that can be used on floors are slate, terrazzo, marble, brick, and finished concrete patterns.

Carpeting is sometimes used as a finished flooring. It can be laid over slab or rough subflooring with a fiber or foam rubber underlayment.

Summary

Working on the interior means finishing everything that will show on the inside of the house. This kind of work is generally slow because care must be taken to do a good job. A poor job will detract from the quality of the house.

Most interior work is done in the following order: (1) insulating, (2) covering inside walls and ceilings, (3) putting in staircases, (4) installing inside doors, (5) trimming, and (6) floor work.

Terms to Know

insulation
batts
blankets
rigid slabs
loose fill
plaster
scratch coat
drywall
scored sheets of plywood
adhesives
hardboard
tongued and grooved
plastic laminates
spiral stairway
angular stairway
resilient flooring
underlayment

stairway parts
- a. stringer
- b. treads
- c. risers

door parts
- a. jambs
- b. casings
- c. door stops
- d. hinges
- e. locksets

inside trim
- a. casing
- b. baseboard
- c. stool
- d. apron
- e. mitered joint
- f. coped joint

Think About It!

1. How many different types of tradesmen or craftsmen can you name that would be employed to *finish out* a newly built home?
2. What interior work, if any, can be done during or before exterior work and the *roughing in* of utilities? Why?

READING 89

Completing the House

The steps remaining to complete the house are painting, decorating, and installing accessories. This reading is about that work.

Painting and decorating are done to put protective and decorative coatings on interior and exterior surfaces. The materials may be applied in the form of a liquid such as paint or in the form of thin sheets such as wallpaper. Paint and similar finishing materials dry to form a thin, continuous surface covering. Sheet materials for finishing walls are generally called *wallpaper* although some are made of plastic, cloth, or other materials.

The last step before completing a house is the installation of fixtures and *accessories.* Much of a person's happiness with his home depends on the taste used in choosing these fixtures and accessories and the skill with which they are installed.

Fig. 89-1. The walls of this room have been finished with stain and varnish. Had the walls been another surface, an opaque color finish could have been used.

Painting Materials

Painting refers to the application of paint, varnish, shellac, lacquer or stain on surfaces. Oil base paint, which is very popular, is a mixture of colored pigment and a *liquid vehicle,* usually linseed oil. Thinners, such as mineral spirits or turpentine, generally are added to the oil.

There are many other paints which use water as the vehicle. These include latex, polyvinyl, acetate, and alkyd paints.

Varnishes are combinations of *resins* (either natural or synthetic) and *drying oils.* The resins and drying oils are mixed with an evaporating thinner such as turpentine. The mixture (varnish) is applied to a wood surface, and it dries to a hard finish as the thinner evaporates. The varnished surface has a good resistance to water, Fig. 89-1.

Shellac is a natural resin which forms a sealer or gum finish. It dissolves in alcohol and has a poor resistance to water.

Lacquers are quick drying solutions of nitrocellulose and resins. They give a brilliant, smooth finish. Water clear lacquer gives a natural finish.

Applying Paints

Before any paint is applied, the surface to be painted must be *conditioned.* The surface should be clean of dirt, grease, or other foreign materials. Loose paint should be removed by scraping.

There are many ways to put on paint. Brushes used to be the only way. Large surfaces are now painted using rollers and spray devices. Rollers are very popular among do-it-yourself painters. They are easy to handle and do the job quickly with nearly professional results, Fig. 89-3.

Spraying often is used in factory or shop painting. The spraying machine can be attached to a central air system, and the spray can be controlled. On a site, however, an independent air compressor is needed for spraying.

Fig. 89-2. This plasterer is applying colored plaster to decorative wall plaques.

Fig. 89-3. On large, flat surfaces, paint can be applied with a roller. This one has a long handle so the painter can stand erect while painting the floor.

Traditional practice for both inside and outside painting is to use three coats. First, a *primer coat* is used to seal the surface. Next, an *undercoat* which must have a good hiding quality is put on. Finally, a *hard outside coat* is applied. Recently developed paints will cover some surfaces in fewer coats.

The increase of masonry block construction has brought about a growing use of *masonry paint*. Portland cement paint has benefited from the water-resistant silicones now used in it. It can be put on new concrete, fresh cement plaster, or stucco while they are still damp.

Wallpaper

Modern technology has improved wallpaper. Electric trimming and prepasting may be done at the factory. Low-cost machine-printed sectional landscape panels are becoming popular. It is now possible to buy wallpaper that matches drapery and upholstery fabrics. Also plastic-coated wallpaper is now available. Patterned, coated canvas, formerly used mostly in kitchens and bath-

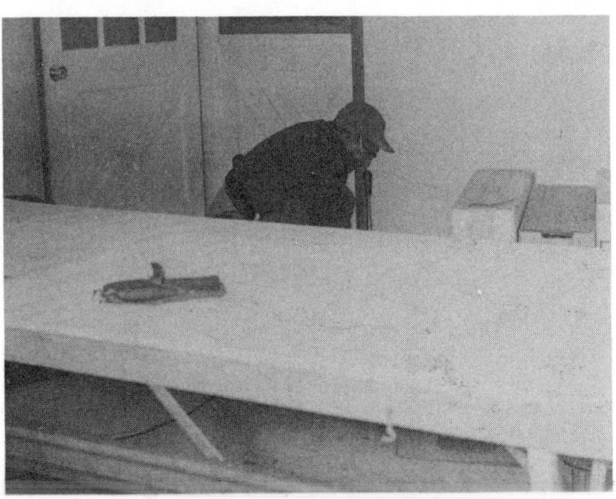

Fig. 89-4. This man is hanging wallpaper. On the table in the foreground, paste is applied to the back of the wallpaper.

rooms because it is washable, now comes in attractive patterns for other rooms. See Fig. 89-4.

Cabinet Work

After the painting and decorating are completed, accessories are installed. The installing of cabinets may be a large part of this work. Cabinets can be prefabricated or custom-built on the job. Kitchen cabinets used to be free standing pieces of furniture. These had special compartments such as flour bins and silverware drawers. Developments in recent years have leaned toward prefabricated units. Today nearly all kitchen storage is in permanent fixtures.

Cabinets are of three general kinds. These are *base units, wall units,* or *full-length units*. More and more kitchen cabinets are now factory-made of either steel or wood. They are installed on the job very quickly.

Counter tops generally are made of plastic laminates in single-length units which cover several base cabinets. They can have short back splashes or full-length back splashes that extend to the bottom of the wall cabinets.

Built-in cabinets are made on the job. Many times, cabinet work involves the installation of prefabricated units along with some custom (on the site) work, Fig. 89-5.

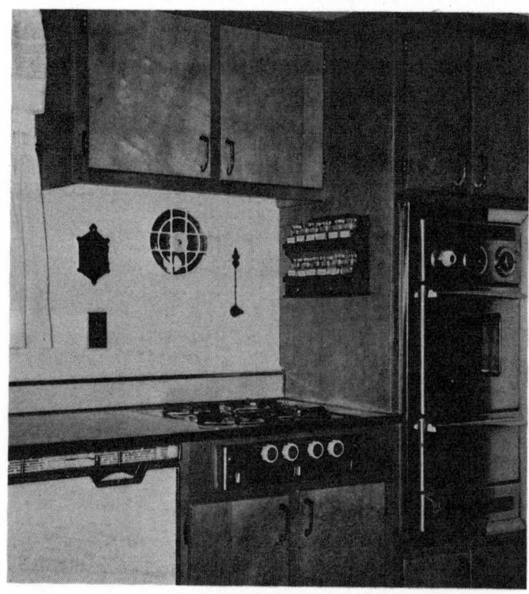

Fig. 89-5. Kitchens often contain many built-ins.

Plumbing Fixtures and Accessories

Bathroom fixtures include toilets, lavatories (washbasins), bathtubs, and showers together with their traps and hardware. A toilet is screwed or bolted to the floor or wall with a water-proof seal between the fixture and the surface to which it is attached. It requires a cold water supply and valve.

Washbasins can be fastened to the wall with hanger brackets, or they can be attached to counter tops, Fig. 89-6. Water supply lines and faucets then are connected. Lavatories generally need an exposed trap in their drain connections.

Most bathtubs and shower stalls are installed during the roughing-in period unless they are freestanding units. They also must have water supplies and drain connections installed.

Bathroom accessories then are installed. These are things such as toilet seats, paper

Fig. 89-6. The lavatories in this bathroom are countertop-mounted. Notice the number of other accessories.

holders, towelbars, washbasin legs, tumbler and toothbrush holders, soap holders, bathtub or shower doors, shower curtain rods, and shower arms and heads.

Kitchen fixtures include sinks, stoves, refrigerators, garbage-disposal units, and dishwashers. Faucets and strainers must be attached to the sink before it is put in. The water lines then are attached to the faucets.

There are many other accessories that must be connected to the plumbing. Examples are water heaters, outside faucets, humidifiers, gas stoves, and sump pumps (surface water pumps).

Heating and Air Conditioning Accessories

The kind of accessories used depends on the kind of heating system used. Most of these systems must have controls, heating unit covers (registers), and humidifiers. Heating systems also may require vents and covers or enclosures, Fig. 89-7.

Electric Fixtures and Accessories

Electric light fixtures are attached to outlet boxes in different ways, depending on the style of fixtures used. The electrical connections are made from the proper wires in the outlet box to the proper wires in the fixture. Switches and receptacles are wired and fastened to the wall boxes. These are finished off with plates that are fastened to the receptacles or switches with small machine screws.

At this time, when fixtures and accessories are being installed, an electrician also connects wires to other appliances, fixtures, and accessories such as garbage disposal units, dishwashers, kitchen fans, heating units, water heaters, stoves, and other built-in conveniences, Fig. 89-8.

Miscellaneous

New developments are adding many new accessories and appliances for use in houses. Some of these accessories are electric garage door operators, central vacuum cleaner

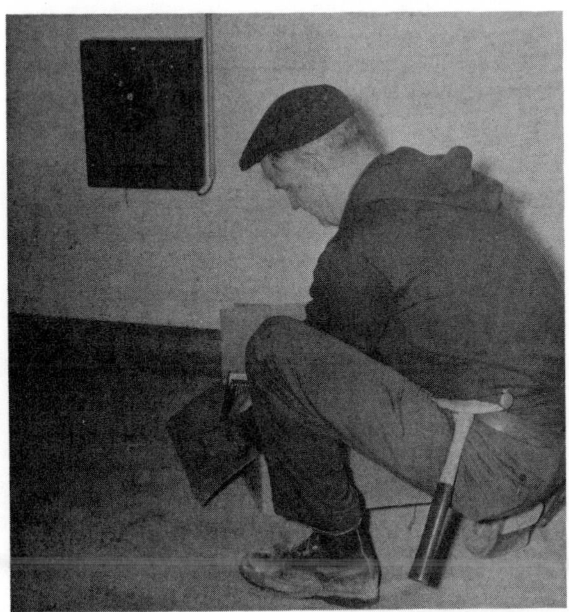

Fig. 89-7. This workman is about ready to install the grill cover on the electric space heater.

Fig. 89-8. This electrician is wiring a kitchen exhaust fan.

systems, home fire alarm systems, open-hearth prefabricated fireplaces, and communication systems or sound systems. This work probably will continue to expand as a part of house construction.

makers, electricians, plumbers, sheet metal workers, and other tradesmen. Usually this work is done on a return visit to the site, some time after roughing in or preliminary work was done.

Summary

The most common way of decorating and protecting interior and exterior surfaces is *painting,* a term which actually refers to the application of paint, varnish, shellac, lacquer, or stain. Wallpaper and similar wall coverings are also very popular. They are available in many patterns, colors, and materials. Wallpaper is applied with an adhesive which sometimes is bought separately and sometimes is applied to the paper at the factory.

One of the last steps in completing a house is putting in fixtures and accessories. Most of these are manufactured away from the job and are delivered to the site as units or components. Much time and effort should go into the selection and installation of these articles because the home owner will see them and have to live with them for a long time.

The final work of installing fixtures and accessories is done by carpenters, cabinet-

Terms to Know

wallpaper	air compressor
accessories	primer coat
paint	undercoat
varnish	hard outside coat
shellac	*hanging* wallpaper
lacquer	silicones
stain	plastic laminates
liquid vehicle	cabinets
linseed oil	lavatory
thinner	trap
resins	humidifier

Think About It!

1. Can you think of reasons why fixtures and accessories should not be installed before painting and decorating?
2. In your home, how many different fixtures and accessories can you name that are in your kitchen? What room in your house has the most fixtures and accessories?

Landscaping Homesites

The project is not completed until the lot is landscaped. Landscaping begins with the landscape plan and ends when the landscapers do the final cleanup on the site.

Landscaping Plan

A landscape architect may be hired to develop and draw a landscape plan of the home site. This plan shows the kinds and locations of shrubs, trees, hedges, and ground cover. The location of the house, garage, driveways, walks, and other structures also are shown on the plan, Fig. 90-1. The landscape architect also may suggest changes to the topography of the land to improve the appearance of the house and the function of the site.

A landscape contractor may be hired to develop the landscape plan. He usually will develop the plan at no cost to get the contract for the landscaping. The landscape plan, whether prepared by the landscape ar-

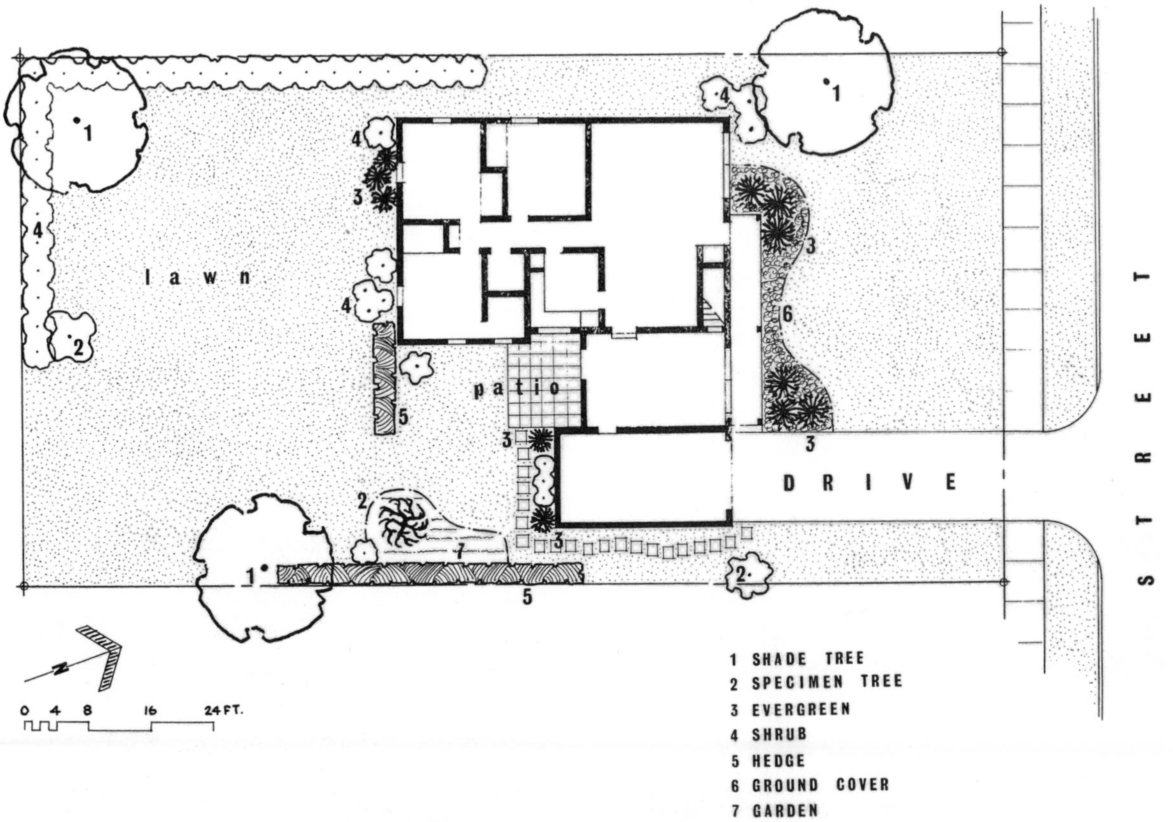

lawn
patio
DRIVE
STREET
0 4 8 16 24 FT.

1 SHADE TREE
2 SPECIMEN TREE
3 EVERGREEN
4 SHRUB
5 HEDGE
6 GROUND COVER
7 GARDEN

Fig. 90-1. Landscape plan.

chitect or the landscape contractor, is usually developed with the help of the architect who designs the house.

Building Accesses and Features

Before final shaping and finishing of the earth can begin, *building accesses* and *features* should be added to the house. *Building accesses* include driveways, walkways, and parking areas. The *features* added to the house include patios, fences, walls, benches, pools, lights, sculptures or statues, and plant boxes.

The building accesses usually are added to the site after the foundation has been backfilled. The features such as bases for statues, patios, walls, fences, and pools also are constructed at this time, Fig. 90-2.

Shaping and Finishing the Earth

The next step in landscaping is shaping the land surface as shown on the landscape plan. The contractor must keep the flow of water in mind during this stage of landscaping. The ground can't be too steep, or the soil will wash away. If the ground is too flat, water will gather in puddles.

The earth is rough graded to give the needed slope. Stones and other debris are taken from the site. Then the lot is graded for the last time to the exact slope and conditions wanted.

Fig. 90-2. With the accent on outdoor living, garden rooms, patios, lawns, flower beds, and swimming pools are combined into a functional and attractive setting.

Preparing the Soil for Planting

The *topsoil* is put back over the site. If more topsoil is needed, the contractor will have it hauled in.

The topsoil can be put back in two ways. It may be done by hand using a wheelbarrow, shovel, and rake; or it may be done by machine using a bulldozer. The bulldozer method is used often and is low in cost as compared to the hand method if the area is very large. If the grading is done with a bulldozer, the soil is packed down and must be loosened. To do this a tractor with a plow may be used to plow up the soil several inches deep.

The ground is then cultivated to cut up the chunks of soil. When this is done, the ground is dragged to level out the soil. The next step is raking the plot to remove any debris. After raking, the soil may have lime and fer-

Fig. 90-3. Soil must be cultivated and fertilized to receive grass seed.

tilizer added to it to enrich the soil for good plant growth, Fig. 90-3.

Planting Trees and Shrubs

It is at this point that lawn, trees, and shrubs are added. The trees and shrubs are planted first, Fig. 90-4. Using the landscape plan as the guide, the gardener marks the locations of the trees and shrubs with stakes.

Fig. 90-4. Trees and shrubs are planted according to the landscape plan.

Fig. 90-5. Sod is laid to give the site a finished look.

Holes are dug, and the trees and shrubs are planted. Extra soil is removed if it has sand and silt in it. If needed, fertile soil is brought in and placed around the trees and shrubs.

Laying Lawns

The *lawn* is the most important part of landscaping. Lawns control surface water and give the site a pleasing look. The two methods commonly used for laying lawns are sodding and seeding.

Sodding gives an almost ready lawn. Strips of sod are laid out on the prepared ground surface. They are placed closely together and rolled or tamped in place to insure root growth, Fig. 90-5.

Seeding is not as expensive as sodding. The soil is prepared by adding lime and fertilizer and by removing any debris from the topsoil. The seed is spread by hand or by machine so there is an even grass growth. The seed is then raked into the soil and the lawn is rolled to compact the soil to keep the seed from blowing or washing away. The ground may be covered with straw or burlap and watered to encourage growth.

Planting Flowers

While the gardener is waiting for the lawn to come in (three to four weeks), he begins planting flowers. The flower beds are prepared by adding topsoil or peat moss to the beds. Using the landscape plan, the gardener then plants the flowers where they are wanted.

Removing Temporary Facilities and Equipment

When the trees, shrubs, lawn, and flowers have been planted, the contractor and landscaper begin removing their equipment and temporary facilities. These items are no longer needed for construction and may hinder the cleanup.

Cleaning Up

After removing temporary facilities and equipment, the clean-up job begins. Since the landscaping is finished, the debris cannot be burned or buried. Therefore, all debris left on the site must be hauled away.

Removing the Equipment

Removing the equipment is the last job on the site. The landscaper and contractor remove all equipment, tools, materials, and supplies from the site. These items are returned to the storage yards and made ready for future use.

Multiphase Landscaping

It is best to complete landscaping when the house is built. However, some homeowners may not be able to do this because of cost. Then the landscaping operations may be *phased.* This means that the landscaping is done in steps over a period of time. The lawn and major trees should be put in the first year. More landscaping may be done in later years.

Fig. 90-6. Here is a new house which has been landscaped according to plan. This site would look unfinished without plants or features.

Summary

The landscaping of the building site is the last step in the constructing of a house. It begins with the landscape plan. The operations used to complete the landscaping job include (1) building accesses and features, (2) shaping and finishing the earth, (3) preparing the soil for planting, (4) planting trees and shrubs, (5) laying the lawn, (6) planting flowers, (7) removing temporary facilities and equipment, (8) cleaning up, and (9) removing equipment.

No matter how well or poorly designed a home is, a good landscape will make it more pleasing to look at, Fig. 90-6.

Terms to Know

shrubs
hedges
ground cover
landscape
building access
building features
topsoil
rough graded
cultivated
dragged
gardener
lawn
sodding
seeding
lime
fertilizer
peat moss
debris
phased

Think About It!

1. What effect does weather or climate have on landscaping,
2. Why is landscaping usually the last step in completing a new home?

City and Regional Planning Factors

READING 91

Construction projects such as houses, streets, sewers, schools, and parks are built when there is a need for them and if the people want them enough to pay for them. Each forms part of a city or regional system. Proper planning can help projects serve people better and longer. These final readings in your text will help you to understand some of the things city and regional planners have to consider and the practices they use in planning the constructed parts of cities and regions.

Primary Construction

Construction that causes the birth of a community is called *primary construction.* It creates continuing employment and causes more construction to be done. Some of the needs that cause primary construction to be built are the following:

1. Need for the use of a natural resource.
2. Need for a change in transportation.
3. Need for a place to change the form of materials (a place to manufacture things).
4. Need for defense from enemies.
5. Need for political action.

Hoover Dam was built because of a *need for the use of a natural resource,* the Colorado River, to produce electrical power. Thus, Boulder City, Nevada, grew up around the primary construction of the Hoover Dam.

The location of New York City was determined by a *need for a change in transportation.* At that location, land and river routes met at a great harbor used for ocean shipping. This meant that wharves, warehouses, and railroad yards had to be built to store and distribute goods. There was a need for workers to handle the goods. Therefore, places to live, stores, and other construction not directly related to transportation also were built.

The steel producing cities on the shores of the Great Lakes are examples of cities which grew because of a *need for a place to change the form of materials.* Iron ore could

Fig. 91-1. Municipal and state buildings result from a demand for political action.

be brought to them by ship, and other resources were close at hand. So it followed that many cities on the Great Lakes became manufacturing centers.

The city of San Francisco is an example of a community which grew from a *need for defense from enemies.* A Spanish fortress was constructed to control the entrance to San Francisco Bay. The city of San Francisco grew from the building of the fort because more construction was needed to meet the social and economic demands of the people at the fort.

State capitals are examples of communities which grew from a *need for political action.* Generally, more than one of these needs, in the same place, is the reason for primary construction. Boston is an example of a city which has had to meet all of these needs. Fig. 91-1.

Fig. 91-2. As communities expand, there will be a demand for new streets.

Fig. 91-3. New waste treatment plants and their piping systems are needed to serve the growing communities.

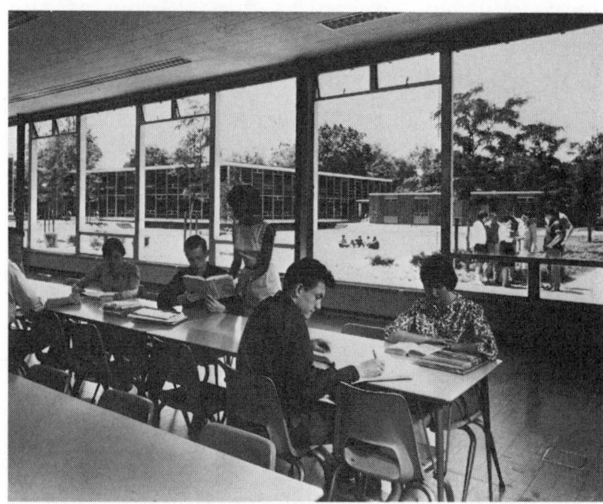

Fig. 91-4. As more families move into a community, more schools must be built.

Building in the Community

Workers are needed for primary construction, and workers will be needed for its maintenance and operation after it is built. As the number of people increases in an area, there will be a greater need for housing. Then there may be a need for such projects as: outdoor recreation facilities, housing, schools, and stores. The community grows as its people have new needs that must be satisfied. These needs may be expressed as demands for new construction. Only then are the needs satisfied. See Figs. 91-2, 91-3, 91-4, and 91-5.

Construction Factors

A construction project should be economical to *justify* its reason for being in a community. To be economical, it must meet three conditions:

1. There must be a *demand* for the construction.
2. The construction must satisfy the demand, providing a *service.*

3. The construction must be located on a suitable *site.*

Demand means that a person, or the community has a reason for wanting the construction project and is both willing and able to pay for the cost of building it. It would not be economical to build something people did not want or need.

Service means what the construction can do for the community. The community must be able to use the constructed object, and it must be in a place or location where it is easy to use.

Site means the ground upon which the construction object is built. A construction project is not economical if the cost of building it on a certain piece of ground is greater than the value of the service it provides.

To be built and maintained, both primary construction and that which results from it should meet *demand factors, service factors, and site factors.*

Demand Factors

1. There must be a demand for the *general type* of project.
2. There must be a demand for the *exact characteristics* or qualities of the project.
3. There must be a demand for a certain *number* of the projects to be provided.

Fig. 91-5. Electrical power and communication services must be distributed to the users.

Service Factors

1. The construction must be located where it can *best serve people and be conveniently located relative to other construction.*
2. The construction project must be located where it can *best provide for or meet its own needs.*

Site Factors

1. The construction must be located on *soils* that allow a low development cost.
2. The construction must be located on a *land slope* that allows a low development cost.
3. The project must be located on a site where the *land price* will allow low development cost.

Summary

Construction that causes the birth of a community is called *primary construction.* Primary construction creates employment which, in turn, creates the need for more construction. The needs that cause primary construction to be built, which in turn, cause communities to develop, include: (1) the need for the use of natural resources, (2) the need for a change in transportation, (3) the need for a place to change the form of materials (manufacturing), (4) the need for defense from enemies, and (5) the need for political action.

Communities come into being when workers who are needed to build and operate a construction project move to or near its site. These workers have families that need housing, schools, and places to shop. A community grows as its people have additional needs to be satisfied.

A construction project must be economical to justify its reason for being in a community. To be economical it must meet three conditions: (1) there must be a demand for the project, (2) the project must satisfy the demand by providing a service, and (3) the project must be located on a site suitable for construction.

Terms to Know

primary construction
political action
site
maintenance
demand
service
justify

Think About It!

1. Is your community growing in population? What plans do you know of that manage (plan, organize, and control) its growth?
2. What are some of the primary construction objects in your community? When were they built?

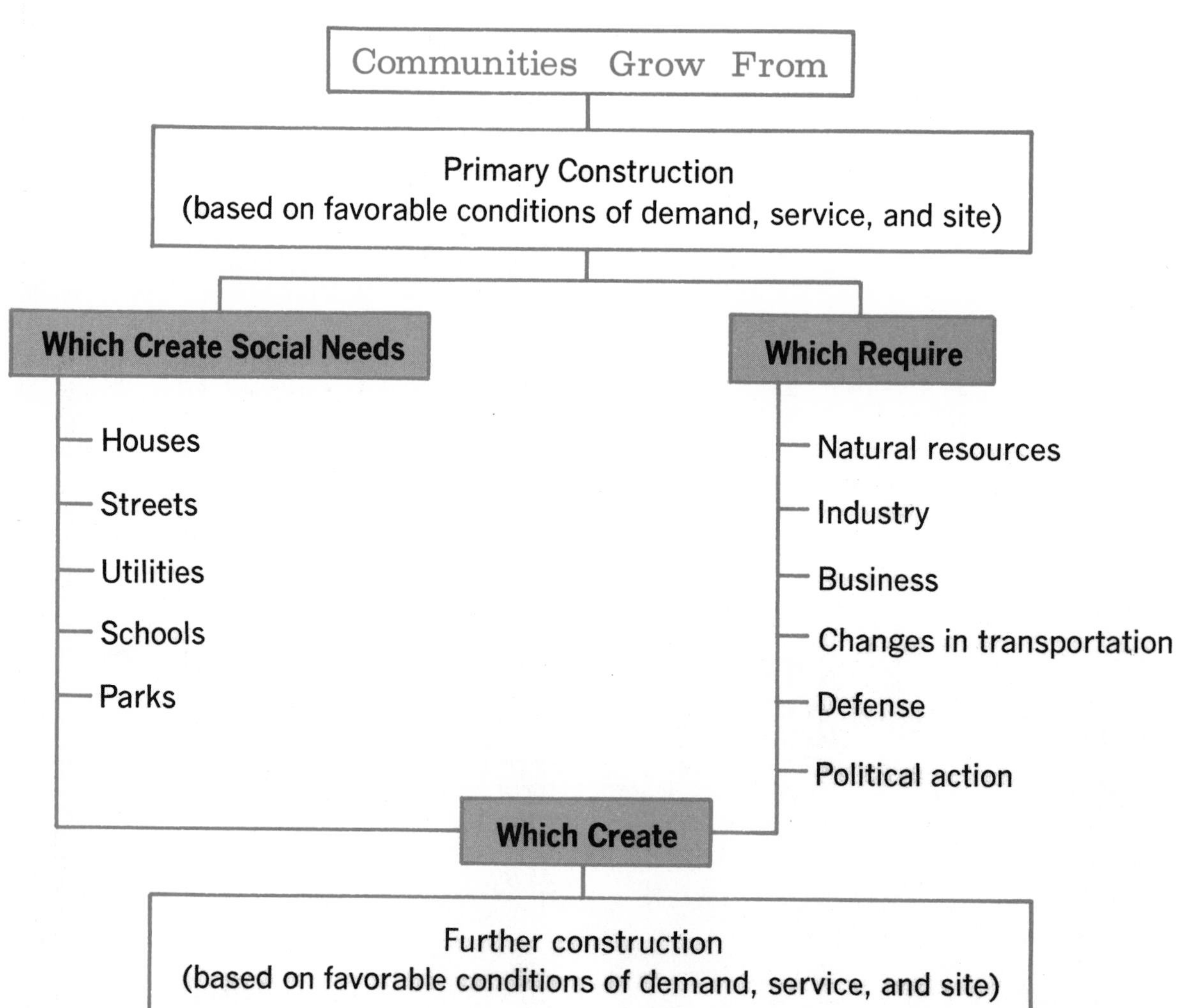

Planning Community Services

READING 92

Primary construction must have more than people to serve its needs. Primary construction must have *services* also. Just as primary construction must meet the construction factors of demand, service, and site, so must *service construction.*

Most primary construction projects need transportation services to their sites. This demand brings about the construction of roads and streets, railroads, docks, airports, and pipelines.

Primary construction also creates the need for utility services. Water treatment plants, underground sewer pipes, electric lines, and telephone lines are kinds of construction that bring utility services to primary construction projects, Fig. 92-1. Without transportation and utility services, most primary construction cannot serve its purposes.

Transportation

Different kinds of service construction are needed for primary construction. In this section we will look at the five major kinds of transportation construction: (1) highways, (2) railways, (3) airways, (4) waterways, and (5) pipelines.

Fig. 92-1. Utilities must be available to construction projects at reasonable cost.

Roads and Streets

Roads are considered to be those routes outside of an urban area for cars and trucks. With the development of modern roads or highways, traffic runs through urban areas as freely as it once did only in the open countryside. More than 2,400 vehicles an hour can move in each direction over modern roads, Fig. 92-2.

Fig. 92-2. This modern highway carries passengers and freight. Trucks carry everything from automobiles to livestock.

Roads are generally built on flat or sloped land because loaded trucks have trouble climbing steep hills. Where necessary, tunnelling, bridging, and earthmoving are used to reduce or avoid steep grades. These all increase the cost of construction. Hard or firm soils also are needed to hold up heavy trucking loads. In addition, roads should be as straight as possible to make them safer and more efficient.

Streets are built to service urban areas. The three basic kinds of streets are: (1) service streets, (2) collector streets (Fig. 92-3), and (3) arterial streets (Fig. 92-4). They have street capacities respectively of 600, 1,200, and 1,800 to 2,400 cars per hour, Table 92-1. Intersections with signals are the main cause of limited street capacity. Signals can be done away with on highspeed, arterial streets by building interchanges, Fig. 92-5.

Things to be considered when locating streets are:

1. The kinds of streets needed,
2. The shortest possible distance between origins and destinations,
3. The use of as few streets as possible to give the whole community fairly short travel routes,
4. Land slope and soil condition,
5. Streets built at an earlier time,
6. The shape of private properties (Fig. 92-6), and
7. Structures in developed areas.

Street building costs include: (1) the cost of the road and (2) the cost of the land the road is on.

Fig. 92-3. Collector streets collect rush hour traffic from service streets and move it to arterial streets.

Fig. 92-4. Arterial streets collect traffic from many collector streets.

Fig. 92-5. Intersections are the main cause of low traffic capacity. Here highway interchanges provide uninterrupted traffic flow.

Table 92-1

Street Capacities at Signalized Intersections for the Three Basic Kinds of Streets

Type of Street	Number of lanes moving in one direction	Street Capacity
Service street	1	600 cars an hour
Collector street	2	1200 cars an hour (600 cars an hour in each lane)
Arterial street	3	1800 cars an hour (600 cars an hour in each lane)
Arterial street widened at intersection to eight lanes	4	2400 cars an hour (600 cars an hour in each lane)

Railways

When large amounts of heavy loads must be moved many miles, *railway service* is often the least expensive means of transportation. Railroad tracks are generally built on hard or firm, flat land. Heavy train loads are hard to pull up even very small hills, Fig. 92-7.

Airways

Transportation by *airplane* is often needed when the primary construction project makes lightweight things of very high value. Air service is also used for both men and materials when travel time must be short. To construct an airplane landing strip, hard or firm soils and a large amount of flat, low-priced land are needed. The landing strip should be close to the primary construction which it serves.

Airways also require, in addition to landing strips, such things as terminals, navigation aids, and repair facilities, Fig. 92-8.

Waterways

Water transport is another way to move heavy loads. The waterway must be close to the primary construction to be useful. These waterways also must be deep enough and wide enough to be used by boats and barges. Using waterways causes a need for more service construction. Docks must be built at the water's edge for loading freight. Roads

Fig. 92-6. Streets that are built around properties leave odd sized and shaped land that is difficult to develop.

Fig. 92-7. Railroad tracks are generally built on hard or firm, flat land.

or railroads also must be close to docks. Flat or sloped land and hard soils are needed near the docks for transporting and holding up the weight of the freight being loaded.

Fig. 92-8. Airways include, in addition to landing strips, such things as terminals, aids to navigation, and storage and repair facilities.

Fig. 92-9. Pipelayers at work building a pipeline to serve the community.

Pipelines

Some things can be carried more cheaply by *pipelines*, Fig. 92-9. Oil, gasoline, and natural gas are often carried by pipelines. Some solids, such as finely ground coal, are carried with the help of water through pipelines. Pipelines generally run underground following the shortest distance between the places wanting pipeline service. Most pipelines are under pressure. Thus, their contents can run uphill and downhill following the slope of the land. Pumping stations must be built along the path of the pipeline to keep pressure in the piping system.

Utilities

In addition to transportation construction, primary construction also need gas, electrical, communications, water, and sewer services. The construction of these services is called *utility construction.*

Most areas can easily get gas, electric, and communication services. To get these services at primary construction sites, usually only additional lengths of pipeline or cable must be used. These lengths bring the utility from the system already in use to the new primary construction site.

Water Systems

Water utilities generally require more construction than gas, electric, or communication services. Water systems are made up of three things:

1. A water treatment plant,
2. A water pump and pressure tank, and
3. Underground water piping.

Water is brought in pipes from the water supply (river, reservoir, or well) to the water treatment plant. At the water treatment plant the water is filtered and chemicals are added. This makes the water safe for human use.

After the water is treated, it is piped to the places needing water service. When the water source itself is higher than the highest site to be served, water can be sent to users directly from the water treatment plant. Then more pressure is not needed. However, where the water source is not higher than all the sites it serves, a water pump and pressure tank are needed.

Water leaves the treatment plant or pressure tower in large, underground pipes. These pipes are large because they carry all the water used to the areas to be served. Pipes that branch from these large pipes are smaller. The smaller pipes take the water to the sites where it will be used. A treelike network of pipelines is formed. The large pipes leaving the water tower are like a tree trunk and are called *trunk lines*. The smaller pipes, delivering water to the separate sites, are like small branches. These are called *branch lines*.

Site factors for pipelines are less important than they are for other construction. Although trunk lines need hard or firm soils to hold them, this need is less important for smaller pipes. The location of the pipeline does not depend on the slope of the land, since the water can be pumped under pressure and can flow uphill as well as downhill. Since the pipes are usually put in publicly owned property along roads, the price of land is less important than it is for most other construction. Study Fig. 92-10.

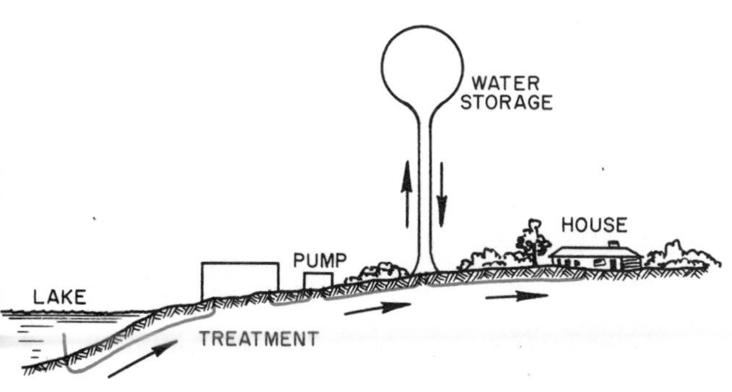

Fig. 92-10. This diagram shows how water gets from a lake to your home.

Sewer Systems

The sewer system has two parts. The first is the *underground collection system*. The second is the *treatment plant*.

The operation of the sewer system is almost the opposite of the water system. The waste enters another treelike piping system at each site. But it enters the ends of the small branches and flows into the larger trunk pipes that then lead to the treatment plant.

Unlike the water system, the sewer system does not operate under pressure. The flow of the waste water in the sewer system is caused by gravity. Therefore sewage can flow downhill only. At the treatment plant, the solids are settled (separated) from the liquid. Then the water is treated and returned to a natural water channel.

Like water pipes, sewer pipes are laid along the roadbed in publicly owned land. Therefore, land price is not a problem. *Since the flow of the sewer system depends on grav-*

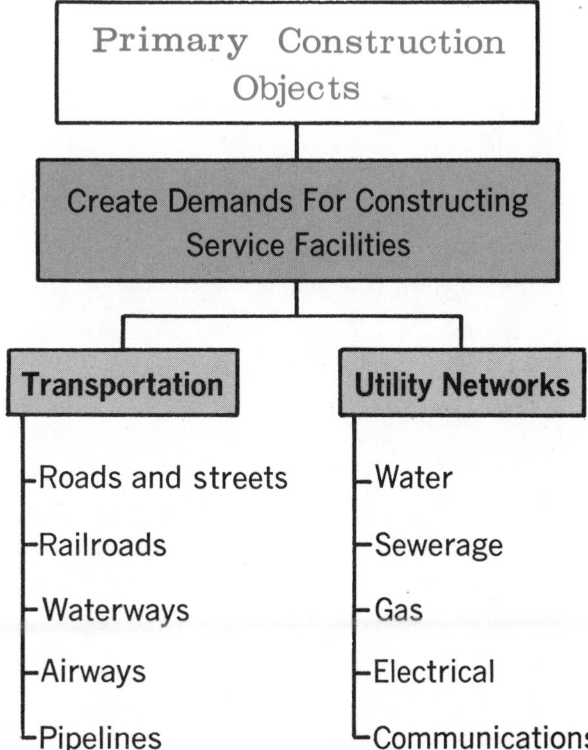

ity, the slope of the land where the pipes are laid is important. Each pipe in the system must be placed so that the waste entering the pipe will flow downhill toward the treatment plant. To let all sewage flow downhill, the treatment plant must be placed at the lowest level in the area being served.

Summary

After places where people work are built, it is necessary to provide the workers with service facilities. These services may generally be classed under the headings of *transportation* and *utilities.*

Roads and streets, railways, airways, waterways, and pipelines provide transportation services. Gas, electrical, communication, water and sewer services are called utilities. Both transportation and utility services construction must meet the construction factors of demand, service, and site.

When *primary* construction has all of the different kinds of *service* construction it needs, it is ready to be operated by workers.

Terms to Know

transportation	water treatment plant
service streets	water pressure
collector streets	water tower
arterial streets	trunk lines
water transport	branch lines
pipelines	underground collection system
utility construction	gravity
filtered	

Think About It!

1. Is automobile traffic slow in your community? If so, what could be done to move it faster?
2. What is the source of your drinking water? Is there ever a shortage of water? Why?

Housing People

Workers employed at primary construction have families who need places to live. This section will show how a demand for housing for workers adds to community development.

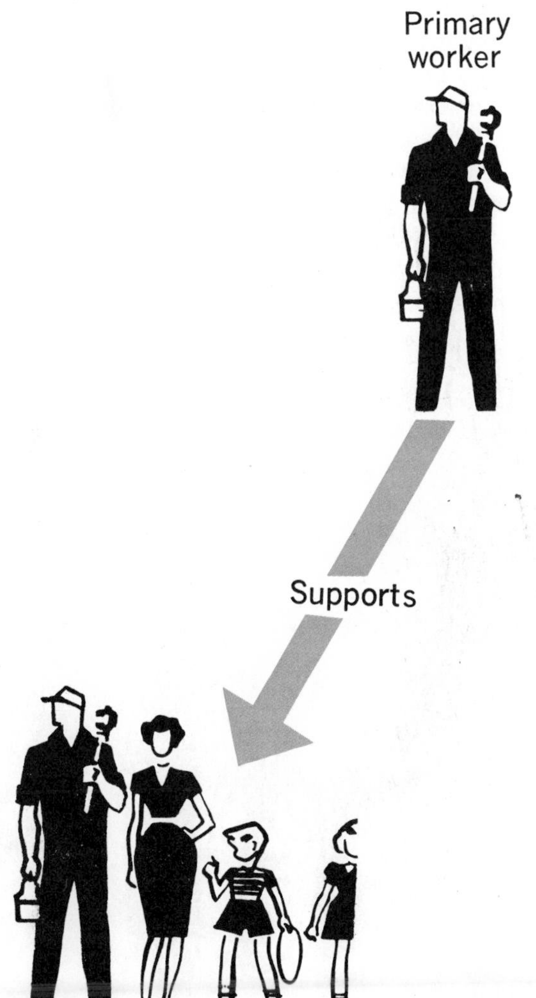

Fig. 93-1. One primary worker supports himself and his family.

The Population Multiplier

It has been found that the average number of people in an American family is 3½. Because of this, each job site will usually have a population around it equal to about 3½ times the number of workers employed there, Fig. 93-1. For example, a production plant (primary construction) which has 100 workers will generally have about 350 people that are directly supported by it.

The production workers are called *primary workers*. Their families need goods and services. This means bankers, doctors, dentists, and shopkeepers are needed. The people who provide these goods and services are called secondary workers.

A community can generally support 1½ secondary workers for each primary worker. If the production plant has 100 workers, there will usually be about 150 secondary workers in the area to give services to the whole community. Because of this, each job at the plant (primary construction) will generally create a market or a demand for 2½ housing units. One of these units is needed by the primary worker and his family and 1½ are needed by the secondary workers and their families, Fig. 93-2.

Housing Density and Income Levels

Houses must be built to fit the price levels and wants of the workers. If housing is more expensive than most of the workers can afford, it will not be sold. If the houses are too small for what the workers with large families want, they will not be sold.

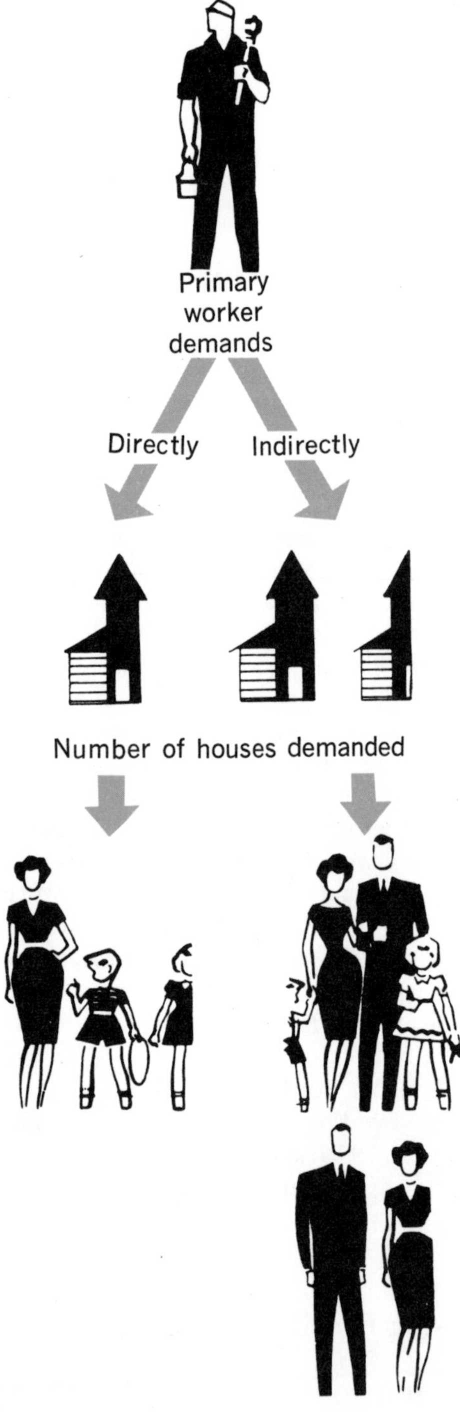

Fig. 93-2. One primary worker creates a demand for 1 house directly and 1½ houses indirectly. Consequently, 8¾ people are housed (primary worker and his family plus 1½ secondary workers and their families).

One way to find the quality of housing needed is to study family incomes to see what general housing density is needed. *Housing density* means the number of houses or apartments per acre.

We can usually estimate the price of housing in an area from its density. Single family housing units on large lots in new areas are generally expensive because they are constructed at a density of from 1-3 houses on an acre of land, Fig. 93-3. This makes the land cost per unit high. *Low density housing* like this is called SF (1) : a single family unit to the acre; SF (2) : two single family units to the acre; and SF (3) : three single family units to the acre.

Single family housing units for middle-income families are constructed at a density of 4 or 5 houses to the acre, SF (4) or SF (5). This is called *medium density housing.*

Lower income housing units are generally constructed at 6 or more units per acre, SF (6), etc. *Multiple family units* often begin to be used at this density. This is called *high density housing.* With it, land, street, and utility costs per housing unit are lower, Fig. 93-4.

Generally no more upper, middle or lower income housing units will be sold than there

Fig. 93-3. The suburbs provide single family housing units.

are workers of those income levels. Knowing the income levels of the people who need housing helps in planning for housing density.

Service and Site Factors in Housing Construction

The sale price of housing is made up of three things:

1. The developer's cost to build the units and develop their sites,
2. The cost of the land the houses are on, and
3. The developer's business costs and profit.

The developer's profit is cut down by a high land cost.

Housing should be close to the owner's job in order to lower travel costs and shorten travel time. While housing should be close, it should not be right next to a worker's job. This is because places of work often produce traffic, noise, and other things not desired in a residential area. Housing also should be close to all utilities.

All housing types need firm or hard soils to support them. Soft soils cause uneven settlement of even the lightest housing units. The slope of housing sites is not too important. Steep slopes raise the cost of the construction. However, the higher cost of construction can usually be made up in the higher sale price of each low density housing unit. With high density housing, cost can be spread across a large number of units.

The Effect of Land Price on Housing Density

Community growth causes a rise in the price of sites close to places of employment because the sites are convenient. Sometimes land prices are so high that single family housing will not make a profit for the developer.

Suppose he builds single family housing units on an expensive site. He must sell housing at the same prices as on low-cost sites and get less profit. Few contractors will do this. It is generally impractical for him to raise the price of single family housing units. The same kind of housing can usually be found on the edge of community develop-

Fig. 93-4. This high density housing unit has apartments on all 24 floors. A great many families can live in each unit.

Fig. 93-5. Space has been provided near this high density housing unit for park and picnic facilities.

ment. There the prices are lower because the cost of the land is less.

As a result, the contractor must build a greater number of housing units on a site close to places of work if he is to make a profit. This lowers the land cost per housing unit by spreading this cost over many units, Figs. 93-5 and 93-6.

Fig. 93-6. Most urban populations live in multiple-family housing units.

Fig. 93-7. This high density housing complex is in the city. In the center of the picture can be seen the school which serves the entire complex.

Summary

To check what you know about population, housing density, and income levels, follow this example of an industrial plant that has 450 primary workers. A community that has 450 primary workers can also support 675 secondary workers. (For each primary worker, the community can support $1\frac{1}{2}$ secondary workers, $450 \times 1\frac{1}{2} = 675$.) The total employment of the community will be about 1,125 people ($450 + 675$). The total population of the community would then be about 3,938 people (1,125 housing units or 1,125 families x $3\frac{1}{2}$ people per family $= 3{,}938$ people).

In general, housing must be built to fit the price levels and wants of the people. For high income families, houses are usually built 1, 2, or 3 to an acre; for low income, 6 or more to an acre.

Because of higher land price near employment centers and a great demand for housing in an area, high density housing may be needed, Fig. 93-7. Both the kind and height of structures constructed for high density housing are usually determined by land price and demand.

Terms to Know

population
primary workers
secondary workers
housing density
income level
low density housing
medium density housing
high density housing
multiple family units

Think About It!

1. Do you live in low density, medium density, or high density housing? How do you know?
2. Why is high density housing usually found close to places of major employment?

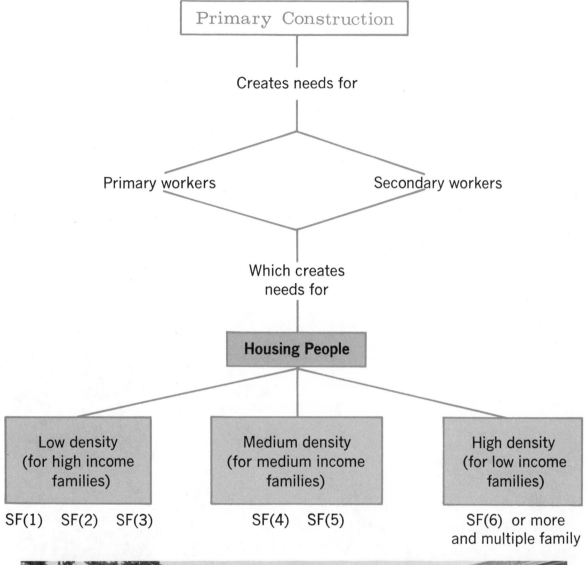

Primary Construction

Creates needs for

Primary workers

Secondary workers

Which creates needs for

Housing People

Low density (for high income families)	Medium density (for medium income families)	High density (for low income families)
SF(1) SF(2) SF(3)	SF(4) SF(5)	SF(6) or more and multiple family

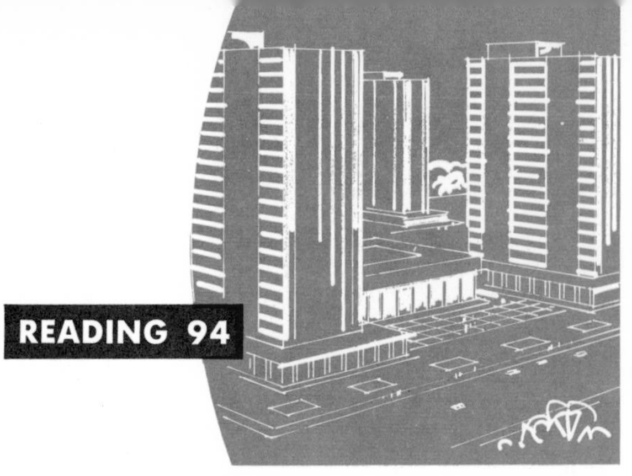

READING 94

Planning Business Facilities

Many people earn a living by working in business places. Everyone in a community, including those who work in industry, has needs that are filled by these business places.

Businesses include such things as banks, grocery stores, and cafeterias. In addition, they may include offices for people such as doctors, insurance agents, and realtors.

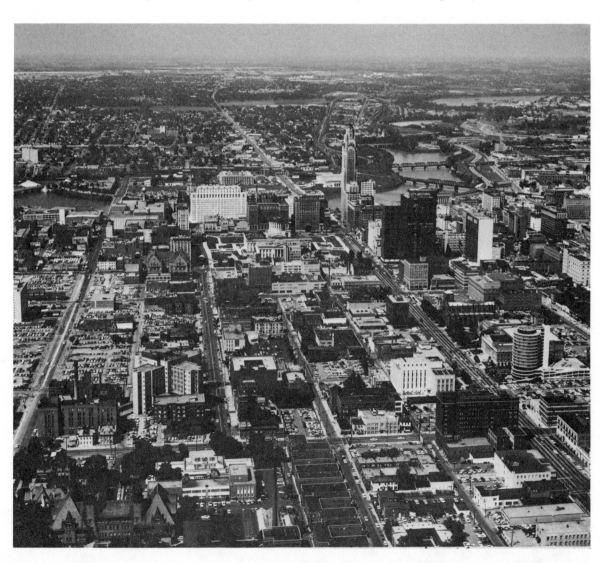

Fig. 94-1. This is the downtown (central business) area of a large midwestern city. It provides services for the surrounding area.

Businesses serve areas of housing called *trade areas.* A trade area is generally small and close to the businesses which serve it. Therefore, a total small community may be a trade area. Large cities generally have several trade areas. A central business district may serve all of these areas, Fig. 94-1. In addition, each trade area may have a business section of its own.

Central Business Construction

Whenever there is a need for services for the whole community, central business construction is undertaken to fulfill this need. The result of this is the construction of such structures as office buildings, theaters, stores, government buildings, and parking lots.

In the past, all central business construction was done at the center of the community. This is the area called *downtown.* This location gave quick access along major roads and streets from all parts of the community. These downtown areas became tightly packed with buildings built right up to the street, Fig. 94-2.

As the community population grew, car use also grew. The streets in the downtown areas became congested (filled) with traffic. This caused traffic jams, and it took more time to make trips from housing units to the central business places. Because large buildings were built right at the side of the downtown streets, it was not possible to widen the streets to make room for the extra traffic. In addition, as the communities grew, new housing areas were built farther and farther away from the downtown areas. This made the time it took for trips to the central area even longer. These developments have caused *shopping centers* to grow outside of the downtown area.

In general, no more than one acre of central business construction will be supported by each 350 housing units in a community. Much less space than this is needed if central business needs are met through the con-

Fig. 94-2. Here are two different faces of a major U.S. city, Pittsburgh, Pennsylvania. Above is the "Golden Triangle" downtown area as it looked in 1947. Below, following vast redevelopment, is the same area in 1964. The "New Golden Triangle" boasts modern traffic facilities, buildings, and park and recreation areas.

struction of tall buildings. If there is a need and a market for central business construction, the facilities will be constructed and maintained. However, they should be well located on land which gives economical development. They also should be planned in relation to shopping center construction.

Site Location

To give community service efficiently, central business construction needs sites that are at the intersections of the most important streets of the community. This permits quick access from all areas of the community. These major streets often intersect (cross) at or near the center of the developed areas of the community. This is why the facilities which give shopping and business services to the whole community are called *central business construction.*

Site Costs

Sites for central business construction generally have the highest land price of all the sites in a community. However, profits from their development are also high. As with high density housing, the higher the land price, the taller the structures must be in order to spread the high price of the land over more facilities.

Shopping Center Construction

Within large communities it is sometimes more efficient to break up the total trade area into smaller areas that are served by *shopping centers.* These are of two kinds, *strip* and *local.*

A strip area is formed when business places are spread out along a length of busy street, Fig. 94-3. Each business is separate from the others. Each of them usually advertises its location by putting up signs beside the street. There are also many separate small parking areas and hundreds of signs. Drivers must park on the streets or enter parking areas from heavily traveled streets. This can slow down traffic and cause accidents.

Local shopping centers differ from strip shopping centers. They are generally constructed on large sites which are set back from busy streets. They are made up of a group of large structures. Each of these large buildings has a number of separate stores or offices in it. These centers are generally much better planned and designed than are the strip centers. There is generally one large parking lot for all the stores and offices in the center. Service roads from main streets to the parking lot help cut down on confusion and slowing of traffic on the main streets.

A local shopping center gets the attention of people passing it. It is easy to see as a whole. People tend to drive to the centers rather than to any one store or office in it. There are not as many signs along the street as there are in a strip center. Sometimes there is only one large sign which has the center's name on it, Fig. 94-4.

All housing units need business services. However, not all communities can support shopping centers. The smallest center needs at least 1,000 housing units in its trade area for support. If there are less than this, shopping centers probably won't be built and separate stores will satisfy business needs.

Fig. 94-3. Here is one section of a strip shopping center under construction.

Site Requirements

The best places for shopping centers are along main streets or where important streets cross. Sometimes these sites are too expensive because of buildings which are there. The cost of developing a shopping center there might be too high for a profit to be made. Then sites along important streets which are not at major intersections are often chosen for shopping centers.

Even then, the price of land is generally high. The price is even higher if there are buildings on the land which must be torn down. However, a high profit can be made by the successful construction and sale of shopping centers. This is true when the land around the center is priced low enough that housing units are built on it. The center would not be built at all if the land price is too high and construction costs would be too great to sell the center with a profit.

Firm or hard soils are needed to support the weight of buildings in shopping centers. The land also should be flat or only a little sloped. Steep land raises construction costs. It would also make unsafe and inefficient parking areas.

Local shopping centers are generally from 1-10 acres in size. The parking lots take up at least ⅔ of the site, Fig. 94-4. If the number of stores built cannot be supported by the trade area, they will fail. The kind and size of each store must be supportable by the families in its trade area.

Summary

Central business construction fills a community's need for centrally placed businesses and offices. A community must reach a certain size before central business construction can begin. At least 350 housing units are needed to support one acre of central business construction. The sites for this construction must have all utilities available. They must have either firm or hard soils and must be flat or slightly sloped. Most importantly, they must be at the intersections of the most important streets in the community.

Fig. 94-4. Many local shopping centers are located on or near heavily traveled streets. Adequate parking areas must be provided for customers.

Fig. 94-5. Large parking areas are needed in local shopping centers.

Shopping centers may be part of a community system. Their location, kind, and number are determined by the need for local business services. These needs are created by the construction and sale of housing units.

Local shopping centers generally serve the community better than strip shopping areas if the community is large enough to support them. In addition to being more attractive, local shopping centers cut down on motorist confusion and the slowing of traffic, Fig. 94-5. Shopping centers also must be near at least 1,000 housing units. The land should be firm or hard to support the weight of construction. Flat or only slightly sloped land is needed. Then the parking areas will be safe and construction costs will be lower.

Terms to Know

trade area
downtown
central business construction
shopping centers
  a. strip shopping center
  b. local shopping center

Think About It!

1. Does your community have a central business area? Have there been new shopping centers developed in the past few years? Why?
2. How would a high-speed mass transportation system affect the central business district of a large city? Would central businessmen be likely to support building one?

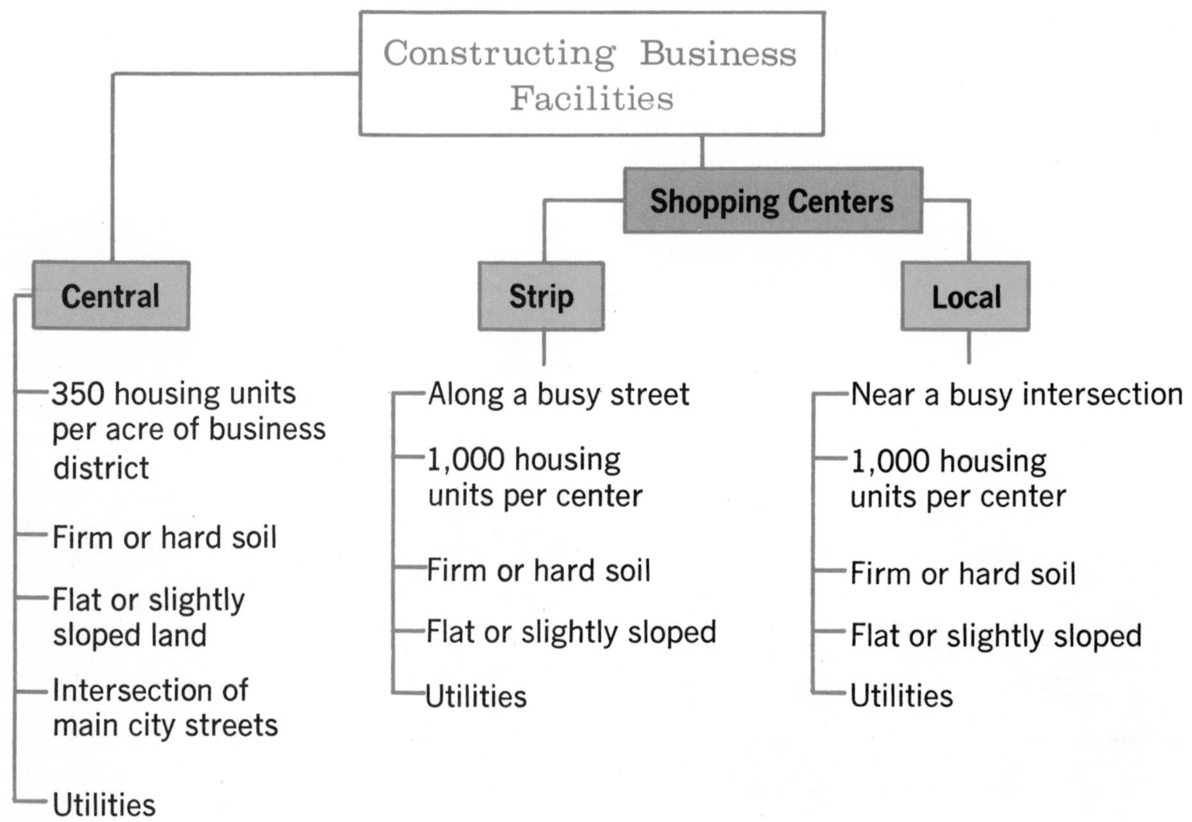

Planning Schools and Recreational Facilities

All communities need schools in which to educate their youth. In addition, all communities need outdoor space for play and recreation.

This reading presents some of the basic knowledge which city planners use in making their plans for schools and recreational areas. Unless they are planned for, every person in the community may have a much less satisfying life.

Kinds of Schools

Two kinds of schools are often constructed in a community. These are: (1) elementary schools, and (2) secondary (high) schools.

In some areas, *elementary schools* hold grades one through eight. The *secondary schools* hold grades nine through twelve. In other areas, the secondary schools are divided into *junior high schools* which hold grades seven through nine and *senior high schools* which hold grades ten through twelve.

In still other areas, grades one through six are in the elementary schools. Grades seven through twelve are in a junior-senior high school. This last kind of school system is the one used as an example in this reading.

Supporting Schools

All housing units need school service. Before a school can be built, however, it must be shown that a school can be supported (paid for) and be kept up. A community which has 550 or more housing units can generally support the construction of an elementary school, Fig. 95-1. If there are less than 550 housing units, there are usually too few children of elementary school age to support a school. When this occurs, communities often go together and jointly construct a school.

More support is needed for junior-senior high school construction. Junior-senior high

Fig. 95-1. The neighborhood elementary school is supported by at least 550 housing units.

Fig. 95-2. This high school, with 3 acres under roof, is supported by at least 3,000 housing units.

schools will generally be built in a community if it has more than 3,000 housing units, Fig. 95-2.

Schools also have a maximum (highest number) of housing units they can service. When a school has too many students, it is so big that it cannot operate efficiently. An elementary school generally cannot efficiently service more than 2,300 housing units. Junior-senior high schools cannot efficiently service more than 11,000 housing units. When there are more housing units than a school can service well, another school must be built.

Location of Schools

Schools must be placed to give good service to housing units. Elementary schools are generally put where young children can walk to school from their homes. Each child in elementary school should not have to walk more than one-half mile from his home to school. The walk from home to school also must be safe. Children should not have to cross heavily traveled streets on their way to and from school, Fig. 95-3.

Youth attending junior-senior high schools are able to walk further than elementary age children. However, it is believed that the older pupils should not have to walk more than $1\frac{1}{2}$ miles on their way to school. Junior-senior high schools also must be on or near a major street. Many activities at the school such as football games, plays, and community meetings means there will be much traffic to and from the school.

Service Needs

Schools have their own service needs. Both elementary and junior-senior high schools must have sites where there is utility service. They also need parking lots (Fig. 95-4) and streets leading to the school for automobile traffic and maintenance and repair vehicles.

All schools need sites with firm or hard soils to support the school construction. Schools need flat playing fields. Therefore, steep land would take a great deal of ex-

Fig. 95-3. Busy intersections should be avoided in locating schools. Youth should not have to cross heavily traveled streets to get to school.

Fig. 95-4. Access and parking facilities for schools must also be provided.

pensive earth moving. Land for schools should be undeveloped and low in price. If buildings must be torn down to clear land for a school, the cost of the school goes up. Schools need large amounts of land. An elementary school generally takes a site of from 5-10 acres or more. A junior-senior high school needs at least twenty acres.

Kinds of Community Recreational Facilities

Community recreational facilities will not be built and maintained if they do not fill special needs. There are many kinds of recreational facilities. Examples are playgrounds, playfields, neighborhood parks, and community parks. Each meets a different need, as described in the next section.

Locating Recreational Facilities

Playgrounds are built for elementary school age children. They generally have playground equipment such as swings, slides, sand boxes, and small open spaces for games, Fig. 95-5. Playgrounds generally need from 1-10 acres of land. This depends on the number of children they serve.

Playfields are constructed for adults and junior and senior high school age youth. They generally have all the equipment of a playground. They also may supply facilities for basketball, softball, football, tennis, and baseball, Fig. 95-6. Playfields also have parking areas and seats for people who watch sports. They also often have indoor areas for dancing, table tennis, and arts and crafts. Playfields usually cover from 10-20 acres depending on the number of people they serve.

Neighborhood parks are built near housing areas. They generally have shady places and large lawns. When housing density is less than five housing units an acre, each yard generally has this kind of area. In areas with a greater housing density, this is not the case. Then neighborhood parks must be constructed. The size of the neighborhood parks depends on how much land is available and the number of people needing the facility.

Fig. 95-5. Playgrounds meet the special recreational needs of elementary school children.

Fig. 95-6. This durable basketball facility will meet the community's needs for many years.

Community parks have a different purpose. They are for outings, picnicing, hiking, and water sports for all members of the community, Fig. 95-7. Areas that have heavy woods, streams with rapids and waterfalls, and attractive river fronts or lake shores are often used as sites for community parks, Fig. 95-8. The community park preserves this natural setting for use by members of the community and for the enjoyment of future generations. Because community parks serve the whole community they are usually 20 acres or more in area.

Fig. 95-7. Riverside improvements can offer many refreshing and relaxing hours.

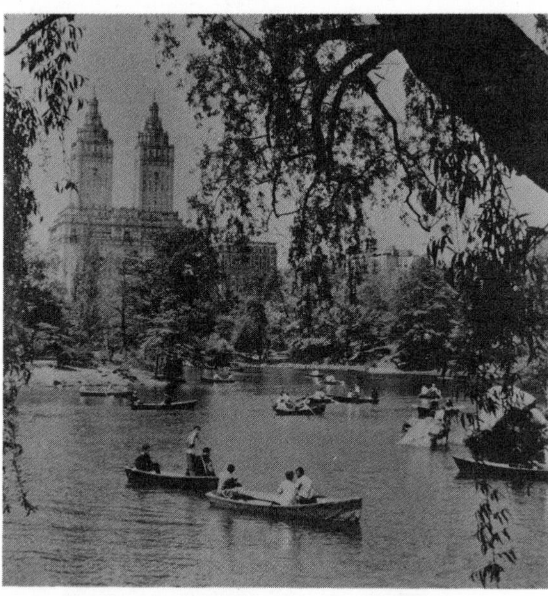

Fig. 95-8. There are 35,760 acres of parks in New York City. Boaters enjoy rowing on the lake in Central Park.

All the land used for recreation must be equal to the demands of the community. Generally, at least 10 acres of space are needed for every 300 housing units. We can use the following formula for figuring the amount of land needed for recreation:

$$\frac{\text{Number of housing units}}{300} \times 10 \text{ acres} =$$

total acres of land needed. For example, a community of 3,000 housing units would need at least 100 acres of land for recreation.

All types of land may be used for recreational areas, although playfields require large, flat areas. Parks may be developed in areas where little other construction is likely to be done, Fig. 95-9.

Summary

Communities often construct elementary and secondary schools. A community must have enough housing units to support their schools.

Choosing the location of schools is very important. They must be built on sites that

Fig. 95-9. Many secluded areas can be opened for public enjoyment with only a few facilities.

efficiently serve the community. They should be built on flat or sloped ground.

Communities also need recreational areas such as playgrounds, playfields, neighborhood parks, and community parks. Usually, there should be at least 10 acres of recreation space in a community for every 300 housing units.

The sites of recreational facilities must be located in an area where they efficiently provide their services to the people living in the housing units. Except for playfields, they may be on any soils or land slope. Playfields require flat and firm or hard sites.

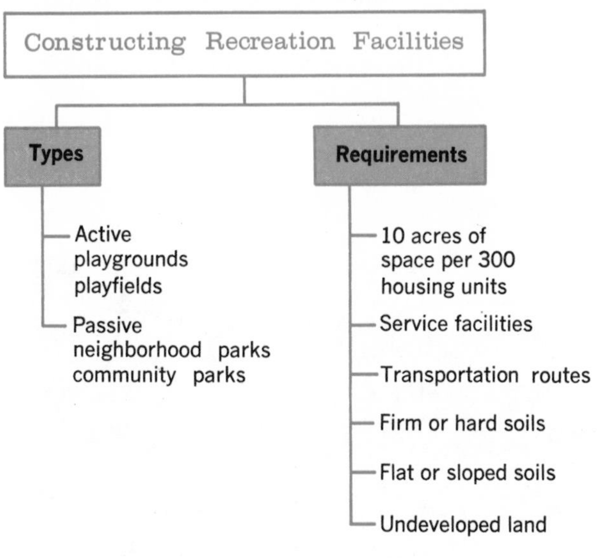

Terms to Know

elementary schools
secondary schools
  a. junior high school
  b. senior high school
recreational facilities
housing units
neighborhood park
community park

Think About It!

1. About how many housing units does your school serve?
2. Does your community have adequate recreation facilities? How could you figure this out if you are not sure?

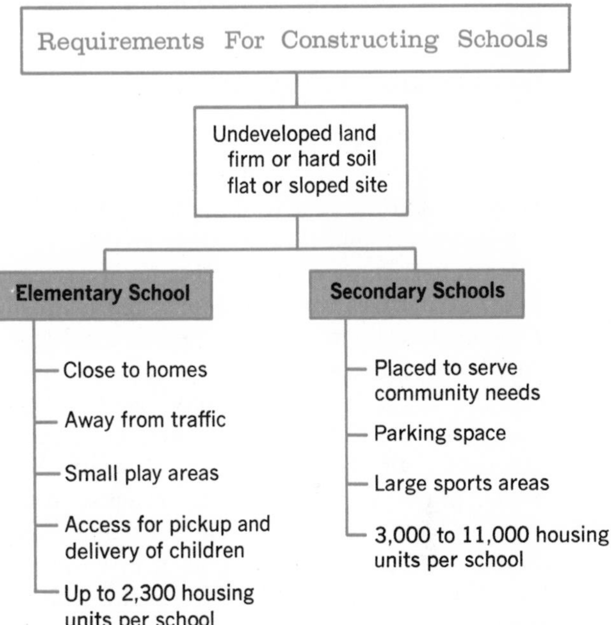

READING 96

The Economics of Community Development

Every community is born with the building of primary construction that makes employment available. The community grows when more construction is needed for the workers and their families. This cycle continues in a prosperous community.

Deterioration of Construction

In a healthy community, all structures are used and all are in good physical condition. They are *maintained* well so they serve their purposes and hold their value.

However, most communities have at least a few structures that are poorly maintained. This causes them to be in poor condition. Such structures are said to be *deteriorated,* Fig. 96-1. At first, they may need only a coat of paint. If time passes and no repairs are made, wooden parts of a structure rot, metal parts rust, brickwork cracks, roofs sag, and the structure itself becomes unstable. It finally collapses into a pile of rubble. All structures deteriorate like this if they are not cared for properly.

Many communities have large deteriorated areas. In time, some of these communities cannot economically maintain a single structure. Then they die. This generally happens when primary construction is abandoned or given up. Then there is no work to provide the needed market support for construction in the community. The first results of the economic death of a community is a "ghost town," Fig. 96-2. No one lives there, and the structures deteriorate until they become piles of rubble. This has happened, over centuries of time, even to many great cities. Constructed objects will be maintained only if the cost of the repairs will be made up in some way. The main ways these costs may be made up are: (1) by increased profit from rental or sale because of the repairs or (2) by making repairs that are needed to stop economic loss.

Parts of a community may deteriorate for many reasons.

1. A major employer of people in a community could move to another city or state. The unemployed people have less reason to remain in the community. This *reduces*

Fig. 96-1. The deteriorating housing shows a great need for general maintenance.

Fig. 96-2. This community in Nevada was a thriving business center in the middle 1800's. It is now a "ghost town," a decaying reminder of what used to be.

the market for quality construction. In turn, property owners have less reason to invest money in improvements.

2. The structure (building, road, bridge, etc.) may lose *location value.* This usually occurs when a community changes and the "old" location is no longer desirable.
3. Construction also may deteriorate because of what is around it (*environmental value*). For example, the value of housing units will generally go down if they are close to a railroad, heavy industry, sewer plant, or a very heavily traveled road. This is because the noise, smells, smoke, and danger to children made by these facilities makes the houses less wanted. Fig. 96-3.

When resale market and sales price fall rapidly, few repairs are made and structures deteriorate.

Other Economic Losses

Deterioration losses are not the only ones a community may have. Great value is also lost through construction inefficiency. This occurs mainly when good facilities must be replaced before they are worn out. For example, a costly 4″ water pipe might be laid to serve the existing needs of an area of a community. If the area grows, this pipe cannot provide all the water service that is needed. Then the expensive 4″ pipe, even though it could give service for many years, must be replaced by a larger pipe. If the growth of the area had been foreseen, the larger pipe could have been laid initially, at

Fig. 96-3. This house has a railway running nearby. Would this place the owner in an undesirable economic situation?

Fig. 96-4. This pile of rubble is the result when a house similar to others in the picture is demolished. The site will be cleared so that a better use may be made of the property.

Fig. 96-5. According to redevelopment plans, urban renewal projects help to clear deteriorated areas.

a large savings. Another example is in street interchange construction. Often, expensive developed property must be bought by the community for this construction. The same ground could have been bought before it was developed at much less cost to the community, Fig. 96-4.

Need for Planning

Costs resulting from both deterioration and *inefficiency* must be paid for by the community citizens. They pay it in taxes. Each land owner in a community pays a share of these costs that have no economic return or social service. Community deterioration and inefficiency are economic illnesses. They take away the economic strength of the community. Effective long-range planning can reduce economic losses and support efficient community development.

Summary

The deterioration of construction in a community usually results from: (1) a reduced market, (2) loss of locational value, or (3) loss of environmental value. Deterioration of construction results in great economic loss to the whole community. Losses also may result from construction inefficiency or a lack of community planning.

Communities should be economically strong and satisfying places in which to work and live. Planning community construction will help them to be such places.

Terms to Know

maintained
deterioration
location value
environmental value
inefficiency

Think About It!

1. What area or areas in your city or community are deteriorating? If there is such an area, can you give the street boundaries?
2. Do you know of any plans to improve your community by rebuilding parts of it? If so, what are they?

Managing Community Development

READING 97

Most people want to live in a community where life is satisfying, efficient, and economical. To reach these goals, nearly every community in the United States of any great size manages its community development. This, as in all management activities, takes planning, organizing, and controlling.

The planning, organizing, and controlling of community development is done by men who are educated to do this. These men are called *city planners*. They spend their lives trying to improve communities, Fig. 97-1.

The General Plan

The city planner predicts the probable number of jobs in the community and the resulting community growth. He then develops statements which outline possible community *objectives* (goals) in managing this growth. These statements of objectives are accepted by the community and are used as a guide to direct community development. These statements are called the *general plan*.

The general plan may include such statements as: (1) to provide high-speed inner and outer traffic belts, (2) to rehabilitate the inner city area, (3) to provide elementary schools within a half mile of most homes, and (4) to provide a park for every township.

Fig. 97-1. The city planner studies plans of the whole community.

The Development Plan

Many details must be added to the general plan before the objectives can be reached. These details become a *development plan*. Standards must be set up for such things as street widths, school site sizes, the size and location of neighborhood parks, housing site sizes, and all other construction in the community.

The development plan also must show those facilities that will be constructed during the next few years. The total cost of community-owned facilities to be constructed during this period must be estimated. Then their construction must be scheduled to make sure that every structure will be constructed where it is wanted and when it is needed.

The schedule for constructing these facilities is called a *capital improvements program*. The way they will be paid for is called a *capital budget*. After a general plan and a development plan have been made, the management of community development must be organized to make sure that the plans are followed.

The Planning Board

Organization for community development takes more than just the services of the city planner. At the earliest stages of the community planning process, a *planning board* or *commission* is made up. This board is made up of a group of citizens chosen to represent the people of the community. The members of the planning board tell the city planner what they want and help him to make a plan that the citizens of the community will support, Fig. 97-2.

Community Development Laws

After a general plan is approved by the planning board, the planner and the board propose regulations or laws that are needed to control the community development. This is done so that the first stage of the development plan proposals are realized. The elected public officials review the suggestions of the planning board and pass laws which regulate community construction.

These laws set up standards for such things as construction methods, the location of buildings, their greatest height and size, and the use of the property around buildings for parking and landscaping. They also give standards for such things as property shape, street width, facilities which must be provided by developers, street slopes, general street patterns, and many other standards for land development.

Control of Community Development

Planning and organization does not mean much without *control.* Laws serve no purpose unless they are followed. For this reason, *the community's building inspector and planning board are given the power to enforce laws.*

The building inspector's job is to see that every building in the community is safe for human use. He generally must check the plans for every building to be built in the community. This is done to make sure that it meets all the legal requirements. If it does, a building permit is issued. The permit states that the structure is approved for construction.

The community's planning board is usually given the power to review land development laws. When a proposed plan does not meet the requirements, it will not be approved, and the site will not be developed.

By enforcing laws, community development is controlled to fulfill the goals of the general plan. These goals are never completely fulfilled, however. The community always grows or changes. Then the general plan must be changed to fit the new conditions. Also, the development plan must be pushed further and further into the future as first goals are reached. The management of community development is a process which never ends, Fig. 97-3.

The Community and Its Region

A region is a certain section or area of the country. Every community is a part of

Fig. 97-2. The managed development of expanding suburbs increases the desirability of the whole community as a place to live and work.

a region. Many characteristics of a community are like those of the areas around it.

Many community problems can only be solved regionally. The construction of highways for the movement of cars and trucks from one community to another within a region and between regions cannot be undertaken by each community alone. Such highways must be planned as a complete regional system that efficiently and economically serves all of the communities of a region, Fig. 97-4. The generation of electricity is another example of a regional problem, Figs. 97-5 and 97-6.

Regional development also must be managed. The full potential for the economic growth and prosperity of the region depends

Fig. 97-3. Central business areas are changing with the demands of the community.

Fig. 97-4. Shown here is a completed interchange area for two interstate highways in Ohio. These highways link communities together.

Fig. 97-5. The switch yard and power lines of the Oahe Dam in South Dakota is shown. This power facility and dam is on the Missouri River.

Fig. 97-6. The transmission towers and lines to the left are part of the vast power distribution system of the state power authority near Niagara Falls, New York.

Fig. 97-7. This area model shows development of a hydroelectric power complex, highway, and park system near Niagara Falls, New York.

Fig. 97-8. A number of communities are located on a river. Characteristics such as weather and economic conditions may be the same for each community.

on this. It is the best way to efficiently solve problems of the whole region, Fig. 97-7. Lack of regional planning, just as a lack of community planning, results in great losses. Many states have state planning divisions. These divisions employ regional planners to plan, organize, and control their regional development. Good regional planning results in continued construction and maintenance of construction in each of the region's communities, Fig. 97-8. It also helps solve problems about regional transportation, flood protection, recreation, and utility services.

Summary

Successful management of community development programs depends on three things:

1. People wanting a better community and willing to support the city planner, planning board, and the elected officials in their efforts to bring it about,

2. A group of elected officials willing to adopt and demand strict enforcement of community development control laws, and

3. A professionally trained and experienced city planner who is able to forecast, plan, and write control laws that can effectively guide the development of the community.

Each constructed project in a community is related to all other construction in that community. In turn, each community is part of a larger region.

The individual housing unit located on a service street in a small town is a part of a constructed system that relates it to all other construction within an area of hundreds, and perhaps thousands, of square miles. This is the world of construction.

Terms to Know

city planners
objectives
general plan
development plan
capital improvement program
capital budget
planning board
commission
building inspector
region

Think About It!

1. Does your city contribute to air or water pollution? If so, what can be done about it?
2. Ask your parents if they know of ways to make your home, your community, and your region of the country a better place in which to live. How might well-planned construction assist in reaching such a goal?

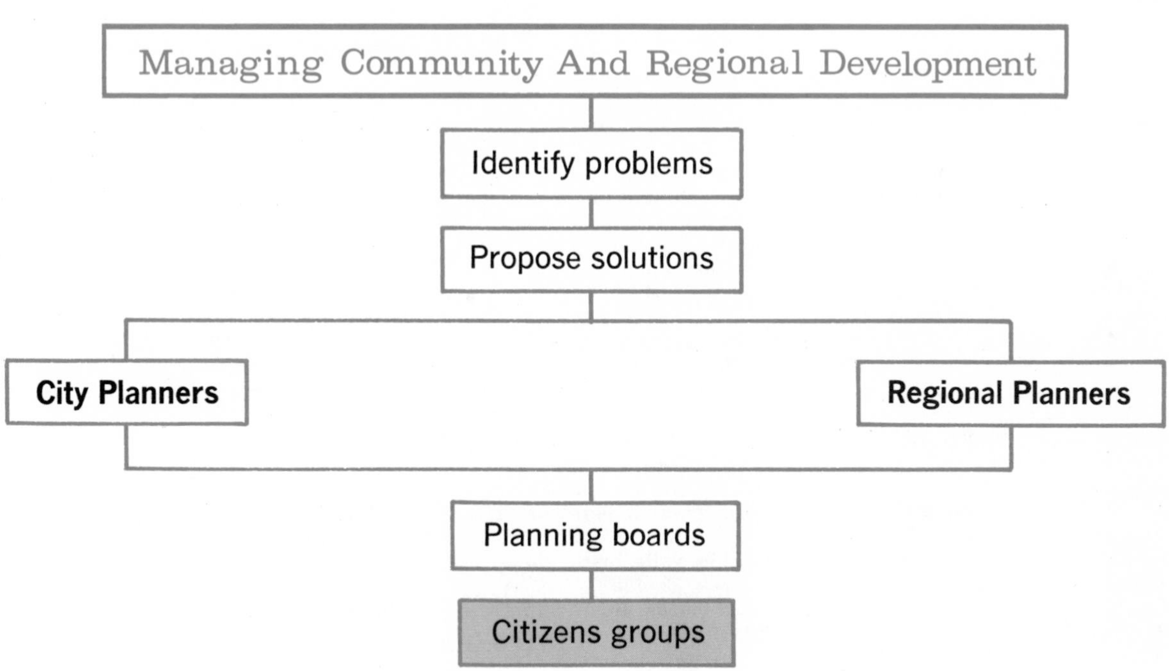

Index

Absorption, 355
Abstract of title, 42
Abutments, 415, 417, 421, 426
Accelerators, 229, 239
Acceptance, of construction project, 400-404
Accessories, 376
installing, 387-392, 510
Access road, 394
Acoustical tile, 333, 364
installing, 490
Activities, in home, 453
Adhesives, in future, 437
Administrators, of contractor, 121
Admixtures, 226, 229
Advertising for bids, 102
Aerial survey, 45
photographs as, 50
Aeronautical engineer, 141
AFL-CIO, history, 126
Aggregates—
cemented, 249
coarse, 227
fine, 227
Agreement, as contract, 105
Agronomist, 393
Air conditioning, 282, 285-290
finishing installation, 513
installing fixtures, 389
plan, 466
Air hammers, 168
for compacting, 196
Air lanes, 317
Airways, 525
Alkyd paints, 383
Alterations, 408
Altimeter, in surveying, 49
Aluminum siding, 345
American Arbitration Association, 326
Amperage, 305
Anchor bolts, 235, 257, 268
Appearance, of design, 61
Application forms, 134-136
Apprentices, 130, 142
Apron, window, 379, 508
Aptitude tests, 137
Aqueducts, 7
Arbitration, 129, 192, 325-329
Arch bridge, 418
Architect, 63, 141
agreement with owner, 474
education of, 141
landscape, 515
and project transfer, 400-404
Architect-engineer, responsibilities, 120
Architect-engineer-contractor, 97
Architectural drawings, 83
Arterial street, 524
Armored cable, 307
Asbestos flooring, 371
Asphalt, 251
to waterproof concrete, 239
Asphaltic base paint, 383
Assembly, steel frame, 257
Assets, 445
Astrodome, 437
Atomic energy, 280
Attic, ventilating, 498
Axeman, 47

Backfill, 298, 483
Backhoe, 185, 297, 481
Banks and mortgages, 451, 476
Bar Chart Schedule, 114
Bascule bridge, 420
Baseboard, 379, 508
Base lines, 40
Basement plan, 465
Base plate, 257
Bathroom—
finishing, 513
planning, 454
Bathtubs, installing, 512
Batt insulation, 354, 356, 505
Batter boards, 177, 481
Battering ram, 169
Beams, 211, 430
bridge, 418
concrete, 262
floor, 488
making concrete, 263
placing steel, 257
Bearing surface, 207, 210
Bearing wall superstructure, 202, 245, 246
Bearing walls, brick, 252
Bedrock, 53, 430
Bench marks, 46, 47, 175
Bid, 19
invitation to, 108, 425
opening, 103
proposal, 111
Bid bond, 104
Bidding, 107-113
documents for, 103
in specifications, 87
Binder money, 450
Bitumen, 338
Bituminous concrete, 246, 251
Blasting, 168, 186, 249
Boards, 213
Boathouse, planning example 71, 76
Boilermakers, 126, 291
Bolts, 431
installing in concrete, 235
Bond, of concrete, 262
Bonded roof, 340
Bonds—
bid, 104
payment, 105
performance, 105
Boom, of derrick, 255
Borings, test, 424
Boulders, 53
Boundaries, of lands, 39
Box cable, 307
Box sill, 270
Braces, 216
Bracing, 196
for concrete forms, 263
of wall section, 271
Breakwaters, 249
Brick, 251, 343
Bricklaying, 252, 345
Brick walls, 252, 486
Bridges, 7
constructing, 417-422
drawings of, 85
laying out, 178
locating, 423
movable, 420
superstructure, 201
Bridging, between joists, 269, 270, 489
Broom finish, 369
Brown coat, 334, 347, 506
Brushes, paint, 383, 511
Bucket—
earthmoving, 183
for moving concrete, 231
Budget, for home building, 456
Buggies, concrete, 232, 264
Builder, selecting, 97-101
Building code, 321, 441, 459, 479, 548
Building and construction trades, 126
Building permit, 160
Buildings—
laying out, 481
surveying for, 177

Built-up roof, 331, 338
Bulldozers, 168, 479
  grading with, 516
Burlap, 395
Business, planning area for, 534-538
Butt hinges, 378, 507
Bypass detour, 424

Cabinetwork, 378, 379
  installing, 512
Cables—
  for bridges, 419
  on derrick, 256
  telephone, 312
Caisson, 173
Camp, as problem, 65, 69
Cantilever bridge, 419
Cape Cod house, 440
Capital improvements program, 547
Capitals, location of, 30
Carpenters, 126, 378, 405
  and form work, 212
  measuring tools of, 214
Carport, 491
Career patterns, 149
Carpeting, 372, 509
Casings, 378, 507
Caulking, 347, 357, 383
  walls, 498
Caves, as housing, 439
Cavity wall, 485
Ceilings, 332, 364, 367, 489
  building, 487-490
  residence, 505
  suspended, 365
Ceiling tile, 365
Cement, 228
Cement finisher, 210, 234
Center line, roadway, 175
Centers, in wood framing, 269, 270
Chain drag, 170
Chainmen, 48
Chairs, in concrete, 224, 264
Chalk, 383
Chalk line, 214
Change, process of, 434
Character reference, 138
Char services, 406
Chases, 288
Churches, 8
Chute, for dumping, 233
CIO, 126
Circuit breaker, 281, 307
Circuits, electrical, 307
Cities, rebuilding, 434
City, services of, 523-528
City planning, 519-522, 547
Civil drawings, 83
Civil engineers, 141
Claim, contractor's, 401
Clamshell, 184
Clay, 53
  vitrified, 300
Clay pipe, 294
Clay tile walls, 344
Cleaning, excavation, 194
Cleanup, 376, 379, 396, 518
Clerk, job, 122
Client, 96
Climate—
  and design, 445
  and site selection, 34
Clinker, 228
Closed circuit TV, 317
Closing, real estate, 42
Coatings—
  for concrete, 240
  protective, 376
Cobblestone, 53, 345
Coffee break, 14
Cofferdam, 172, 173, 196, 415
Collar beam, 272
Collective bargaining, 125-132, 325, 349
  agreement, 146
Collector street, 524
Colonial house, 440
Color, of paint, 384
Column clamps, 262
Columns, 211, 430
  concrete, 262
  setting, 257
Combination set, 214
Common brick, 344
Communications, 282, 310-319
  installing accessories, 390
Community—
  building in, 520
  economics, 544-546
  planned development, 547-551
  planning, 519-522
  services of, 523-528
  and site selection, 33
Compacting, 195, 196, 487
Compaction, soil, 54, 55, 298, 426
Compaction, soil, 54, 55, 298, 426
Compression joint, 299
Computers, future uses, 436
Concrete, 212, 349
  bituminous, 246
  blocks, 252, 344
  in bridges, 418
  cast-in-place, 261
  finishing, 385
  floors, 368, 369, 465
  for footings, 209
  forms, 216
  mixing, 226, 229, 230
  patching, 239
  pipe, 298
  placing and finishing, 231-236, 264
  precast, 261
  precast and prestressed, 265
  setting of, 237
  in skyscrapers, 430
  for slab, 488
  strength of, 261
  subfloors, 487
  use in future, 436
  wall panels, 346
  workers, 11
Concrete frames, erecting, 247, 261-267
Condemnation, 35
Condensation, 353
Conditions, in specifications, 468
Conduction, heat, 353
Conductors, electrical, 305
Conduit, 280
  electrical, 308
Conservation—
  soil, 412
  wildlife, 412
Construction, 3, 4, 398, 399
  basic steps, 152-153, 157
  beginning a project, 23-29
  consultant, 26, 97
  contractor prepares for, 160-167
  of dam, 415
  defined, 157
  deterioration of, 544
  employees as group, 121
  finishing, 375
  in future, 433-438
  primary, 519
  survey of, 45
  as system, 154-159
  workers in, 13
Construction Specifications Institute outline, 91
Construction technology, 7-11
Contemporary house, 446
Contour map, 50
Contract—
  for building, 97
  legal, 451
  road construction, 425
  in specifications, 87, 89
  types of, 98
Contract drawings, 86
Contractor and contracting, 102-106, 474-477
  agreement with owner, 474
  cleans site, 517
  inspects work, 321
  organizes people and work, 120
  prepares bid, 107-113
  selecting, 97-101
  transfers project to owner, 400-404
  work of, 10, 20, 119, 124
Control, temperature, 288
Controlling, 154, 320
  as managing, 17, 20
Control points, 175
  building location, 177
Convection, 354, 501
Conveyors, concrete, 232
Cooling, 285, 290
Coped joint, 508
Copper pipe, 293
Cored concrete block, 344
Cores, soil, 56
Cork flooring, 372
Cornice, 498
Cost—
  of design, 61
  of house, 456
  of walls, 484

Cost-plus contract, 98, 424
Countertops, 512
Couplings, 294
Craftsman, education of skilled, 142
Crane, 431
to lay pipe, 298
mobile, 258
to place steel, 255
to pour concrete, 264
Crawler tractor, 169, 170, 482
Crawl space, 481
Creativity, 68
Critical Path Method, 114, 436
Crowbar, 169
Curing, of concrete, 237, 238
Curtain wall, 330, 342
Custom details, 464
Cut, and fill, 175
Cutting, 170

Damper, 288
Dams, 8, 250
building, 171, 410-416
laying out, 178
as mass superstructures, 200, 246
selecting site, 413
Datum level, 459
Dead air space, 333
Dead weight, 74
Deck, roof, 337
Decorating, 376, 381, 386
Deed, 41
registering, 451
Deformed rods, 220
Dehumidifier, 285
Demand, 521
Demolition, 168, 430
Demoting, 150
Den, 454
Density, of housing, 530
Density tests, soil, 56
Depreciation, 110
Derrick, 255
Design—
of bridge, 420
of home, 445
presenting, 80
of road, 424
selecting, 78-82
skyscraper, 429
Designing, 19, 60, 61, 64
analysis step, 74-77
of bridge, 417
considerations in, 61
cycle, 94-96
home, 453-458
identifying problem, 65-67
implementation phase, 95
information for, 94
preliminary ideas, 68-70
refining ideas, 71-73
Detail drawings, 83, 462
Detour, 424
Developer, costs of, 531
Development, plan for city, 547

Dimension lumber, 213
Dimensions—
in designing, 72
on drawings, 83
Directing, 20
Discharging, 150
Disposing, 171
Docks, 525
Domed roof, 493
Doors—
installing, 497, 507
parts of, 378
Door stop, 507
Dormer, 493
Dowels—
in concrete, 224
in concrete frame, 262
Downspouts, 494
Draft, 286, 354
Dragline, 183
Drainage, 394
of foundation, 482
of slab, 487
of site, 34, 75, 479
of soil, 54
Drawings, 19
of ideas, 68
preparing house, 459-467
working, 81, 83, 86
Dream house, 443-447
Dredging, 185
Driveways, 516
Dry heat, 501
Drywall, 361, 506
ceiling, 364, 365
Ductwork, 280, 282, 286
installing, 288
roughing in, 500

Earth—
as construction material, 249
stabilizing, 194-199
Earth auger, 185
Earthmoving, 8, 152, 158, 171, 180, 188, 426
Earthquake, 429
Easement, 41, 306
Eating space, 453
Eave, 272, 494, 499
Economic system, beginning of, 2-3
Education and training, 140-144
Eiffel Tower, 247
Electrical communications systems, 310-319
Electrical drawings, 83
Electrical engineer, 141
Electrical fixtures, installing, 389
Electrical power system, 304-309, 466
Electric heat, 501
Electrician, 305, 311, 378, 405
Electricity, 279
finishing installations, 513
roughing in, 503
temporary, 163
Electron, 279

Elementary school, 539
Elevations, 46, 83, 461
Elevation survey, 49
Elevator, building, 428
Ells, 294
Embankment, 413, 426
Eminent domain, 36
Enamel, 383
Encapsulate, 438
Encroachment, 41
Engineers, 63
education, 141
field, 122
operating, 311
and project transfer, 400-404
schooling of, 141
Engineering, 19, 60, 64
of contractor, 121
cycle, 94-96
Entraining agents, 229
Environment—
control of, 437
working, 145
Epoxy resins, 437
Equipment—
estimating costs, 109
installing, 408
moving, 161
in specifications, 473
Erector, steel, 255
Erosion, 411
Estimating, 19, 107, 108, 113
preparing, 92
Estimator, 108
Evaluation—
in design, 66
during refinement of idea, 72
Excavating, 183, 185
for house, 481
nuclear, 436
Exhaust fan, 389
Expansion joint, 337
Explosives, 168
Exterior elevations, 461
Exterior walls, 496-499

Face brick, 344
Facing, 216
Facsimile transmission, 314
Fascia, 499
Feasibility study, 25, 26, 30, 413, 423, 520
skyscraper, 429
Federal Mediation and Conciliation Service, 326
Felt, roofing, 338
Felt paper, 498
Fences, 516
Fiber glass, 436
Field engineer, 122
Field office, 122
File, specifications, 90
Fill, 187
for bridge, 426
and cut, 175
gravel, 487
on site, 479

Filter, air, 285
Financing, 474-477
Finished floor, 332
Finishing, 158, 347, 376, 380, 510, 514
Fire alarm system, 514
Fire blocks, 271
Fireplace, 514
Fire protection, 449
Fish tape, 308
Fission, 280
Fixed price contract, 98, 104
Fixtures, 376
  installing, 387-392, 510
Flagpole schedule, 114
Flanges, 294
Flashing, 339
Flat paint, 383
Flat roof, 336, 491
Float finish, 234, 369
Floating footing, 208
Flood coat, 339
Flood control, 24, 410
Floor plan, 83, 455, 459
Flooring, house, 508
Floors, 332, 368, 375
  building, 487-490
  finished, 489
  finishing, 384
  skyscraper, 431
  wood framing, 268
Flowers, planting, 517
Footings, 206, 207, 465, 482
Forced air heat, 501
Foremen, job, 122
Forms, concrete, 212
  assembling, 216
  building, 212-219
  removing, 237
Fossil fuels, 280
Foundations, 152, 204, 211
  completing, 237-243
  excavating for, 481
  parts of, 207
  plans, 83, 465
  for road, 251
  setting, 158, 209, 212, 482
  skyscraper, 429, 430
  and substructure, 200
  and superstructure, 244
  support for, 58
  trimming for, 194
Frame, 202, 245, 247
  building, 428
  door, 378
  enclosing, 330-335
  erecting concrete, 261-267
  roof, 337
  wood, 268-277
Framework, skyscraper, 430
Framing—
  partitions, 360
  steel, 255-260
Free enterprise system, 351
Freehand drawings, 68, 70
Frescos, 384
Friction piles, 196
Frieze, 499
Fringe benefits, 128, 146
Frost, in soil, 54, 58
Fuel, selection, 501
Functions—
  of dams, 410
  of designs, 61
Funding, for road, 423
Furnaces, 285, 500
Furnishings, 387
Furniture, and room planning, 455
Furring strips, 365
Fuse box, 281, 307
Future—
  of construction, 433-438
  housing in, 441

Gable roof, 491
Gains, 378, 507
Gambrel roof, 492
Game refuge, 412
Garage door opener, 513
Gas, fuel, 281, 291
Gasket, 299
Gas pipeline, 301
Gates, of dam, 415
General conditions, of specifications, 89
General contractor, 100
Georgian house, 440
Ghost town, 544
Girder, assembling in wood framing, 270
Glass wall panels, 346
Glazier, 405
Goals—
  of city plan, 547
  setting, 19, 154
Go-devil, 302
Goods, economic, 3
Government, and strikes, 351
Government lands, 38
Grade, 176
Grading, 394, 479, 516
  of aggregate, 227
  excavation, 195
Granite cutters, 126
Graphs, uses, 66, 80
Gravel, 53, 226
  fill, 487
  roof, 338
Green concrete, 237
Grid system, survey map, 50
Grievances, 189-193
  in writing, 191
  process, 325
Gross National Product, 8
Grout, 259, 269, 300, 363
Guard rail, 377
Gutters, 494, 499
Guy derrick, 431
Guy wires, 259
Gypsum, 228
Gypsum, uses, 497, 506

Hardboards, for walls, 506
Hardware, installing, 391
Hardwood floor, 508
Header, 270
Header course, 252
Heat, transfer methods, 353
Heating, 282, 285, 290, 466
  finishing installation, 513
  installing fixtures, 389
  roughing in, 500
Heat loss, 500
Heat rays, 354
Helicopter—
  to erect steel, 258
  use in construction, 172
High chairs, in concrete, 224
High density housing, 530
Highways, 249, 250, 523
  planning, 549
  surveying for, 174
Hinges, door, 378
Hip roof, 492, 493
Hiring practices, 20, 133, 134, 139
Hod carrier, 345
Hoist, 264
Hoops, in piers, 225
Hot air heat, 501
House—
  drawings for, 459-467
  dream, 443-447
  finishing, 510-514
Housekeeping services, 406
Housing—
  construction of, 439-442
  need for, 434
  people, 529-533
  styles of, 440
Humidity, 285, 288
Hydration, 228
Hydraulic engineer, 413
Hydroelectric plant, 411
Hydrographic survey, 45
Hyperparabolic roof, 493

Ideas, recording, 68
  preliminary, 68-70
Incentive contract, 99
Income, and housing, 443
Inducting workers, 133, 138
Industrial arts, 5
Industrial engineer, 141
Industrial production, 155
Industrial technology, 7
Industry, defined, 5
Initiator, 23, 30
Inspections, 21, 320-324
  of final project, 400-404
  of road, 427
Installers, telephone, 311
Instrument man, 47
Insulation, 330, 332, 334, 335, 337, 353, 358
  on ductwork, 288
  installing, 505
  joist floors, 488
  materials, 356
  of slab, 487
  steam lines, 300
Insulation board, 506
  sheathing, 497

Insulators, 305
Insurance, title, 42
Interest, on loan, 477
Interior, of house, 505-509
Interior walls, 359-363
Intersections, 524
Interview, job, 137
Investment cost, 110
Invitation to bid, 102
Ironwork, installing, 391
Ironworkers, 126, 255
Irrigation, 410

Jack rafter, 493
Jacks, 312
Jamb, 378, 507
Jetties, 249
Job descriptions, 133
Joint—
drywall, 361, 506
masonry, 344
in molding, 379
Joint Apprenticeship Committee, 142
Joint venture, 412
Joist hanger, 271
Joists, 268, 465
ceiling, 489
assembling, 269
in concrete slab form, 264
wood, 488
Journeyman, 131
Junior high school, 539
Jurisdictional dispute, 327

Kiln, 343
Kitchen, finishing, 513
Kitchen cabinets, 512
Knights of Labor, 126

Labor, 12, 32
estimating, 109
legislation, 128, 160
relations, 121
strike costs to, 351
union, 125
Laboratory tests, soil, 57
Lacquer, 510
Land—
acquiring for dam, 415
effect of price, 531
survey of, 45
Land development standards, 548
Land holdings, history of U.S., 38
Land restrictions, 35
Landscaping, 10, 150, 393, 399, 459 515, 518
Laser system, 314
Lath, 361
and plaster, 364, 365, 505
Lavatories, installing, 512
Lawn, laying, 517
Lawyer, 450
Laying off, 150

Leaching lines, 459
Lead joint, 299
Lead solder, 294
Ledger strip, 270
Legal description, land, 39
Legal documents, 468
Letter of commitment, 474
Level, 48, 49, 174
Lever, principle of, 74
Lien, 42, 402
Lift bridge, 420
Light fixtures, installing, 387, 390
Lime, and cement, 228
Linemen, 305, 311
Linoleum, 371
Load-bearing surface, 53
Load bearing walls, 333, 342, 359
skyscraper, 430
Loads, analyzing, 74
Loan—
arranging for, 474
house, 451
payment schedule, 477
Lockout, 325
Lockset, 507
Loose-fill insulation, 356
Lot, 40
selecting and purchasing, 448-452
Louvers, 498
Low chairs, in concrete, 224
Low density housing, 530
Lumber, 213

Machine, 2
Mains, water, 279
Maintenance, 10
need for, 544
property, 407
workers, 405
Man and technology, 1-6
Management, 17, 21, 90, 140
and bid proposal, 112
of construction, 17-22
of future, 436
and grievances, 191
strike cost to, 350
Manhole, 300
Mansard roof, 492
Manufacturing technology, 3, 4, 7
workers in, 12
Mapping, 45-52, 174
Marble wall panels, 346
Market, and site, 32
Marking gage, 214
Markup, 111
Maser system, 314
Mason, 252, 345
Masonry—
finishing, 385
paint, 511
superstructures, 249-254
use inside, 506
walls, 247, 343, 485
Mass superstructures, 201, 245, 249-254
Mast, of derrick, 255

Mastic, 365, 370
Materials, 3, 61
for bridge, 418
change in value, 155
for dams, 412
estimating, 109
for footings, 209
for forms, 212
of future, 434, 436
inspecting, 322
local use, 445
for mass superstructures, 246
moving excavated, 186
and site selection, 34
in specifications, 473
Mean sea level, 46
Mechanical drawings, 83
Mechanical engineer, 141
Mechanical joint, 299
Mediation, 129, 192, 325, 329
Meridians, 40
Mesh, reinforcing, 220
Metal flooring, 371
Metal lath, 361, 505
Metal wall panels, 346
Metals, of future, 436
Meter, electric, 307
Metes and bounds, 40
Microwaves, 282, 310, 313
Millwork, 376
Mitered joint, 508
Mixer operator, 209
Mobile units, radio/TV, 315
Models, 20, 80, 455
Modular system, 434
Modulation, 311
Mold, concrete form as, 212
Molding, 379
Monitor, 21, 318
TV, 315
Monuments, 250
of pipelines, 302
survey, 46
Morale, 148
Mortar, 252
Mortgage, 41
application for, 475
payments, 443
Mosaic, 362
Movable partitions, 360
Mulch, 396
Multiple family housing, 530
Mural, 384

National labor policy, 128
Nature, products of, 5
Navigation system, 310-319
Needs—
and housing, 443
identifying, 65
Negotiation, 35, 99
labor, 125, 147
Network, radio/TV, 315
Neutral party, 325
Nonmetallic-sheathed cable, 307

Oakum, 294
Obstacles, on site, 478
Office communication, 318
Office workers, 140
Oil base paint, 383, 510
Operating personnel, 405
Organizing, 154
as managing, 17, 20
Oriental house, 440
Ornamental ironwork, 391
Outline specifications, 89
Outlet box, 390
Overall Progress Chart, 117
Overhead, 98, 111, 350
Overload, 307
Owner, 24
accepts project, 400-404
agreement with architect, 474
agreements with contractors, 120, 474
of bridge, 417
inspects, 321
responsibilities, 120
selects builder, 97
selects design, 78-82
selects site, 30
skyscraper, 428

Painters, 378, 382
Painting, 376, 381, 386, 510
Panama Canal, 25, 30
Paneled floor systems, 489
Paneled walls, 362, 485
Panels—
for concrete forms, 262
exterior wall, 346
Paperhangers, 382
Parallels, 40
Parcel, of land, 38
Parks, 539-543
Parking—
location of, 75
need for, 537
at schools, 540
Parquet floor, 370
Partitions, 333, 359, 360
Patios, 491, 516
Pavement, pouring, 251
Paver, bituminous concrete, 251
Payment bond, 105
Pencils, carpenter's, 215
People—
housing, 529-533
organizing, 120
and technology, 12-16
Performance bond, 105
Permit, building, 548
Personnel technology, 10, 14, 15, 133
PERT, 436
Petitions, 24
Petroleum pipeline, 301
Picketing, 350
Pictorial drawings, 80
Piers, 196, 211, 421
bridge, 417, 426
forms for, 218
Pigment, 381, 510
Pile cap, 208
Pilings, 58, 75, 196, 207, 208, 421 430
Pins, wood, 268
Pipe—
laying, 298
sizes, 293
Pipe dope, 294
Pipelines, 278, 279, 297, 303, 526
records of, 302
as structures, 202
Piping, 293
in slab, 487
Pisa, tower of, 207
Pitch, of roof, 336, 491
Plane table, 48
Planking, 213
floors, 488
roof, 365
Planks, as joists, 269
Planning, 154
of bridge, 420
city and region, 519-522
for construction, 10-11
house, 453-458
as managing, 17, 19
need for community, 546
Planning Commission, 548
Plaster, 362, 364, 365, 505
Plasterboard, 361
Plasterers, 334, 347
Plastic laminates, 506
Plastic pipe, 295
Plastic wall panels, 346
Plastics, in future, 436
Plat, 40
Plate, of roof, 493
Plate bearing test, soil, 56
Plates, 216
Playgrounds, 541
Plot plan, 177, 459
Plumb bob, 178, 217, 259
Plumber, 291, 378
Plumbing, 291-296, 467
installing fixtures, 387, 388, 512
roughing in, 502
steel frame, 259
Plywood, 213
sheathing, 497
walls, 506
Pneumatic conveyor, 286
Pneumatic tamper, 299
Point support pile, 196
Police communication, 318
Pollution, 410
Polyvinyl acetate paint, 383
Pontoons, 420
Population density, 31
Population multiplier, 529
Porous material, 354
Portland cement, 228
Post and beam wall system, 486
Postprocessing, 10, 14, 156, 405
Power lines, 305
Precast concrete, 265
beams, 418
wall panel, 485
Precut house, 441
Prefabrication, 163, 379
doors and windows, 497
forms, 213
in future, 434
house, 441
wall panels, 485
Preprocessing, 10, 155
Primary construction, 519
Primary workers, 529
Primer, 384, 511
Private projects, 23
Problem, identifying, 61
design, 65-67
Processing, 3, 10, 155
Production technology, 2, 10, 154
Production workers, 140
Proficiency tests, 134
Profit, 111
and managing, 17
Project—
feasibility of, 25
manager, 122
specifications, 90
transfer to owner, 400-404
Promotions, 148-153
Property line, 177
Proposal, bid, 103
Public hearing, 24
Public projects, 23
Pumping, to clear water, 187
Pumps, concrete, 232
Punch list, 400-404
Purchase offer, 450
Purchasing section, 121
Push-pull rule, 214
Putty, 383
Pyramids, 8

Qualifications, to bid, 102
Quality control, 321
Quarrying, 249
Quarter section, 40
Quotation, price, 110

Radar, 316, 317
Radiation, 354, 501
Radiators, 501
Radio system, 310-319
Raft footing, 207, 208
Rafters, 268, 272
types, 493
Railroad spur, 394
Ranch house, 440
Readymixed concrete, 229
Real estate, buying, 35, 38-44
Realtors, 35, 450
Recorder of deeds, 39, 451
Recreation, planning facilities, 539-543
Recruiting, 133
Redevelopment, 545
Reducer, 293
References, personal, 138
Refinery, 301

Refining, of design, 62
Reflection, 354
Region, services of, 523-528
Regional planning, 519-522, 549
Registers, air handling, 282, 389
Registrar, county, 39, 451
Reinforcing concrete, 209, 220-225, 262
Relaxing space, 453
Relay stations, 283
Release of claims, 400, 401, 403
Relocating, 150
Repairman, 405, 407
Reporting, 21
Reproduction, 3
Resale value, 450
Research, 19, 45
Reservoir, 410
Resilient flooring, 371, 508
Responsive bid, 104
Resurvey, 46
Retarders, 229
Retirement, 125, 131, 150
Reveal, 378
Ribbon stone, 345
Ridge, 272, 493
Riggers, 256
Right-of-way, 306
Ripping, 186
Rip-rap, 415
Rise, of roof, 494
Risers, 507
    pipe, 295
River, diverting, 171
Rivets, 431
Roadbed, 176, 523
    building, 423-427
    compacting, 196
Rock, 249
    crushed, 226
Rock lath, 361, 505
Rocket assembly building, 9
Rodman, 47
Rods, reinforcing, 220
Rodsetter, 209, 223
Rollers, paint, 383, 511
Roofing, 336-341
Roofs, 83, 331, 465
    building, 491-495
    decking, 273
    wood framing, 268, 272
Roof trusses, 490
Room divider, 360
Rooms, planning, 454
Row-lock course, 252
Rubber base paint, 383
Rubber flooring, 372
Rule, bench, 214
Run, of roof, 493

Sack-rubbed finish, concrete, 240
Safety, 146, 161
    electrical, 305
    programs, 129
    and schools, 540
Safety factor, 74
Sailor course, 252
Salvaging, 169
Sand, 53, 227
Sandwich panels, 489
Sanitary engineers, 141
Sanitary sewer, 279, 300
Satellites, communications, 313
Savings and loan companies, 476
Sawing, 215
Scale drawings, 71, 79, 83
Scarifying, 186
Scheduling, 114-118
Schools, planning, 539-543
Scraper, 182
Scratch coat, 334, 347, 506
Screeds, 233
Screening job applicants, 134
Sea lanes, 317
Seawater, desalting, 434
Secondary school, 539
Secondary workers, 529
Sections, 40, 83
    structural, 461
Seeding, 396
    lawn, 517
Separating, 150
    materials, 155, 156
Septic tank, 459
Serpentine roof, 493
Service entrance, 307, 312
Services—
    business, 535
    of constructed project, 405-409
    of community, 523-528
    of facility, 521
    at home site, 449
    of house, 456
    for schools, 540
    workers in, 13
Setbacks, 448, 479
Sewage system, 279, 291, 300, 527
Sewer pipes, 298
Sewing room, 454
Shakes, cedar, 494
Sheathing, 213, 345
    excavation, 196
    outside wall, 496
    roof, 494
    wood framing, 272
Shed roof, 491
Sheepsfoot roller, 426
Sheet metalworkers, 287
Shellac, 383, 510
Shelter, 7
    man's early, 439
    temporary on site, 162
Shims, 257
Shiner course, 252
Shingles, types, 494
Shoe, 379
Shop drawings, 83, 221, 257
Shopping centers, 534, 535
Shoring, 58, 196, 216, 263
    for concrete slab, 263
Shovel, power, 182
Showers, installing, 512
Shrubs, planting, 395, 517
Siding, exterior, 498
Signals, steelworker's, 257
Silicone, in roofing material, 340
Sill, 268, 269, 378, 379
Silt, 53
Single family dwelling, 530
Site, 4, 521
    access to, 162
    of businesses, 536, 537
    clearing, 152, 166-173, 478
    completing, 393-399
    cost of, 449, 531
    for dam, 413
    factors regarding, 168
    for house, 448-452
    information about, 66
    key to construction/manufacturing definition, 157
    preparing, 158
    protecting, 161
    for recreation, 541
    for school, 540
    selecting, 30-37, 75
    skyscraper, 429
    use of, 480
Site plan, 71, 83
Skeleton frame, 330
Sketches, idea, 62
Skilled craftsmen, education, 142
Skyscrapers, building, 428-432
Slab floor, 332, 481, 487
Slabs—
    forms for, 216
    making suspended, 263
Slaking, of clay, 54
Sleeping space, 453
Slope—
    of roof, 331, 336, 491
    of sewer, 528
Slope stakes, 176, 195
Snake, 300
Snowshoes, as footing, 207
Social Security, 109
Society, industrial, 7
Sod, 396, 517
Soffit, 389, 499
    ventilating, 499
Soil—
    analysis, 55, 75
    as construction material, 249
    and footings, 482
    preparing for seeding, 516
    of site, 34
    testing, 53-59, 448
    types, 53
Soil pipe, 294
    installing, 502
Solder, 294
Soldier course, 252
Sole plate, 271
Solvents, 383, 510
Sound waves, 312
Space communication, 9, 318
Spacing, wood framing, 270, 271
Span—
    of roof, 493
    of wood framing, 270
Spandrel braced arch, 419
Spanish house, 440
Spar varnish, 383

Specialization, 3, 10
Specifications, 19, 87, 93
writing, 468-473
Spigot end, 294
Spillway, 415
Spoil, 185, 186, 187
Spray painting, 384, 511
Spread footing, 207
Sprigging, 396
Spud wrench, 257
Square, framing, 214
Stains, 383
Stairs, 379, 507
Stakes, 216
for plantings, 395
survey, 46
Standard details, 462
Standards specifications, 89
Status, social, 150
Steam curing, 239
Steam fitters, 291
Steam heat, 286
Steam lines, 300
Steel—
kinds of reinforcing, 220
making structural, 255
Steel frames, erecting, 247, 255-260
Stilts, as footing, 207
Stone, 249
floor, 370
masonry, 345, 486
Stoned finish, concrete, 240
Stone mason, 252, 345
Stool, 508
window, 379
Storm sewer, 279, 300
Streets, 523
Stressed skin panels, 489
Stretcher course, 252
Strikes, 129, 325, 349-352
Stringer, 507
for concrete slab, 264
Strip, shopping, 536
Structural analysis, 74, 461
Structural drawings, 83
Structural steel, 255
Structures, 7, 200-203
locating, 174-181
plans for, 83
stabilizing, 194-199
Stucco, 347, 486
Studs, 216, 268, 271
Stud wall, 484
Study, 454
Subcontract, 100, 110
Subcontractor, agreement with owner, 474
Subdivision, 40
Subfloor, 271, 487
Substation, electrical, 306
Substructures, 158, 200, 206, 244
building, 478-483
of road, 251
Suburbs, 441
Summary sheet, estimator's, 111, 112
Sump pumps, 187
Superintendent, job, 122
Superstructures, 153, 158, 200, 242-248
bridge, 421
design of, 244
enclosing, 330-335
of house, 201
mass and masonry, 249-254
Supplies, contract, 100
Supports, foundation, 207
Survey, 45-52, 174
land, 42
of site, 479
types of, 45
Surveyors, 40, 450
Suspended ceiling, 332, 365
Suspension bridge, 419
Sweated joint, 294
Sweets catalog, 90
Swing bridge, 420
Switchgear, telephone, 312

Tackless strips, 373
Tag line, 257
Takeoff, 109
Tape, measuring, 174
Tar paper, 331
Taxes, and site selection, 35
Tax rates, 449
T-bevel, 214
Teamwork, 145
Technology—
and man, 1-6, 12-16
use of new, 434
Teepees, 439
Tees, 294
Telegraph system, 310-319
Telephone, 310-319
installing, 390
on site, 163
Television, 310-319
Temperature control, 288
Termites, 269
Terrazzo, 368
floor, 369
Theodolite, 49
Thermopane, 355
Thermostat, 282, 288
Thinner, 383, 510
Threads, pipe, 294
Threshold, 378
Through bridge, 417
Ties, 216
in forms, 218
in wall, 485
Tile, 506
ceiling, 364
clay wall, 344
drain, 482
floor, 370, 509
installing ceiling, 490
laying floor, 372
roof, 494
on subfloor, 488
wall, 362
Tilt-up slab, 347
Title, 41, 42
Title insurance, 42
Title page, of specifications, 92
Toenailing, 270
Toilet, installing, 512
Tongue and groove flooring, 271
Tool, 1
Topography, 45, 448
Top plate, 271
Topping out, 260, 331
Topsoil, 54, 395
spreading, 516
stripping, 478
Torque wrench, 258
Tower, as framed superstructure, 244, 247, 317
Tower of Babel, 246
Tower crane, 431
Township, 40
Tract, of land, 38
Trade, in economics, 3
Trade area, 535
Tradition, and style of house, 445, 446
Traffic, 523
flow in house, 455
Trailers, as temporary office shelters, 163
Training and education, 129, 140-144
Transferring, 150
Transformer, 280, 306
Transit, 48, 174
Transmission lines, 305
Transportation, 523
need for, 434
and site, 33
Trap, plumbing, 502
Treads, 507
Trees—
planting, 395, 517
on site, 478
Trench, digging, 185, 297, 482
Trencher, 297
Triangulation, 46
Trim, inside, 507
Trimming, 376, 378
excavation, 194
Trowel finish, 234, 369
Trowel trades, 347
Trussed bars, 263
Trussed roof, wood framing, 273
Trusses—
bridge, 418
roof, 490
Try square, 214
Tudor house, 441
Tunneling, 185
Tunnels, as structures, 202
Turnkey job, 97

Undercoat, 511
Underlayment, 368, 489
Underpinnings, 430
Unions, 125, 293
joining, 130
membership standards, 131
Unit heaters, 501
Unit price contract, 98, 104, 110

Utilities, 24, 153, 276, 284, 526
during construction, 163
installing, 158
roughing in, 500-504
and site, 33, 449
in skyscrapers, 432
Utility, of site, 31
Urban housing, 532
Urban renewal, 545

Vacations, 128
Vacuum systems, 286, 354
Valley, of roof, 493

Value, of structures, 545
Valves, 293
Vapor barrier, 332, 334, 338, 345, 353, 487, 505
walls, 498
Varnish, 383, 510
Vaulted roof, 493
Vehicle, 382, 510
Veneer, brick, 344
Ventilating, 285-290
of attic, 498
installing fixtures, 389
plan, 466
Vents, 389
plumbing, 502
Vertical control, survey, 46
Vinyl flooring, 333, 371
Vinyl paint, 381
Vinyl siding, 345
Vitrified clay, 300
Voids, in so[illegible] 4
Voltage, 280, 305

Wages, 125, 128, 146
Walers, 216, 261, 262
Walks, 516
Wallpaper, 384, 511
Walls—
building, 484-486
exterior, 331, 342, 348
forms for, 217
inside, 333
interior, 359-363, 505
skyscraper, 431
wood framing, 268, 271
Warranty, 403
Washing—
excavation, 194
sand, 227
Washing space, 453
Water, 279
in concrete, 228, 238
diverting, 172, 173, 525
need for, 434
removing unwanted, 187
on site, 163
Water base paint, 383, 510
Waterproofing, concrete, 239
Water reducing agents, 229
Water system, 291, 526
Water table, 54
Weather, and construction, 162
Weather-stripping, 357, 498
Welfare program, 131
Wet heat, 501
Windows—
installing, 497
parts of, 379
Wiremen, electrical, 305
Wood, in future, 436
Wood floor, 370
construction, 465
subfloors, 488
Wood frames, building, 247, 268-277
Wood siding, 346
Work, managing, 154
Workers—
hiring, 133-139
and technology, 12-16
types and number, 12, 13
Working conditions, 125, 128, 145, 147, 190
and promotions, 148-153
Working drawings, 81, 83, 86, 459, 467
Working hours, 128
Workmanship, inspecting, 322
Workmen's Compensation, 109
Work promotion, 130
Workshop, 454
Work stoppage, *see* Strikes
Wrecking, 168, 169, 430
Writer, specifications, 90
Wythe brick wall, 252

Zig-zag rule, 214
Zoning, 35, 160, 448, 548